Everyday Mathematics®

The University of Chicago School Mathematics Project

Teacher's Lesson Guide
Volume 2

Grade

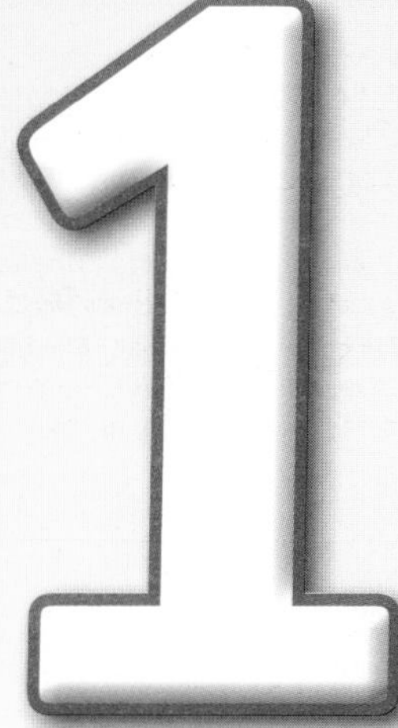

McGraw Hill Education

Chicago, IL • Columbus, OH • New York, NY

Everyday Mathematics®

The University of Chicago School Mathematics Project (UCSMP)

Max Bell, Director, UCSMP Elementary Materials Component, Director, *Everyday Mathematics* First Edition; James McBride, Director, *Everyday Mathematics* Second Edition; Andy Isaacs, Director, *Everyday Mathematics* Third Edition; Amy Dillard, Associate Director, *Everyday Mathematics* Third Edition; Rachel Malpass McCall, Associate Director, *Everyday Mathematics* Common Core State Standards Edition

Authors
Max Bell, Jean Bell, John Bretzlauf, Amy Dillard, Robert Hartfield, Andy Isaacs, James McBride, Rachel Malpass McCall, Kathleen Pitvorec, Peter Saecker

Technical Art
Diana Barrie

UCSMP Editorial
Rossita Fernando
Lila K. Schwartz

ELL Consultant
Kathryn B. Chval

Mathematics and Technology Advisor
James Flanders

Third Edition Teachers in Residence
Jeanine O'Nan Brownell, Andrea Cocke, Brooke A. North

Contributors
Regina Littleton (Office Manager), Kriszta Miner (Project Manager), Allison Greer, Meg Schleppenbach, Cynthia Annorh, Amy DeLong, Debra Fields, Jenny Fischer, Nancy Glinka, Serena Hohmann, Robert Balfanz, Judith Busse, Mary Ellen Dairyko, Lynn Evans, James Flanders, Dorothy Freedman, Nancy Guile Goodsell, Pam Guastafeste, Nancy Hanvey, Murray Hozinsky, Deborah Arron Leslie, Sue Lindsley, Mariana Mardrus, Carol Montag, Elizabeth Moore, Kate Morrison, William D. Pattison, Joan Pederson, Erenda Penix, June Ploen, Herb Price, Danette Riehle, Ellen Ryan, Marie Schilling, Sheila Sconiers, Susan Sherrill, Patricia Smith, Kimberli Sorg, Robert Strang, Jaronda Strong, Kevin Sweeney, Sally Vongsathorn, Esther Weiss, Francine Williams, Michael Wilson, Izaak Wirzup

Photo Credits
Cover (l)C Squared Studios/Getty Images, (r)Tom & Dee Ann McCarthy/CORBIS, (bkgd)Ralph A. Clevenger/CORBIS; **Back Cover** C Squared Studios/Getty Images; **iii** (t)Simon Brown/Digital Vision/Getty Images, (b)The McGraw-Hill Companies; **iv v** The McGraw-Hill Companies; **vi** Brand X Pictures/PunchStock; **vii** The McGraw-Hill Companies; **522** (t)Lenscap/Alamy, (b)The McGraw-Hill Companies; **533 535 565 571** The McGraw-Hill Companies; **608** (l)Burazin/Photographer's Choice/Getty Images, (r)The McGraw-Hill Companies; **609** (tl cl b)The McGraw-Hill Companies, (r)Bloomimage/CORBIS; **619** (t)The McGraw-Hill Companies, (b)CORBIS; **620** The McGraw-Hill Companies; **621** (t)The McGraw-Hill Companies, (b)Ingram Publishing/Alamy; **640 662** The McGraw-Hill Companies; **663** Tanya Constantine/Digital Vision/Getty Images; **673** (t)The McGraw-Hill Companies, (b)Spencer Grant/PhotoEdit; **674** Photodisc Collection/Eyewire/Getty Images; **675** David Young-Wolff/PhotoEdit; **721 728 729 740 765 788** The McGraw-Hill Companies; **789** (l)VEER Steve Cicero/Photonica/Getty Images, (r)The McGraw-Hill Companies; **799 823 862 865** The McGraw-Hill Companies; **876** Image Source/Alamy; **880 881 883 885** The McGraw-Hill Companies; **Icons** (NCTM l-r)Sharon Hoogstraten/Courtesy of Dave Wyman, Jules Frazier/Photodisc/Getty Images, Comstock/PunchStock, Sundell Larsen/Getty Images, PhotoAlto/PunchStock, Four Elements/V262/CORBIS, Juan Silva/Stockbyte/Getty Images, Digital Vision/Getty Images; (iTLG)C Squared Studios/Getty Images; (Online Content Support)Image Source; (Objective)Brand X Pictures/PunchStock/Getty Images.

---

everyday**math**.com

Education

Send all inquiries to:
McGraw-Hill Education
STEM Learning Solutions Center
P.O. Box 812960
Chicago, IL 60681

ISBN: 978-0-07-657684-5
MHID: 0-07-657684-1

Printed in the United States of America.

1 2 3 4 5 6 7 8 9 RMN 17 16 15 14 13 12 11

McGraw-Hill is committed to providing instructional materials in Science, Technology, Engineering, and Mathematics (STEM) that give all students a solid foundation, one that prepares them for college and careers in the 21st century.

Contents

Volume 1

Everyday Mathematics®

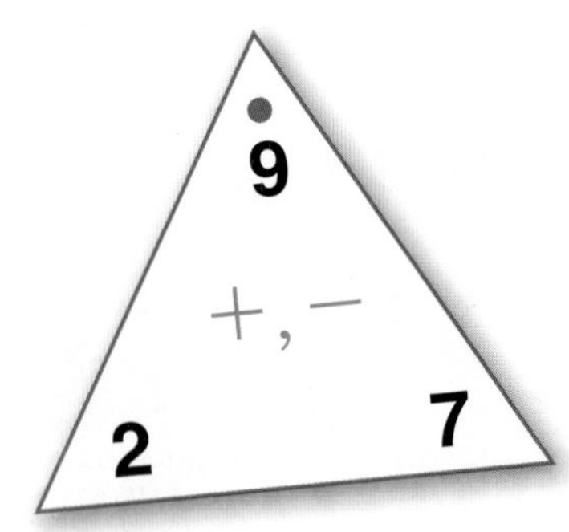

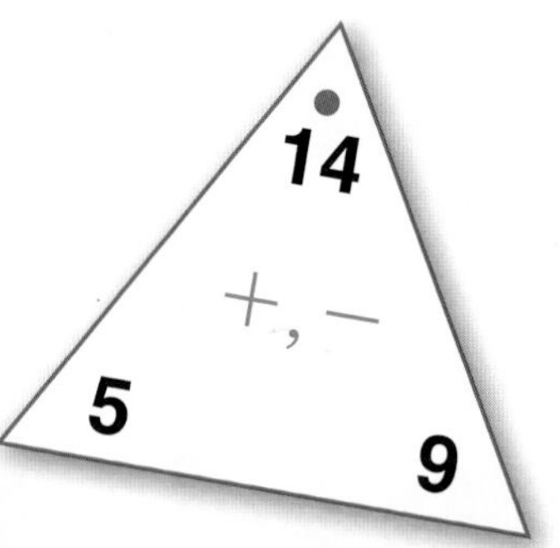

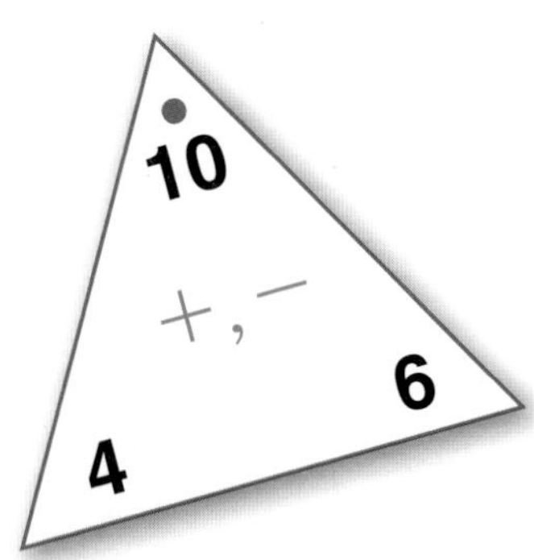

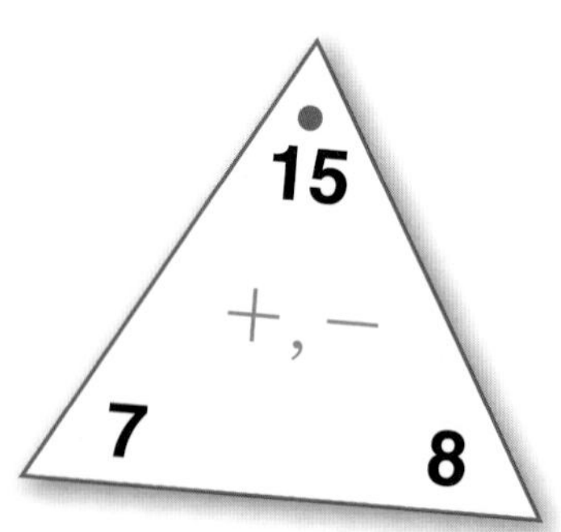

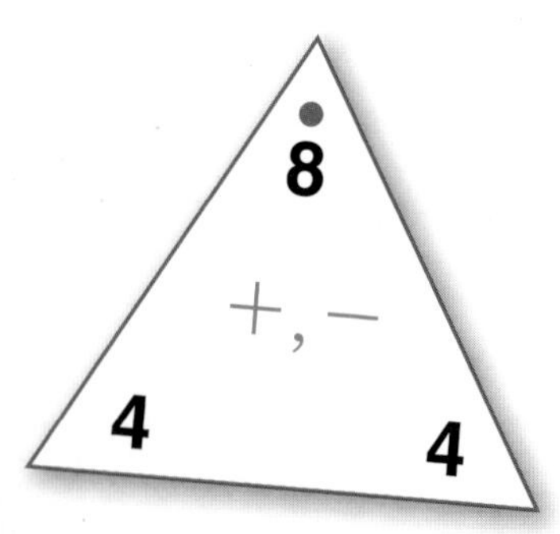

Volume 2

50
40
30
20
10
0
-10
-20
-30
-40
120
100
80
60
40
20
0
-20
-40
°C
°F

Unit 6 Organizer

Developing Fact Power

Overview

The main focus of Unit 6 is developing fact power. It is the expectation that with frequent practice throughout the school year, most children will know the simple addition facts by the end of first grade. Unit 6 has four main areas of focus:

- To introduce fact-finding strategies,
- To review coin values, measurements, and time,
- To develop procedures for addition/subtraction problems, and
- To introduce *My Reference Book.*

Linking to the Common Core State Standards

The content of Unit 6 addresses the Common Core State Standards for Mathematics in *Operations and Algebraic Thinking* and *Measurement and Data.* The correlation of the Common Core State Standards to the *Everyday Mathematics* Grade 1 lessons begins on page CS1.

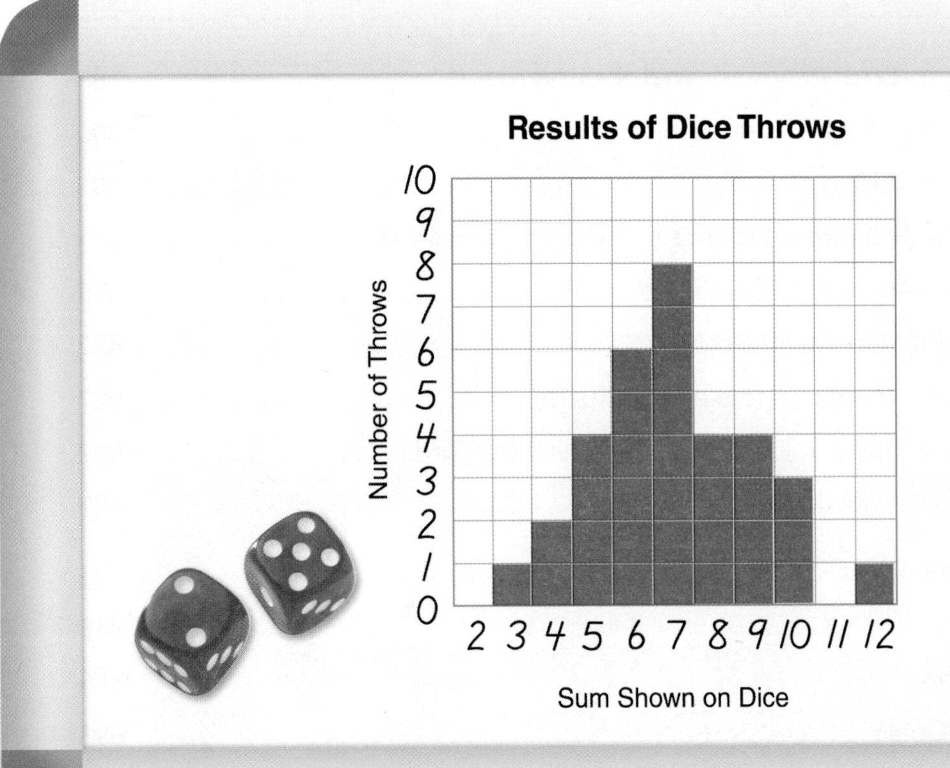

Contents

Unit 6 Organizer

Learning In Perspective

	Lesson Objectives	Links to the Past	Links to the Future
6•1	To provide experience exploring patterns in sums of two dice; and to introduce the Addition/Subtraction Facts Table.	In Units 3–5, children describe and extend patterns. They also explore addition and subtraction, and easy addition facts. In Kindergarten, children work with addition.	In Grades 1–3, children continue to use the Addition/Subtraction Facts Table as a reference and to develop fact power.
6•2	To introduce name-collection boxes as devices for collecting equivalent names for numbers.	In Units 2–5, children show amounts of money using different coins. They use tally marks. In Kindergarten, children use different names for the same number.	In Grades 1–3, children continue to find equivalent names for numbers and fractional parts of a whole.
6•3	To introduce addition/subtraction fact families.	In Units 3–5, children explore addition and subtraction, addition facts, and number models. Children work with addition and subtraction in Kindergarten.	In Grades 1–3, children continue to use addition/subtraction fact families to develop fact power.
6•4	To introduce Fact Triangles.	In Units 3–5, children explore addition and subtraction, addition facts, and number models. Children work with addition and subtraction in Kindergarten.	In Grades 1–3, children continue to use Fact Triangles to develop fact power.
6•5	To provide experience revisiting the relationship between addition and subtraction; and to introduce subtraction fact strategies using ten.	In Units 2 and 4–6, children are introduced to the relationship between addition and subtraction. In Kindergarten, children work with single-digit addition and subtraction.	In Grades 1–3, children continue to explore the relationship between addition and subtraction.
6•6	To introduce the centimeter as a unit of measure in the metric system; and to provide experience measuring and drawing line segments to the nearest centimeter.	In Unit 4, children measure and estimate length to the nearest foot or inch. In Kindergarten, children use nonstandard and standard units to measure length.	In Grades 1 and 2, children continue to measure and compare lengths using standard and nonstandard units to the nearest inch and centimeter.
6•7	To develop readiness for fractions; to provide practice with addition facts; and to provide for the exploration of various shapes of triangles.	In Units 3–5, children explore addition and subtraction, addition facts, and 2-dimensional shapes. In Kindergarten, children work with single-digit addition and triangles.	In Units 8 and 9, children use pattern blocks to model fractions of equal parts. They continue to develop fact power, and identify and describe plane shapes.
6•8	To provide an extension for the "What's My Rule?" routine which includes finding missing input numbers.	In Unit 5, children solve "What's My Rule?" problems with missing rules and output numbers. In Kindergarten, children are introduced to "What's My Rule?"	In Units 8 and 9, children continue to solve "What's My Rule?" problems with missing rules, input numbers, and output numbers.
6•9	To provide experience finding the value of collections of quarters, dimes, nickels, and pennies; and showing money amounts with coins.	In Units 2–5, children are introduced to coins, cents notation, and dollars-and-cents notations. They find the values of coin combinations. In Kindergarten, children are introduced to quarters.	In Units 8 and 10, children are introduced to dollar bills and calculate combinations of coins and dollar bills.
6•10	To provide experience identifying the number of minutes around the face of an analog clock; and to introduce digital time.	In Units 2–4, children begin telling time to the nearest hour, half-hour, and quarter-hour. Children begin telling time to the nearest hour in Kindergarten.	In Unit 10, children tell time to the nearest hour, half-hour, quarter-hour, and 5 minutes. In Grade 2, they tell time to the nearest half-hour and 5 minutes.
6•11	To introduce *My Reference Book.*		In Grades 1 and 2, children use *My Reference Book* as a mathematical reference. In Grade 3, they use the *Student Reference Book* as a mathematical reference.
6•12	To introduce the statistical landmarks *range* and *middle value;* and to provide practice collecting data and making bar graphs.	In Units 1, 3, and 4, children use tally marks to record and analyze data and create line plots. In Kindergarten, children collect and organize data.	In Grades 1–6, children continue to collect, organize, and analyze data.

	Key Concepts and Skills	Grade 1 Goals*
6•1	Compare sums of whole numbers.	Number and Numeration Goal 7
	Find sums of whole numbers.	Operations and Computation Goal 1
	Use the Addition/Subtraction Facts Table to find sums of 1-digit whole numbers.	Operations and Computation Goal 1
	Identify and describe simple numerical patterns.	Patterns, Functions, and Algebra Goal 1
6•2	Find different sets of 2 or more addends with the same sum.	Number and Numeration Goal 6
	Use dominoes, drawings, tally marks, base-10 blocks, and manipulatives to give equivalent names for numbers.	Number and Numeration Goal 6
	Write number sentences to express equivalencies.	Patterns, Functions, and Algebra Goal 2
6•3	Write parts-and-total number models.	Operations and Computation Goal 4
	Write addition and subtraction number models using +, –, and =.	Patterns, Functions, and Algebra Goal 2
	Generate fact families.	Patterns, Functions, and Algebra Goal 3
6•4	Find sums of 1-digit numbers with and without a calculator.	Operations and Computation Goal 1
	Write addition and subtraction number models, using +, –, and =.	Patterns, Functions, and Algebra Goal 2
	Generate fact families.	Patterns, Functions, and Algebra Goal 3
6•5	Use the Addition/Subtraction Facts Table to find sums and differences.	Operations and Computation Goal 1
	Use subtraction fact strategies to find differences.	Operations and Computation Goal 1
	Use addition to check answers for subtraction facts.	Patterns, Functions, and Algebra Goal 3
6•6	Count forward by 1s.	Number and Numeration Goal 1
	Estimate length to the nearest centimeter.	Measurement and Reference Frames Goal 1
	Measure and draw line segments to the nearest centimeter.	Measurement and Reference Frames Goal 1
	Measure lengths in nonstandard units and compare lengths.	Measurement and Reference Frames Goal 1
6•7	Count pattern blocks.	Number and Numeration Goal 2
	Identify even and odd numbers.	Number and Numeration Goal 5
	Find sums of randomly generated whole numbers.	Operations and Computation Goal 1
	Use a tally chart to organize data.	Data and Chance Goal 1
	Model triangles.	Geometry Goal 1
6•8	Count forward and backward by 1s.	Number and Numeration Goal 1
	Find the missing input and output numbers in "What's My Rule?" problems.	Patterns, Functions, and Algebra Goal 1
6•9	Count forward by 25s.	Number and Numeration Goal 1
	Calculate the value of combinations of quarters, dimes, nickels, and pennies.	Operations and Computation Goal 2
	Identify a quarter and know its value.	Measurement and Reference Frames Goal 2
	Make exchanges between coins.	Measurement and Reference Frames Goal 2
6•10	Count forward by 1s and 5s.	Number and Numeration Goal 1
	Tell time on a digital clock given the time on an analog clock.	Measurement and Reference Frames Goal 4
	Tell time on an analog clock given the time on a digital clock.	Measurement and Reference Frames Goal 4
	Tell time to the quarter-hour in digital notation.	Measurement and Reference Frames Goal 4
6•11	Find numbers in a sequence.	Number and Numeration Goal 7
	Calculate the value of combinations of coins.	Operations and Computation Goal 2
	Find and draw plane shapes.	Geometry Goal 1
6•12	Count forward by 1s on a calculator.	Number and Numeration Goal 1
	Compare and order whole numbers.	Number and Numeration Goal 7
	Create a tally chart and a bar graph to organize data.	Data and Chance Goal 1
	Find landmarks; ask and answer questions about a data set.	Data and Chance Goal 2

*See the Appendix for a complete list of Grade 1 Goals.

A Balanced Curriculum

Ongoing Practice

Mental Math and Reflexes activities promote speed and accuracy in mental computation.

Math Boxes offer mixed practice and are paired across lessons as shown in the brackets below. This makes them useful as assessment tools. The last one or two boxes on each page preview the next unit's content.

Mixed practice	[6•1, 6•3], [6•2, 6•4], [6•5, 6•7], [6•6, 6•8], [6•9, 6•11], [6•10, 6•12]
Mixed practice with multiple choice	6•1, 6•4, 6•7, 6•8, 6•11, 6•12
Mixed practice with writing/reasoning opportunity	6•1, 6•4, 6•5, 6•8, 6•10, 6•11

Home Links are daily homework assignments that review the content of the lesson and often contain ongoing facts practice.

Minute Math+ problems are offered for additional practice in Lessons 6•2, 6•4, 6•6, 6•9, and 6•11.

EM Facts Workshop Game provides online practice of basic facts and computation.

EXTRA PRACTICE **Extra Practice** activities are included in Lessons 6•2, 6•3, 6•5, 6•6, 6•9, 6•10, and 6•11.

Practice through Games

Games are an essential component of practice in the *Everyday Mathematics* program. Games offer skills practice and promote strategic thinking. See the *Differentiation Handbook* for ways to adapt games to meet children's needs.

Lesson	Game	Skill Practiced
6•1, 6•2, 6•5	*Addition Top-It*	Finding and comparing sums [NN Goal 7 and OC Goal 2]
6•1	*Difference Game*	Subtraction [OC Goal 2]
6•4	*Beat the Calculator*	Addition facts [OC Goal 2]
6•4, 6•7	*Fact Power Game*	Solving addition problems [OC Goal 2]
6•5	*Penny Plate*	Finding sums of 10 [OC Goal 1]
6•8, 6•12	*Tric-Trac*	Solving addition problems [OC Goal 2]
6•9	*Coin Top-It*	Calculating and comparing the values of combinations of coins [OC Goal 2]
6•9, 6•10	*Penny-Nickel-Dime Exchange Coin Exchange*	Making coin exchanges [MRF Goal 2]
6•9	*Quarter-Dime-Nickel-Penny Grab*	Counting coin combinations [OC Goal 2]
6•10	*Time Match*	Matching analog and digital clocks [MRF Goal 4]

[NN] Number and Numeration
[MRF] Measurement and Reference Frames
[OC] Operations and Computation
[GEO] Geometry
[DC] Data and Chance
[PFA] Patterns, Functions, and Algebra

Problem Solving 

Good problem solvers use a variety of strategies, including the following:

- Draw a picture.
- Act out the problem.
- Make a table, chart, or list.
- Look for a pattern.
- Try a simpler version of the problem.
- Make a guess and try it out.

The table below lists some of the opportunities in this unit for children to practice these strategies.

Lessons that teach *through* problem solving, not just *about* problem solving

Lesson	Activity
6•1	Explain why 7 comes up most often when rolling two dice.
6•3	Find the number of dots missing on dominoes.
6•4	Find the missing numbers on Fact Triangles.
6•8	Find input numbers in a "What's My Rule?" table.
6•12	Find how high children can count on a calculator.

See Chapter 18: Problem Solving in the *Teacher's Reference Manual* for more information.

The Language of Mathematics

Everyday Mathematics provides lesson-specific suggestions to help all children acquire, process, and express mathematical ideas. Throughout Unit 6, there are lesson-specific language development notes that address the needs of English language learners, indicated by ELL.

ELL SUPPORT Activities to support English language learners are in Part 3 of Lessons 6•4, 6•6, 6•7, 6•9, and 6•12.

The *English Learners Handbook* and the *Differentiation Handbook* have suggestions for promoting language development and acquisition of mathematics vocabulary. See Unit 6 in each handbook.

Unit 6 Vocabulary

Addition/Subtraction Facts Table
centimeter
cm
digital clock
equivalent names
fact family
Fact Triangle
metric system
middle value
My Reference Book
name-collection box
quarter
range
table of contents

Literacy Connection

Lesson 6•9 *26 Letters and 99 Cents,* by Tana Hoban, Greenwillow Books, 1995

Lesson 6•9 *Deena's Lucky Penny,* by Barbara deRubertis, Kane Press, 1999

For more literacy connections, see the *Home Connection Handbook,* Grades 1–3.

Cross-Curricular Links 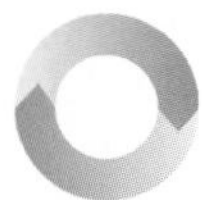

Language Arts
Lesson 6•9 Children learn the meaning of the word *quarter.*

Literature
Lesson 6•9 Children read *Deena's Lucky Penny.*

Science
Lesson 6•10 Children measure how different substances work in an hourglass.

Social Studies
Lesson 6•9 Using state quarters, children find the states on a map of the United States.
Lesson 6•11 Children explore encyclopedias.

Balanced Assessment

Daily Assessments

- **Recognizing Student Achievement** – A daily assessment that is included in every lesson to evaluate children's progress toward the Grade 1 Grade-Level Goals.
- **Informing Instruction** – Notes that appear throughout the unit to help anticipate children's common errors and suggest appropriate problem-solving strategies.

Lesson	Recognizing Student Achievement	Informing Instruction
6•1	Estimate costs for items. [NN Goal 7]	
6•2	Write addition facts. [OC Goal 1]	
6•3	Find parts and totals. [OC Goal 4]	Write subtraction facts in a fact family.
6•4	Do stop-and-start counting by 10s, then 5s, and then 1s. [NN Goal 1]	
6•5	Use the Addition/Subtraction Facts Table to solve addition problems. [OC Goal 1]	
6•6	Analyze and interpret data. [DC Goal 2]	Align zero-mark on rulers.
6•7	Solve easy addition facts. [OC Goal 1]	
6•8	Find the rule in "What's My Rule?" problems. [PFA Goal 1]	Find the input number in "What's My Rule?" problems. Count all uncovered numbers when playing *Tric-Trac.*
6•9	Answer probability questions. [DC Goal 3]	Find the value of coin combinations including quarters.
6•10	Solve number stories. [OC Goal 4]	Write time using digital notation.
6•11	Show and tell time. [MRF Goal 4]	
6•12	Solve addition facts. [OC Goal 1]	

[NN] Number and Numeration [OC] Operations and Computation [DC] Data and Chance
[MRF] Measurement and Reference Frames [GEO] Geometry [PFA] Patterns, Functions, and Algebra

Portfolio Opportunities

The following lessons provide opportunities to gather samples of children's mathematical writings, drawings, and creations to add balance to the assessment process: Lessons 6•1, 6•3, 6•4, 6•5, 6•7, 6•8, 6•10, 6•11, 6•12, and 6•13.

See pages 16 and 17 in the *Assessment Handbook* for more information about portfolios and how to use them.

Say several addition facts. Children use the paper and facts table to find the sums and then record the sums on their slates. Circulate and check that children are using their papers correctly.

NOTE It is okay for children to look up either 6 and 8 or 8 and 6 on the Addition/Subtraction Facts Table. This is a good opportunity to discuss turn-around facts. Also, children can use the Addition/Subtraction Facts Table located on the inside front cover of their journals to find answers.

▶ Introducing *Addition Top-It*

PARTNER ACTIVITY

(*Math Journal 2,* inside front cover)

Children play *Addition Top-It* to practice addition facts. The game is played with a deck of number cards, 4 cards for each number 0–9. (As many as 4 children can play, but at first, just 2 children should play.) Provide directions and then have children play at least one game. Children should play this game often in the next few weeks to practice the facts.

Directions

1. Shuffle the deck and place it number-side down.
2. Each player turns over 2 cards and calls out the sum of the numbers. If the players don't know the sum, they may find it in the Addition/Subtraction Facts Table (*Math Journal 2,* inside front cover). Players should check each other's sums, using the table.
3. The player with the largest sum wins the round and takes all of the cards.
4. In case of a tie for the largest sum, each tied player turns over 2 more cards and calls out the sum of the numbers. The player with the largest sum takes all of the cards from both plays.
5. The game ends when not enough cards are left for each player to have another turn.
6. The player with the most cards wins.

Variation: Have children practice finding sums of 3 addends using the Associative Property of Addition while playing *Addition Top-It.* Have children turn over 3 cards rather than 2 cards.

As children play *Addition Top-It,* visit each partnership. Notice which facts children are solving and ask them to share their strategy for finding the sum. When necessary, direct children to the Fact Strategy Wall to assist them in finding a strategy.

Playing *Addition Top-It*

NOTE The facts table is one source for looking up facts. Do not expect all children to find the table easy to use at first. Encourage them to use the table so that they can eventually use it with ease.

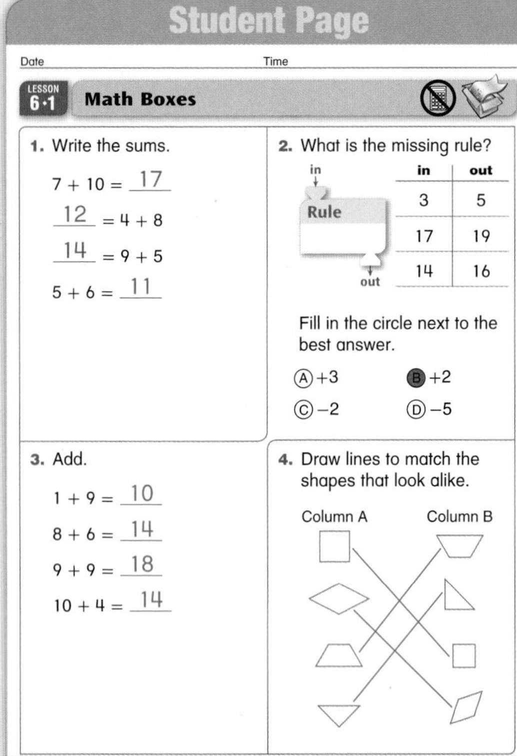
Student Page

Date Time

LESSON 6·1 **Math Boxes**

1. Write the sums.

7 + 10 = 17

12 = 4 + 8

14 = 9 + 5

5 + 6 = 11

2. What is the missing rule?

in → Rule → out

in	out
3	5
17	19
14	16

Fill in the circle next to the best answer.

Ⓐ +3 ● +2

Ⓒ −2 Ⓓ −5

3. Add.

1 + 9 = 10

8 + 6 = 14

9 + 9 = 18

10 + 4 = 14

4. Draw lines to match the shapes that look alike.

Column A Column B

Math Journal 2, p. 110

NOTE Remember to use the Dice Roll Activity on a regular basis to practice fact strategies. See Lesson 5-10 for detailed instructions. When your class is ready, you may wish to try some of the variations listed in Lesson 5-10.

2 Ongoing Learning & Practice

▶ Playing the *Difference Game*

Children practice subtraction skills with coins by playing the *Difference Game*. For detailed instructions, see Lesson 5-7.

Adjusting the Activity

Have children record number models on half-sheets of paper for each round of play. For example, if Player 1 has 8 pennies and Player 2 has 10 pennies, the number model is 10 − 8 = 2.

AUDITORY ◆ KINESTHETIC ◆ TACTILE ◆ VISUAL

▶ Math Boxes 6·1

(*Math Journal 2*, p. 110)

Mixed Practice Math Boxes in this lesson are paired with Math Boxes in Lesson 6-3. The skills in Problem 4 preview Unit 7 content.

Portfolio Ideas

Writing/Reasoning Have children draw, write, or verbalize an answer to the following question: *How do turn-around facts help you learn math facts?* A reasonable answer should explain that if you know one fact, then you also know its turn-around fact.

its the Same
thing inSept
you torn arawn
the numbrs.

3+2
2+3

One child's work in response to the Writing/Reasoning prompt

▶ Home Link 6•1

INDEPENDENT ACTIVITY

(*Math Masters,* pp. 162 and 163)

Home Connection Children find sums, using the Addition/Subtraction Facts Table and complete a color-by-number picture. This Home Link consists of two pages.

NOTE If you wish to have children practice sums to 20 using the Addition/Subtraction Facts Table, go to www.everydaymathonline.com.

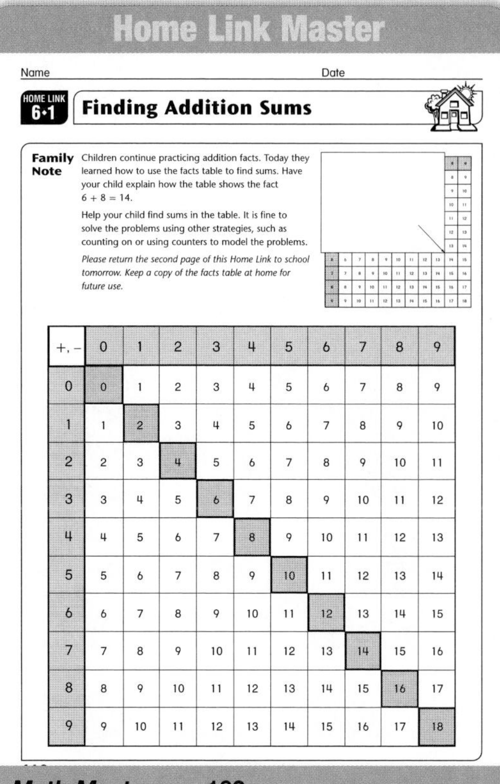

Home Link Master

Name Date

HOME LINK 6•1 **Finding Addition Sums**

Family Note Children continue practicing addition facts. Today they learned how to use the facts table to find sums. Have your child explain how the table shows the fact 6 + 8 = 14.

Help your child find sums in the table. It is fine to solve the problems using other strategies, such as counting on or using counters to model the problems.

Please return the second page of this Home Link to school tomorrow. Keep a copy of the facts table at home for future use.

+, −	0	1	2	3	4	5	6	7	8	9
0	0	1	2	3	4	5	6	7	8	9
1	1	2	3	4	5	6	7	8	9	10
2	2	3	4	5	6	7	8	9	10	11
3	3	4	5	6	7	8	9	10	11	12
4	4	5	6	7	8	9	10	11	12	13
5	5	6	7	8	9	10	11	12	13	14
6	6	7	8	9	10	11	12	13	14	15
7	7	8	9	10	11	12	13	14	15	16
8	8	9	10	11	12	13	14	15	16	17
9	9	10	11	12	13	14	15	16	17	18

Math Masters, p. 162

3 Differentiation Options

READINESS

SMALL-GROUP ACTIVITY

▶ Charting Domino Sums

5–15 Min

ELL

To provide experience charting sums using a concrete model, have children sort and chart domino sums. Children put each domino in the column labeled with the corresponding sum. (See Advance Preparation.) Encourage children to lay the dominoes in the columns horizontally and from the bottom of the column to the top. With a second set of 6|6 dominoes, children can add the turn-around facts to the chart. After the dominoes are sorted, discuss patterns on the chart. Sample answers: There are more dominoes in the middle columns. There is one domino in the 2 column and one domino in the 12 column. To support English language learners, review the meaning of the word *sum.*

ENRICHMENT

FACTS PRACTICE

PARTNER ACTIVITY

▶ Exploring Polyhedral Dice Rolls

15–30 Min

ELL

To apply children's understanding of randomly generated dice sums, have them predict the results of rolling a pair of 8-sided dice. Discuss which of the true statements for the 6-sided dice roll might be true for the 8-sided dice roll. Then partners take turns rolling a pair of 8-sided dice and recording each roll as an addition fact and as its turn-around fact in the correct column on the chart. (See Advance Preparation.) Review the charted results to see if the predictions were accurate. To support English language learners, review the meaning of the word *predict.*

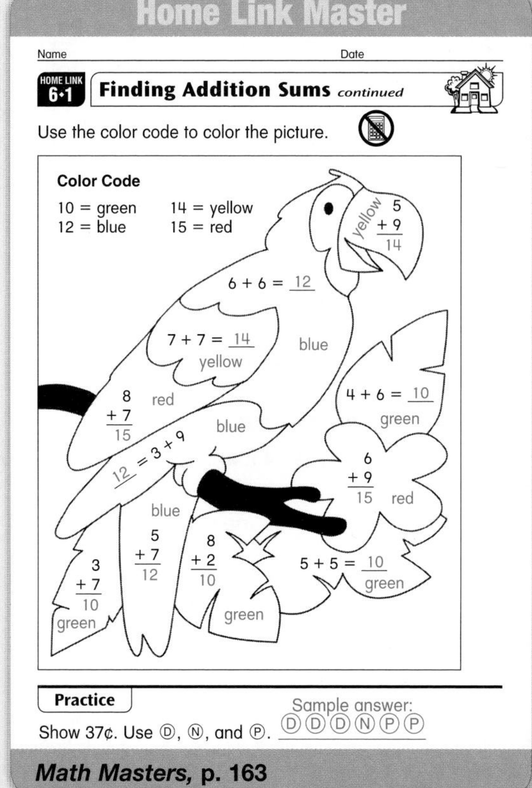

Home Link Master

Name Date

HOME LINK 6•1 **Finding Addition Sums** *continued*

Use the color code to color the picture.

Practice

Show 37¢. Use Ⓓ, Ⓝ, and Ⓟ. Sample answer: ⒹⒹⒹⓃⓅⓅ

Math Masters, p. 163

6•2 Equivalent Names

Objective To introduce name-collection boxes as devices for collecting equivalent names for numbers.

www.everydaymathonline.com

ePresentations

eToolkit

Algorithms Practice

EM Facts Workshop Game™

Family Letters

Assessment Management

Common Core State Standards

Curriculum Focal Points

Interactive Teacher's Lesson Guide

1 Teaching the Lesson

Key Concepts and Skills

- Find different sets of 2 or more addends with the same sum.
  [Number and Numeration Goal 6]
- Use dominoes, drawings, tally marks, base-10 blocks, and manipulatives to give equivalent names for numbers.
  [Number and Numeration Goal 6]
- Write number sentences to express equivalencies.
  [Patterns, Functions, and Algebra Goal 2]

Key Activities

Children are introduced to equivalent names for numbers. They find equivalent names for numbers and record them in name-collection boxes.

Ongoing Assessment: Recognizing Student Achievement Use the Math Message.
[Operations and Computation Goal 1]

Key Vocabulary

equivalent names ◆ name-collection box

Materials

Math Journal 2, p. 111
Home Link 6•1
pan balance ◆ 14 identical objects ◆ slate

2 Ongoing Learning & Practice

Playing *Addition Top-It*
Math Journal 2, inside front cover
per partnership: 4 each of number cards 0–9 (from the Everything Math Deck, if available)
Children practice addition skills.

Math Boxes 6•2
Math Journal 2, p. 112
Children practice and maintain skills through Math Box problems.

Home Link 6•2
Math Masters, pp. 164 and 165
Children practice and maintain skills through Home Link activities.

3 Differentiation Options

READINESS

Modeling Equivalent Names
per partnership: counters
Children use counters to explore finding equivalent names.

ENRICHMENT

Doing Musical Name-Collection Boxes
per group: 5 large sheets of chart paper, CD or tape player, CDs or tapes
Children write or draw representations of numbers in name-collection boxes posted around the classroom.

EXTRA PRACTICE

Minute Math+
Minute Math®+, pp. 11 and 12
Children practice finding equivalent names.

Advance Preparation

For Part 1, each of the 14 identical objects should weigh enough so that if one pan has one more object than the other, the pans will clearly not balance. For example, use longs rather than cubes, since an unequal number of cubes may appear to balance.

***Teacher's Reference Manual,* Grades 1–3** pp. 17, 69, 76

Getting Started

Mental Math and Reflexes

Dictate a number. Have children write on their slates the number that comes before (or after) the given number. Then have them circle the tens digit.

●○○ Number before: 12, 22, 31 ①1, ②1, ③0
Number after: 29, 30, 35 ③0, ③1, ③6

●●○ Number before: 39, 44, 49 ③8, ④3, ④8
Number after: 45, 55, 63 ④6, ⑤6, ⑥4

●●● Number before: 79, 88, 97 ⑦8, ⑧7, ⑨6
Number after: 100, 107, 129 1⓪1, 1⓪8, 1③0

Math Message ★

On your slate, write as many addition facts as you can that have 7 as a sum.

Home Link 6·1 Follow-Up

Briefly go over the answers.

1 Teaching the Lesson

▶ Math Message Follow-Up

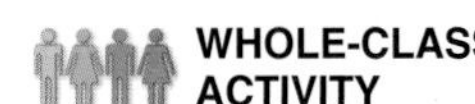

List addition facts on the board in horizontal and vertical formats. These facts will be used later in this lesson.

Ongoing Assessment: Recognizing Student Achievement

Math Message 

Use the **Math Message** to assess children's ability to write addition facts. Children are making adequate progress if they are able to write at least 3 different facts with sums of 7. Some children may be able to write more facts.

[Operations and Computation Goal 1]

▶ Discussing Equivalent Names in Everyday Life

Discuss the fact that the same thing or person can have different names, or **equivalent names.** For example, Mrs. Jones, Nancy Jones, Nancy, Nan, Mom, and Aunt Nan could all be names for the same person. To support English language learners, write the word *equivalent* on the board.

Point out that numbers also have different names. Many math problems are really exercises in finding an equivalent name for a number. For example, when solving $7 + 5 = ?$, you are really looking for another name for $7 + 5$, such as 12.

NOTE If the pans on your balance are deep, put a piece of cardboard on top of each pan as a platform to make the objects visible. If you do not have a pan balance, you might draw one on the board or on a transparency.

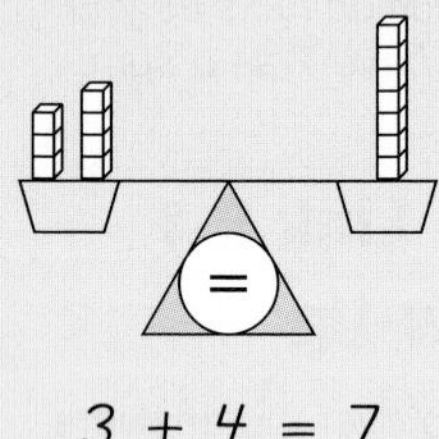

3 + 4 = 7

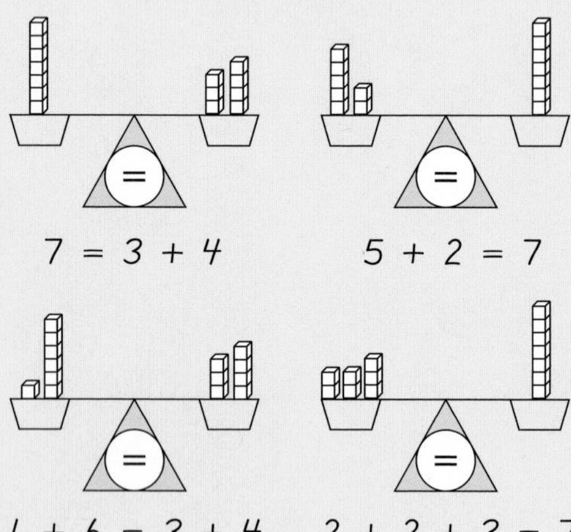

▶ Illustrating Equivalence Using a Pan Balance

WHOLE-CLASS ACTIVITY

Algebraic Thinking Set up a pan balance in full view of the whole class and place seven identical objects on each of the two pans. Separate the objects on one of the pans into two groups.

Write a number model to represent this arrangement of objects. (*See margin.*)

Repeat this procedure with other arrangements of seven objects, as suggested by children. Alternate between putting the two groups of objects in the right-hand pan and then in the left-hand pan. Depending on the arrangement of the objects, the number 7 will appear either to the right or to the left of the equal sign in the number model.

Children may suggest arrangements where the objects are grouped on both pans or where the objects in one pan are arranged into three or more groups. Accept such responses, but concentrate on the basic addition facts for 7.

▶ Introducing Name-Collection Boxes

WHOLE-CLASS ACTIVITY

Draw a **name-collection box** with 7 written on the tag and two addition names for 7 inside the box. (*See margin.*) Explain that name-collection boxes will be used to record equivalent names for numbers.

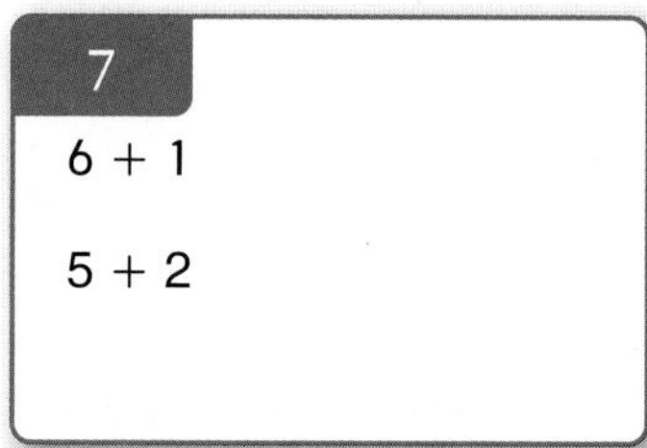

NOTE Name-collection boxes can be posted on the Class Data Pad or on the board for children to add new entries over several days. When they realize that they can use subtraction names as well, the sky is the limit!

Discuss the addition names for 7: 6 + 1 is 7, and so is 5 + 2. *What are some other addition problems with 7 as the answer?* As children give names, write them in the name-collection box. Write the sums for 7 in various ways: horizontally, vertically, and as turnarounds of names already listed.

7 | ~~////~~ // | seven

6 + 1

5 + 2

$\begin{array}{r} 3 \\ +4 \\ \hline \end{array}$ $\begin{array}{r} 4 \\ +3 \\ \hline \end{array}$

Ask children for other names for 7. Write some suggestions in the 7 box.

Examples:

$1 + 1 + 1 + 1 + 1 + 1 + 1$

1 more than 6

$8 - 1$

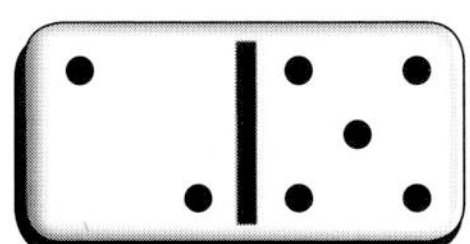

▶ Finding Equivalent Names for Numbers

INDEPENDENT ACTIVITY

(*Math Journal 2,* p. 111)

In Problems 1 and 2, children record equivalent names for numbers in name-collection boxes. In Problem 3, they determine which names do not belong in a name-collection box. In Problem 4, children make up their own name-collection box.

NOTE At first, many children may use only addition facts to name the number in the name-collection box. Encourage them to use money, make a representation with base-10 blocks, or make tally marks for the number. As the year progresses, children will expand their strategies for naming numbers.

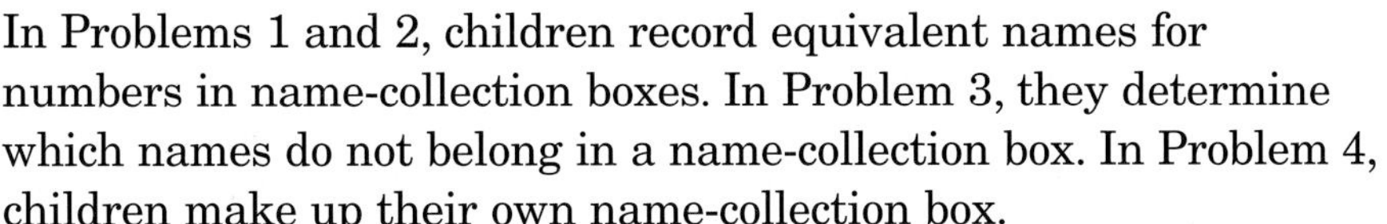

▶ Playing *Addition Top-It*

PARTNER ACTIVITY

(*Math Journal 2,* inside front cover)

Children practice addition skills for numbers from 0 through 9 by playing *Addition Top-It*. For detailed instructions, see Lesson 6-1.

▶ Math Boxes 6•2

INDEPENDENT ACTIVITY

(*Math Journal 2,* p. 112)

Mixed Practice Math Boxes in this lesson are paired with Math Boxes in Lesson 6-4. The skills in Problem 4 preview Unit 7 content.

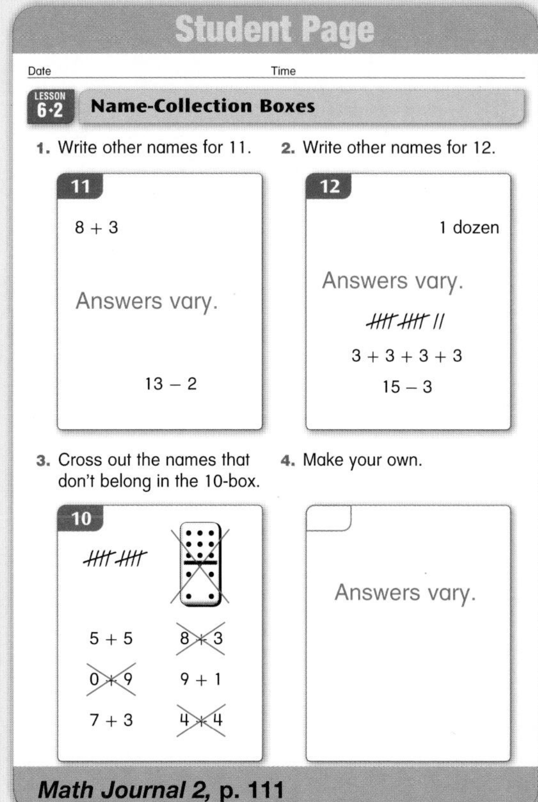

Math Journal 2, p. 111

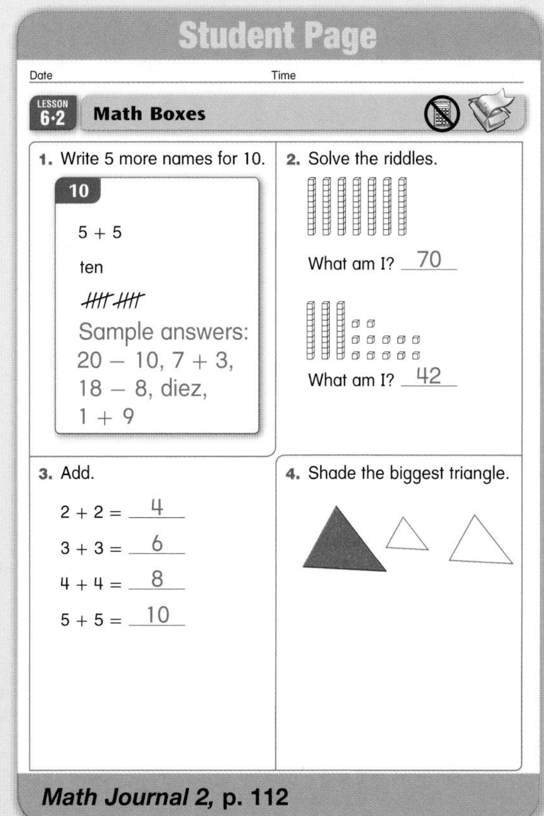

Math Journal 2, p. 112

Home Link Master

Name Date

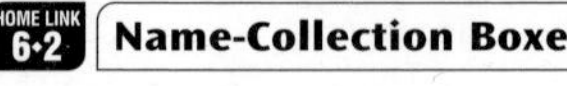

HOME LINK 6•2 **Name-Collection Boxes**

Family Note Today we began working with name-collection boxes. See the attached letter for more information about this routine.

Please return this Home Link to school tomorrow.

1. List all of the addition facts you know that have a sum of 10.

2. Write as many names as you can in the name-collection boxes.

15 Sample answers:
10 + 5 20 − 5
~~||||~~ ~~||||~~ ~~||||~~
quince
7 + 8

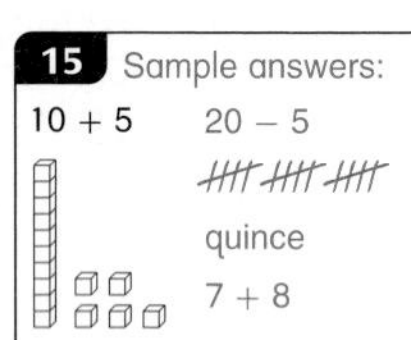

18 Sample answers:
10 + 8 9 + 9
~~||||~~ ~~||||~~ ~~||||~~ |||
diez y ocho

Practice

3. How old were you 2 years ago? Answers vary.

4. Odd or even? Answers vary.

Math Masters, p. 164

NOTE Remember to reserve time every day to complete the number-line, attendance, calendar, weather, and temperature routines.

Home Link Master

Name Date

HOME LINK 6•2 **Family Letter**

Name-Collection Boxes

People, things, and ideas often have several different names. For example, Mary calls her parents Mom and Dad. Other people may call them Linda and John, Aunt Linda and Uncle John, or Grandma and Grandpa. Mail may come addressed to Mr. and Mrs. West. All of these names are for the same two people.

Your child is bringing home an activity with a special format for using this naming idea with numbers. We call this format a name-collection box. The box is used by children to collect many names for a given number.

The box is identified by the name on the label. The box shown here is a 25-box, a name-collection box for the number 25.

Names can include sums, differences, products, quotients, or combinations of operations, as well as words (including words in other languages), tally marks, and arrays. A name-collection box can be filled by using any equivalent names.

With repeated practice, children gain the power to rename numbers for a variety of different uses.

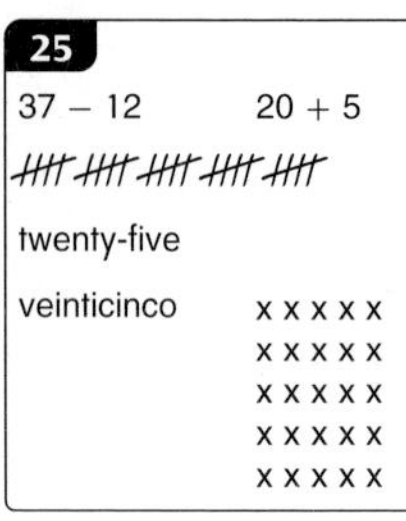

25
37 − 12 20 + 5
~~||||~~ ~~||||~~ ~~||||~~ ~~||||~~ ~~||||~~
twenty-five
veinticinco
X X X X X
X X X X X
X X X X X
X X X X X
X X X X X

Math Masters, p. 165

▶ Home Link 6•2

INDEPENDENT ACTIVITY

FACTS PRACTICE

(*Math Masters,* pp. 164 and 165)

Home Connection Children write as many facts as they can with a sum of 10 and complete two name-collection boxes. A Family Letter (*Math Masters,* page 165) that describes the name-collection box routine accompanies this Home Link.

3 Differentiation Options

READINESS

PARTNER ACTIVITY

▶ Modeling Equivalent Names

5–15 Min

To explore equivalent names for numbers using a concrete model, have children explore combinations of counters for a given number. Model the following process:

1. Write the number 5 on a half-sheet of paper and circle it.
2. Place 5 counters on the table in a line.
3. Say: *No counters are covered.* Write 0.
4. Say: *5 counters are not covered.* Write + 5.
5. Say: *There are a total of 5 counters.* Write = 5.

(5)

0 + 5 = 5

Recording Sheet for Modeling Equivalent Names

Repeat the process, covering 1 counter and writing the number sentence 1 + 4 = 5. Have children work with a partner to write additional number sentences for 5. Have children read their number sentences aloud. Children can repeat the activity using different numbers of counters.

ENRICHMENT

▶ Doing Musical Name-Collection Boxes

To apply what children know about equivalent names, draw 5 name-collection boxes (with numbers on the tags) on chart paper and post them around the room. Play music as children walk around the room. Stop the music and ask each child to sit by the nearest name-collection box. Have each child write an equivalent name in the box that follows a "rule." For example, children record a name that has subtraction in it or record coin combinations for a name. Continue this activity, providing opportunities for children to stop at as many name-collection boxes as possible.

EXTRA PRACTICE

▶ *Minute Math+*

Use *Minute Math+,* pages 11 and 12 to provide practice finding name equivalents for whole numbers and money amounts.

Planning Ahead

Beginning in Lesson 6-4, each child will need a set of Fact Triangles found in *Math Journal 2*, Activity Sheets 9 and 10.

6·3 Fact Families

Objective To introduce addition/subtraction fact families.

www.everydaymathonline.com

ePresentations

eToolkit

Algorithms Practice

EM Facts Workshop Game™

Family Letters

Assessment Management

Common Core State Standards

Curriculum Focal Points

Interactive Teacher's Lesson Guide

1 Teaching the Lesson

Key Concepts and Skills

- Write parts-and-total number models. [Operations and Computation Goal 4]
- Write addition and subtraction number models using +, −, and =. [Patterns, Functions, and Algebra Goal 2]
- Generate fact families. [Patterns, Functions, and Algebra Goal 3]

Key Activities

Children are introduced to addition/subtraction fact families, using dominoes as a source for number triples. Children generate fact families for number triples.

Ongoing Assessment: Recognizing Student Achievement Use the Math Message. [Operations and Computation Goal 4]

Ongoing Assessment: Informing Instruction See page 551.

Key Vocabulary

fact family

Materials

Math Journal 2, p. 113
Home Link 6•2
Math Masters, pp. 166–168
per child: 2 dominoes ◆ slate ◆ counters (optional)

2 Ongoing Learning & Practice

Practicing with Name-Collection Boxes

Math Journal 2, p. 114
Children practice filling in name-collection boxes.

Math Boxes 6•3

Math Journal 2, p. 115
Children practice and maintain skills through Math Box problems.

Home Link 6•3

Math Masters, p. 169
Children practice and maintain skills through Home Link activities.

3 Differentiation Options

READINESS

Playing Concentration with Number Cards and Dominoes

per partnership: number cards 0–9 (from the Everything Math Deck, if available), 10 dominoes with a total of 0–9 dots
Children practice matching dots on dominoes with numerals.

EXTRA PRACTICE

Solving Fact Families

Math Masters, p. 326
double-9 dominoes
Children practice with fact families.

Advance Preparation

For Part 1, make one copy of *Math Masters,* page 166 per two children. Cut the sheets in half and place them near the Math Message.

***Teacher's Reference Manual,* Grades 1–3** pp. 16, 17, 196–198

Getting Started

Mental Math and Reflexes

Tell simple number stories. Children may solve them by using a number line, number grid, tally marks, pictures, counters, or base-10 blocks. Have children share their strategies for each problem. Summarize solutions with an appropriate diagram and number model. Do not force a number story into a particular mold by saying that there is a "best" diagram for the problem.

Suggestions:

●○○ *Mona had 25¢ when she went to school. She bought milk at lunchtime for 5¢. How much money did she have left after buying the milk?* 20¢

●●○ *Dwayne received 12 helium balloons for his seventh birthday. By the next day, 6 balloons had lost their helium. How many balloons still had helium the next day?* 6 balloons

●●● *Michele read 24 books. Regina read 8 more books than Michele. How many books did Regina read?* 32 books

Math Message

Display *Math Masters,* page 166.

Take a half-sheet of paper and complete the problems.

Home Link 6·2 Follow-Up

Ask children to help you list all of the addition facts with sums of 10. Have children share some of the names in their name-collection boxes. Highlight names that are especially creative.

1 Teaching the Lesson

▶ Math Message Follow-Up

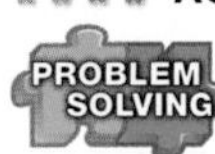

Algebraic Thinking Have children share how they solved the problems on *Math Masters,* page 166. Solutions to Problem 2 may include:

▷ Counting up to 11, starting at 7 (8, 9, 10, 11, while counting on fingers).

▷ Using a guess-and-check approach: "I will try 2. 7 + 2 is 9, so 2 is not enough. 7 + 3 is 10. 3 is not enough, so I will try 4. 7 + 4 is 11, so there are 4 missing dots."

▷ Solving an unknown addend problem: Solve $11 - 7 = \square$ by finding the number that makes 11 when added to 7, as in $7 + \square = 11$.

For each problem, write three numbers on the board: the number of dots in each half of the domino and the total number of dots. For example, for Problem 1, write 4, 3, 7. Point out that we can always associate three numbers with any domino. Tell children that they will practice making number models for dominoes by using the three related numbers. Ask them to suggest number models for each problem.

Ongoing Assessment: Recognizing Student Achievement

Math Message

Use the **Math Message** to assess children's ability to find parts and totals. Children are making adequate progress if they are able to answer all 3 problems correctly.

[Operations and Computation Goal 4]

Teaching Master

Name Date

LESSON 6·3 **Domino Totals**

1. Find the total.

Unit: domino dots

7

Draw the missing dots.

2. 11

3. 8

Name Date

LESSON 6·3 **Domino Totals**

1. Find the total.

Unit: domino dots

7

Draw the missing dots.

2. 11

3. 8

Math Masters, p. 166

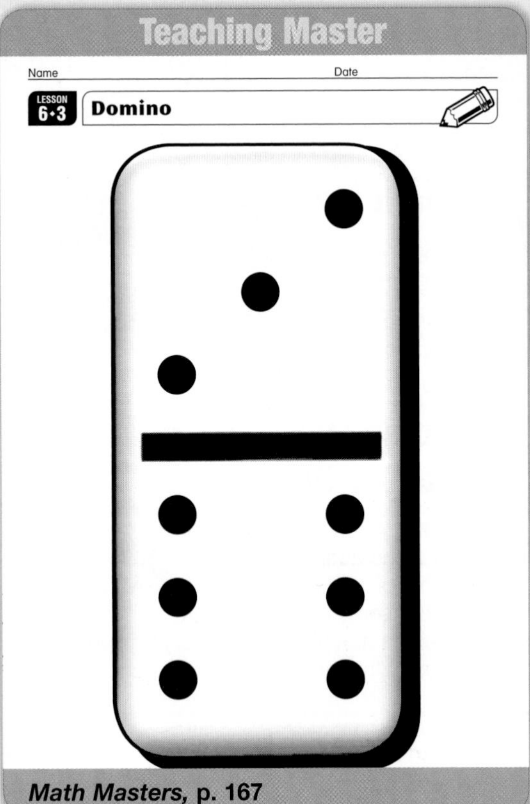

Math Masters, p. 167

▶ Introducing Addition/Subtraction Fact Families

(*Math Masters,* pp. 167 and 168)

Tape the 3|6 demonstration domino (*Math Masters,* page 167) to the board (or draw a 3|6 domino). Then ask:

- What three numbers go with this domino? 3, 6, 9 (Write 3, 6, 9 on the board.)
- What two number models show how to find the total number of dots? $3 + 6 = 9$; $6 + 3 = 9$ (Write the number models on the board.)
- What two subtraction number models can you make up that use 3, 6, and 9? $9 - 3 = 6$ and $9 - 6 = 3$ (Write both number models on the board.)

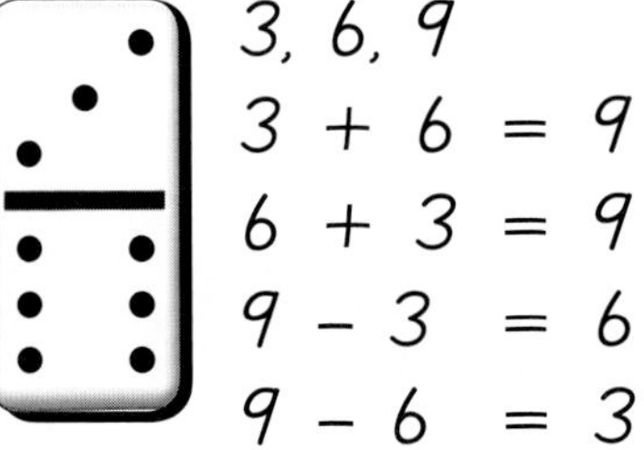

NOTE To encourage further understanding of the +, −, and = symbols, have children fill in missing symbols in number sentences that you write.

Adjusting the Activity

ELL

For subtraction, have children draw a line down the middle of their slates and place counters in each half to model the domino. They can count the total and then remove the counters from one side to generate a subtraction fact.

AUDITORY ◆ KINESTHETIC ◆ TACTILE ◆ VISUAL

Repeat this routine with the 5|4 demonstration domino (*Math Masters,* page 168). Focus on the three numbers associated with this domino and the four number models that can be written using these numbers.

Explain that the addition and subtraction facts that can be written using the three domino numbers make up a **fact family.** Fact families show the relationship between addition and subtraction.

Distribute two dominoes to each child. Ask children to write on their slates the fact family for each of their dominoes. Facts can be written in horizontal or vertical format. If children have difficulty with the addition turn-around rule, rotate your demonstration domino to model these relationships.

You might mention that a subtraction answer can be checked by doing addition. For many first graders, it is helpful to think about $8 - 5 = ?$ as $5 + ? = 8$. This approach encourages "counting up" to subtract, a strategy that also works well with multidigit numbers. This also encourages children to look for the unknown number that makes the number model true.

Teaching Master

Name Date

LESSON 6·3 **Domino**

Math Masters, p. 168

Have several children share their fact families. In one column, list the dominoes that have four different number models (all dominoes except doubles). In another column, list the dominoes that have only two facts (all doubles).

Summarize by stating that except for doubles, a fact family has two addition and two subtraction facts. A fact family for doubles has only one addition and one subtraction fact.

▶ Writing Addition/Subtraction Fact Families

(*Math Journal 2,* p. 113)

Children write fact families for dominoes.

NOTE Generating fact families reinforces the inverse relationship between addition and subtraction.

Ongoing Assessment: Informing Instruction

Watch for children who assume incorrectly that since the two addition facts are turn-around facts, the two subtraction facts must also be turn-around facts, and therefore write subtraction number models such as $5 - 9 = 4$. Remind children to write the largest number first when writing a subtraction problem.

Student Page

Date ______ Time ______

LESSON 6·3 **Fact Families**

Write the 3 numbers for each domino.
Use the numbers to write the fact family.

1. Numbers: 3, 5, 8
Fact Family: 3 + 5 = 8; 5 + 3 = 8; 8 − 5 = 3; 8 − 3 = 5

2. Numbers: 4, 6, 10
Fact Family: 4 + 6 = 10; 6 + 4 = 10; 10 − 4 = 6; 10 − 6 = 4

3. Numbers: 9, 3, 12
Fact Family: 9 + 3 = 12; 3 + 9 = 12; 12 − 3 = 9; 12 − 9 = 3

4. Make up your own.
Draw the dots.
Numbers: Answers vary.
Fact Family: ___ + ___ = ___; ___ + ___ = ___; ___ − ___ = ___; ___ − ___ = ___

Math Journal 2, p. 113

2 Ongoing Learning & Practice

▶ Practicing with Name-Collection Boxes

INDEPENDENT ACTIVITY

(*Math Journal 2,* p. 114)

Use *Math Journal 2,* page 114 to provide more practice with name-collection boxes.

▶ Math Boxes 6·3

INDEPENDENT ACTIVITY

(*Math Journal 2,* p. 115)

Mixed Practice Math Boxes in this lesson are paired with Math Boxes in Lesson 6-1. The skills in Problem 4 preview Unit 7 content.

▶ Home Link 6·3

INDEPENDENT ACTIVITY

(*Math Masters,* p. 169)

Home Connection Children generate fact families for dominoes.

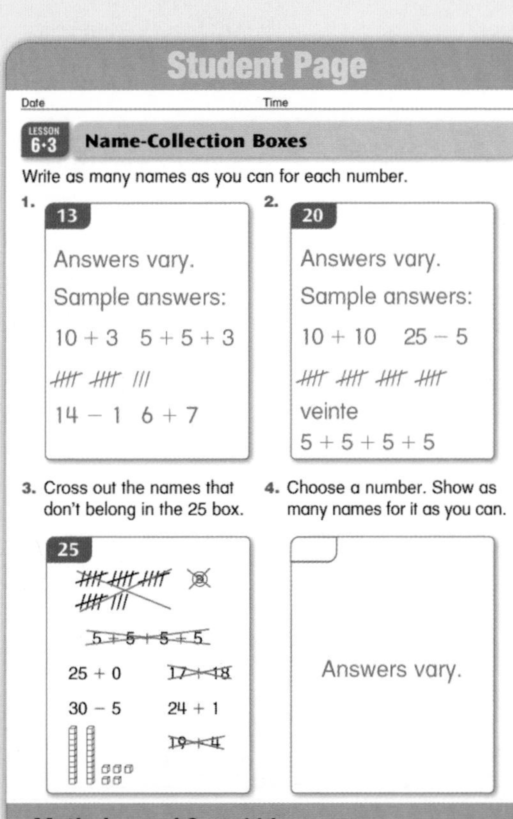

Student Page

Date ______ Time ______

LESSON 6·3 **Name-Collection Boxes**

Write as many names as you can for each number.

1. 13
Answers vary.
Sample answers:
10 + 3   5 + 5 + 3
tally marks (13)
14 − 1   6 + 7

2. 20
Answers vary.
Sample answers:
10 + 10   25 − 5
tally marks (20)
veinte
5 + 5 + 5 + 5

3. Cross out the names that don't belong in the 25 box.
25
~~tally marks~~   ~~(crossed out)~~
~~5 + 5 + 5 + 5~~
25 + 0   ~~17 + 18~~
30 − 5   24 + 1
base-10 blocks   ~~19 + 4~~

4. Choose a number. Show as many names for it as you can.
Answers vary.

Math Journal 2, p. 114

Student Page

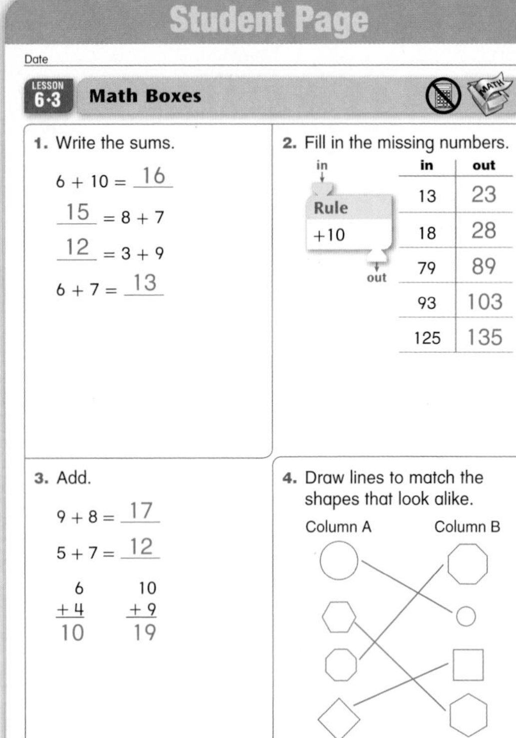
Date

LESSON 6·3 Math Boxes

1. Write the sums.

6 + 10 = 16

15 = 8 + 7

12 = 3 + 9

6 + 7 = 13

2. Fill in the missing numbers.

Rule +10

in	out
13	23
18	28
79	89
93	103
125	135

3. Add.

9 + 8 = 17

5 + 7 = 12

6 + 4 = 10

10 + 9 = 19

4. Draw lines to match the shapes that look alike.

Column A Column B

Math Journal 2, p. 115

Home Link Master

Name Date

HOME LINK 6·3 Fact Families

Family Note We have extended our work with facts to subtraction facts by introducing fact families. Your child will generate addition facts and subtraction facts for the numbers pictured on the dominoes below.

Note that for each problem, there are two addition facts and two subtraction facts.

Please return this Home Link to school tomorrow.

Write the 3 numbers for each domino. Use the numbers to write the fact family.

1. Numbers: 7, 5, 12

Fact family:

7 + 5 = 12

5 + 7 = 12

12 - 5 = 7

12 - 7 = 5

2. Numbers: 6, 9, 15

Fact family:

6 + 9 = 15

9 + 6 = 15

15 - 6 = 9

15 - 9 = 6

Practice

3. Write the missing numbers.

Rule −2

32, 30, 28, 26, 24

Math Masters, p. 169

3 Differentiation Options

READINESS

PARTNER ACTIVITY

▶ Playing Concentration with Number Cards and Dominoes

15–30 Min

To provide experience writing number sentences, children record number sentences based on domino-card pairs they collect. Players place number cards facedown in 2 rows of 5 cards each. They also arrange the dominoes facedown in 2 rows of 5 dominoes each. Players take turns turning over 1 card and 1 domino. If the numbers on the card and the domino match, the player takes the card-domino pair and continues playing. If they do not match, the player puts them back in their original place after the other player has seen them. The game ends when there are no more cards and dominoes left. Have children record the domino-card pairs they won in the form of a number sentence. For example, if they had a 3|0 domino, they should record 3 + 0 = 3.

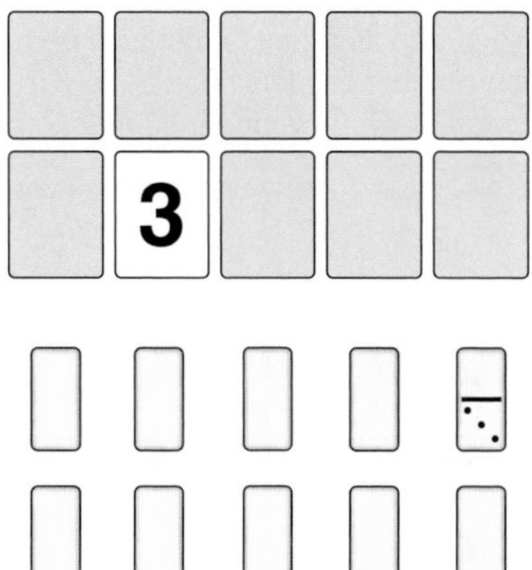

EXTRA PRACTICE

INDEPENDENT ACTIVITY

FACTS PRACTICE

▶ Solving Fact Families

(*Math Masters,* p. 326)

Have children practice finding fact families by choosing dominoes and filling in *Math Masters,* page 326.

6•4 Fact Triangles

Objective To introduce Fact Triangles.

www.everydaymathonline.com

ePresentations

eToolkit

Algorithms Practice

EM Facts Workshop Game™

Family Letters

Assessment Management

Common Core State Standards

Curriculum Focal Points

Interactive Teacher's Lesson Guide

1 Teaching the Lesson

Key Concepts and Skills

- Find sums of 1-digit numbers with and without a calculator.
  [Operations and Computation Goal 1]
- Write addition and subtraction number models, using +, −, and =.
  [Patterns, Functions, and Algebra Goal 2]
- Generate fact families.
  [Patterns, Functions, and Algebra Goal 3]

Key Activities

Children learn to use Fact Triangles to generate fact families. They play *Beat the Calculator* in groups of three.

Ongoing Assessment: Recognizing Student Achievement
Use Mental Math and Reflexes.
[Number and Numeration Goal 1]

Key Vocabulary

Fact Triangle

Materials

Math Journal 2, p. 116 and Activity Sheets 9 and 10
Home Link 6•3
Math Masters, p. 170 (optional)
per group: calculator ◆ slate ◆ paper clip or envelope

2 Ongoing Learning & Practice

Playing the *Fact Power Game*

Math Masters, p. 343
game markers
per partnership or group: die
Children practice addition facts.

Math Boxes 6•4

Math Journal 2, p. 117
Children practice and maintain skills through Math Box problems.

Home Link 6•4

Math Masters, pp. 171 and 172
Children practice and maintain skills through Home Link activities.

Minute Math+

Minute Math®+, p. 6
Children practice with ordinal numbers.

3 Differentiation Options

READINESS

Constructing Fact Families

per child: 2 different-colored dice
Children generate and record fact families with dice.

ENRICHMENT

Exploring Patterns Using Fact Triangles

Math Masters, pp. 173 and 174
Children use Fact Triangles to explore patterns based on easy addition facts.

ELL SUPPORT

Making a Fact Family House

per group: construction paper, dominoes (optional)
Children use triangle roofs and square houses to generate fact families.

Advance Preparation

***Teacher's Reference Manual,* Grades 1–3** pp. 58, 59

Getting Started

Mental Math and Reflexes 

Practice "stop-and-start" counting by 10s, 5s, and 1s. Use the following routine:

- Start at 0. Count together by 10s to 50. Stop. Have children write the next count on their slates. 60
- Continue from 60, counting together by 5s. Stop at 80. Have children write the next count on their slates. 85
- Continue from 85, counting together by 1s. Stop at 89. Have children write the next count on their slates. 90

Repeat this routine, stopping at different numbers.

Math Message

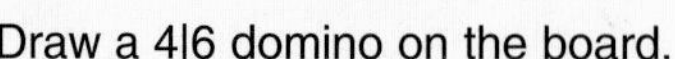
Draw a 4|6 domino on the board.

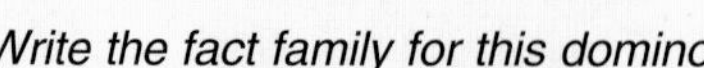
Write the fact family for this domino.

Home Link 6·3 Follow-Up

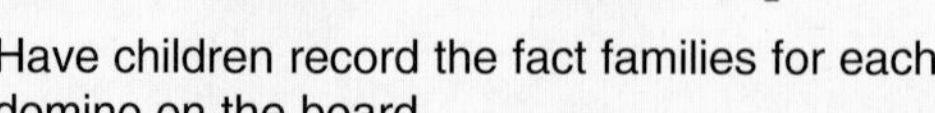
Have children record the fact families for each domino on the board.

Ongoing Assessment: Recognizing Student Achievement

Mental Math and Reflexes 

Use **Mental Math and Reflexes** to assess children's ability to do "stop-and-start" counting. Children are making adequate progress if they are able to successfully make the transition between counts by 10s, counts by 5s, and counts by 1s. Some children may continue to have difficulty with this skill.

[Number and Numeration Goal 1]

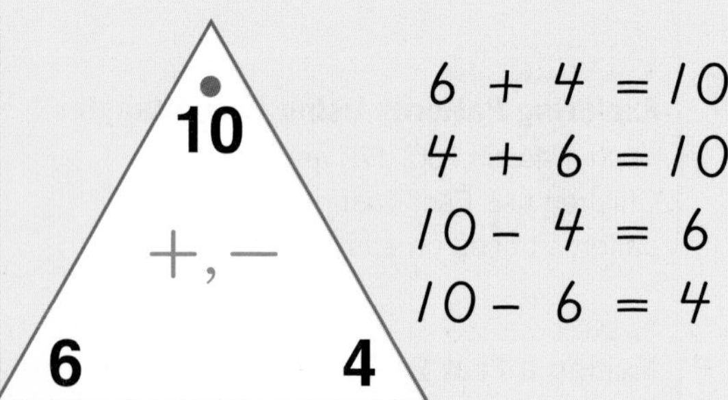
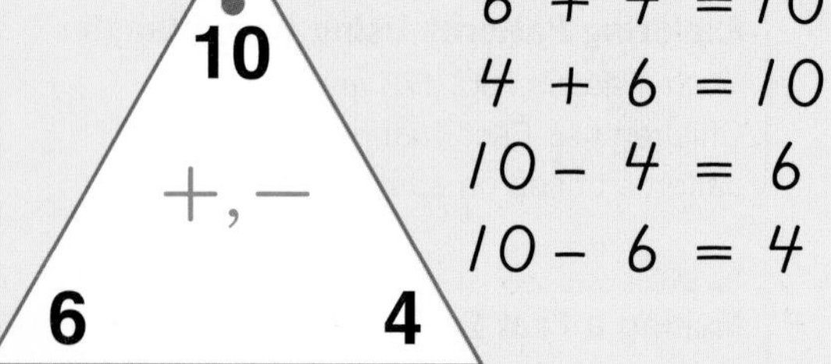

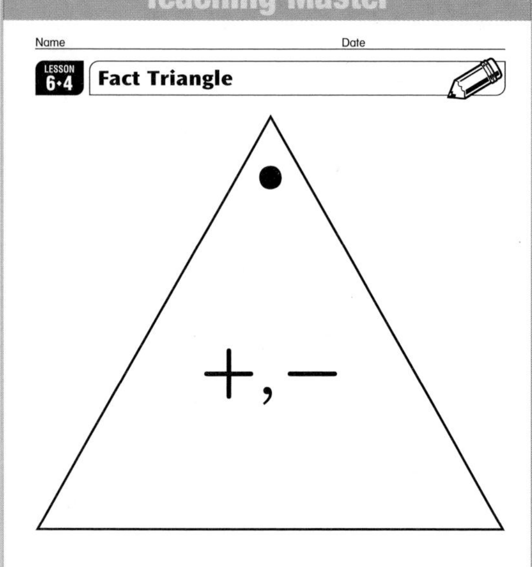

Math Masters, p. 170

1 Teaching the Lesson

▶ Math Message Follow-Up

Ask children to name the facts in the fact family. Record the facts using horizontal and vertical formats. $4 + 6 = 10$; $6 + 4 = 10$; $10 - 6 = 4$; $10 - 4 = 6$

Review the idea that three related numbers make up a fact family. Tell children that today they will learn another way to practice fact families.

▶ Introducing Fact Triangles

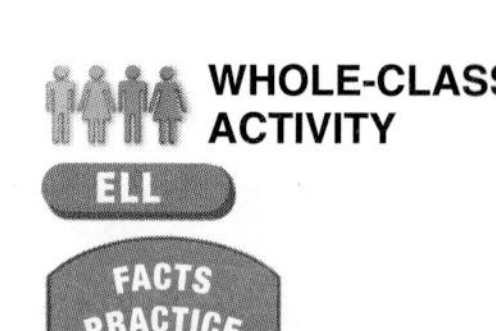

(*Math Masters,* p. 170)

▷ Write 6, 4, and 10 on the three corners of a demonstration Fact Triangle (*Math Masters,* page 170) or draw it on the board. Make sure that 10 is at the top, under the dot. (*See margin.*)

▷ Point to the 10 and ask how we can use the other two numbers to get 10. Add 6 and 4 Write the two addition number models next to the triangle. $6 + 4 = 10$; $4 + 6 = 10$

▷ Point to the 6 and ask how we can use the other two numbers to get 6. Subtract 4 from 10 Write the number model next to the triangle. $10 - 4 = 6$

▷ Finally, point to the 4 and ask how we can use the other two numbers to get 4. Subtract 6 from 10 Write the number model next to the triangle. $10 - 6 = 4$

Explain that this kind of triangle is called a **Fact Triangle** and that children will use Fact Triangles to practice the basic addition and subtraction facts. To support English language learners, write *Fact Triangle* on the board next to an example. Remind children that the word *fact* has an everyday meaning and a mathematical meaning. Discuss the different meanings.

▶ Generating Fact Families

WHOLE-CLASS ACTIVITY

(*Math Journal 2,* Activity Sheets 9 and 10)

Each child needs a set of Fact Triangles. Give children time to examine several Fact Triangles. Ask them to check that the number under the dot on each triangle is always the sum of the other two numbers.

With a child as your partner, demonstrate the following:

1. Cover one corner of a Fact Triangle.
2. Have your partner give an addition or subtraction fact that has the number you are concealing as its answer. For example, if you cover the 3 on a 3, 6, 9 Fact Triangle, your partner should give the subtraction fact $9 - 6 = 3$. If you cover the 9, there are two possibilities: $3 + 6 = 9$ and $6 + 3 = 9$.
3. Repeat, covering each of the other numbers.

Partners practice this procedure as you circulate and help. They say, or write on their slates, the number models that go with the numbers shown.

NOTE Once the doubles, 0-facts, and 1-facts are learned, there are 36 more challenging facts to learn. Half of these facts are given now. The other half are given in Lesson 6-7.

When children are not using the Fact Triangles, they can clip them together or put them in an envelope and store them in their tool-kits.

▶ Playing *Beat the Calculator*

(*Math Journal 2,* p. 116)

In Lesson 5-11, children began to play *Beat the Calculator* as a class. The game can also be played in groups of three: one child is the "Caller" (says a fact); the second child is the "Calculator" (uses a calculator to find the answer); the third child is the "Brain" (finds the answer mentally). The Caller selects a fact randomly from the Fact Power Table on *Math Journal 2,* page 116. Children trade roles about every five facts.

Student Page

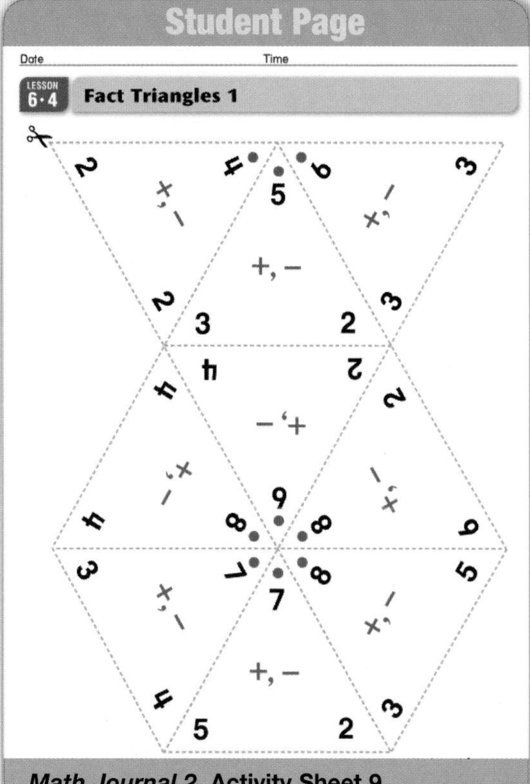

Math Journal 2, Activity Sheet 9

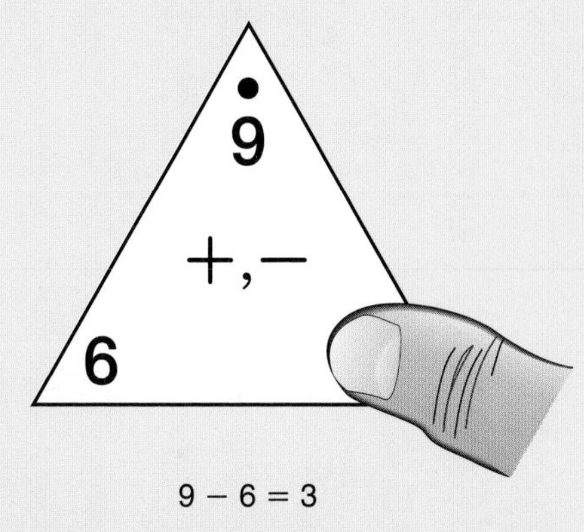

$9 - 6 = 3$

Student Page

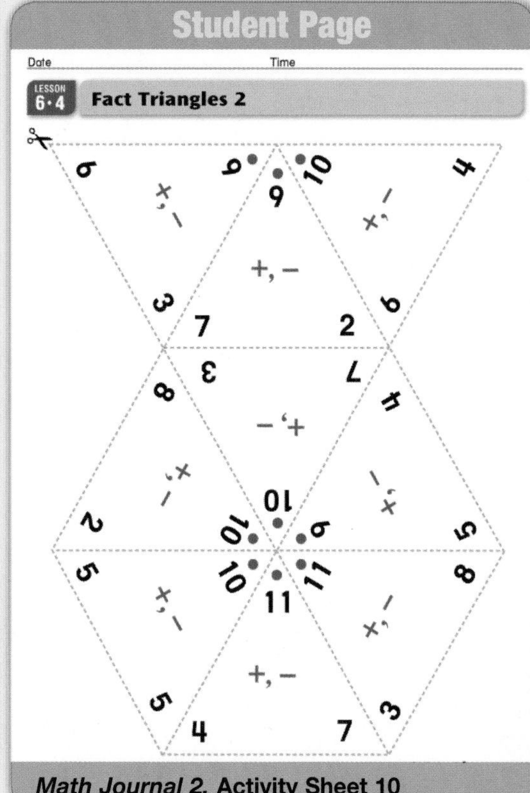

Math Journal 2, Activity Sheet 10

Student Page

Date ______ Time ______

LESSON 6·4 **Fact Power Table**

0 + 0 0	0 + 1 1	0 + 2 2	0 + 3 3	0 + 4 4	0 + 5 5	0 + 6 6	0 + 7 7	0 + 8 8	0 + 9 9
1 + 0 1	1 + 1 2	1 + 2 3	1 + 3 4	1 + 4 5	1 + 5 6	1 + 6 7	1 + 7 8	1 + 8 9	1 + 9 10
2 + 0 2	2 + 1 3	2 + 2 4	2 + 3 5	2 + 4 6	2 + 5 7	2 + 6 8	2 + 7 9	2 + 8 10	2 + 9 11
3 + 0 3	3 + 1 4	3 + 2 5	3 + 3 6	3 + 4 7	3 + 5 8	3 + 6 9	3 + 7 10	3 + 8 11	3 + 9 12
4 + 0 4	4 + 1 5	4 + 2 6	4 + 3 7	4 + 4 8	4 + 5 9	4 + 6 10	4 + 7 11	4 + 8 12	4 + 9 13
5 + 0 5	5 + 1 6	5 + 2 7	5 + 3 8	5 + 4 9	5 + 5 10	5 + 6 11	5 + 7 12	5 + 8 13	5 + 9 14
6 + 0 6	6 + 1 7	6 + 2 8	6 + 3 9	6 + 4 10	6 + 5 11	6 + 6 12	6 + 7 13	6 + 8 14	6 + 9 15
7 + 0 7	7 + 1 8	7 + 2 9	7 + 3 10	7 + 4 11	7 + 5 12	7 + 6 13	7 + 7 14	7 + 8 15	7 + 9 16
8 + 0 8	8 + 1 9	8 + 2 10	8 + 3 11	8 + 4 12	8 + 5 13	8 + 6 14	8 + 7 15	8 + 8 16	8 + 9 17
9 + 0 9	9 + 1 10	9 + 2 11	9 + 3 12	9 + 4 13	9 + 5 14	9 + 6 15	9 + 7 16	9 + 8 17	9 + 9 18

Math Journal 2, p. 116

Game Master

Name ______ Date ______

***Fact Power Game* Mat**

START →	0 + 0	0 + 1	0 + 2	0 + 3	0 + 4	0 + 5	0 + 6	0 + 7	0 + 8	0 + 9
	1 + 0	1 + 1	1 + 2	1 + 3	1 + 4	1 + 5	1 + 6	1 + 7	1 + 8	1 + 9
	2 + 0	2 + 1	2 + 2	2 + 3	2 + 4	2 + 5	2 + 6	2 + 7	2 + 8	2 + 9
	3 + 0	3 + 1	3 + 2	3 + 3	3 + 4	3 + 5	3 + 6	3 + 7	3 + 8	3 + 9
	4 + 0	4 + 1	4 + 2	4 + 3	4 + 4	4 + 5	4 + 6	4 + 7	4 + 8	4 + 9
	5 + 0	5 + 1	5 + 2	5 + 3	5 + 4	5 + 5	5 + 6	5 + 7	5 + 8	5 + 9
	6 + 0	6 + 1	6 + 2	6 + 3	6 + 4	6 + 5	6 + 6	6 + 7	6 + 8	6 + 9
	7 + 0	7 + 1	7 + 2	7 + 3	7 + 4	7 + 5	7 + 6	7 + 7	7 + 8	7 + 9
	8 + 0	8 + 1	8 + 2	8 + 3	8 + 4	8 + 5	8 + 6	8 + 7	8 + 8	8 + 9
END ←	9 + 0	9 + 1	9 + 2	9 + 3	9 + 4	9 + 5	9 + 6	9 + 7	9 + 8	9 + 9

Math Masters, p. 343

Whenever the Brain beats the Calculator, the Brain writes the answer to the fact on the Fact Power Table in his or her journal and colors the cell with a light-colored crayon. Children should continue to keep a record of the facts for which they beat the Calculator.

Summarize by inviting children to tell why they think the Brain is faster or slower than the Calculator.

2 Ongoing Learning & Practice

▶ Playing the *Fact Power Game*

(*Math Masters,* p. 343)

This game can be played with two players or in small groups. For each new game, use the game mat of one of the players. Unused game mats can be used at another time.

Directions

1. Players place their markers on START. They take turns rolling a die and moving their markers the correct number of spaces across the rows, as indicated by the arrows on the game mat.
2. When a player lands on a space, he or she says the sum. The others check that the sum is correct. If correct, the player marks the space with his or her initials. If a player lands on a marked space, he or she moves to the next open space.
3. A round is over when a player reaches or passes END. At that point, there will be some spaces marked and some not. Players then start again at the beginning.
4. When time is up or all of the spaces have been marked, players count their marked spaces. The player with the greatest number of marked spaces wins the game.

Adjusting the Activity

Use only the first six rows of the Fact Power Game Mat and increase the number of rows used as appropriate.

AUDITORY ◆ KINESTHETIC ◆ TACTILE ◆ VISUAL

▶ Math Boxes 6◆4

INDEPENDENT ACTIVITY

(*Math Journal 2,* p. 117)

Mixed Practice Math Boxes in this lesson are paired with Math Boxes in Lesson 6-2. The skills in Problem 4 preview Unit 7 content.

Writing/Reasoning Have children draw, write, or verbalize an answer to the following question: *How do you know what to write on the name-collection box?* A reasonable answer should explain the need to label the box and find multiple names for that number. Sample answer: I write different things that are all like the same number that's there. I write it in Spanish or write math facts.

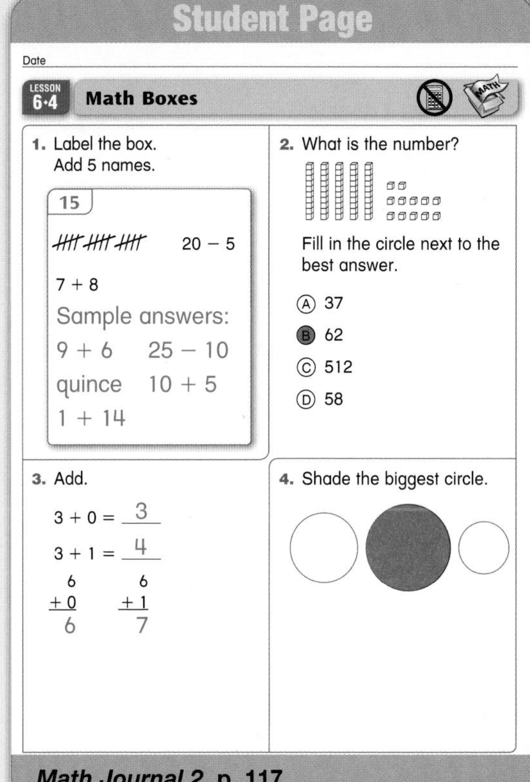

Student Page

Date

LESSON 6◆4 **Math Boxes**

1. Label the box. Add 5 names.

15

//// //// //// 20 − 5

7 + 8

Sample answers:

9 + 6 25 − 10

quince 10 + 5

1 + 14

2. What is the number?

Fill in the circle next to the best answer.

Ⓐ 37

Ⓑ 62 (filled)

Ⓒ 512

Ⓓ 58

3. Add.

3 + 0 = 3

3 + 1 = 4

6 + 0 = 6

6 + 1 = 7

4. Shade the biggest circle.

Math Journal 2, p. 117

▶ Home Link 6◆4

INDEPENDENT ACTIVITY

(*Math Masters,* pp. 171 and 172)

Home Connection Children cut out Fact Triangles and show someone at home how they can use them as flash cards. This Home Link is accompanied by a Family Letter (*Math Masters,* page 171).

▶ *Minute Math+*

WHOLE-CLASS ACTIVITY

Use *Minute Math+,* page 6 to provide more practice with ordinal numbers.

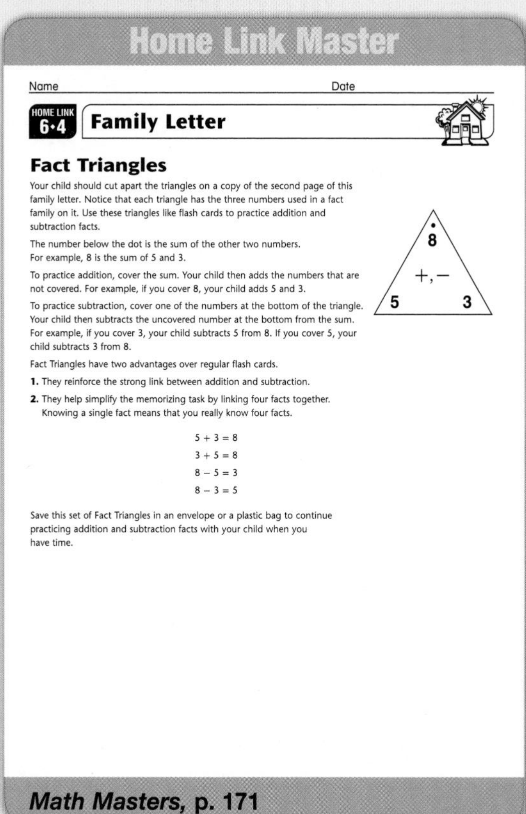

Home Link Master

Name Date

HOME LINK 6◆4 **Family Letter**

Fact Triangles

Your child should cut apart the triangles on a copy of the second page of this family letter. Notice that each triangle has the three numbers used in a fact family on it. Use these triangles like flash cards to practice addition and subtraction facts.

The number below the dot is the sum of the other two numbers. For example, 8 is the sum of 5 and 3.

To practice addition, cover the sum. Your child then adds the numbers that are not covered. For example, if you cover 8, your child adds 5 and 3.

To practice subtraction, cover one of the numbers at the bottom of the triangle. Your child then subtracts the uncovered number at the bottom from the sum. For example, if you cover 3, your child subtracts 5 from 8. If you cover 5, your child subtracts 3 from 8.

8 +, − 5 3

Fact Triangles have two advantages over regular flash cards.

1. They reinforce the strong link between addition and subtraction.
2. They help simplify the memorizing task by linking four facts together. Knowing a single fact means that you really know four facts.

5 + 3 = 8

3 + 5 = 8

8 − 5 = 3

8 − 3 = 5

Save this set of Fact Triangles in an envelope or a plastic bag to continue practicing addition and subtraction facts with your child when you have time.

Math Masters, p. 171

3 Differentiation Options

READINESS

SMALL-GROUP ACTIVITY

▶ Constructing Fact Families

5–15 Min

To provide experience with the Commutative Property of Addition, have children generate fact families by rolling two different-colored dice. Children roll the dice and record each number, using the corresponding crayon color. Children determine the third number in the fact family and write it in pencil. Then children can manipulate the dice to show the two addition facts and two subtraction facts in the fact family. Children record each number sentence, using the corresponding colors.

Home Link Master

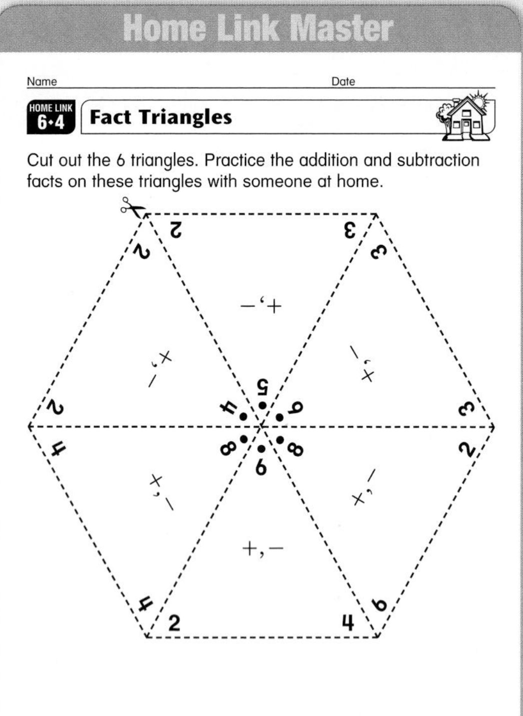
Name Date

HOME LINK 6•4 **Fact Triangles**

Cut out the 6 triangles. Practice the addition and subtraction facts on these triangles with someone at home.

Math Masters, p. 172

ENRICHMENT

INDEPENDENT ACTIVITY

▶ Exploring Patterns Using Fact Triangles

5–15 Min

(*Math Masters*, pp. 173 and 174)

To further explore fact families, children use Fact Triangles to extend easy addition facts. Children complete *Math Masters*, pages 173 and 174 and discuss the patterns in the sets of related fact families.

ELL SUPPORT

▶ Making a Fact Family House

5–15 Min

To provide language support for fact families, use construction paper to make triangular roofs and square houses representing fact families. Have children write the three numbers of a fact family on the roof and write the family of number sentences on the house. Remind children that only the numbers on the roof can live in the house of number sentences. Children can choose dominoes to help them make additional fact family houses.

Teaching Master

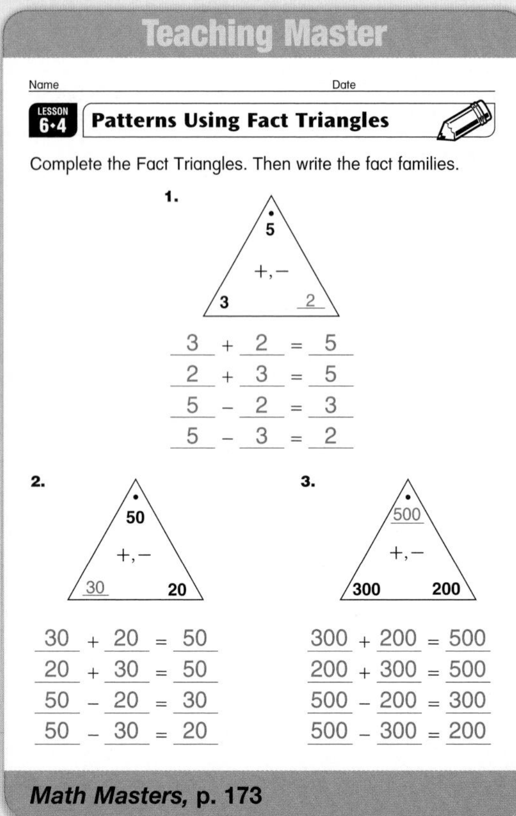
Name Date

LESSON 6•4 **Patterns Using Fact Triangles**

Complete the Fact Triangles. Then write the fact families.

1. Triangle: 5 (top), 3, 2; +, −

3 + 2 = 5
2 + 3 = 5
5 − 2 = 3
5 − 3 = 2

2. Triangle: 50 (top), 30, 20; +, −

30 + 20 = 50
20 + 30 = 50
50 − 20 = 30
50 − 30 = 20

3. Triangle: 500 (top), 300, 200; +, −

300 + 200 = 500
200 + 300 = 500
500 − 200 = 300
500 − 300 = 200

Math Masters, p. 173

Teaching Master

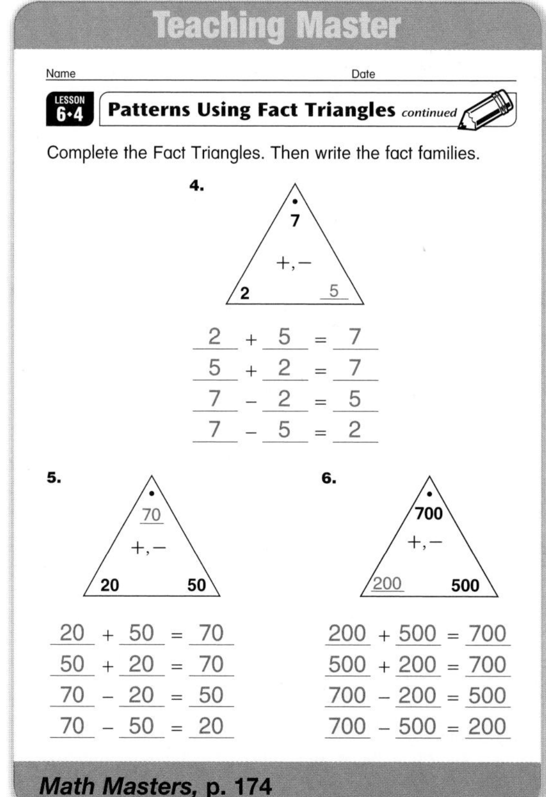
Name Date

LESSON 6•4 **Patterns Using Fact Triangles** *continued*

Complete the Fact Triangles. Then write the fact families.

4. Triangle: 7 (top), 2, 5; +, −

2 + 5 = 7
5 + 2 = 7
7 − 2 = 5
7 − 5 = 2

5. Triangle: 70 (top), 20, 50; +, −

20 + 50 = 70
50 + 20 = 70
70 − 20 = 50
70 − 50 = 20

6. Triangle: 700 (top), 200, 500; +, −

200 + 500 = 700
500 + 200 = 700
700 − 200 = 500
700 − 500 = 200

Math Masters, p. 174

6•5 Using Strategies to Solve Subtraction Facts

Objectives To provide experience revisiting the relationship between addition and subtraction; and to introduce subtraction fact strategies using ten.

www.everydaymathonline.com

ePresentations

eToolkit

Algorithms Practice

EM Facts Workshop Game™

Family Letters

Assessment Management

Common Core State Standards

Curriculum Focal Points

Interactive Teacher's Lesson Guide

1 Teaching the Lesson

Key Concepts and Skills

- Use the Addition/Subtraction Facts Table to find sums and differences.
  [Operations and Computation Goal 1]
- Use subtraction fact strategies to find differences.
  [Operations and Computation Goal 1]
- Use addition to check answers for subtraction facts.
  [Patterns, Functions, and Algebra Goal 3]

Key Activities

Children learn to use the Addition/Subtraction Facts Table to solve subtraction problems. They use subtraction fact strategies focused on the number ten to find differences.

Ongoing Assessment: Recognizing Student Achievement
Use journal page 118.
[Operations and Computation Goal 1]

Materials

Math Journal 2, p. 118 and inside front cover
Home Link 6•4
Math Masters, p. 336
transparency of *Math Masters,* p. 324 (optional) ◆ Number-Grid Poster ◆ slate ◆ calculator ◆ counters

2 Ongoing Learning & Practice

Playing *Addition Top-It*
Math Journal 2, inside front cover
per partnership: 4 each of number cards 0–9 (from the Everything Math Deck, if available)
Children practice addition skills.

Math Boxes 6•5
Math Journal 2, p. 119
Children practice and maintain skills through Math Box problems.

Home Link 6•5
Math Masters, p. 175
Children practice and maintain skills through Home Link activities.

3 Differentiation Options

ENRICHMENT

Coloring Patterns in the Facts Table
Math Masters, p. 176
Children find patterns in the Addition/Subtraction Facts Table.

EXTRA PRACTICE

Playing *Penny Plate*
per partnership: paper plate, 10–20 pennies
Children review counting up to determine the total amount.

Getting Started

Mental Math and Reflexes

Play *Beat the Calculator.*
See Lesson 6-4 for directions.

FACTS PRACTICE

Math Message

Use the table on the inside front cover of your journal to solve:

6 + 7 = _____

13 − 6 = _____

Home Link 6·4 Follow-Up

Remind children to practice with their Fact Triangles at home.

NOTE This lesson contains a significant amount of content; you may wish to complete it over two days.

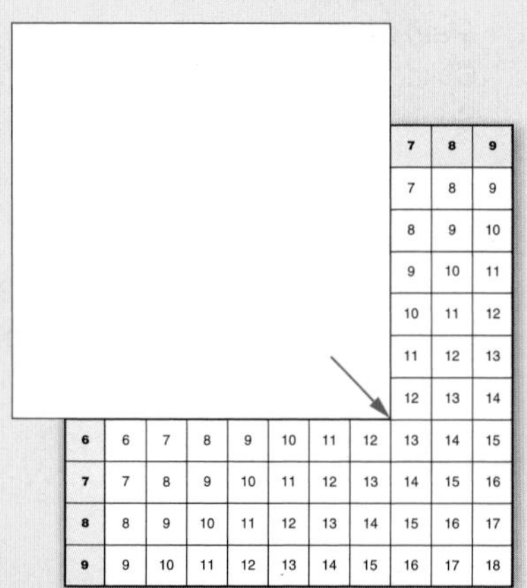

Student Page

Date Time

LESSON 6·5 **Using the Addition/Subtraction Facts Table 2**

+,−	0	1	2	3	4	5	6	7	8	9
0	0	1	2	3	4	5	6	7	8	9
1	1	2	3	4	5	6	7	8	9	10
2	2	3	4	5	6	7	8	9	10	11
3	3	4	5	6	7	8	9	10	11	12
4	4	5	6	7	8	9	10	11	12	13
5	5	6	7	8	9	10	11	12	13	14
6	6	7	8	9	10	11	12	13	14	15
7	7	8	9	10	11	12	13	14	15	16
8	8	9	10	11	12	13	14	15	16	17
9	9	10	11	12	13	14	15	16	17	18

Add or subtract. Use the table to help you.

1. 5 + 6 = 11
2. 11 − 5 = 6
3. 8 + 4 = 12
4. 12 − 4 = 8
5. 7 + 8 = 15
6. 15 − 8 = 7
7. 9 + 9 = 18
8. 18 − 9 = 9
9. 9 + 7 = 16
10. 16 − 9 = 7

Math Journal 2, p. 118

1 Teaching the Lesson

▶ Math Message Follow-Up

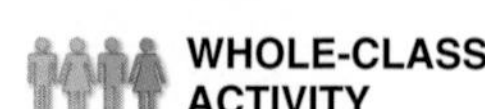

(*Math Journal 2,* inside front cover)

Have children share solution strategies. They have not used the Addition/Subtraction Facts Table to solve subtraction problems before, so children may not have figured out how to do it. Some children may have found the answers with the help of the table, but are not able to describe what they did.

Use the transparency of the Addition/Subtraction Facts Table (*Math Masters,* page 324), as you model 6 + 7 and 13 − 6. Children follow along on the table on the inside front cover of their journals.

- To find the sum of 6 and 7, use a large piece of paper with an arrow drawn in the corner. Cover the Facts Table so that the 6 row and the 7 column are visible at the bottom and right edges of the paper. The arrow will point to the answer, 13.
- To find the answer to 13 − 6, keep the sheet of paper in place. Ask yourself: "6 plus what number is 13?" To find the number, move along the 6 row to 13. Then go up the sheet to the number in the top row, 7. To check that 7 is the correct answer, use the table to find 6 plus 7 is 13.

▶ Using the Addition/Subtraction Facts Table to Solve Subtraction Problems

WHOLE-CLASS ACTIVITY

(*Math Journal 2,* p. 118)

Pose a few subtraction problems. Ask children to use the table to find the answers, even if they know the facts. Have them check each answer, using addition. They write answers on their slates.

Use the transparency of the table to model the solution to each problem. When you think that children are comfortable using the table to solve subtraction problems, have them complete journal page 118.

Ongoing Assessment: Recognizing Student Achievement

Journal Page 118 

Use the addition problems on **journal page 118** to assess children's ability to use the Addition/Subtraction Facts Table to solve addition problems. Children are making adequate progress if they are able to solve the addition problems correctly. Some children may be able to use the table to solve the subtraction problems, as well.

[Operations and Computation Goal 1]

NOTE If you wish to have children practice sums to 20 using the Addition/Subtraction Facts Table, go to www.everydaymathonline.com.

NOTE Some children may find it difficult to use the Facts Table when solving subtraction facts. Children may use other strategies to solve the problems and/or to check their answers. However, since the goal of this activity is to learn to use the table, children should be encouraged to turn to it for answers they don't know. Keep in mind that this is the first exposure to using a Facts Table to solve subtraction problems.

▶ Subtracting Using a Ten Frame

(*Math Masters*, p. 336)

Remind children that in Lessons 6-3 and 6-4 they learned that one good strategy for solving subtraction facts is to use the relationship between addition and subtraction. Explain that children will explore other strategies for solving subtraction facts, specifically strategies that use 10.

Write 16 − 9 = ☐ on the board. Have children place 9 counters on their ten frames. Ask: *How many more counters are needed to show 16?* Help children see that they need *one more counter to get ten* plus the rest of the number, in this case 6.

Encourage the following thought process:

- Start with 9.
- How many do I need to get 10? 1
- How many more do I need to get 16? 6
- 1 + 6 = 7, so 16 − 9 = 7.

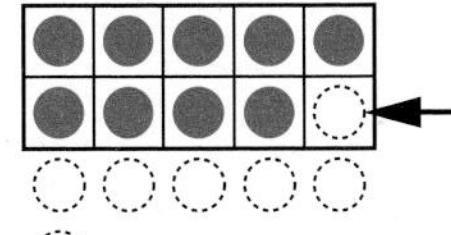

One more to get to 10. Then 6 more.

Have children use their ten frames and counters to practice other −9 subtraction facts, such as 14 − 9 and 18 − 9.

Repeat the same procedure to introduce −8 facts using the ten frame. Focus on the idea that children need *two more counters to get 10* and then some number more to get to the larger number. Have children describe the steps they take to solve the problems.

NOTE Be sure to add this strategy, Subtracting Using a Ten Frame, to your Fact Strategy Wall. This strategy is especially helpful for −8 and −9 facts; however, using a ten frame to visualize subtraction may help children with other subtraction facts.

Adjusting the Activity

Using ten to subtract can also be demonstrated using a number line. Given 16 − 9 = ☐, start at 9 and think *How many do I need to get 10? How many more do I need to get 16?*

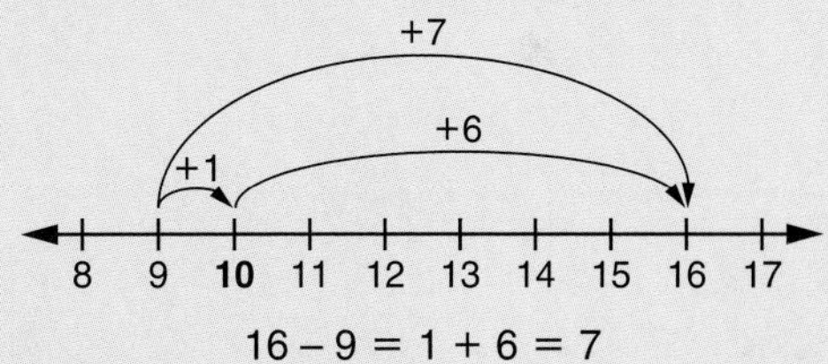

AUDITORY ◆ KINESTHETIC ◆ TACTILE ◆ VISUAL

Teaching Aid Master

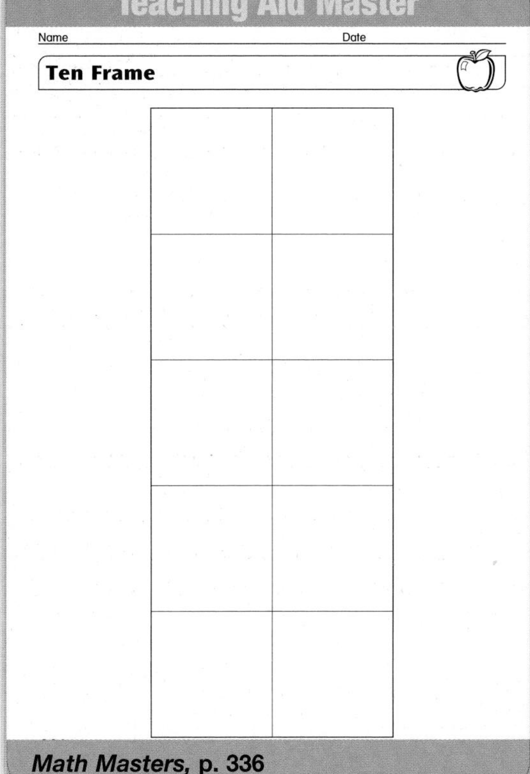

Math Masters, p. 336

▶ −8 and −9 Shortcuts

WHOLE-CLASS ACTIVITY

$13 - 9 = 4$ $13 - 10 = 3$
$17 - 9 = 8$ $17 - 10 = 4$
$15 - 9 = 6$ $15 - 10 = 5$
$16 - 9 = 5$ $16 - 10 = 6$

Write the following −9 facts on the board without including the differences: 13 − 9, 17 − 9, 15 − 9, and 16 − 9. Ask children to copy these facts onto their slates and find the differences. Then have children write the differences on the board. Ask children if they can figure out a shortcut for the −9 facts. Children might suggest that the difference is one more than the ones digit of the minuend. If children need help, write related −10 facts beside each of these facts.

Ask children to use the −10 facts to help explain the −9 shortcut. Add the −9 shortcut to the Fact Strategy Wall in children's own words. Children may describe it as *Subtract 10 instead of 9 and then add 1.*

You may wish to show children the −9 shortcut on the Number-Grid Poster as well. As you model the process on the class number grid, have children use the number grid in their journals to follow along. To find the difference between 13 and 9, place your finger on the number 13; subtract 10 by moving your finger straight up to the row above; add one by moving to the right one space. The difference is 4.

1	2	3 →	4	5	6	7	8	9	10
11	12	(13) ↑	14	15	16	17	18	19	20

Repeat the procedure for −8 facts. Begin by listing several −8 facts on the board and have the children find the differences. Some children may discover the −8 shortcut without seeing pairs of −10 facts, but writing the related −10 facts on the board may be helpful to those children who are still struggling to grasp these shortcuts. Be sure to demonstrate this shortcut on the class number grid. Encourage children to describe the −8 shortcut in their own words for the Fact Strategy Wall. Children may describe it as *Subtract 10 instead of 8 and then add 2.*

Have children practice mixed −9 and −8 facts. Write subtraction facts on the board and have children write the differences on their slates.

▶ Using Ten Subtraction Strategy

WHOLE-CLASS ACTIVITY

By now children should be very comfortable with the sum-equals-ten addition and subtraction facts, such as 4 + 6 = 10 and 10 − 7 = 3. Knowing these facts will help children use another strategy, sometimes called "decomposing a number leading to ten."

Write 13 − 5 = □ on the board. Explain to children that they are going to use 10 as a stopping point to solve this subtraction problem. Doing so, they will uncover a sum-equals-ten subtraction fact that they will solve to find the difference between 13 and 5.

Ask: *What could you do to 13 to get 10?* Subtract 3 Remind children that they have subtracted 3; they need to subtract a total of 5. Ask: *How many more do we need to subtract?* 2 more $13 - 3$ leads to the sum-equals-ten subtraction fact, $10 - 2 = 8$. Thus, $13 - 5 = 8$. Demonstrate this using a number line. (*See margin.*)

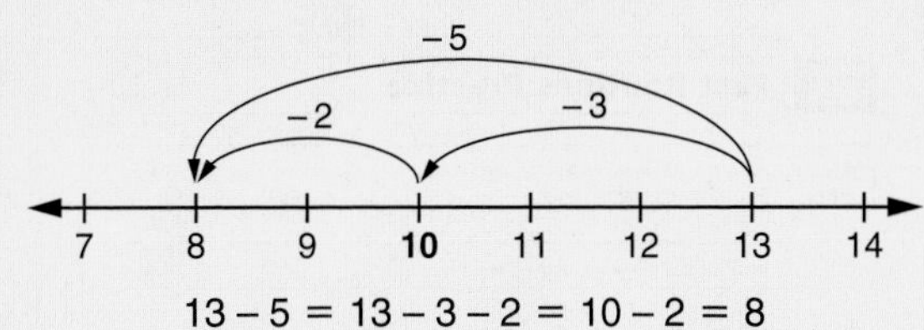

It is important to note that this is a difficult strategy that may not be intuitive for many children. However, by repeating the strategy with other facts in which the minuend is greater than 10, such as $16 - 7$, $12 - 4$, and $14 - 8$, many children will begin to understand and internalize the strategy. With practice it will likely become a favorite subtraction strategy for some children.

NOTE Be sure to add this strategy to your Fact Strategy Wall. It will help children if you include an example, including steps like those shown in the diagram in the margin.

2 Ongoing Learning & Practice

▶ Playing *Addition Top-It*

(*Math Journal 2,* inside front cover)

Children practice addition skills by playing *Addition Top-It*. For detailed instructions, see Lesson 6-1.

▶ Math Boxes 6·5

INDEPENDENT ACTIVITY

(*Math Journal 2,* p. 119)

Mixed Practice Math Boxes in this lesson are paired with Math Boxes in Lesson 6-7. The skills in Problem 4 preview Unit 7 content.

Writing/Reasoning Have children draw, write, or verbalize an answer to the following question: *What is a fact family?* A reasonable answer should include a discussion of four related number models.

A fact family is a family of facts. You need a domino. There are three numbers in a domino. There is one number on each side. The third number is both of the numbers added together. Then you use the three numbers to make two addition and subtraction facts.

One child's work in response to the Writing/Reasoning prompt

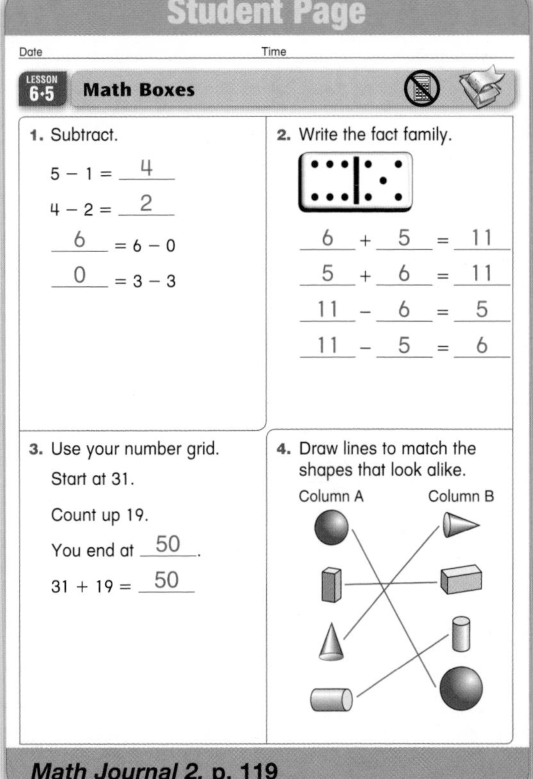

Student Page

Date Time

LESSON 6·5 **Math Boxes**

1. Subtract.

$5 - 1 =$ 4

$4 - 2 =$ 2

6 $= 6 - 0$

0 $= 3 - 3$

2. Write the fact family.

6 + 5 = 11

5 + 6 = 11

11 − 6 = 5

11 − 5 = 6

3. Use your number grid.

Start at 31.

Count up 19.

You end at 50.

$31 + 19 =$ 50

4. Draw lines to match the shapes that look alike.

Column A Column B

Math Journal 2, p. 119

Getting Started

Mental Math and Reflexes

Practice rounding skills. Have children write their answers on their slates.

●○○ Is 18 closer to 10 or 20? 20

●●○ Is 44 closer to 40 or 50? 40

●●● Is 126 closer to 120 or 130? 130

Math Message ★

Draw the function machine on the board. Put a question mark in the rule box.
Find the rule.

in

Rule

?

out

in	out
1	3
2	4
3	5
4	6
7	9
10	12

Home Link 6•7 Follow-Up

Encourage children to practice their facts at home as often as possible, even if only for 5 minutes at a time.

1 Teaching the Lesson

▶ Math Message Follow-Up

WHOLE-CLASS ACTIVITY

Discuss the rule that fits the table. The rule may be phrased in various ways, such as "Add 2," "Count up by 2," or "2 more." If a child offers an incorrect rule, test it on several input numbers to show that it doesn't work. (Incorrect answers can be an opportunity for you to "think out loud" to model how to approach these problems.)

Write the rule in the rule box. Then extend the table, write a new input number in the "in" column, and ask children to write the output number on their slates. Record it in the "out" column.

Repeat the procedure with several other input numbers.

NOTE You may wish to show children how finding the rule for the in/out box is like finding the unknown that makes these number sentences true:

1 + □ = 3
2 + □ = 4
3 + □ = 5
4 + □ = 6
7 + □ = 9
10 + □ = 12

Ongoing Assessment: Recognizing Student Achievement

Math Message ★

Use the **Math Message** to assess children's ability to find the rule in "What's My Rule?" problems. Children are making adequate progress if they are able to name the rule.

[Patterns, Functions, and Algebra Goal 1]

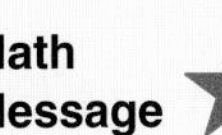

Tell children that today they will learn how to figure out missing input numbers.

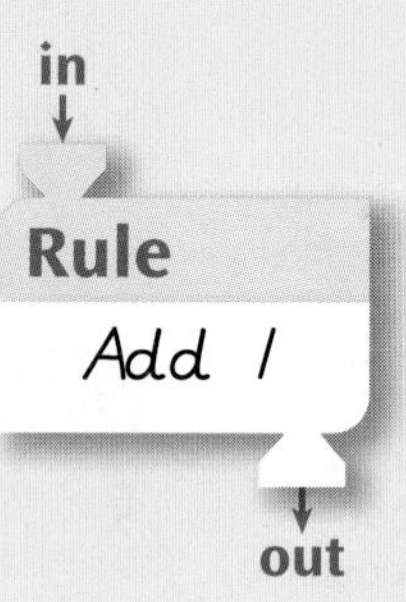

in	out
1	
4	
	7
	10
27	
	39

in

Rule

Add 3

out

in	out
	5
	6
	9
	3
	12
	10

▶ Reviewing the "What's My Rule?" Routine

(*Math Journal 2,* p. 124)

Algebraic Thinking Erase the rule in the rule box and replace it with the rule "Add 1." Replace the numbers in the table with those shown in the margin.

Point out that this table is different from the last one because some of the input numbers are missing. Ask children to name the missing numbers as you record them in the table. Answers can be recorded on slates or given orally. *What did you do to find the missing input numbers?* Sample answers: Found the number that comes before the output number; subtracted 1 from the output number

Explain to children that they can check that an input number is correct by applying the rule to the input number; the result should be the output number.

Change the rule to "Add 3." Have children name the missing numbers and describe what they did to find the missing input numbers. Subtracted 3 from the output number

Adjusting the Activity

Suggest ways to find the input number when children are given a rule and an output number:

- Before children find the missing "in" numbers, have children look for a pattern in the table. Are the "out" numbers larger or smaller than the "in" numbers?
- Use a number grid. For example, for the rule "Add 3" and the output number 12, count back 3 on the number grid from 12. You land on 9. Check the answer by adding 3 to the input number 9.
- Guess and check. Test sample inputs until one is found that works. In the above example, you might try 6. It is too small because 6 + 3 is less than 12. If you try 10, the output number is 13—too big. Continue until you get the correct input number.

AUDITORY • KINESTHETIC • TACTILE • VISUAL

Practice finding inputs with several tables in which all of the inputs are missing. Use rules and output numbers that are appropriate for your class. When you think that most children understand the process, have them do the "What's My Rule?" problems on journal page 124.

Ongoing Assessment: Informing Instruction

Watch for children who have difficulty finding the input number. You may want to have these children use the guess-and-check strategy suggested above.

Student Page

Date Time

LESSON 6·8 **"What's My Rule?"**

1. Find the rule.

Rule: +4

in	out
5	9
8	12
10	14

Your turn: Answers vary.

2. Fill in the blanks.

Rule: −10

in	out
16	6
22	12
23	13

Your turn: Answers vary.

3. What comes out?

Rule: +5

in	out
5	10
20	25
32	37

Your turn: Answers vary.

4. What goes in?

Rule: −2

in	out
7	5
11	9
5	3

Your turn: Answers vary.

Make up your own. Answers vary.

5. Rule

in	out

6. Rule

in	out

Math Journal 2, p. 124

2 Ongoing Learning & Practice

▶ Playing *Tric-Trac*

PARTNER ACTIVITY

(*Math Masters,* p. 360)

Divide the class into partnerships. Model rolling the dice quietly and finding the sum. Make a list of possible numbers that could equal the sum.

Tell children that they will be playing *Tric-Trac* to practice addition facts. Ask children to help you determine which number or numbers to cover in a demonstration game.

Directions

1. Cover the empty circles with pennies.
2. Take turns. When it is your turn:
   - ▷ Roll the dice. Find the total number of dots. This is your sum.
   - ▷ Move 1 of your pennies and cover your sum.
   - ▷ OR move 2 or more of your pennies and cover any numbers that can be added together to equal your sum.
3. Play continues until no more numbers can be covered on your gameboard. Your partner may continue playing even after you are finished.
4. The game is over when neither player can cover any more of the numbers on his or her gameboard.
5. Find the sum of your uncovered numbers. The player with the lower sum wins.

Ongoing Assessment: Informing Instruction

Watch for children who simply count the number of uncovered circles at the end of the game. Remind children to find the sum of all of the uncovered numbers to determine who wins the game.

Discuss any patterns children noticed while playing *Tric-Trac*.

For example:

- It is important to cover high numbers early in the game so that your sum will be lower when the game is complete.
- Numbers such as 6, 7, and 8 often get covered early in the game because you are more likely to roll these numbers than some of the other numbers.
- Numbers are covered more quickly if you cover two numbers that equal a sum rather than covering the sum.

Game Master

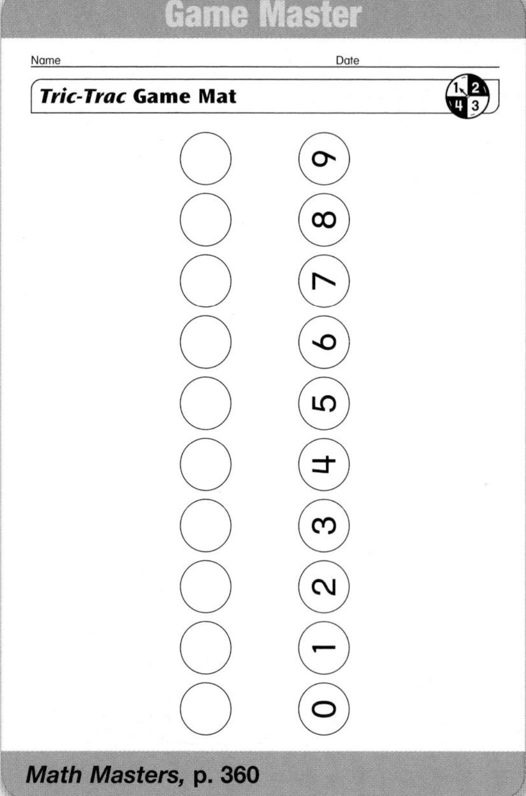

Math Masters, p. 360

Adjusting the Activity

For each turn, have children write a number sentence showing the sum and the numbers they covered.

AUDITORY ◆ KINESTHETIC ◆ TACTILE ◆ VISUAL

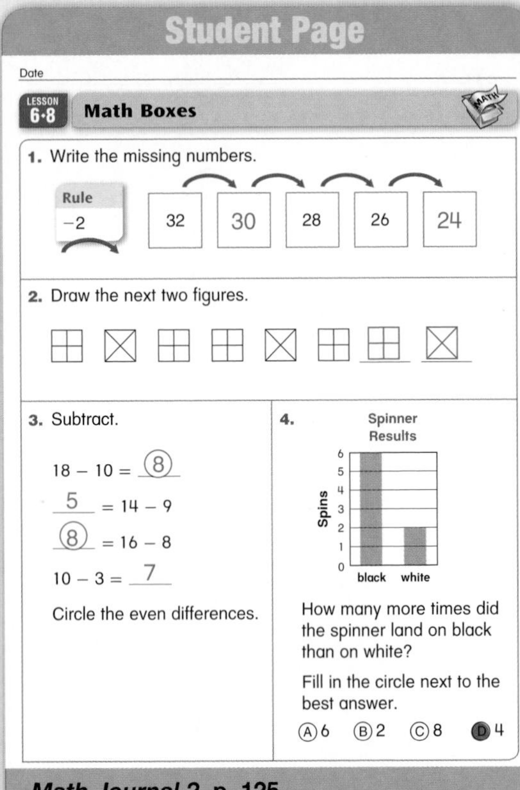

Student Page

Date

LESSON 6·8 **Math Boxes**

1. Write the missing numbers.

Rule: −2

32	30	28	26	24

2. Draw the next two figures.

3. Subtract.

18 − 10 = 8

5 = 14 − 9

8 = 16 − 8

10 − 3 = 7

Circle the even differences.

4. Spinner Results

How many more times did the spinner land on black than on white?

Fill in the circle next to the best answer.

Ⓐ 6 Ⓑ 2 Ⓒ 8 Ⓓ 4

Math Journal 2, p. 125

▶ Math Boxes 6·8

INDEPENDENT ACTIVITY

(*Math Journal 2*, p. 125)

Mixed Practice Math Boxes in this lesson are paired with Math Boxes in Lesson 6-6.

Writing/Reasoning Have children draw, write, or verbalize an answer to the following question: *How do you compare numbers on a graph?* A reasonable answer should describe a strategy to find the difference, such as counting up.

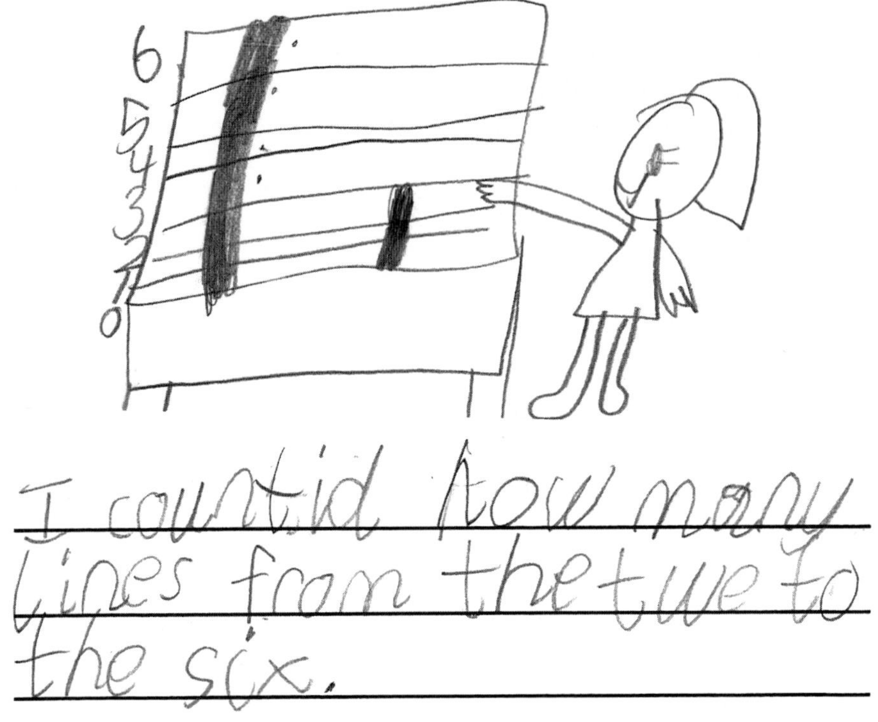

One child's work in response to the Writing/Reasoning prompt

Home Link Master

Name Date

HOME LINK 6·8 **Counting Coins**

Family Note This Home Link reviews finding the value of combinations of dimes, nickels, and pennies. If your child is having trouble finding the value of collections of coins, you might try the following method, using real coins, if possible:

1. Show the amount with pennies.
2. Trade the pennies for nickels.
3. Trade the nickels for dimes.

Beginning tomorrow, children will add quarters to their work with coins. In preparation, please give your child two quarters to bring to school.

Please return this Home Link to school tomorrow.

Use Ⓟ, Ⓝ, and Ⓓ to show each amount in two different ways.

1. 43¢	Sample answer: Ⓓ Ⓓ Ⓓ Ⓓ Ⓟ Ⓟ Ⓟ	Sample answer: Ⓓ Ⓓ Ⓝ Ⓝ Ⓝ Ⓝ Ⓟ Ⓟ Ⓟ
2. 67¢	Sample answer: Ⓓ Ⓓ Ⓓ Ⓓ Ⓓ Ⓓ Ⓝ Ⓟ Ⓟ	Sample answer: Ⓓ Ⓓ Ⓝ Ⓝ Ⓝ Ⓝ Ⓝ Ⓝ Ⓝ Ⓝ Ⓝ Ⓟ Ⓟ

3. Ask someone at home for two quarters. Bring them to school.

Practice

Find the total number of dots for each one.

4. 9 5. 9 6. 5

Math Masters, p. 183

▶ Home Link 6·8

INDEPENDENT ACTIVITY

(*Math Masters*, p. 183)

Home Connection Children show amounts of money with two different coin combinations.

3 Differentiation Options

READINESS

▶ Reviewing Missing Output Numbers

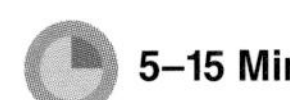

Algebraic Thinking To explore the "What's My Rule?" table, put the following tables on the board and have children use a calculator to find the missing "out" numbers. Invite children to describe any connections they see between the two completed tables.

in

Rule

+6

out

in	out
5	11
3	9
7	13
15	21

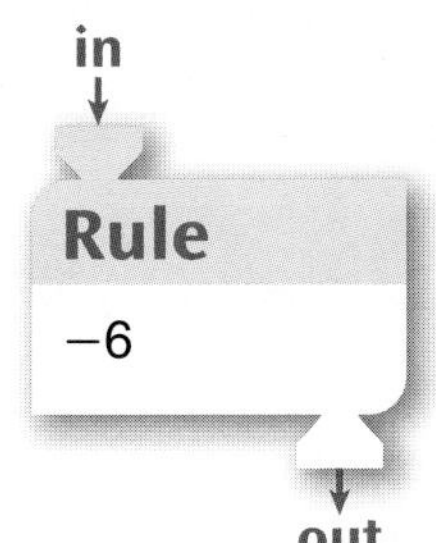

in	out
11	5
9	3
13	7
21	15

ENRICHMENT

▶ Filling in Frames and Rules

(*Math Masters*, p. 184)

Algebraic Thinking To apply children's understanding of finding and using rules, have them solve Frames-and-Arrows problems in which the first few frames are blank. Children complete *Math Masters*, page 184. Discuss how filling in the first frames of a Frames-and-Arrows problem is similar to finding missing input numbers in a "What's My Rule?" table.

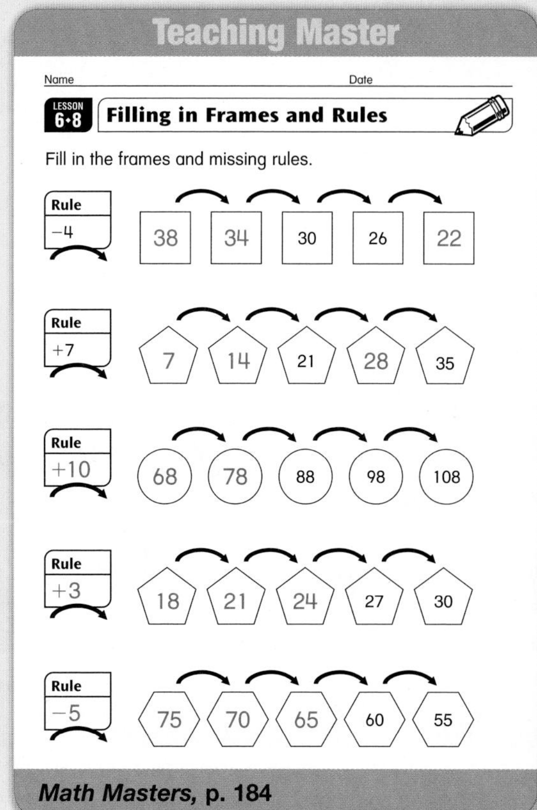
Teaching Master

Name Date

LESSON 6·8 Filling in Frames and Rules

Fill in the frames and missing rules.

Rule −4: 38, 34, 30, 26, 22

Rule +7: 7, 14, 21, 28, 35

Rule +10: 68, 78, 88, 98, 108

Rule +3: 18, 21, 24, 27, 30

Rule −5: 75, 70, 65, 60, 55

Math Masters, p. 184

6•9 Quarters

Objectives To provide experience finding the value of collections of quarters, dimes, nickels, and pennies; and showing money amounts with coins.

www.everydaymathonline.com

ePresentations

eToolkit

Algorithms Practice

EM Facts Workshop Game™

Family Letters

Assessment Management

Common Core State Standards

Curriculum Focal Points

Interactive Teacher's Lesson Guide

1 Teaching the Lesson

Key Concepts and Skills

- Count forward by 25s.
  [Number and Numeration Goal 1]
- Calculate the value of combinations of quarters, dimes, nickels, and pennies.
  [Operations and Computation Goal 2]
- Identify a quarter and know its value.
  [Measurement and Reference Frames Goal 2]
- Make exchanges between coins.
  [Measurement and Reference Frames Goal 2]

Key Activities

Children examine quarters and practice counting by 25s. They find the value of coin collections that include quarters, dimes, nickels, and pennies and use these coins to show amounts of money.

Ongoing Assessment: Informing Instruction See page 583.

Key Vocabulary

quarter

Materials

Math Journal 2, p. 126
Home Link 6•8
Story of Money Poster ◆ slate ◆ tool-kit coins ◆ overhead coins (optional) ◆ calculator (optional) ◆ per partnership: 1 magnifying lens

2 Ongoing Learning & Practice

Playing *Coin Top-It*
per partnership: coin cards
Children practice counting and comparing collections of coins.

Math Boxes 6•9
Math Journal 2, p. 127
Children practice and maintain skills through Math Box problems.

Ongoing Assessment: Recognizing Student Achievement
Use Math Boxes, Problem 1.
[Data and Chance Goal 3]

Home Link 6•9
Math Masters, p. 185
Children practice and maintain skills through Home Link activities.

Minute Math+
Minute Math®+, pp. 35 and 39
Children practice counting money and finding missing parts in number models.

3 Differentiation Options

READINESS

Playing *Penny-Nickel-Dime Exchange*
per partnership: tool-kit coins, 2 dice
Children make exchanges with pennies, nickels, and dimes.

ENRICHMENT

Playing *Quarter-Dime-Nickel-Penny Grab*
Math Masters, p. 351
per partnership: tool-kit coins
Children compare and find the values of coin combinations including quarters.

EXTRA PRACTICE

Reading About Money
Math Masters, p. 305
Children read *Deena's Lucky Penny* to practice with money.

ELL SUPPORT

Discussing Meanings of the Word *Quarter*
Children discuss various meanings of the word *quarter.*

Advance Preparation

Add two quarters to each child's tool-kit coins. For Part 2, cut 3" by 5" index cards in half to make *Coin Top-It* cards with quarters. Add these cards to those made for Lessons 2•13 and 3•11.

For the optional Extra Practice activity in Part 3, obtain a copy of ***Deena's Lucky Penny*** by Barbara deRubertis (The Kane Press, 1999). You may wish to find the book ***26 Letters and 99 Cents*** by Tana Hoban (Greenwillow Books, 1995), as it relates to lesson content.

***Teacher's Reference Manual,* Grades 1–3** pp. 163–165

Getting Started

Mental Math and Reflexes

Ask children to show the coins needed to solve each of the following problems. Encourage them to use the fewest number of coins. Have children share their solution strategies after solving each problem. Record solutions using Ⓟ, Ⓝ, and Ⓓ.

●○○ Fernando had 45¢ in his piggy bank. His father gave him 25¢ for walking the dog. How much money did Fernando have then? 70¢

●●○ Rose wants to buy a new jump rope for $1.00. She has saved 70¢. How much more money does Rose need? 30¢

●●● Juanita is making a fruit salad that uses 3 pounds of bananas. Bananas cost 12¢ a pound. How much money will Juanita need? 36¢

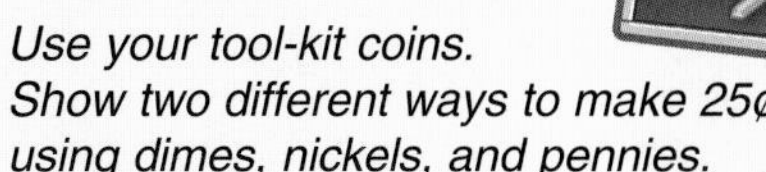

Math Message

Use your tool-kit coins. Show two different ways to make 25¢ using dimes, nickels, and pennies.

Home Link 6·8 Follow-Up

Ask children what can be purchased with a quarter.

1 Teaching the Lesson

▶ Math Message Follow-Up

WHOLE-CLASS DISCUSSION

Have children describe different ways of showing 25¢ using a combination of dimes, nickels, and pennies. Record combinations on the board using coin symbols.

Tell children that today they will learn about the **quarter**, a coin that is worth 25¢. Write *quarter* on the board.

▶ Introducing the Quarter

WHOLE-CLASS DISCUSSION

Children share magnifying lenses for a closer inspection of what is on a quarter. Mention the following information about the quarter:

- The quarter was first issued in 1932 to commemorate the 200th anniversary of George Washington's birth.
- George Washington is on the heads side. For quarters minted through 1998, an eagle with inverted wings over two laurel branches is shown on the tails side. Starting in 1999, quarters were introduced on which the tails side represents one of the 50 states in the United States. These quarters were introduced gradually, in the order in which the states became part of the Union.
- John Flanagan designed the bust of George Washington. His initials, JF, appear on the very bottom of the bust toward the rear of Washington's head.

At this time, you may want to fill in the "Quarter" column on your Story of Money Poster begun in Lesson 2-8. (*See margin.*)

Story of Money

	Penny 1¢ $0.01	Nickel 5¢ $0.05	Dime 10¢ $0.10	Quarter 25¢ $0.25	
Heads	Head of Lincoln	Head of Jefferson	Head of Roosevelt	Head of Washington	
Tails	Lincoln Memorial	Monticello	Torch with Olive and Oak Branches	Eagle or State Designs	
Equivalencies	None	5 Ⓟ	10 Ⓟ 2 Ⓝ	25 Ⓟ 5 Ⓝ	

Language Arts Link Note the words *QUARTER DOLLAR* at the bottom of the tails side of the coin. Explain that a "quarter" of something is one-fourth of that thing. *Quarter* comes from the Latin word *quartarius,* which means "fourth part".

Social Studies Link Display a laminated map of the United States. Using available state quarters, ask the children to find the states that the quarters represent. Tape available state quarters to the map to make a geography connection.

▶ Counting by 25s

Have each child in the class hold up one quarter. Ask for and record estimates of the total amount of money shown by the class. Then count the quarters, first by cents, and then by dollars and cents, with each child adding to the count in turn. You may want to record the counts on the board. Note that when counting by cents, the total goes over 500¢ for a class of more than 20 children.

Ask children to name things that can be purchased for about the total amount.

NOTE To help children find the value of collections of quarters, consider using a table such as the following and having children complete it.

Number of Quarters	Total Amount in Dollars and Cents
1	\$0.25
2	\$0.50
3	\$0.75
4	\$1.00
5	\$1.25

Adjusting the Activity

Have children program a calculator to count by 25s. This will help them find sums of various groups of quarters.

AUDITORY ◆ KINESTHETIC ◆ TACTILE ◆ VISUAL

▶ Counting Combinations of Quarters, Dimes, Nickels, and Pennies

Review counting coins. Ask children to come to the front of the class, as follows:

▷ 2 children, each with a quarter

▷ 3 children, each with a dime

▷ 1 child with a nickel

▷ 4 children, each with a penny

Have the 10 children form a line, with the "quarters" at the left end of the line, followed by the "dimes," "nickels," and "pennies." Walk behind the children, starting with the quarters, and tap each on the head as the class counts the value of the coins together. 25, 50, 60, 70, 80, 85, 86, 87, 88, 89 Write 89 cents in cents notation (89¢) and dollars-and-cents (\$0.89) notation on the board.

Practice finding the value of coins. Use overhead pennies, nickels, dimes, and quarters or draw the coins on the board. Children count their own coins and write the total value on their slates, using either cents or dollars-and-cents notation. Write the answers on the board, using both notations. Children then count the coins in unison.

Suggestions:

What is the value of:

- 2 quarters and 2 dimes? 70¢, or $0.70 Count: 25 cents, 50 cents, 60 cents, 70 cents.
- 1 quarter, 3 dimes, and 2 nickels? 65¢, or $0.65 Count: 25 cents, 35 cents, 45 cents, 55 cents, 60 cents, 65 cents.
- 3 quarters, 1 dime, 3 nickels, and 2 pennies? 102¢, or $1.02 Count: 25 cents, 50 cents, 75 cents, 85 cents, 90 cents, 95 cents, 100 cents (or 1 dollar), 101 cents (or 1 dollar and 1 cent), 102 cents (or 1 dollar and 2 cents).
- 4 quarters, 6 nickels, and 1 penny? 131¢, or $1.31 Count: 25 cents, 50 cents, 75 cents, 1 dollar, 1 dollar and 5 cents, 1 dollar and 10 cents, 1 dollar and 15 cents, 1 dollar and 20 cents, 1 dollar and 25 cents, 1 dollar and 30 cents, 1 dollar and 31 cents.

Ongoing Assessment: Informing Instruction

Watch for children who have difficulty with coin combinations that include quarters. For those children, pose quarter-only coin combination problems. Then add dimes or nickels to the set of coins as the children become more comfortable counting quarters.

▶ Showing Money Amounts with Different Coin Combinations

Write an amount such as $0.46 (or 46¢) on the board. (Initially, use amounts of money less than a dollar and work up to about $3.00.) Ask each partnership to show the exact amount with their coins. Let them share some possibilities with the rest of the class; for example, for 46 cents:

Ⓓ Ⓓ Ⓓ Ⓓ Ⓝ Ⓟ

Ⓠ Ⓝ Ⓝ Ⓝ Ⓝ Ⓟ

Ⓝ Ⓝ Ⓝ Ⓝ Ⓝ Ⓝ Ⓝ Ⓝ Ⓝ Ⓟ

Then ask them to show the amount, using the *fewest* number of coins. Ⓠ Ⓓ Ⓓ Ⓟ

Do more problems as needed.

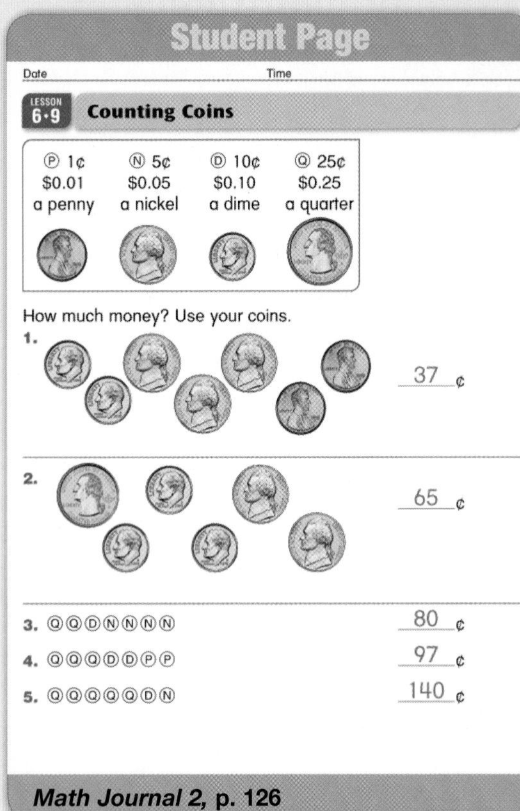
Student Page

Date Time

LESSON 6·9 Counting Coins

Ⓟ 1¢	Ⓝ 5¢	Ⓓ 10¢	Ⓠ 25¢
$0.01	$0.05	$0.10	$0.25
a penny	a nickel	a dime	a quarter

How much money? Use your coins.

1. 37 ¢

2. 65 ¢

3. ⓆⓆⒹⓃⓃⓃⓃ 80 ¢

4. ⓆⓆⒹⒹⒹⓅⓅ 97 ¢

5. ⓆⓆⓆⓆⓆⒹⓃ 140 ¢

Math Journal 2, p. 126

▶ Counting Coins

INDEPENDENT ACTIVITY

(*Math Journal 2,* p. 126)

Children work independently or in partnerships to complete the journal page. They should use their coins to model the problems. When children are finished, go over the answers.

Adjusting the Activity

Have children write the amount that each coin is worth above or below the coin and/or show the value of each coin with tally marks.

AUDITORY ◆ KINESTHETIC ◆ TACTILE ◆ VISUAL

2 Ongoing Learning & Practice

▶ Playing *Coin Top-It*

PARTNER ACTIVITY

Children practice counting and comparing collections of coins by playing *Coin Top-It.* See Lesson 2-13 for directions. Adjust the level of difficulty of the cards by adding harder coin combinations to the deck. Combinations should include some cards with quarters.

▶ Math Boxes 6·9

INDEPENDENT ACTIVITY

(*Math Journal 2,* p. 127)

Mixed Practice Math Boxes in this lesson are paired with Math Boxes in Lesson 6-11. The skills in Problem 4 preview Unit 7 content.

Ongoing Assessment: Recognizing Student Achievement

Math Boxes Problem 1 

Use **Math Boxes, Problem 1** to assess children's ability to answer probability questions. Children are making adequate progress if they are able to answer the question correctly. Some children may be better able than others to explain their reasoning using probability language.

[Data and Chance Goal 3]

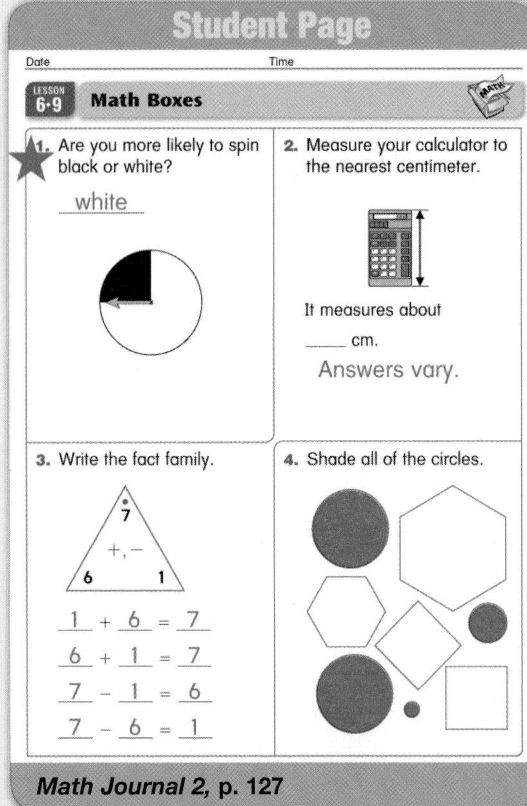
Student Page

Date Time

LESSON 6·9 Math Boxes

1. Are you more likely to spin black or white? white

2. Measure your calculator to the nearest centimeter. It measures about ____ cm. Answers vary.

3. Write the fact family. 7, 6, 1 (+, −)

1 + 6 = 7

6 + 1 = 7

7 − 1 = 6

7 − 6 = 1

4. Shade all of the circles.

Math Journal 2, p. 127

▶ Home Link 6•9

INDEPENDENT ACTIVITY

(*Math Masters,* p. 185)

Home Connection Children count combinations of quarters, dimes, nickels, and pennies. They record the totals, using cents and dollars-and-cents notation.

▶ *Minute Math+*

WHOLE-CLASS ACTIVITY

Use *Minute Math+,* pages 35 and 39 to provide more practice with counting money and finding missing parts in number models.

3 Differentiation Options

READINESS

PARTNER ACTIVITY

▶ Playing *Penny-Nickel-Dime Exchange*

5–15 Min

To provide experience with making coin exchanges, have children play *Penny-Nickel-Dime Exchange*. See Lesson 5-13 for game directions. When children have finished the game, briefly review how many pennies are in a dollar, how many nickels are in a dollar, and how many dimes are in a dollar.

ENRICHMENT

PARTNER ACTIVITY

▶ Playing *Quarter-Dime-Nickel-Penny Grab*

5–15 Min

(*Math Masters,* p. 351)

To apply children's understanding of counting coin combinations including quarters, children play a variation of *Dime-Nickel-Penny Grab* including quarters. For detailed instructions, see Lesson 3-13.

Home Link Master

Name Date

HOME LINK 6•9 **More Counting Coins**

Family Note Children have begun to find the value of coin combinations that include quarters. If your child is having difficulty because coins are not shown in any particular order, use real coins to model the problems. Sort the coins into groups of like coins (all dimes together, all nickels together) before counting.

Children also continue to use dollars-and-cents notation (for example, $1.05). If your child has trouble recording amounts in this notation, don't worry—this is a skill we will continue to practice throughout the year.

Please return this Home Link to school tomorrow.

(P)	(N)	(D)	(Q)
1¢	5¢	10¢	25¢
$0.01	$0.05	$0.10	$0.25
	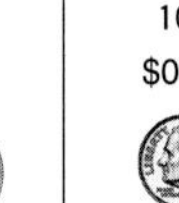		

Find the value of the coins.

Write the total in cents and in dollars-and-cents notation.

1. (N)(Q)(D)(N)(N) 50 ¢ or $ 0.50
2. (Q)(Q)(D)(N)(D)(N)(P)(P) 82 ¢ or $ 0.82
3. (D)(P)(P)(N)(P)(Q) 43 ¢ or $ 0.43
4. (D)(N)(P)(Q)(Q) 66 ¢ or $ 0.66

Practice

5. Fill in the blanks.

72 73 74 75 76 77

***Math Masters,* p. 185**

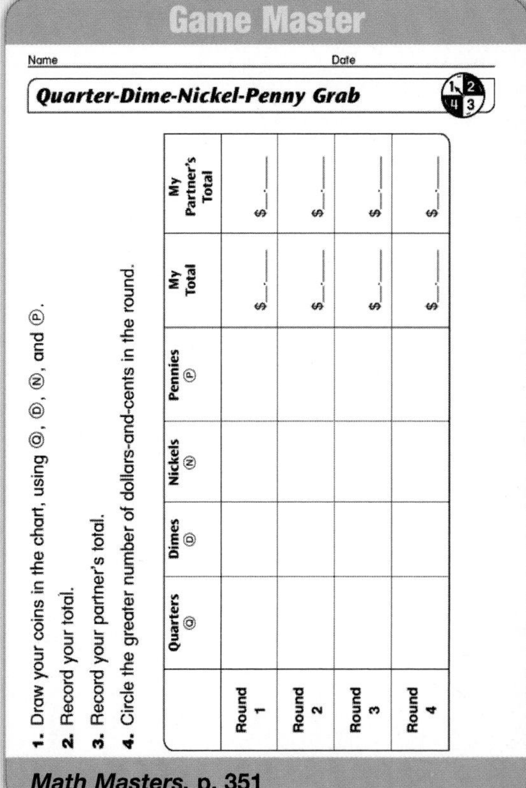

Game Master

Name Date

Quarter-Dime-Nickel-Penny Grab

1. Draw your coins in the chart, using (Q), (D), (N), and (P).
2. Record your total.
3. Record your partner's total.
4. Circle the greater number of dollars-and-cents in the round.

	Quarters (Q)	Dimes (D)	Nickels (N)	Pennies (P)	My Total	My Partner's Total
Round 1					$ ___	$ ___
Round 2					$ ___	$ ___
Round 3					$ ___	$ ___
Round 4					$ ___	$ ___

***Math Masters,* p. 351**

EXTRA PRACTICE

▶ Reading About Money

5–15 Min

(*Math Masters,* p. 305)

Literature Link To provide practice making money amounts, children read ***Deena's Lucky Penny*** by Barbara deRubertis (The Kane Press, 1999). On an Exit Slip (*Math Masters,* page 305), have children show two ways to make 50¢.

ELL SUPPORT

▶ Discussing Meanings of the Word *Quarter*

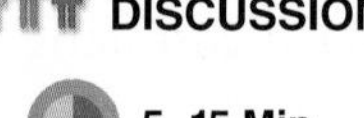

To provide language support for money, have children discuss various meanings of the word *quarter.* They may be familiar with the word in various contexts. Discuss some of these contexts; for example, as a length of time in a basketball game; a football game, or another sporting event; as an amount in a measuring cup; as a portion of an hour or of a pizza. Explain the relationship between the various uses of the word *quarter*.

6•10 Digital Clocks

Objectives To provide experience identifying the number of minutes around the face of an analog clock; and to introduce digital time.

Technology Resources www.everydaymathonline.com

ePresentations

eToolkit

Algorithms Practice

EM Facts Workshop Game™

Family Letters

Assessment Management

Common Core State Standards

Curriculum Focal Points

Interactive Teacher's Lesson Guide

1 Teaching the Lesson

Key Concepts and Skills

- Count forward by 1s and 5s. [Number and Numeration Goal 1]
- Tell time on a digital clock given the time on an analog clock. [Measurement and Reference Frames Goal 4]
- Tell time on an analog clock given the time on a digital clock. [Measurement and Reference Frames Goal 4]
- Tell time to the quarter-hour in digital notation. [Measurement and Reference Frames Goal 4]

Key Activities

Children identify the number of minutes that have elapsed as the minute hand passes each hour number of an analog clock. They are introduced to digital clocks and digital notation for times. They practice writing times to the quarter-hour in digital notation.

Ongoing Assessment: Recognizing Student Achievement Use Mental Math and Reflexes. [Operations and Computation Goal 4]

Ongoing Assessment: Informing Instruction See page 590.

Key Vocabulary

digital clock

Materials

Math Journal 2, pp. 128 and 129
Home Link 6•9
transparency of *Math Masters,* p. 186 (optional) ◆ demonstration clock (minute/hour hands) ◆ digital clock (optional)

2 Ongoing Learning & Practice

Playing *Coin Exchange*

per partnership: tool-kit coins, 2 dice, polyhedral dice (optional)
Children practice exchanging coins with equivalent values.

Math Boxes 6•10

Math Journal 2, p. 130
Children practice and maintain skills through Math Box problems.

Home Link 6•10

Math Masters, p. 187
Children practice and maintain skills through Home Link activities.

3 Differentiation Options

READINESS

Exploring the Minutes on a Clock Face

Math Masters, p. 188 (2 copies per small group)
scissors ◆ tape or glue
Children make circular number lines.

EXTRA PRACTICE

Playing *Time Match*

Time Match Cards (*Math Masters,* pp. 354–357)
Children practice telling time.

Advance Preparation

Place half-sheets of paper, one for each child, near the Math Message. For the optional Extra Practice activity in Part 3, each small group needs a deck of 24 cards.

***Teacher's Reference Manual,* Grades 1–3** p. 173

Getting Started

Mental Math and Reflexes 

Tell number stories such as those suggested below. Children solve them any way they can. Have children share their solution strategies after solving each problem. Summarize their solutions by drawing an appropriate diagram and by writing a number model.

●○○ Grace collects stones. She had 14 stones from the park. She collected 3 more from her neighbors' yards. How many stones has Grace collected in all? 17 stones; 14 + 3 = 17

●●○ Sheena was 48 inches tall at the end of first grade. She grew 5 inches during first grade. How tall was Sheena at the beginning of first grade? 43 inches; Sample number model: 43 + 5 = 48

●●● Jamie is trying to finish reading a book. It is 32 pages long. He has read some pages already. Jamie still has 12 pages left to read. How many pages did Jamie read? 20 pages; Sample number model: 32 − 20 = 12

Math Message

Take a half-sheet of paper. Write the numbers you say when you count by 5s to 60.

Home Link 6·9 Follow-Up

Briefly go over the answers.

Ongoing Assessment: Recognizing Student Achievement

Mental Math and Reflexes 

Use **Mental Math and Reflexes** to assess children's ability to solve number stories. Children are making adequate progress if they are able to answer the first and second problems correctly. Some children may be able to answer all 3 problems correctly.

[Operations and Computation Goal 4]

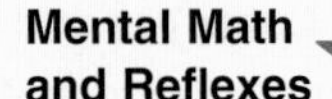

1 Teaching the Lesson

▶ Math Message Follow-Up

Collect the Math Message papers. Look through them to assess readiness for today's lesson.

▶ Counting the Minutes in an Hour

Remind children that it takes 1 minute for the minute hand to move from one mark to the next. Move the minute hand on your demonstration clock slowly around the clock face, starting at 12 o'clock. Children count by 1s to 60 as the minute hand passes each minute mark. Point out that the hour hand has moved from 12 to 1. *How many minutes are there in 1 hour?* 60 minutes

Science Link Use salt, sugar, or sand and plastic bottles taped together at the mouths to make hourglass timers. Make different timers, using different-sized pairs of bottles. Measure how long it takes each timer to empty. Help children determine why the bottles empty at different rates. Discuss the historic and present-day uses of hourglass timers.

▶ Introducing the 5-Minute Interval Marks on the Analog Clock

(*Math Journal 2,* p. 128)

Point to the hour numbers on the clock face: 1, 2, 3 ... 12. To check that it takes 5 minutes for the minute hand to move from one hour number to the next, count the minute marks between two or three pairs of hour numbers. Then set your demonstration clock to 12 o'clock and move the minute hand slowly around the clock face. Have children count by 5s as the minute hand passes the number for each hour.

Children fill in the numbers of minutes at 5-minute intervals around the clock face on journal page 128 and then record the number of minutes in 1 hour, half an hour, a quarter hour, and three-quarters of an hour. After children have completed the journal page, set your demonstration clock to 3 o'clock and move the minute hand slowly around the clock. As the minute hand passes each hour number, say the time with children: *5 minutes after 3, 10 minutes after 3, 15 minutes after 3,* and so on.

Show times on the demonstration clock, such as 8:00, 4:10, 7:30, 10:15, 5:35, and 11:45. Have children say the time, referring to the clock face in their journals as needed.

Adjusting the Activity

Have children show the position of the minute hand for an "o'clock" time by raising an arm vertically. Have children position their arms to show "quarter-past," "half-past," and "quarter-before."

AUDITORY ◆ KINESTHETIC ◆ TACTILE ◆ VISUAL

Links to the Future

Both analog and digital clocks have advantages and disadvantages. It is more difficult to tell time with an analog clock than with a digital clock. However, analog clocks help develop an intuitive understanding of time measurement because they show time more graphically. Since both kinds of clocks are used in everyday life, it is important that children learn to read and understand time on both clocks. This lesson introduces children to time at 5-minute intervals. They are not expected to master this skill in first grade. Telling time to the nearest 5 minutes is a Grade 2 Goal.

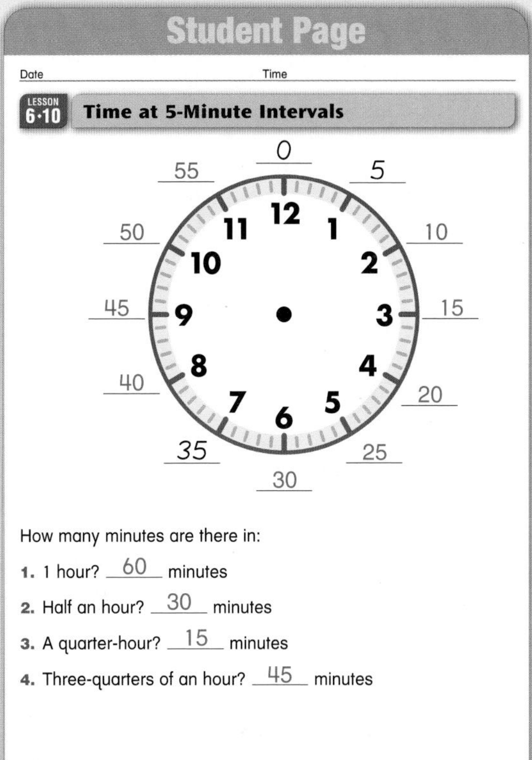

Student Page

Date Time

LESSON 6·10 **Time at 5-Minute Intervals**

How many minutes are there in:

1. 1 hour? 60 minutes
2. Half an hour? 30 minutes
3. A quarter-hour? 15 minutes
4. Three-quarters of an hour? 45 minutes

Math Journal 2, p. 128

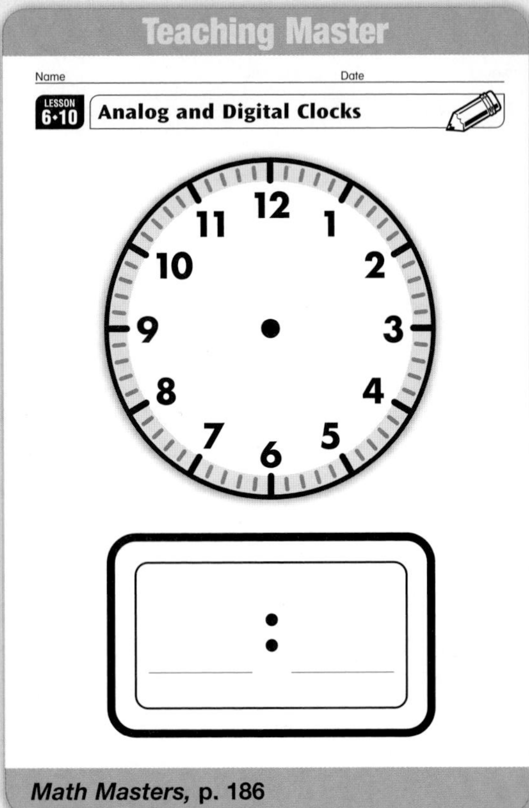

Math Masters, p. 186

▶ Introducing the Digital Clock

Show 5 o'clock on the demonstration clock. Ask if anyone has a clock at home that shows "5 o'clock" with numbers only. Explain that this is called a **digital clock.** Write *digital clock* on the board. Display a digital clock. Use a transparency of *Math Masters,* page 186 for the following routine.

1. Draw hands on the analog clock face on the transparency to show 5 o'clock. Then write "5:00" on the digital clock on the transparency. Explain that these two clocks show the same time.
2. Show 10 minutes after 7 on the analog clock and write "7:10" on the digital clock. Again, point out that the two clocks show the same time. We can say that the time shown is "10 minutes after 7," or "seven-ten."
3. Show 5 minutes after 6 on the analog clock and write "6:05" on the digital clock. We can say that the time shown is "5 minutes after 6" or "six-o-five." It may be curious to children that 605 is read "six hundred five", but 6:05 is read, "six-o-five." Explaining this difference may be important. Emphasize other ways to read 6:05 such as "5 past six."

Repeat with several other times. Then show a time with the minute hand pointing to an hour number on the analog clock and ask children what time is shown. Write the time on the digital clock. After a few examples, give a time and ask volunteers to draw the hands on the analog clock and write the time on the digital clock. Include times such as "half-past 9," "a quarter past 4," and "a quarter to 10."

Explain what the numbers and symbol on the digital clock mean.

- The numbers are separated by a *colon* (:).
- The number before the colon tells the hour.
- The number after the colon tells the minutes after the hour.
- To support English language learners, write the following on the board:

6:05

hour:minutes

Ongoing Assessment: Informing Instruction

Watch for children who:

- write 2:00 as 2:60.
- write 2:00 as 2:12.
- write 2:00 as 10:00.

Discuss the similarity between dollars-and-cents notation for money and digital notation for time. In dollars-and-cents notation, two places are needed after the decimal point to accommodate cents amounts up to 99 cents. In digital notation for time, two places are needed after the colon to accommodate numbers of minutes up to 59. Just as we write 6 dollars and 5 cents as $6.05, not $6.5, we write 5 minutes after 6 as 6:05, not 6:5.

Adjusting the Activity

Tell the class that "00" is the smallest number of minutes that can be displayed on a digital clock.

- What is the largest number of minutes that can be displayed? 59
- What is the smallest number of hours that can be displayed? 1
- What is the largest number of hours that can be displayed? 12

AUDITORY ◆ KINESTHETIC ◆ TACTILE ◆ VISUAL

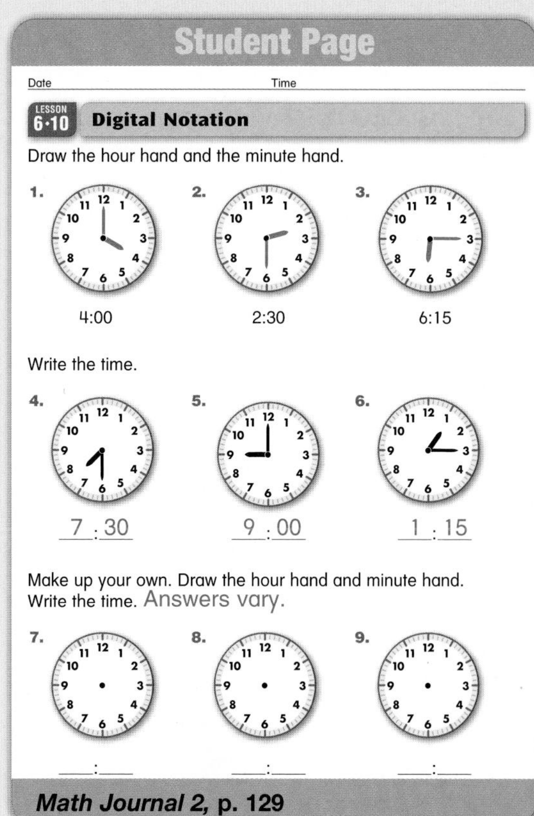

▶ Using Digital Notation

INDEPENDENT ACTIVITY

(*Math Journal 2,* p. 129)

Children draw the hour and minute hands to show a time given in digital notation. They write the time shown on an analog clock face in digital notation. Children who are having difficulty with this page can refer to the clock face on journal page 128 for help.

2 Ongoing Learning & Practice

▶ Playing *Coin Exchange*

PARTNER ACTIVITY

Partners put 20 pennies, 10 nickels, 10 dimes, and 4 quarters in a pile. This pile is the bank.

Directions

1. Players take turns. When it is your turn, roll both dice and collect from the bank the amount shown on the dice.
2. Whenever you can, exchange 5 pennies for a nickel in the bank; exchange 2 nickels, or 5 pennies and a nickel, for a dime; and exchange a combination of nickels and dimes for a quarter.
3. The game ends when there are no more quarters in the bank.
4. The player with more money wins.

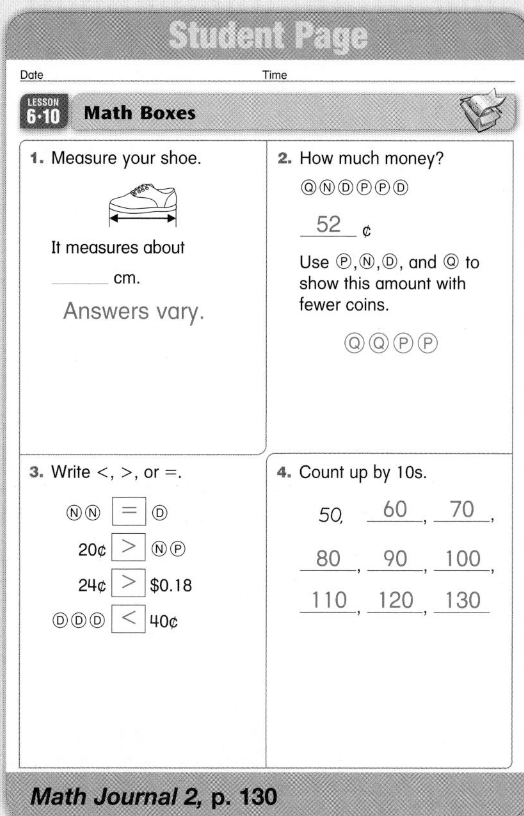

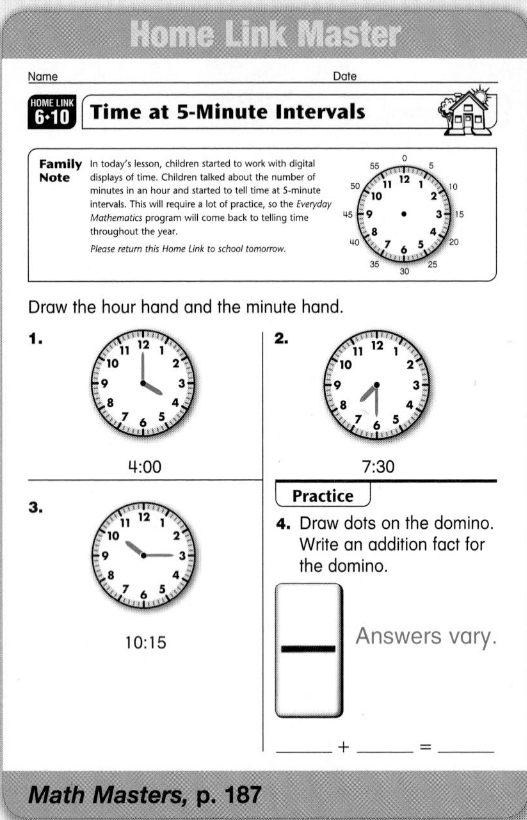

Home Link Master

Name Date

HOME LINK 6•10 **Time at 5-Minute Intervals**

Family Note In today's lesson, children started to work with digital displays of time. Children talked about the number of minutes in an hour and started to tell time at 5-minute intervals. This will require a lot of practice, so the *Everyday Mathematics* program will come back to telling time throughout the year.

Please return this Home Link to school tomorrow.

Draw the hour hand and the minute hand.

1. 4:00

2. 7:30

3. 10:15

Practice

4. Draw dots on the domino. Write an addition fact for the domino.

Answers vary.

____ + ____ = ____

***Math Masters,* p. 187**

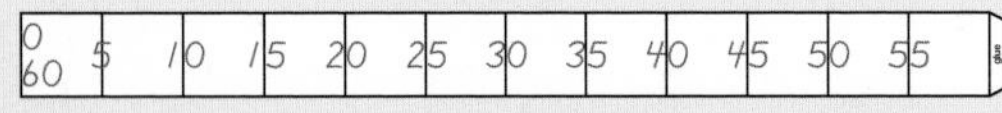

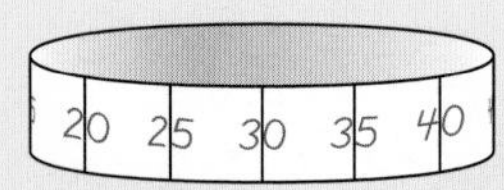

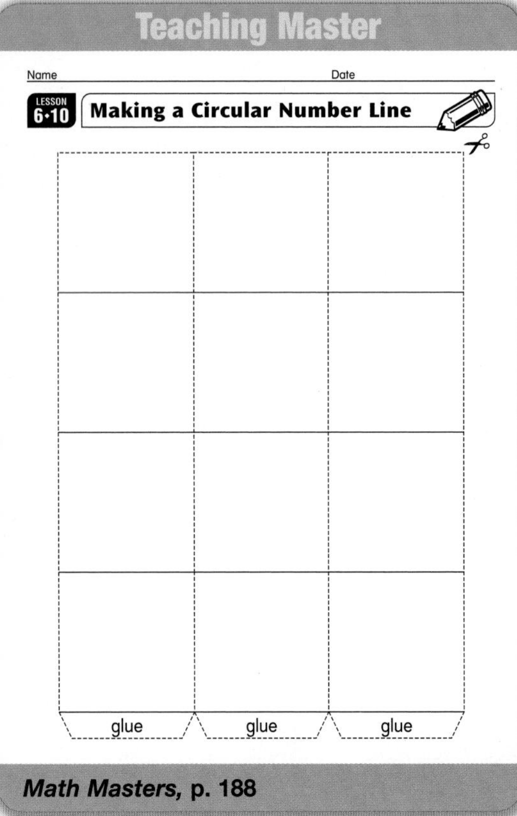

Teaching Master

Name Date

LESSON 6•10 **Making a Circular Number Line**

glue glue glue

***Math Masters,* p. 188**

▶ Math Boxes 6•10

INDEPENDENT ACTIVITY

(*Math Journal 2,* p. 130)

Mixed Practice Math Boxes in this lesson are paired with Math Boxes in Lesson 6-12.

Writing/Reasoning Have children draw, write, or verbalize an answer to the following question: *How do you count a handful of coins?* A reasonable answer should show a strategy for counting a mixed group of coins, such as sorting coins by type and counting the coins with the larger values first.

▶ Home Link 6•10

INDEPENDENT ACTIVITY

(*Math Masters,* p. 187)

Home Connection Children draw the hands on analog clocks for times shown in digital notation.

3 Differentiation Options

READINESS

SMALL-GROUP ACTIVITY

▶ Exploring the Minutes on a Clock Face

(*Math Masters,* p. 188)

To explore the number of minutes in an hour, have children make a circular number line. Have children cut and glue together the three parts of *Math Masters*, page 188 to make a "number line." Instruct children to label each line with a count by 5s from 0–55. (*See margin.*) Instruct children to write 60 under the 0 because the minute hand of the clock starts and ends at the same place. Then they should tape the ends of the number line together to form a circle. Have them compare their circular "number line" to the clock face.

EXTRA PRACTICE

SMALL-GROUP ACTIVITY

▶ Playing *Time Match*

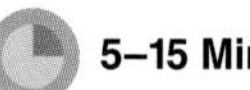

Children practice identifying time on clocks by playing *Time Match*. For detailed instructions, see Lesson 4-4.

6•11 Introducing *My Reference Book*

Objective To introduce *My Reference Book.*

Technology Resources www.everydaymathonline.com

ePresentations | eToolkit | Algorithms Practice | EM Facts Workshop Game™ | Family Letters | Assessment Management | Common Core State Standards | Curriculum Focal Points | Interactive Teacher's Lesson Guide

1 Teaching the Lesson

Key Concepts and Skills

- Find numbers in a sequence.
  [Number and Numeration Goal 7]
- Calculate the value of combinations of coins.
  [Operations and Computation Goal 2]
- Find and draw plane shapes.
  [Geometry Goal 1]

Key Activities

Children are introduced to *My Reference Book.* They use it to answer questions in a scavenger hunt.

Ongoing Assessment: Recognizing Student Achievement Use Mental Math and Reflexes.
[Measurement and Reference Frames Goal 4]

Key Vocabulary

My Reference Book ◆ table of contents

Materials

Math Journal 2, p. 131
Grades 1–2 My Reference Book
Home Link 6•10
tool-kit clock ◆ slate ◆ stick-on notes (optional)

2 Ongoing Learning & Practice

Practicing Measuring in Centimeters

Math Journal 2, p. 132
centimeter ruler
Children practice measuring in centimeters.

Math Boxes 6•11

Math Journal 2, p. 133
Children practice and maintain skills through Math Box problems.

Home Link 6•11

Math Masters, p. 189
Children practice and maintain skills through Home Link activities.

3 Differentiation Options

READINESS

Ordering Ourselves

per group: 12 ordinal number cards
Children use ordinal numbers through 12th.

EXTRA PRACTICE

Minute Math+

Minute Math®+, pp. 32 and 33
Children practice identifying digits in numbers.

Advance Preparation

For the optional Readiness activity in Part 3, on each of 12 large index cards, write the ordinal number and word. For example, on the first card, write *1st* and *first.*

***Teacher's Reference Manual,* Grades 1–3** p. 16

Getting Started

Mental Math and Reflexes ★

Have children show a time on their tool-kit clocks and write the time in digital notation on their slates.

●○○ 4:00, 12:00, 9:00

●●○ 8:30, 6:30, 11:30

●●● 5:45, 3:15, 1:45

Math Message

Look through your My Reference Book. *Be ready to share something you find interesting. Think about how this book can help you.*

Home Link 6·10 Follow-Up

Briefly go over the answers.

Ongoing Assessment: Recognizing Student Achievement

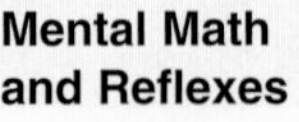

Use **Mental Math and Reflexes** to assess children's ability to show and tell time. Children are making adequate progress if they can show times on an analog clock. Some children will be successful writing digital time, as well.

[Measurement and Reference Frames Goal 4]

1 Teaching the Lesson

▶ Math Message Follow-Up

Display a *Grades 1–2 My Reference Book* and explain to children that this book may be used as a reference during math time in first and second grade. Tell children that they will be exploring *MRB* today to see what kinds of things are in it.

Have children share some of the things they found while exploring ***My Reference Book.*** Make a list of ways that children think *My Reference Book* may be helpful during mathematics.

Tell children that the **table of contents** may be used to find the page number of the first page of a topic. Write *table of contents* on the board as you discuss it. Have children use the table of contents to look up information on time. *To what page does the table of contents send you?* Page 78 Discuss the information in *My Reference Book* related to time. Return to the table of contents. *What other topics in the table of contents look familiar to you?* Allow time for children to explore topics found in the table of contents.

Next, turn to the games section. Discuss times when this section might be useful. Directions can help children play games at home and during free time in class.

Adjusting the Activity

As the *Table of Contents* and *Games* sections are introduced, have children put stick-on notes on the first page of each part to make it easy to find these parts again.

AUDITORY ◆ KINESTHETIC ◆ TACTILE ◆ VISUAL

▶ *My Reference Book* Scavenger Hunt

PARTNER ACTIVITY

(*Math Journal 2,* p. 131)

Ask children if anyone has ever done a scavenger hunt. Allow a few children to share their experiences. Tell children that a scavenger hunt is an activity where you are given clues telling you to hunt for a specific item in a certain area. After finding the item, you are given a new clue and a new item for which to hunt. Let children know that they are doing a scavenger hunt today in their *Grades 1–2 My Reference Book*. Partnerships use page 131 in their journals. Encourage children to complete the page by filling in each of the boxes with their responses.

Adjusting the Activity

Scavenger hunts can also be done in teacher-led small groups or as a whole-class activity.

AUDITORY ◆ KINESTHETIC ◆ TACTILE ◆ VISUAL

Social Studies Link Display an age-appropriate set of encyclopedias for children to explore. Compare the encyclopedias to the *Grades 1–2 My Reference Book*. Encourage children to make their own scavenger hunts using the encyclopedias.

2 Ongoing Learning & Practice

▶ Practicing Measuring in Centimeters

INDEPENDENT ACTIVITY

(*Math Journal 2,* p. 132)

Use *Math Journal 2,* page 132 to provide more practice measuring in centimeters.

Student Page

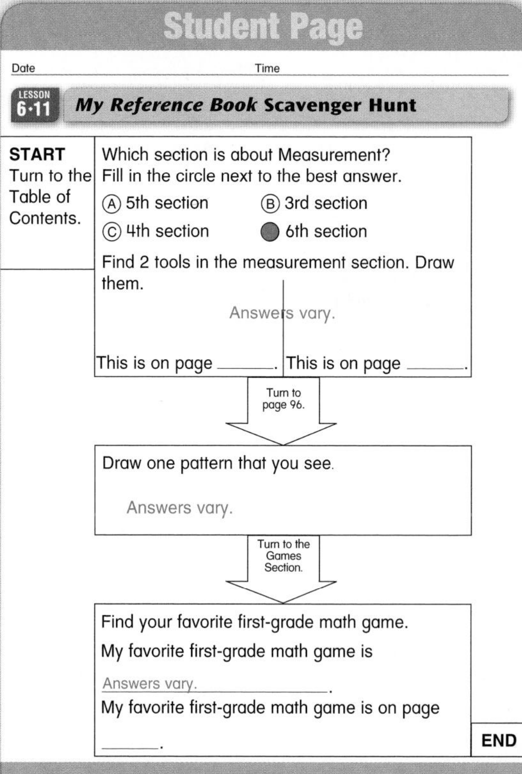
Date Time

LESSON 6·11 ***My Reference Book* Scavenger Hunt**

START Turn to the Table of Contents.

Which section is about Measurement? Fill in the circle next to the best answer.

Ⓐ 5th section Ⓑ 3rd section

Ⓒ 4th section ● 6th section

Find 2 tools in the measurement section. Draw them.

Answers vary.

This is on page ____. This is on page ____.

Turn to page 96.

Draw one pattern that you see.

Answers vary.

Turn to the Games Section.

Find your favorite first-grade math game.

My favorite first-grade math game is

Answers vary.

My favorite first-grade math game is on page ____.

END

***Math Journal 2,* p. 131**

Student Page

Date Time

LESSON 6·11 **1- and 10-Centimeter Objects**

1. Find 3 things that are about 1 centimeter long.
   Use words or pictures to show the things you found.
   Answers vary.

2. Find 3 things that are about 10 centimeters long.
   Use words or pictures to show the things you found.
   Answers vary.

***Math Journal 2,* p. 132**

Student Page

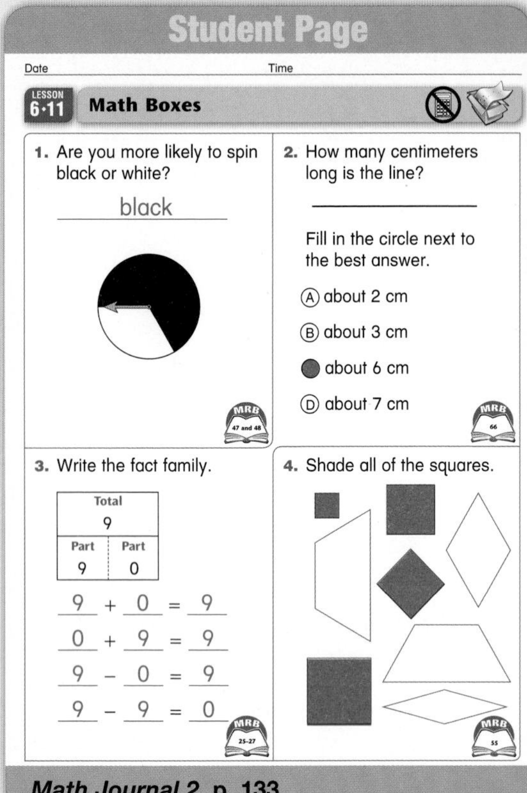
Date Time

LESSON 6•11 **Math Boxes**

1. Are you more likely to spin black or white?

black

2. How many centimeters long is the line?

Fill in the circle next to the best answer.

(A) about 2 cm
(B) about 3 cm
● about 6 cm
(D) about 7 cm

3. Write the fact family.

Total	
9	
Part	Part
9	0

9 + 0 = 9
0 + 9 = 9
9 − 0 = 9
9 − 9 = 0

4. Shade all of the squares.

Math Journal 2, p. 133

▶ Math Boxes 6•11

INDEPENDENT ACTIVITY

(*Math Journal 2,* p. 133)

Mixed Practice Math Boxes in this lesson are paired with Math Boxes in Lesson 6-9. The skills in Problem 4 preview Unit 7 content.

Writing/Reasoning Have children draw, write, or verbalize an answer to the following question: *How do you know which color you are more likely to spin?* A reasonable answer should identify the color covering the greatest region on the spinner.

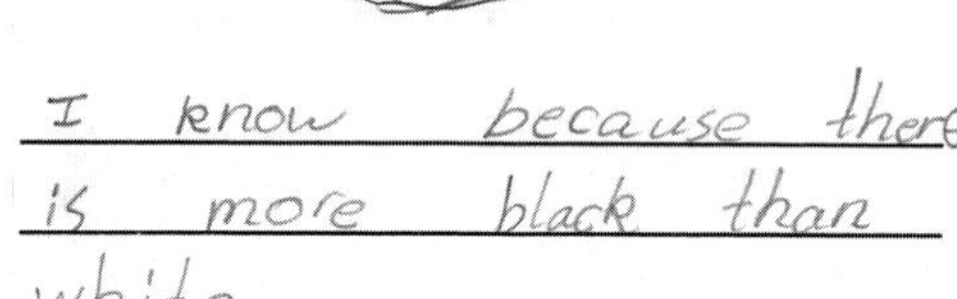

One child's work in response to the Writing/Reasoning prompt

▶ Home Link 6•11

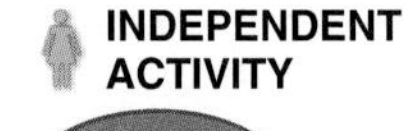
INDEPENDENT ACTIVITY

(*Math Masters,* p. 189)

Home Connection Children cut out a third set of Fact Triangles to continue their fact practice at home.

Home Link Master

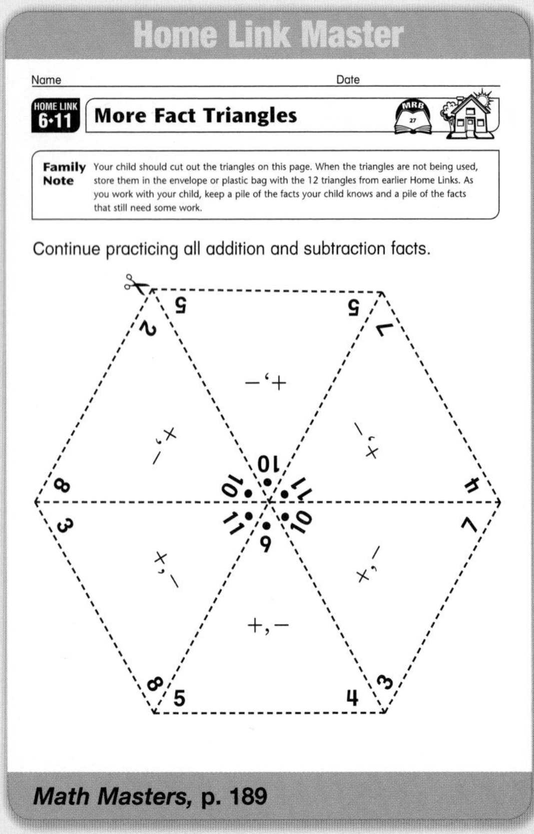
Name Date

HOME LINK 6•11 **More Fact Triangles**

Family Note Your child should cut out the triangles on this page. When the triangles are not being used, store them in the envelope or plastic bag with the 12 triangles from earlier Home Links. As you work with your child, keep a pile of the facts your child knows and a pile of the facts that still need some work.

Continue practicing all addition and subtraction facts.

Math Masters, p. 189

3 Differentiation Options

READINESS

SMALL-GROUP ACTIVITY

▶ Ordering Ourselves

15–30 Min

To explore ordinal numbers, have children sequence number cards. Arrange 12 children in line. Give the 1st and 12th cards to the children on either end of the line. Randomly distribute the remaining 10 cards to the other children in line.

Have children take turns finding their correct place in line and explaining why he or she belongs there. Encourage children to use not only their ordinal number, but also the ordinal number for the person on either side of them to explain their position.

EXTRA PRACTICE

SMALL-GROUP ACTIVITY
5–15 Min

▶ *Minute Math+*

Use *Minute Math+,* pages 32 and 33 to practice using digit clues to identify numbers.

6•12 Data Landmarks

Objectives To introduce the statistical landmarks *range* and *middle value*; and to provide practice collecting data and making bar graphs.

Technology Resources www.everydaymathonline.com

ePresentations

eToolkit

Algorithms Practice

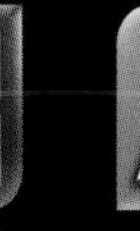
EM Facts Workshop Game™

Family Letters

Assessment Management

Common Core State Standards

Curriculum Focal Points

Interactive Teacher's Lesson Guide

1 Teaching the Lesson

Key Concepts and Skills

- Count forward by 1s on a calculator.
  [Number and Numeration Goal 1]
- Compare and order whole numbers.
  [Number and Numeration Goal 7]
- Create a tally chart and a bar graph to organize data.
  [Data and Chance Goal 1]
- Find landmarks; ask and answer questions about a data set.
  [Data and Chance Goal 2]

Key Activities

Children see how high they can count in 15 seconds using calculators. Children tally the class data, determine various statistical landmarks, and make a bar graph of the data. Children ask and answer questions about the data.

Key Vocabulary

middle value ◆ range

Materials

Math Journal 2, p. 134
Home Link 6•11
Class Data Pad ◆ slate ◆ calculator ◆ stick-on notes (1 per child) ◆ number cards (optional) ◆ overhead coins (optional)

2 Ongoing Learning & Practice

Playing *Tric-Trac*
Math Masters, p. 360
My Reference Book, pp. 156–158
per partnership: 2 dice, 20 pennies
Children practice addition facts.

Ongoing Assessment: Recognizing Student Achievement
Use an Exit Slip (*Math Masters,* page 305).
[Operations and Computation Goal 1]

Math Boxes 6•12
Math Journal 2, p. 135
Children practice and maintain skills through Math Box problems.

Home Link 6•12
Math Masters, p. 190
Children practice and maintain skills through Home Link activities.

3 Differentiation Options

READINESS

Finding the Lowest and Highest Values in Data
Class Data Pad pages from Lessons 4•7 and 5•9
Children find the lowest and highest values in previously collected data.

ENRICHMENT

Collecting and Analyzing Data
Math Masters, p. 191
Children survey their classmates, using a question, and collect and analyze the data.

ELL SUPPORT

Building a Math Word Bank
Differentiation Handbook, p. 126
Children add the term *range* to their Math Word Banks.

Advance Preparation

For Part 1, draw a tally chart on the Class Data Pad with the headings "Counted to" for the first column and "Number of Children" for the second column. In the first column, write the numbers 5–15. See page 598.

***Teacher's Reference Manual,* Grades 1–3** pp. 120–125

Getting Started

Mental Math and Reflexes

Show a coin combination on the overhead or draw it on the board. Have children write the total value of the coins on their slates in both cents and dollars-and-cents notation. To go over the answers, count the coins in unison, using "stop-and-start" counting.

Suggestions:

●○○ Ⓓ Ⓓ Ⓓ Ⓓ Ⓓ Ⓝ Ⓝ Ⓝ Ⓟ Ⓟ Ⓟ 68¢; $0.68
●●○ Ⓠ Ⓠ Ⓓ Ⓓ Ⓓ Ⓝ Ⓟ Ⓟ Ⓟ Ⓟ Ⓟ 90¢; $0.90
●●● Ⓠ Ⓠ Ⓠ Ⓓ Ⓓ Ⓝ Ⓟ Ⓟ Ⓟ Ⓟ 104¢; $1.04

Math Message

Program a calculator to count by 1s. How high can you count on the calculator in one minute?

Home Link 6·11 Follow-Up

List some of the facts that children are still having trouble learning when they practice at home. Draw one or two Fact Triangles on the board and ask volunteers to write the three numbers and the fact family associated with each triangle.

Counted to	Number of Children
5	/
6	
7	//
8	
9	//
10	~~////~~
11	~~////~~ //
12	~~////~~
13	///
14	//
15	/

Student Page

Date ______ Time ______

LESSON 6·12 **Class Results of Calculator Counts**

1. I counted to ______ in 15 seconds. Answers vary.
2. Class results:

Largest count	Smallest count	Range of class counts	Middle value of class counts
______	______	______	______

3. Make a bar graph of the results.

Results of Calculator Counts

Number of Children

Counted to

Math Journal 2, **p. 134**

1 Teaching the Lesson

▶ Math Message Follow-Up

WHOLE-CLASS DISCUSSION

Ask a few volunteers to explain how they programmed their calculators to count by 1s. Record their methods on the board. Tell children that they will use their calculators to count by 1s in a different way today.

▶ Timing a Calculator Count

(*Math Journal 2,* p. 134)

Tell children that they will find out how high they can count on a calculator in 15 seconds by entering 1 [+] 1 [=] [+] 1 [=] [+] 1 [=] and so on.

First, have everyone practice counting to 10:

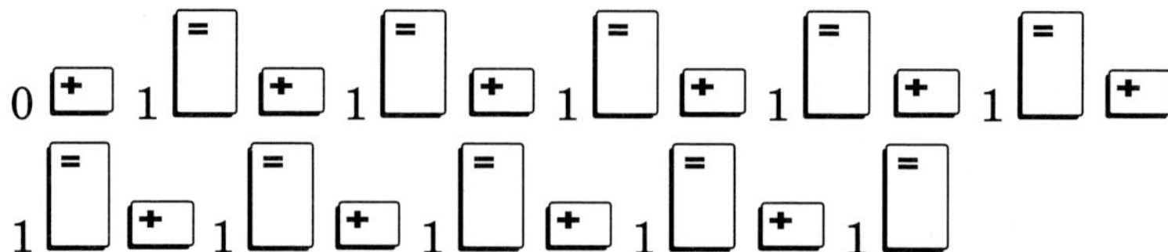

Do this several times until children are comfortable with it.

Then time children for 15 seconds, three times. Have children use a stick-on note, journal page 134, and a slate on which to record the largest number to which they counted.

Ask children, one at a time, to report their largest count and record it with a tally in the Class Data Pad. Discuss the results.

- What was the largest number anyone counted to? What was the smallest number?
- Find the difference between the largest and smallest numbers. (If children don't remember the meaning of the word *difference,* ask: *How much more is the largest number than the smallest number?)*

Explain that the difference between the largest and smallest numbers in a set of data is called the **range.** You can find the range by subtracting the smallest number from the largest number.

Suppose you had to guess about how high a child your age in another school could count on the calculator in 15 seconds. What would be your guess?

Expect answers such as the following:

- Probably higher than the smallest number because most of us counted higher than that.
- Probably less than the largest number because most of us counted less than that.
- It might be somewhere around the middle of all of our counts because a lot of us were near the middle.

One name for the **middle value** is the *median.* The median is a number that describes a typical result. If, when finding the median, there are two middle values, we can call the number halfway between the two middle values the median. At this stage, however, it is appropriate to say that there are two middle values.

Ask for suggestions for finding the number (or numbers) in the middle. Here is one way:

Ask children to bring their slates as they form a line in order from smallest to largest number. Two children who have the same number stand next to each other. Ask the child at each end of the line to sit down. Repeat. Children continue to sit down in pairs until there are either one or two children left. If the total number of children in line is an odd number, there will be one child in the middle and, therefore, one middle value. If it is an even number, there will be two children in the middle and, therefore, two middle values.

ELL The range is often understood to be the spread of a set of numbers from smallest to largest. For example, we might say that the range in the ages of children in a school is from 5 to 12, or that the children's ages range from 5 to 12 years. In mathematics, range is used to refer to a single number—the difference between the largest and smallest number in a set of numbers. To support English language learners, discuss the everyday meanings of the word *range* and provide examples of its meaning in this mathematical context.

NOTE Another typical result is found by adding all of the results and dividing the sum by the number of results. This number is known as the *average*, or to use the mathematical term, the *mean,* of a set of values.

Children act out finding the middle numbers.

At this time, you may wish to introduce another method for finding the middle value.

- ▷ Use children's stick-on notes to create a line plot.
- ▷ Remove the last stick-on note at each end of the line plot and move it below the number line. (If there are several stick-on notes forming a column at one end of the line plot, remove the top one.)
- ▷ Repeat the procedure over and over.
- ▷ Eventually, there will be only one or two notes left above the line. If one note remains, the number on that note is the middle value. If two notes remain, the numbers on those notes are the middle values.

Make sure children record the class results of the largest count, the smallest count, the range of class counts, and the middle value of class counts on journal page 134.

▶ Making a Bar Graph

INDEPENDENT ACTIVITY

(*Math Journal 2,* p. 134)

Children make a bar graph of the class data. If they are able to do so, have them work on their own or with a partner. Otherwise, work with the whole class on the Class Data Pad. Guide children by asking questions, such as the following:

- What numbers go at the bottom of the graph? The numbers in the first column of the chart
- How many squares would you color above the first number? Above the second number? The number of tallies next to that number

Children can color the rest of the bars on their own. See sample results in the margin.

After children have completed their graphs, encourage them to ask questions that can be answered using the graph. Ask questions such as the following to guide them:

- What questions can you ask that compare the data in one column with the data in another column?
- What other questions can you ask that can be answered by using this graph?

Have children pose their questions to their classmates, so that they have the opportunity to both ask and answer questions about the data.

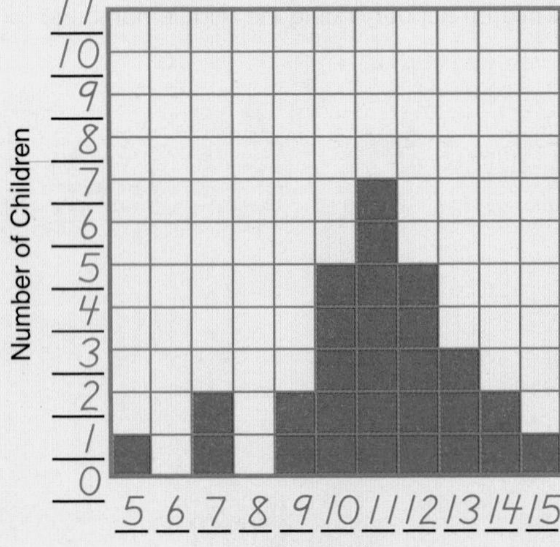

Adjusting the Activity

ELL

Find space on the floor to create a human "bar graph" about the information in the tally chart. Use number cards to label the axes and have children sit in the graph as a representation of their highest counts.

Use a transparency of journal page 134, and fill in the numbers at the bottom of the bar graph together. Have volunteers come to the overhead and shade the correct number of squares for each number.

AUDITORY ◆ KINESTHETIC ◆ TACTILE ◆ VISUAL

NOTE You may want to show children how their graph would look if it were created with graphing software.

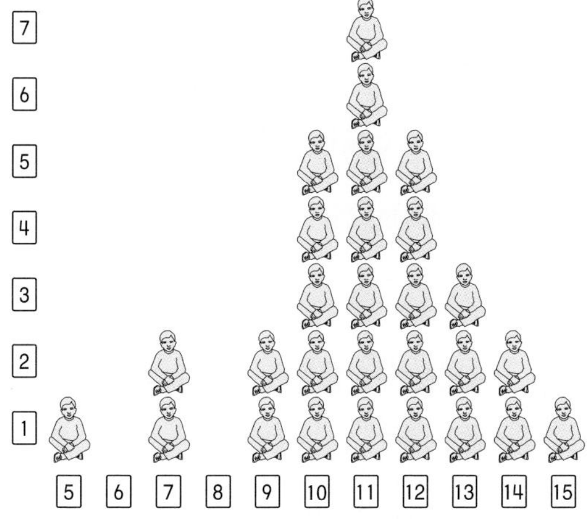

Create a human bar graph showing the results of the calculator counts.

2 Ongoing Learning & Practice

▶ Playing *Tric-Trac*

PARTNER ACTIVITY

FACTS PRACTICE

(*Math Masters*, p. 360; *My Reference Book*, pp. 156–158)

Children practice addition facts by playing *Tric-Trac*. For detailed instructions see Lesson 6-8 or pages 156–158 of *My Reference Book*.

Ongoing Assessment: Recognizing Student Achievement

Exit Slip

Use an **Exit Slip** (*Math Masters*, page 305) to assess children's knowledge of addition facts. For one game of *Tric-Trac*, have children write on an Exit Slip each addition fact they use. Children are making adequate progress if they list accurate addition facts.

[Operations and Computation Goal 1]

Student Pages

Games

Tric-Trac

Materials ❑ 2 six-sided dice
❑ 20 pennies
❑ 1 *Tric-Trac* Game Mat for each player

Players 2

Skill Addition facts 0-10

Object of the game To have the lower sum.

Directions

1. Cover the empty circles on your game mat with pennies.
2. Take turns. When it is your turn:
   - Roll the dice. Find the total number of dots. This is your sum.
   - Move 1 of your pennies and cover your sum on your game mat.

OR

   - Move 2 or more of your pennies and cover any numbers that can be added together to equal your sum.

***My Reference Book*, p. 156–158**

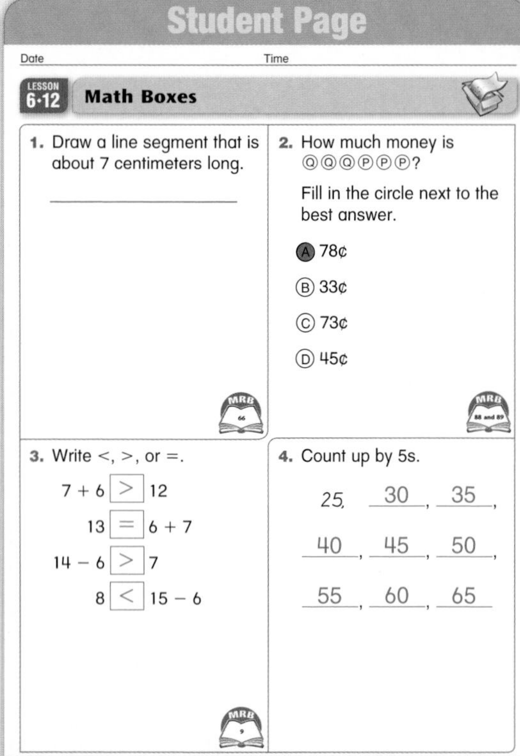
Student Page

Date Time

LESSON 6•12 **Math Boxes**

1. Draw a line segment that is about 7 centimeters long.

2. How much money is Ⓠ Ⓠ Ⓠ Ⓟ Ⓟ Ⓟ?
Fill in the circle next to the best answer.
● 78¢
Ⓑ 33¢
Ⓒ 73¢
Ⓓ 45¢

3. Write <, >, or =.
7 + 6 [>] 12
13 [=] 6 + 7
14 − 6 [>] 7
8 [<] 15 − 6

4. Count up by 5s.
25, 30, 35,
40, 45, 50,
55, 60, 65

Math Journal 2, **p. 135**

Math Boxes 6•12

INDEPENDENT ACTIVITY

(*Math Journal 2,* p. 135)

Mixed Practice Math Boxes in this lesson are paired with Math Boxes in Lesson 6-10.

Home Link 6•12

INDEPENDENT ACTIVITY

(*Math Masters,* p. 190)

Home Connection Children identify the largest and smallest numbers and the range of numbers in a tally chart.

3 Differentiation Options

READINESS

SMALL-GROUP DISCUSSION

Finding the Lowest and Highest Values in Data

5–15 Min

To provide experience with finding data landmarks, have children look at the collected data about children's heights from Lesson 4-7. Help children determine the lowest and highest values of children's heights. Look at the collected data about dice throws in Lesson 5-9. Help children determine the lowest and highest value of dice throws.

NOTE Remember to use the Dice Roll Activity on a regular basis to practice fact strategies. See Lesson 5-10 for detailed instructions. When your class is ready, you may wish to try some of the variations listed in Lesson 5-10.

Home Link Master

Name Date

HOME LINK 6•12 **Analyzing a Set of Data**

Family Note Today we did some calculator counts in class. Ask your child what his or her highest count was at the end of 15 seconds.

Below is a tally chart like one we made in class today. Help your child identify how many children did the counts and the lowest and the highest counts that someone in Casey's class got. Then help your child find the range of the counts. (To find the range, subtract the lowest count from the highest count.)

Please return this Home Link to school tomorrow.

Casey's Class Data for Calculator Counts

Counted to	Number of Children
5	/
7	//
10	卌
11	卌 /
12	////
13	///
15	//
17	/
18	/

1. How many children in Casey's class did the calculator counts? 25 children
2. Find the highest count. 18
3. Find the lowest count. 5
4. Find the range of the counts. 13

Practice

5. Write some names for 12.
Sample answers: 10 + 2, 20 − 8, 卌卌 //, 1 + 3 + 4 + 4

Math Masters, **p. 190**

ENRICHMENT

INDEPENDENT ACTIVITY

15–30 Min

▶ Collecting and Analyzing Data

(*Math Masters,* p. 191)

To apply children's understanding of data sets, have them make a prediction and then collect and analyze data for a question that they ask their classmates. Have each child think of a question along with four answer choices. For example, for the question, *What is your favorite lunch food?,* the answer choices might be hamburger, hot dog, salad, or other. Have children predict which answer will be the most popular. Then have them survey their classmates and record the responses in a tally chart. Children can use *Math Masters,* page 191 to display their results. Ask children if their predictions were accurate.

ELL SUPPORT

5–15 Min

▶ Building a Math Word Bank

(*Differentiation Handbook,* p. 126)

To provide language support for data landmarks, have children use the Word Bank Template found on *Differentiation Handbook,* page 126. Ask children to write the term *range* and to list five numbers in order: 2, 4, 6, 7, 9. Children circle the highest and lowest numbers (2 and 9) and write below the numbers $9 - 2 = 7$ *The range is 7.* To help children remember that 7 is the range for these numbers, consider having them use a brightly colored crayon to trace the number 7 in the number sentence and in the word sentence. Ask children to write other words to describe range, draw a picture representing the term, and write other words that describe it. See the *Differentiation Handbook* for more information.

6•13 Progress Check 6

Objective To assess children's progress on mathematical content through the end of Unit 6.

1 Looking Back: Cumulative Assessment

Input children's data from Progress Check 6 into the **Assessment Management Spreadsheets.**

Materials

- Home Link 6•12
- *Assessment Handbook,* pp. 94–101, 157–160, 182, and 220–223
- slate; 10 pennies, 10 nickels, 10 dimes, and 4 quarters per child

CONTENT ASSESSED	LESSON(S)	ASSESSMENT ITEMS				
		SELF	ORAL/SLATE	WRITTEN		OPEN RESPONSE
				PART A	PART B	
Read, write, and represent with base-10 blocks whole numbers through hundreds. [Number and Numeration Goal 3]	6•2, 6•4, 6•6, 6•11	3		1, 2		
Use concrete materials and pictures to find equivalent names for numbers. [Number and Numeration Goal 6]	6•2, 6•3, 6•4	1		3, 4		
Compare whole numbers. [Number and Numeration Goal 7]	6•1, 6•2, 6•5, 6•12	2	1, 2			
Know addition and subtraction facts. [Operations and Computation Goal 1]	6•1–6•9, 6•12		4	6	9	
Solve problems involving addition; calculate and compare the values of combinations of coins. [Operations and Computation Goal 2]	6•9, 6•10, 6•12			5		✓
Demonstrate and describe change-to-more and change-to-less situations. [Operations and Computation Goal 4]	6•3, 6•9, 6•10	6	3			
Estimate and compare lengths of objects. [Measurement and Reference Frames Goal 1]	6•9, 6•10, 6•12	4			7, 8	
Know and compare the values of coins. [Measurement and Reference Frames Goal 2]	6•9, 6•10–6•12					✓
Create and continue a visual pattern. [Patterns, Functions, and Algebra Goal 1]	6•1					✓
Write number sentences using symbols. [Patterns, Functions, and Algebra Goal 2]	6•2–6•4	2	3	5		
Use the Commutative Property of Addition. [Patterns, Functions, and Algebra Goal 3]	6•1, 6•3–6•7, 6•9, 6•11	5	4			

2 Looking Ahead: Preparing for Unit 7

Math Boxes 6•13

Home Link 6•13: Unit 7 Family Letter

Materials

- *Math Journal 2,* p. 136
- *Math Masters,* pp. 192–195

Getting Started

Math Message • Self Assessment

Complete the Self Assessment (*Assessment Handbook*, p. 157).

Home Link 6·12 Follow-Up

Briefly go over the answers. If you want, challenge children to find the middle value of the counts in the tally chart.

1 Looking Back: Cumulative Assessment

▶ Math Message Follow-Up

INDEPENDENT ACTIVITY

(Self Assessment, *Assessment Handbook*, p. 157)

The Self Assessment offers children the opportunity to reflect upon their progress.

▶ Oral and Slate Assessment

WHOLE-CLASS ACTIVITY

Problems 1 and 2 provide summative information and can be used for grading purposes. Problems 3 and 4 provides formative information that can be useful in planning future instruction.

Oral Assessment

1. Ask children to tell which number is greater.
   - 10 or 15 15
   - 42 or 24 42
   - 37 or 22 37
2. Ask children to tell which number is less.
   - 33 or 13 13
   - 9 or 10 9
   - 60 or 70 60

Slate Assessment

3. Ask children to solve these number stories and record number models on their slates.
   - Lorenzo rides his bike 8 blocks to his grandmother's house. If he rides 2 more blocks, he will be at his friend's house. How many blocks does Lorenzo need to ride to reach his friend's house? 10 blocks; $8 + 2 = 10$
   - Mariana collected 15 rocks for her rock collection. She lost 4 of her rocks on the way home. How many rocks does Mariana have now? 11 rocks; $15 - 4 = 11$ or $4 + 11 = 15$
4. Ask children to write the sum and the turn-around fact for each problem.
   - $8 + 9 = 17$; $9 + 8 = 17$
   - $5 + 8 = 13$; $8 + 5 = 13$
   - $9 + 4 = 13$; $4 + 9 = 13$
   - $5 + 7 = 12$; $7 + 5 = 12$

Assessment Master

Name Date

LESSON 6·13 **Self Assessment** Progress Check 6

Put a check in the box that tells how you do each skill.

Skills	I can do this by myself. I can explain how to do this.	I can do this by myself.	I can do this with help.
1. Fill name-collection boxes.			
2. Use <, >, =.			
3. Name the ones place and tens place in numbers.			
4. Estimate the length of objects.			
5. Write turn-around facts.			
6. Solve change-to-more and change-to-less number stories.			

Assessment Handbook, p. 157

Assessment Master

Name Date

LESSON 6·13 **Written Assessment** Progress Check 6

Part A

1. Write the number. Circle the number in the tens place.
   (3)2
2. Write the number. Circle the number in the ones place.
   5(9)
3. Write five names for 12.
   12
   Sample answers:
   10 + 2
   HHH HHH ||
   20 − 8
   twelve
   6 + 6
4. Label the box. Add 5 names.
   19
   Sample answers:
   20 − 1
   10 + 9
   18 + 1
   HHH HHH HHH ||||
   6 + 6 + 7
   23 − 4
   nineteen

Assessment Handbook, p. 158

Assessment Master

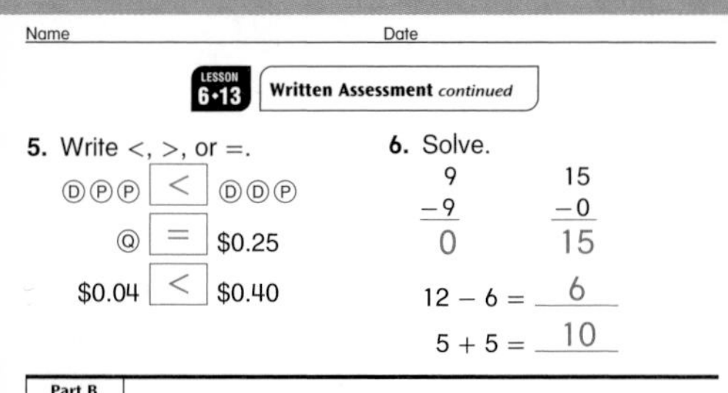

Name Date

LESSON 6·13 Written Assessment *continued*

5. Write <, >, or =.

Ⓓ Ⓟ Ⓟ [<] Ⓓ Ⓓ Ⓟ

Ⓠ [=] $0.25

$0.04 [<] $0.40

6. Solve.

$$\begin{array}{r} 9 \\ -9 \\ \hline 0 \end{array} \qquad \begin{array}{r} 15 \\ -0 \\ \hline 15 \end{array}$$

12 – 6 = 6

5 + 5 = 10

Part B

Use this line for Problems 7 and 8. This line is about 6 cm long.

7. About how long is this row of paper clips?

12 cm

8. About how long is this row of coins?

6 cm

9. Solve.

17 – 7 = 10	14 – 7 = 7
10 – 6 = 4	16 – 9 = 7
15 – 8 = 7	14 – 10 = 4

Assessment Handbook, p. 159

Assessment Master

Name Date

LESSON 6·13 **Open Response** Progress Check 6

Necklace Patterns

You are making a necklace with a bead pattern that repeats three times. Use the beads pictured below. Draw your necklace on the string.

1¢ 2¢ 5¢ 10¢

Use Ⓟ Ⓝ Ⓓ and Ⓠ to show how you can pay for all of the beads using the fewest number of coins.

See the *Assessment Handbook* for rubrics and children's sample work.

Assessment Handbook, p. 160

▶ Written Assessment

INDEPENDENT ACTIVITY

(*Assessment Handbook,* pp. 158–159)

Part A Recognizing Student Achievement

Problems 1–6 provide summative information and may be used for grading purposes.

Problem(s)	Description
1, 2	Read, write, and represent whole numbers through hundreds with base-10 blocks; identify digits and express their values in such numbers.
3, 4	Use concrete materials and pictures to find equivalent names for numbers; use tally marks and numerical expressions involving addition and subtraction of 1-digit and 2-digit whole numbers to represent equivalent names for numbers.
5	Know and compare the value of a penny, nickel, dime, and quarter; calculate and compare the values of combinations of coins.
6	Know addition and subtraction facts.

Part B Informing Instruction

Problems 7–9 provide formative information that can be useful in planning future instruction.

Problem(s)	Description
7, 8	Estimate and compare lengths of objects.
9	Know addition and subtraction facts.

Use the checklists on pages 221 and 223 of the *Assessment Handbook* to record results. Then input the data into the **Assessment Management Spreadsheets** to keep an ongoing record of children's progress toward Grade-Level Goals.

▶ Open Response

INDEPENDENT ACTIVITY

(*Assessment Handbook,* p. 160)

Necklace Patterns

The open-response item requires children to apply skills and concepts from Unit 6 to solve a multistep problem. See *Assessment Handbook,* pages 98–101 for rubrics and children's work samples for this problem.

Beginning in Unit 6, there will no longer be two options for completing the open-response problem. While children may continue to need support in completing the problem, all children will be given the problem in the same format.

Distribute Assessment Master, page 160. Read the problem aloud to children. Allow children to solve the problem and record their solution strategy on the page.

After children have had a chance to complete the page, invite individual children to explain their solution strategies. Encourage them to use words and drawings to explain their strategies as you list them on the board. Be sure to discuss both successful and unsuccessful strategies.

NOTE For this problem, you may wish to encourage children to use tools from their toolkits. This will allow them to act out coin exchanges.

2 Looking Ahead: Preparing for Unit 7

▶ Math Boxes 6•13

(*Math Journal 2,* p. 136)

Mixed Practice This Math Boxes page previews Unit 7 content.

▶ Home Link 6•13: Unit 7 Family Letter

(*Math Masters,* pp. 192–195)

Home Connection The Unit 7 Family Letter provides families with information and activities related to Unit 7 topics.

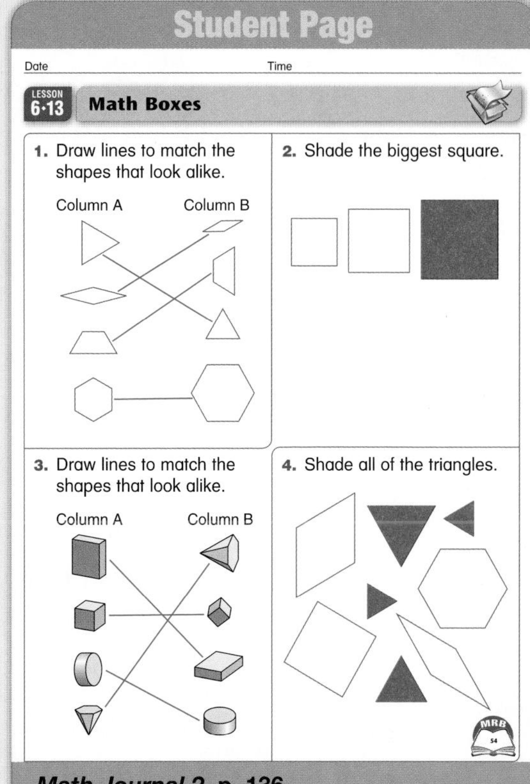

Student Page

Date Time

LESSON 6•13 **Math Boxes**

1. Draw lines to match the shapes that look alike.

Column A Column B

2. Shade the biggest square.

3. Draw lines to match the shapes that look alike.

Column A Column B

4. Shade all of the triangles.

MRB 54

Math Journal 2, p. 136

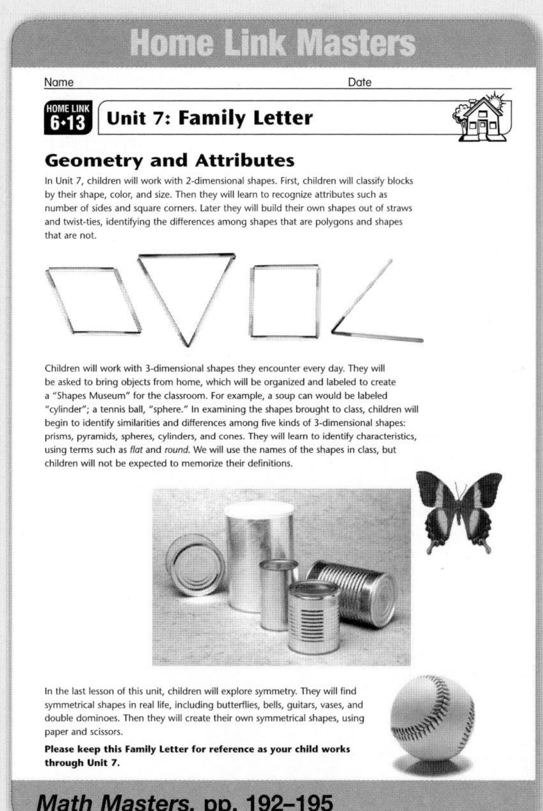

Home Link Masters

Name Date

HOME LINK 6•13 **Unit 7: Family Letter**

Geometry and Attributes

In Unit 7, children will work with 2-dimensional shapes. First, children will classify blocks by their shape, color, and size. Then they will learn to recognize attributes such as number of sides and square corners. Later they will build their own shapes out of straws and twist-ties, identifying the differences among shapes that are polygons and shapes that are not.

Children will work with 3-dimensional shapes they encounter every day. They will be asked to bring objects from home, which will be organized and labeled to create a "Shapes Museum" for the classroom. For example, a soup can would be labeled "cylinder"; a tennis ball, "sphere." In examining the shapes brought to class, children will begin to identify similarities and differences among five kinds of 3-dimensional shapes: prisms, pyramids, spheres, cylinders, and cones. They will learn to identify characteristics, using terms such as *flat* and *round.* We will use the names of the shapes in class, but children will not be expected to memorize their definitions.

In the last lesson of this unit, children will explore symmetry. They will find symmetrical shapes in real life, including butterflies, bells, guitars, vases, and double dominoes. Then they will create their own symmetrical shapes, using paper and scissors.

Please keep this Family Letter for reference as your child works through Unit 7.

Math Masters, pp. 192–195

Unit 7 Organizer

Geometry and Attributes

Overview

This unit introduces children to ideas about 3-dimensional geometric shapes. Children bring various boxes and other 3-dimensional shapes, which they display in a Shapes Museum after they sort the objects into categories (prisms, pyramids, and so on). Children also look for 2-dimensional figures within 3-dimensional shapes and construct polygons with straws and twist-ties. These activities are preliminary exposures to ideas and techniques that will appear again in *Second* and *Third Grade Everyday Mathematics.* Unit 7 has four main areas of focus:

- To sort attribute blocks according to attribute rules,
- To extend children's familiarity with polygons,
- To identify 3-dimensional shapes, and
- To explore symmetrical shapes.

CCSS Linking to the Common Core State Standards

The content of Unit 7 addresses the Common Core State Standards for Mathematics in *Geometry*. The correlation of the Common Core State Standards to the *Everyday Mathematics* Grade 1 lessons begins on page CS1.

Contents

Learning In Perspective

	Lesson Objectives	Links to the Past	Links to the Future
7·1	To reinforce sorting attribute blocks according to attribute rules.	In Units 4 and 6, children describe shapes. In Kindergarten, children use their own criteria to sort attribute blocks and play attribute games.	In Units 9 and 10, children identify, describe, model, and compare plane shapes. In Grade 2, they categorize objects by attributes.
7·2	To reinforce sorting by attribute rules; to facilitate the learning of addition facts.	In Units 3 and 6, children describe shapes and practice addition facts. In Kindergarten, children sort attribute blocks.	Throughout Grades 1–3, children identify, describe, model, and compare plane shapes. They also develop fact power for addition and subtraction facts.
7·3	To guide the identification of plane shapes; and to facilitate investigating some of their characteristics.	In Units 4 and 6, and Kindergarten, children identify and describe plane shapes, including circles, triangles, squares, and rectangles.	Throughout Grades 1–3, children identify, describe, and model plane shapes. In Grade 3, they use geometric terminology to describe figures.
7·4	To extend children's familiarity with polygons.	In Units 4 and 6, and Kindergarten, children identify and describe plane shapes.	Throughout Grades 1–3, children identify, describe, and model plane shapes. In Grade 3, they use geometric terminology to describe figures.
7·5	To guide the identification of spheres, cylinders, and rectangular prisms; and to facilitate the investigation of their characteristics.	In Units 4 and 6, children explore plane shapes. In Kindergarten, children match common objects with rectangular prisms, cylinders, and spheres.	Throughout Grades 1–3, children identify and describe 3-dimensional figures. In Grade 3, they use geometric terminology to describe figures.
7·6	To guide the identification of pyramids, cones, and cubes; and to facilitate the investigation of their characteristics.	In Units 4 and 6, children explore plane shapes. In Kindergarten, children match common objects with cubes and cones.	Throughout Grades 1–3, children identify and describe 3-dimensional figures. In Grade 3, they use geometric terminology to describe figures.
7·7	To facilitate the exploration of symmetrical shapes.	In Units 4 and 6, children explore plane shapes. In Kindergarten, children explore symmetry and identify shapes with line symmetry.	In Unit 9, children identify shapes with line symmetry and complete line-symmetric shapes or designs.

	Key Concepts and Skills	Grade 1 Goals*
7•1	Identify and describe plane shapes.	Geometry Goal 1
	Sort plane shapes by size, shape, and color.	Patterns, Functions, and Algebra Goal 1
7•2	Solve addition problems.	Operations and Computation Goal 1
	Create designs using plane shapes.	Geometry Goal 1
	Identify and apply rules to extend patterns.	Patterns, Functions, and Algebra Goal 1
	Identify rules by which plane shapes are sorted.	Patterns, Functions, and Algebra Goal 1
7•3	Count the sides and corners on plane shapes.	Number and Numeration Goal 2
	Identify, describe, and compare plane shapes.	Geometry Goal 1
	Compose plane shapes.	Geometry Goal 1
7•4	Count the sides and corners on plane shapes.	Number and Numeration Goal 2
	Model polygons, identifying their sides and corners; compare polygon models.	Geometry Goal 1
	Compose plane shapes.	Geometry Goal 1
7•5	Count the flat faces and corners on solid figures.	Number and Numeration Goal 2
	Identify and describe solid figures; identify the flat faces and corners on solid figures.	Geometry Goal 1
	Compose solid shapes.	Geometry Goal 1
7•6	Count the flat faces and corners on solid figures.	Number and Numeration Goal 2
	Identify and describe solid figures.	Geometry Goal 1
	Compare and contrast solid figures.	Geometry Goal 1
	Compose solid shapes.	Geometry Goal 1
7•7	Identify shapes having line symmetry.	Geometry Goal 2
	Create line-symmetric shapes.	Geometry Goal 2

*See the Appendix for a complete list of Grade 1 Goals.

A Balanced Curriculum

Ongoing Practice

Everyday Mathematics provides numerous opportunities for ongoing practice. These activities are embedded throughout the lessons:

Mental Math and Reflexes activities promote speed and accuracy in mental computation.

Math Boxes offer mixed practice and are paired across lessons as shown in the brackets below. This makes them useful as assessment tools. The last one or two boxes on each page preview the next unit's content.

Mixed practice	[7•1, 7•3], [7•2, 7•4, 7•6], [7•5, 7•7]
Mixed practice with multiple choice	7•3, 7•6, 7•7
Mixed practice with writing/reasoning opportunity	7•3, 7•5, 7•6

Home Links are daily homework assignments that review the content of the lesson and often contain ongoing facts practice.

***Minute Math*+** problems are offered for additional practice in Lessons 7•6 and 7•7.

EM Facts Workshop Game provides online practice of basic facts and computation.

EXTRA PRACTICE **Extra Practice** activities are included in Lessons 7•2, 7•3, 7•6, and 7•7.

Practice through Games

Games are an essential component of practice in the *Everyday Mathematics* program. Games offer skills practice and promote strategic thinking. See the *Differentiation Handbook* for ways to adapt games to meet children's needs.

Lesson	Game	Skill Practiced
7•1, 7•7	*Make My Design*	Describing geometric designs and spatial relationships [GEO Goal 1]
7•2, 7•6	*Attribute Train Game*	Identifying attributes of shapes [GEO Goal 1]
7•2	*Time Match*	Matching analog and digital clocks [MRF Goal 4]
7•5	*Coin Exchange*	Exchanging coins [MRF Goal 2]
7•7	*Addition Top-It*	Finding and comparing sums [NN Goal 7 and OC Goal 2]

[NN] Number and Numeration
[MRF] Measurement and Reference Frames
[OC] Operations and Computation
[GEO] Geometry
[DC] Data and Chance
[PFA] Patterns, Functions, and Algebra

Problem Solving 

Good problem solvers use a variety of strategies, including the following:

- Draw a picture.
- Act out the problem.
- Make a table, chart, or list.
- Look for a pattern.
- Try a simpler version of the problem.
- Make a guess and try it out.

The table below lists some of the opportunities in this unit for children to practice these strategies.

Lesson	Activity
7•1	Play *Make My Design.*
7•2	Make an attribute train.
7•2	Use an addition Fact Platter.
7•4	Construct straw polygons.
7•4	Find how many times a penny lands heads up when flipped 10 times.
7•7	Make symmetrical shapes.

Lessons that teach *through* problem solving, not just *about* problem solving

See Chapter 18: Problem Solving in the *Teacher's Reference Manual* for more information.

The Language of Mathematics

Everyday Mathematics provides lesson-specific suggestions to help all children acquire, process, and express mathematical ideas. Throughout Unit 7, there are lesson-specific language development notes that address the needs of English language learners, indicated by ELL.

ELL SUPPORT Activities to support English language learners are in Part 3 of Lessons 7•1, 7•3, and 7•5.

The *English Learners Handbook* and the *Differentiation Handbook* have suggestions for promoting language development and acquisition of mathematics vocabulary. See Unit 7 in each handbook.

Unit 7 Vocabulary

attribute
circle
cone
corner
cube
cylinder
face
hexagon
polygon
pyramid
rectangle
rectangular prism
rhombus
side
sphere
square
square corner
surface
symmetrical
symmetry
trapezoid
triangle

Literacy Connection

Lesson 7•3 *Round Is a Mooncake: A Book of Shapes,* by Roseanne Thong, Chronicle Books, 2000

Lesson 7•6 *Cubes, Cones, Cylinders, & Spheres,* by Tana Hoban, Greenwillow Books, 2000

For more literacy connections, see the *Home Connection Handbook,* Grades 1–3.

Cross-Curricular Links 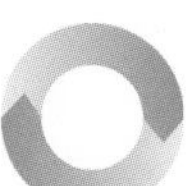

Music
Lesson 7•1 Children learn about various attributes of music.

Language Arts
Lesson 7•3 Children learn the origins of the word *polygon.*

Social Studies
Lesson 7•6 Children learn about the Egyptian pyramids.

Art
Lesson 7•5 Children make models of skyscrapers.

Lesson 7•6 Children construct 3-dimensional creatures.

Literature
Lesson 7•3 Children read *Round Is a Mooncake.*

Lesson 7•6 Children read *Cubes, Cones, Cylinders & Spheres.*

Balanced Assessment

Daily Assessments

- **Recognizing Student Achievement** – A daily assessment that is included in every lesson to evaluate children's progress toward the Grade 1 Grade-Level Goals.
- **Informing Instruction** – Notes that appear throughout the unit to help anticipate children's common errors and suggest appropriate problem-solving strategies.

Lesson	Recognizing Student Achievement	Informing Instruction
7•1	Solve change-to-less problems. [OC Goal 4]	Sort blocks by negative attributes.
7•2	Write fact families. [PFA Goal 3]	
7•3	Identify 2-dimensional shapes. [GEO Goal 1]	
7•4	Count the value of quarters to $1.00. [MRF Goal 2]	Make flat polygons.
7•5	Name numbers represented by base-10 blocks. [NN Goal 3]	
7•6	Recognize attributes of attribute blocks. [GEO Goal 1]	Recognize 3-dimensional shapes given 2-dimensional representations.
7•7	Identify cylinders. [GEO Goal 1]	Make symmetrical shapes.

[NN] Number and Numeration
[MRF] Measurement and Reference Frames
[OC] Operations and Computation
[GEO] Geometry
[DC] Data and Chance
[PFA] Patterns, Functions, and Algebra

Portfolio Opportunities

The following lessons provide opportunities to gather samples of children's mathematical writings, drawings, and creations to add balance to the assessment process: Lessons 7•3, 7•5, 7•6, and 7•8.

See pages 16 and 17 in the *Assessment Handbook* for more information about portfolios and how to use them.

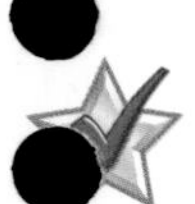

Unit Assessment

Progress Check 7 – A cumulative assessment of concepts and skills taught in Unit 7 and in previous units, providing information for evaluating children's progress and planning for future instruction. These assessments include oral/slate, written, and open-response activities, as shown below in the sample Progress Check lesson opener.

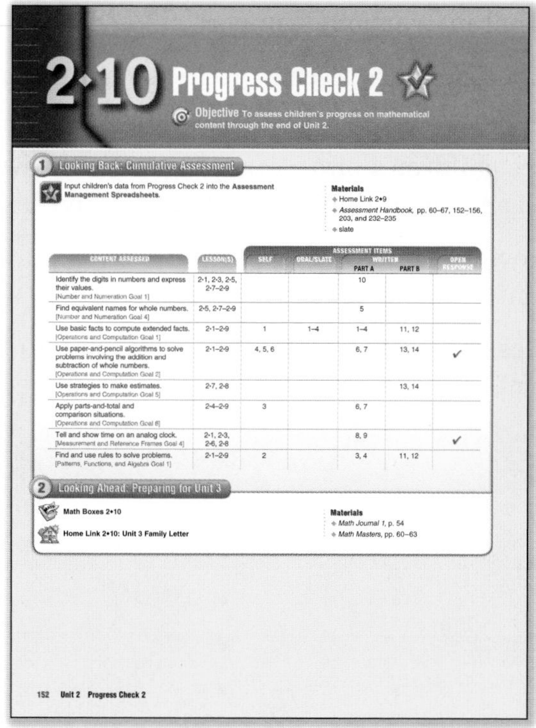

2•10 Progress Check 2

Objective To assess children's progress on mathematical content through the end of Unit 2.

1 Looking Back: Cumulative Assessment

Input children's data from Progress Check 2 into the **Assessment Management Spreadsheets.**

Materials
- Home Link 2•9
- *Assessment Handbook,* pp. 60–67, 152–156, 203, and 232–235
- slate

Content Assessed	Lesson(s)	Assessment Items				
		Self	Oral/Slate	Written Part A	Written Part B	Open Response
Identify the digits in numbers and express their values. [Number and Numeration Goal 1]	2·1, 2·3, 2·5, 2·7–2·9			10		
Find equivalent names for whole numbers. [Number and Numeration Goal 4]	2·5, 2·7–2·9			5		
Use basic facts to compute extended facts. [Operations and Computation Goal 1]	2·1–2·9	1	1–4	1–4	11, 12	
Use paper-and-pencil algorithms to solve problems involving the addition and subtraction of whole numbers. [Operations and Computation Goal 2]	2·1–2·9	4, 5, 6		6, 7	13, 14	✓
Use strategies to make estimates. [Operations and Computation Goal 5]	2·7, 2·8				13, 14	
Apply parts-and-total and comparison situations. [Operations and Computation Goal 6]	2·4–2·9	3		6, 7		
Tell and show time on an analog clock. [Measurement and Reference Frames Goal 4]	2·1, 2·3, 2·6, 2·8			8, 9		✓
Find and use rules to solve problems. [Patterns, Functions, and Algebra Goal 1]	2·1–2·9	2		3, 4	11, 12	

2 Looking Ahead: Preparing for Unit 3

Math Boxes 2•10

Home Link 2•10: Unit 3 Family Letter

Materials
- *Math Journal 1,* p. 54
- *Math Masters,* pp. 60–63

152 Unit 2 Progress Check 2

Core Assessment Resources

Assessment Handbook

- **Unit 7 Assessment Overview,** pages 102–109
- **Unit 7 Assessment Masters,** pages 161–164
- **Unit 7 Individual Profiles of Progress,** pages 224, 225, and 248
- **Unit 7 Class Checklists,** pages 226, 227, and 249
- **Math Logs,** pages 254–256
- **Exit Slip,** page 251
- **Other Student Assessment Forms,** pages 252, 253, 257, and 258

Assessment Management Spreadsheets

The Assessment Management Spreadsheets consist of the Digital Class Checklists and Individual Profile of Progress Checklists. Use them to monitor, record, and report children's progress.

Addressing All Needs

Differentiated Instruction

Adjusting the Activity – suggests adaptations that target advanced learners, English language learners, or learners who need additional instructional support.

ELL SUPPORT / ELL – provides lesson-specific suggestions to help English language learners understand and process the mathematical content.

READINESS – accesses children's prior knowledge or previews content that prepares children to engage in the lesson's Part 1 activities.

EXTRA PRACTICE – provides additional opportunities to apply the mathematical content of the lesson.

ENRICHMENT – enables children to apply or further explore the mathematical content of the lesson.

Lesson	Adjusting the Activity	ELL Support/ ELL	Readiness	Extra Practice	Enrichment
7•1	•	•	•		•
7•2	•		•	•	•
7•3	•	•	•	•	•
7•4	•		•		•
7•5	•	•	•		•
7•6	•		•	•	•
7•7				•	•

Additional Resources

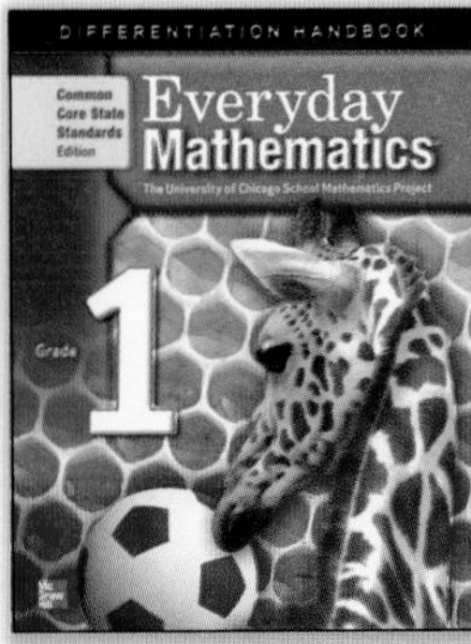

Differentiation Handbook
Provides ideas and strategies for differentiating instruction.
Pages 92–98

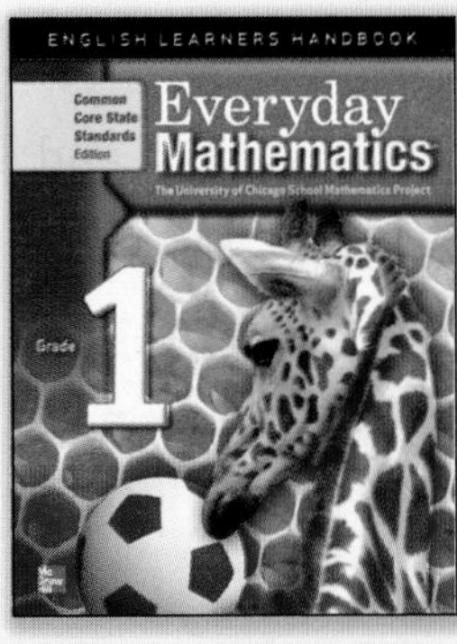

English Learners Handbook
Contains lesson-specific comprehension strategies.
Pages 78–84

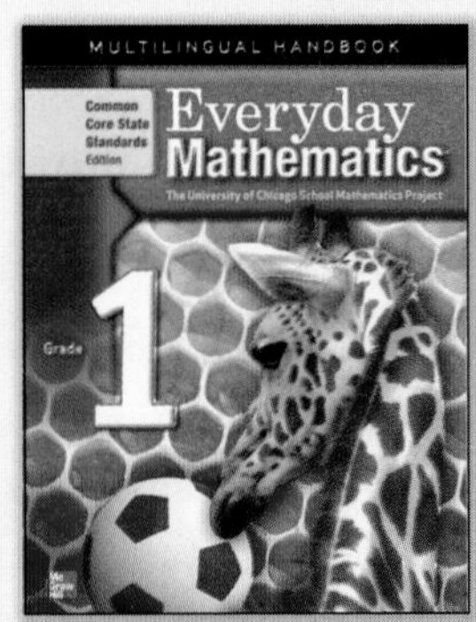

Multilingual Handbook
Previews concepts and vocabulary. It is written in six languages.
Pages 155–168

Planning Tips

Multiage Classroom

Companion Lessons from Grades K and 2 can help you meet instructional needs of a multiage classroom. The full Scope and Sequence can be found in the Appendix.

Grade K	4•13, 5•14	4•13, 5•14	1•2, 4•3	2•1, 2•2, 4•10	6•3	6•3	2•15, 2•16
Grade 1	**7•1**	**7•2**	**7•3**	**7•4**	**7•5**	**7•6**	**7•7**
Grade 2	4•3, 4•7, 5•1	4•3, 4•7, 5•1	5•4, 5•5	5•4, 5•5	5•6, 5•7	5•6, 5•7	5•8

Pacing for Success

Pacing depends on a number of factors, such as children's individual needs and how long your school has been using *Everyday Mathematics*. At the beginning of Unit 7, you may want to use tools available at www.everydaymathonline.com to help you set your pace.

Home Support

Unit 7 Family Letter (English/Spanish) provides families with an overview, Do-Anytime Activities, Building Skills through Games, a list of vocabulary, and answers to the daily homework (Home Links). Family Letters in English, Spanish, and seven other languages are also available online.

Home Links are the daily homework assignments. They consist of active projects and ongoing review problems.

Home Support Resources

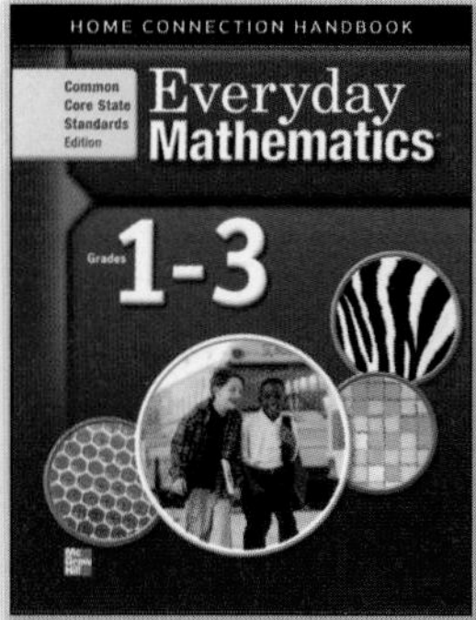

Home Connection Handbook
Offers ideas and reproducible masters for communicating with families. See Table of Contents for unit information.

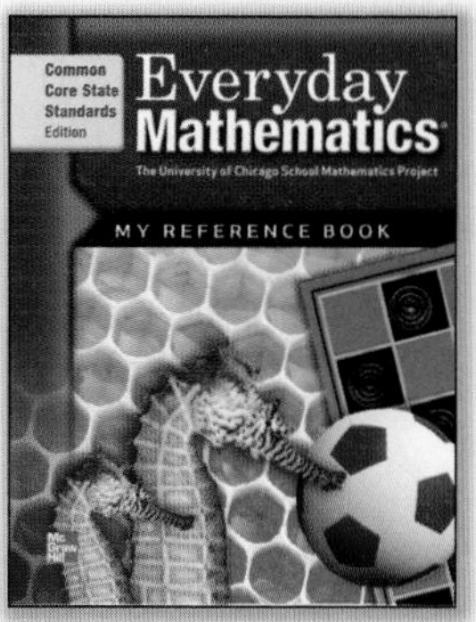

My Reference Book
Provides a resource for children and parents.
Pages 122, 123, 128, 129, 152, 153

Technology Resources

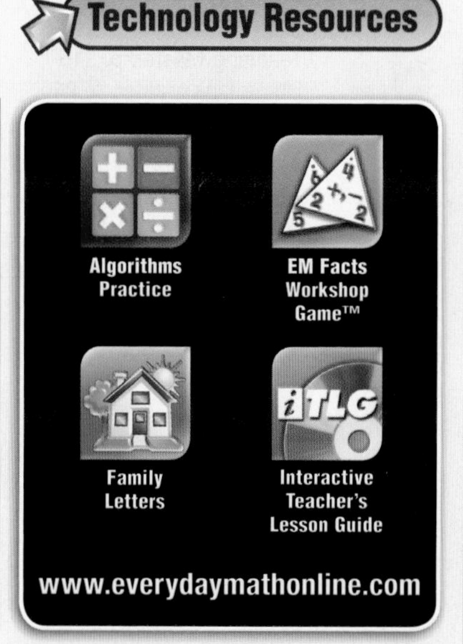

Materials

Technology Resources www.everydaymathonline.com

ePresentations

eToolkit

Algorithms Practice

EM Facts Workshop Game™

Family Letters

Assessment Management

Common Core State Standards

Curriculum Focal Points

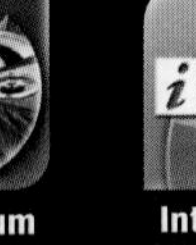

Interactive Teacher's Lesson Guide

Lesson	Masters	Manipulative Kit	Other Items
7•1	Home Link Master, p. 196	attribute blocks; pattern blocks	folder; calculator
7•2	Teaching Masters, pp. 197–199 and 201 Home Link Master, p. 200 Game Masters, pp. 357 and 358	attribute blocks; slate	Fact Triangles; set of classroom objects that can be sorted by attributes, such as crayons, books, or paper
7•3	Home Link Master, p. 203 Teaching Masters, pp. 202 and 204 Teacher Aid Master, p. 305 *Differentiation Handbook,* p. 126	slate; pattern blocks; chart paper	pattern-block shape posters*; *Round Is a Mooncake;* Pattern-Block Template
7•4	Transparencies of *Math Masters,* pp. 205*, 205B, 205C, and 329* Home Link Master, p. 207 Teaching Masters, pp. 205A, 205D, 206, 208, and 209	pattern blocks	per child: 3 each of 8" straws, 6" straws, and 4" straws; 15 twist-ties; pennies; Class Data Pad; poster-size sheets of paper, magazines or catalogs; glue or tape; scissors
7•5	Teaching Masters, pp. 210*, 212, and 212A Home Link Master, p. 211	slate; base-10 blocks (longs and cubes); tool-kit coins; per partnership: 2 dice	ball, can, and box; 3" by 5" index cards; items for the Shapes Museum; 3-dimensional shapes; rectangular prism, cylinder; per small group: 20 twist-ties, 4 each of 8" straws, 6" straws, and 4" straws; scissors; tape
7•6	Teaching Masters, pp. 210*, 212B, and 214 Home Link Master, p. 213 Teaching Aid Master, p. 305	slate; attribute blocks; pattern blocks	*Cones, Cubes, Cylinders and Spheres;* models of pyramid, cone, and cube; 3" by 5" index cards; items for the Shapes Museum; per small group: several paper bags each filled with a different 3-dimensional shape; prisms and pyramids from the Shapes Museum; folder; per small group: twenty twist-ties and twelve 4" straws; scissors; tape
7•7	Teaching Master, p. 215 Home Link Master, p. 216	slate; 4 each of number cards 0–10; pattern blocks	number grid*; scissors; 4" by 6" (or 5" by 8") index cards; magazines to cut up; glue or tape; scissors; small mirrors; folder
7•8	Assessment Masters, pp. 161–164 Home Link Masters, pp. 217–220	slate	Pattern-Block Template

*Denotes optional materials

Mathematical Background

The discussion below highlights the major content ideas presented in Unit 7 and helps establish instructional priorities.

The Importance of Starting Geometry Early in Children's Schooling

Research shows that more than half of students entering high school simply did not have the geometry experiences they should have had much earlier in school and over an extended period of time. One of this program's main objectives is to correct this harmful error in the mathematics education of children.

The gradual approach used in *Everyday Mathematics* for building geometry intuition and skills follows much the same path as that used for building arithmetic intuition and skills. It begins with the everyday experiences of children and then provides additional guided, concrete experiences as well as discussion about what is happening in those experiences.

Prior Geometry Experiences in the *Everyday Mathematics* Curriculum

Assuming children have come from a well-implemented *Kindergarten Everyday Mathematics* experience (or similar Kindergarten program), they will have had much playful experience with 3-dimensional shapes, 2-dimensional shapes, pattern blocks, and attribute blocks. Also, some of the Explorations that preceded this unit have provided informal experiences with pattern blocks and geoboards. Some of the projects you've done may have provided informal experience with geometric shapes. Of course, anything children have done with the Pattern-Block Templates in their tool kits has provided experience with common geometry figures. In addition, there are informal geometry exercises in *Minute Math*®+ (pages 17 and 18 of the Basic Routines and the Geometry section on pages 53–60). If you have been using these and similar routines, continue to do so; if not, please start to do so.

The Vocabulary of Geometry

The authors' research, as well as the research of others, indicates that K–2 children know the names of such common shapes as squares, rectangles, triangles, and circles independent of their school experience. In this early geometry unit, acquisition of the additional special vocabulary of geometry (of which there is a considerable amount) takes second place to developing intuition and relationships. This does not mean you should be reluctant to use the special geometry words. Just do not expect children to master them. Children will not know many of these words initially, but with repeated use, the terms will, over time, become a natural part of their vocabulary. Children will not always use the words correctly; however, if you use the words consistently and correctly, children eventually will build their own correct vocabulary.

Attribute Rules and Games

(Lessons 7◆1–7◆4)

These lessons use the informal attribute experiences that have preceded this unit as the basis for more formal whole-group activities. Because each block has several different attributes, children can focus on both similarities and differences—blocks can be the same shape, but they can be a different color. Children use these comparisons to help determine defining and non-defining attributes of shapes in Lessons 7-3 and 7-4. Children can see that blocks may be grouped in different ways, depending on a particular point of view. The ability to look at similar things in different ways is important for many problem-solving activities. Science educators also identify classification as one of the important "processes" of science.

Two-Dimensional Shapes (Lesson 7◆3)

Through hands-on experience with pattern blocks and by drawing with the template, children identify triangles, squares, trapezoids, rhombuses, hexagons, and circles and explore some of their characteristics.

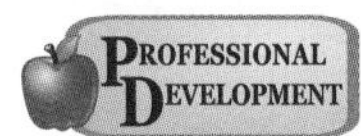

See the *Teacher's Reference Manual,* Sections 13.4.2 and 13.4.3, for further information about 2-dimensional shapes.

Exploring and Making Polygons

(Lesson 7◆4)

Pipe cleaners and chenille sticks (slightly thicker than pipe cleaners) are alternatives to twist-ties. Some *Everyday Mathematics* teachers have found that chenille sticks hold the straws together more reliably without sacrificing flexibility. They should be cut to $1\frac{1}{2}$ to 2 inches long.

Everyday Mathematics teachers have found that using straws in three different colors and cutting straws of each color to a different length makes cleanup much quicker. Straws required for Lesson 7-4 are readily available in green, red, and white at party stores or through restaurant supply companies.

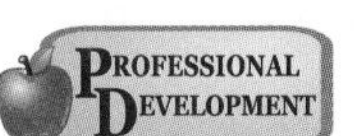

Please see the Geometry Tools and Techniques section of the *Teacher's Reference Manual,* Section 13.10.3, for information about using straws and twist-ties for hands-on geometry constructions.

Three-Dimensional Shapes

(Lessons 7◆5 and 7◆6)

Using objects from the Shapes Museum and the pictures on the 3-Dimensional Shapes Poster (*Math Journal 2,* p. 146), children review similarities and differences among six general kinds of 3-dimensional shapes (spheres, cylinders, rectangular prisms, pyramids, cones, and cubes). They may also find instances of the five regular polyhedrons, some of which are prisms or pyramids.

Take special note that the concepts of faces and bases of prisms and pyramids are sometimes confusing. All of the surfaces of prisms and pyramids are faces; bases are faces that have special additional roles to play.

- The bases of a prism come in pairs that are exactly the same size and shape. They are opposite and parallel to each other. They can be any polygonal shape.
- Prisms are named after the shapes of their bases; for example, *rectangular prism* and *triangular prism.* The other faces of a prism must either be rectangles or nonrectangular parallelograms. For the boxes and other examples that are typical in first grade, these other faces are usually rectangles. In a rectangular prism, any pair of opposite faces can be bases.
- A pyramid has only one base (which is also a face). The other faces are triangular and come together in a point. As with prisms, pyramids are named after the shapes of their bases. In a triangular pyramid, any face can be a base.
- Cylinders are like prisms in that they have a pair of bases that are parallel and the same size and shape. Cones, like pyramids, have just one base. Cylinders and cones differ from prisms and pyramids in that they have curved surfaces.
- Spheres have no faces; they are completely curved.

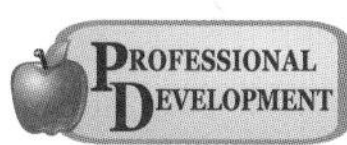

For more information about 3-dimensional shapes, please see Sections 13.5.1, 13.5.2, and 13.5.3 in the *Teacher's Reference Manual*.

Project Notes

Use Project 5, Apple Math, to provide opportunities for children to classify, count, compare, and measure.

Use Project 7, Weather and Probability, to introduce children to the basic language of probability to describe events.

Symmetry (Lesson 7•7)

Children explore the concept of line symmetry through paper folding and cutting. Two topics not covered explicitly—the "line of symmetry" (the line that divides a symmetric shape into two matching halves) and the possibility that a shape may be symmetric in more than one way—could easily be introduced if you wish.

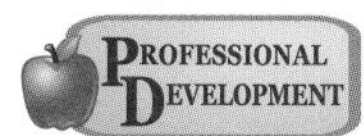

Please read Sections 13.8 and 13.8.1 in the *Teacher's Reference Manual* for additional information about line symmetry.

7•1 Attribute Rules

Objective To reinforce sorting attribute blocks according to attribute rules.

Technology Resources www.everydaymathonline.com

ePresentations

eToolkit

Algorithms Practice

EM Facts Workshop Game™

Family Letters

Assessment Management

Common Core State Standards

Curriculum Focal Points

Interactive Teacher's Lesson Guide

1 Teaching the Lesson

Key Concepts and Skills

- Identify and describe plane shapes. [Geometry Goal 1]
- Sort plane shapes by size, shape, and color. [Patterns, Functions, and Algebra Goal 1]

Key Activities

Children identify shapes of attribute blocks. They sort them into groups according to shape, color, or size. Children also sort attribute blocks according to attribute rules given by the teacher.

Ongoing Assessment: Informing Instruction See page 624.

Key Vocabulary

triangle ◆ square ◆ rectangle ◆ hexagon ◆ circle ◆ attribute

Materials

calculator ◆ attribute blocks

2 Ongoing Learning & Practice

Playing *Make My Design*
Math Journal 2, p. 137
per partnership: pattern blocks, folder
Children practice naming and describing geometric designs and spatial relationships.

Math Boxes 7•1
Math Journal 2, p. 138
Children practice and maintain skills through Math Box problems.

Ongoing Assessment: Recognizing Student Achievement
Use Math Boxes, Problem 3.
[Operations and Computation Goal 4]

Home Link 7•1
Math Masters, p. 196
Children practice and maintain skills through Home Link activities.

3 Differentiation Options

READINESS

Fishing for Attributes
Children figure out attribute rules.

ENRICHMENT

"What's My Attribute Rule?"
per partnership: attribute blocks
Children sort attribute blocks and describe how they sorted them.

ELL SUPPORT

Communicating About Geometry
geometric shapes (optional) ◆ pictures of geometric shapes (optional)
Children use geometric objects or pictures as well as gestures to communicate.

Advance Preparation

Because of the differences among attribute block sets, the activities in Part 1 are generic. Adapt the activities to the blocks that you are using.

Place a set of attribute blocks near the Math Message.

***Teacher's Reference Manual,* Grades 1–3** pp. 134–138, 140, 151–153

Getting Started

Mental Math and Reflexes

Play *Beat the Calculator.* See Lesson 6-4 for directions.

Math Message

Take a block to use today. What shape is it?

1 Teaching the Lesson

Interactive whiteboard-ready ePresentations are available at www.everydaymathonline.com to help you teach the lesson.

▶ Math Message Follow-Up

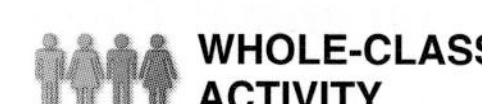

Have children identify the shapes of their blocks. **Triangle, square, rectangle, hexagon,** or **circle** Tell them that they will learn different ways to sort blocks.

▶ Introducing the Attributes of Attribute Blocks

Ask children who have a circle to go to one area of the room, those who have a triangle to go to another area, those who have a rectangle to go to a third area, and those who have a square to go to a fourth area. Ask children who remain seated to show their attribute blocks. *What shape are the blocks?* hexagons

Ask children in each area to tell what their blocks have in common and to identify the shapes. They all have the same shape: circle, triangle, rectangle, square

- Are the shapes all the same color? No. They are red, yellow, or blue.
- Are they all the same size? No. Some shapes are large, and some shapes are small.

Next, have children move so that the blocks are sorted by color. To support English language learners, explain that the process of separating the blocks is called *sorting*.

▷ All children with red shapes should go to one area.

▷ All those with yellow shapes should go to another area.

▷ All those with blue shapes should sit down.

Finally, have children move so that the blocks are sorted by size.

▷ All children with small blocks should go to one area.

▷ All children with large blocks sit down.

Guide children to understand that attribute blocks can be sorted by shape, color, or size. Shape, color, and size are **attributes** of the blocks.

Music Link Help children list various attributes of music such as loud, soft, high, and low. You may wish to play music. Encourage children to listen carefully and describe any attributes heard.

▶ Sorting Attribute Blocks by Attribute Rules

Algebraic Thinking Ask all children who have a blue circle to stand up. Say: *All of you fit the rule because you have a blue circle.*

Continue the activity with other attribute rules. *For example:*

Stand up and show me your attribute block if it is

- a red square.
- not yellow.
- a small rectangle.
- a large circle.
- a small, blue hexagon.
- not red and not large.

Include at least one attribute rule that does not fit any of the blocks.

Ongoing Assessment: Informing Instruction

Watch for children who have a difficult time sorting blocks by negative attributes. Encourage children to listen for the word *not* in the rule. Remind children that *not* is similar to *no.*

▶ Collecting Attribute Blocks According to Rules

Children turn in their attribute blocks according to the attribute rules you write on the board. For example, you might write *large, red blocks, all yellow circles,* and so on, until most of the blocks have been collected; then write *everyone else's blocks* to finish the activity. This is a good opportunity to practice negative attribute rules.

2 Ongoing Learning & Practice

▶ Playing *Make My Design*

PARTNER ACTIVITY

(*Math Journal 2,* p. 137)

In this game, children name and describe geometric figures and the spatial relationships in a design. For directions, see journal page 137.

Adjusting the Activity

Children use more than 6 pattern blocks to make their designs. Children may also enjoy using blocks that are all the same shape.

AUDITORY ◆ KINESTHETIC ◆ TACTILE ◆ VISUAL

▶ Math Boxes 7•1

INDEPENDENT ACTIVITY

(*Math Journal 2,* p. 138)

Mixed Practice Math Boxes in this lesson are paired with Math Boxes in Lesson 7-3. The skills in Problem 4 preview Unit 8 content.

Ongoing Assessment: Recognizing Student Achievement

Math Boxes Problem 3 ★

Use **Math Boxes, Problem 3** to assess children's ability to solve change-to-less problems. Children are making adequate progress if they are able to solve this problem correctly.

[Operations and Computation Goal 4]

▶ Home Link 7•1

INDEPENDENT ACTIVITY

(*Math Masters,* p. 196)

Home Connection Children cut out a fourth set of Fact Triangles to continue their fact practice at home. By separating the triangles into piles to show facts they know and facts that still need work, children can focus on facts they need to practice.

Student Page

Date

LESSON 7•1 **Make My Design**

Materials □ pattern blocks
□ folder

Players 2

Skill Create designs using pattern blocks

Object of the Game To create a design identical to the other player's design

Directions:

1. The first player chooses 6 blocks. The second player gathers the same 6 blocks.
2. Players sit face-to-face with a folder between them.
3. The first player creates a design with the blocks.
4. Using only words, the first player tells the second player how to "Make My Design." The second player can ask questions about the instructions.
5. Players remove the folder and look at the two designs. Players discuss how closely the designs match.
6. Players change roles and play again.

Math Journal 2, p. 137

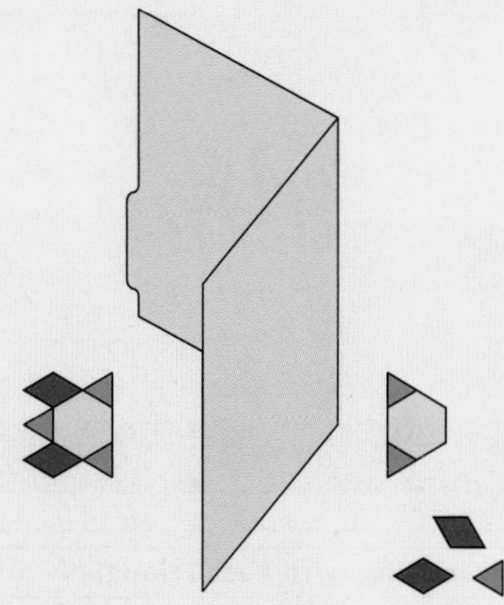

A game of *Make My Design* in progress

NOTE Explain to children that they will need to think carefully about the words they use to describe their patterns because neither partner can look at the other's work until the game is complete. It may be helpful to list words and phrases on the board that children might use to describe the placement of shapes in their designs, such as *above, below, beside, left,* and *right.*

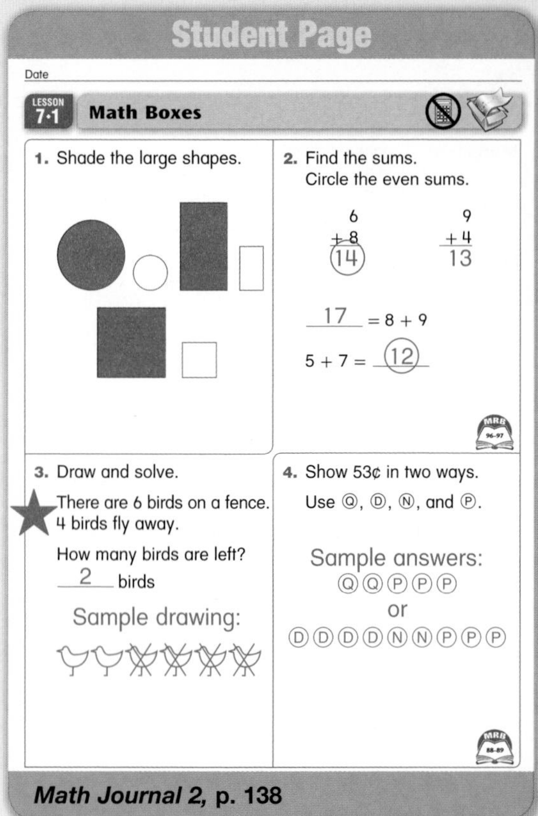
Student Page

Date

LESSON 7·1 Math Boxes

1. Shade the large shapes.

2. Find the sums. Circle the even sums.

6 + 8 = (14) 9 + 4 = 13

17 = 8 + 9

5 + 7 = (12)

3. Draw and solve.

There are 6 birds on a fence. 4 birds fly away.

How many birds are left? 2 birds

Sample drawing:

4. Show 53¢ in two ways.

Use Ⓠ, Ⓓ, Ⓝ, and Ⓟ.

Sample answers: ⓆⓆⓅⓅⓅ or ⒹⒹⒹⒹⓃⓃⓅⓅⓅ

Math Journal 2, p. 138

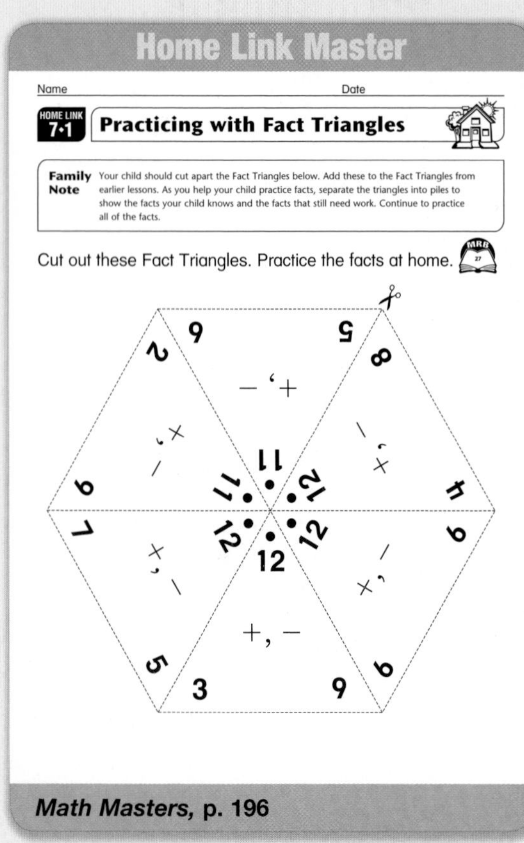
Home Link Master

Name Date

HOME LINK 7·1 Practicing with Fact Triangles

Family Note Your child should cut apart the Fact Triangles below. Add these to the Fact Triangles from earlier lessons. As you help your child practice facts, separate the triangles into piles to show the facts your child knows and the facts that still need work. Continue to practice all of the facts.

Cut out these Fact Triangles. Practice the facts at home.

Math Masters, p. 196

3 Differentiation Options

READINESS

SMALL-GROUP ACTIVITY

▶ Fishing for Attributes

5–15 Min

To explore the meaning and use of attributes, have children figure out attribute rules. Tell children that you are going "fishing," but that you want to "catch" only a certain kind of "fish." Challenge them to determine what kind of fish you want by observing the fish you catch. For example, fish for children wearing blue jeans. Invite children wearing blue jeans to stand in front of the group. Let children guess what you are fishing for until someone says "Children wearing blue jeans." Once children understand the game, let them try fishing.

ENRICHMENT

PARTNER ACTIVITY

▶ "What's My Attribute Rule?"

5–15 Min

To apply children's understanding of formulating rules based on attributes, have them sort a group of attribute blocks into two piles according to an attribute of their choosing. Children grab a small handful of attribute blocks and work with a partner to decide how to sort them. After the blocks are sorted, have children describe how they sorted them. For example, "I sorted them into blocks that are red and blocks that are not red." Other sample categories are shapes that are circles and shapes that are not circles, and shapes that are thick and shapes that are thin.

ELL SUPPORT

SMALL-GROUP ACTIVITY

▶ Communicating About Geometry

5–15 Min

To provide language support for geometry throughout this unit, provide opportunities for children to use geometric objects or pictures as well as gestures to communicate their thinking. Encourage children to use the mathematical terms in the contexts of working with the 2- and 3-dimensional shapes.

7•2 Exploring Attributes, Designs, and Fact Platters

Explorations

Objective To reinforce sorting by attribute rules; to facilitate the learning of addition facts.

Technology Resources www.everydaymathonline.com

ePresentations

eToolkit

Algorithms Practice

EM Facts Workshop Game™

Family Letters

Assessment Management

Common Core State Standards

Curriculum Focal Points

Interactive Teacher's Lesson Guide

1 Teaching the Lesson

Key Concepts and Skills

- Solve addition problems. [Operations and Computation Goal 1]
- Create designs using plane shapes. [Geometry Goal 1]
- Identify and apply rules to extend patterns. [Patterns, Functions, and Algebra Goal 1]
- Identify rules by which plane shapes are sorted. [Patterns, Functions, and Algebra Goal 1]

Key Activities

Review the attributes of attribute blocks. Children guess rules used to sort attribute blocks.

Exploration A: Children play the *Attribute Train Game,* in which they line up blocks differing in just one attribute.

Exploration B: Children make attribute-block designs.

Exploration C: Children practice addition facts with Fact Platters.

Ongoing Assessment: Recognizing Student Achievement Use Mental Math and Reflexes. [Patterns, Functions, and Algebra Goal 3]

Materials

Home Link 7•1
Fact Triangle ◆ slate ◆ attribute blocks

Exploration A: Per group:
attribute blocks

Exploration B: Per group:
Math Masters, pp. 197 and 198
attribute blocks

Exploration C: Per partnership:
Math Masters, p. 199 (optional)

2 Ongoing Learning & Practice

Playing *Time Match*
Math Masters, pp. 357 and 358
My Reference Book, pp. 152 and 153

Math Boxes 7•2
Math Journal 2, p. 139

Home Link 7•2
Math Masters, p. 200

3 Differentiation Options

READINESS

Sorting Classroom Objects by Attributes
per partnership: sets of classroom objects that can be sorted by attributes, such as crayons, books, or paper

ENRICHMENT

Solving an Attribute-Train Puzzle
Math Masters, p. 201
attribute blocks

EXTRA PRACTICE

Practicing Addition and Subtraction
Math Masters, p. 199

Advance Preparation

Place a set of attribute blocks near the Math Message. Provide Fact Platters (see illustration) for Exploration C by doing one of the following: (1) distribute copies of *Math Masters,* page 199; (2) draw a large Fact Platter on the board; or (3) attach copies of *Math Masters,* page 199 to paper plates.

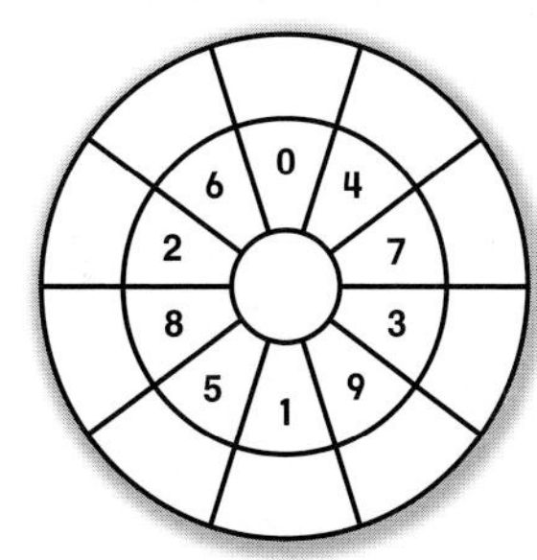

***Teacher's Reference Manual,* Grades 1–3** pp. 147–149

Next, draw on the board some polygons and some figures that are not polygons or display an overhead transparency of *Math Masters,* page 205. Have children identify the shapes that are polygons and explain why the others are not polygons.

Since many children enjoy making these constructions, you might make the materials available to children for several days.

NOTE The polygon constructions make great displays. Choose a few to add to a bulletin board or another display. Consider including several in the Shapes Museum. For the rest of the polygons, allow time for children to dismantle their constructions and return the straws and twist-ties to the proper boxes.

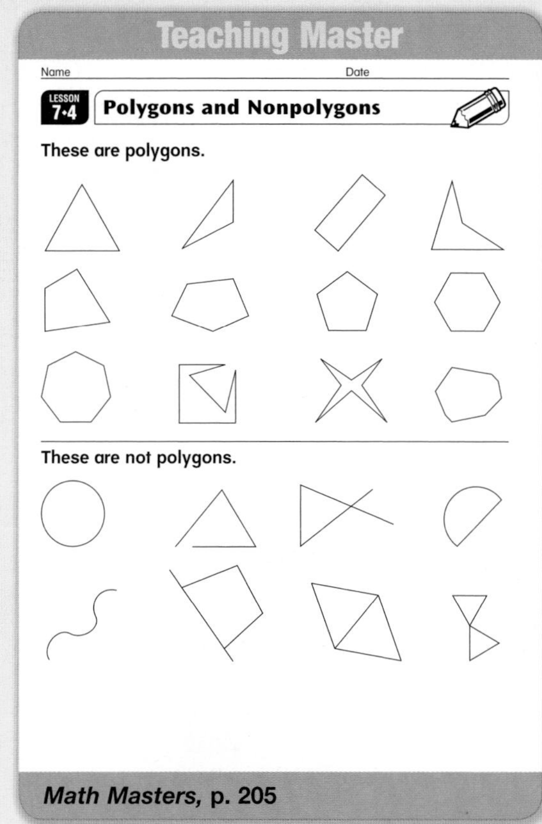

Math Masters, p. 205

Composing New Shapes

WHOLE-CLASS ACTIVITY

(*Math Masters,* pp. 205A–205D)

Group children into pairs for the beginning of this activity. Provide each partnership with three pattern blocks of each shape and with a set of circle blocks from *Math Masters,* page 205A. Discuss the circle blocks with children, introducing the terms *half-circle* and *quarter-circle*.

Tell children that they are going to practice making new shapes from pattern blocks and circle blocks. Display overhead transparencies of *Math Masters,* pages 205B and 205C. Work through Problems 1 through 4, first letting each partnership make a composite shape for the given problem and then asking the following questions:

- ▷ Ask: *What shape did you make?* Answers vary. Trace the outline of several of the children's shapes in the space provided under each problem.
- ▷ Ask: *Could you use any other blocks to make these shapes?* Answers vary. Encourage children to come to the overhead and try placing different pattern blocks on the new shape outlines.
- ▷ Ask: *Do any of these new shapes remind you of other shapes you know? Which ones?* Answers vary.

After this discussion, have partners complete *Math Masters,* page 205D. Each child creates a composite shape with pattern blocks and circle blocks and traces the outline of the shape. Children then trade papers and try to fill each other's shapes with pattern blocks and circle blocks.

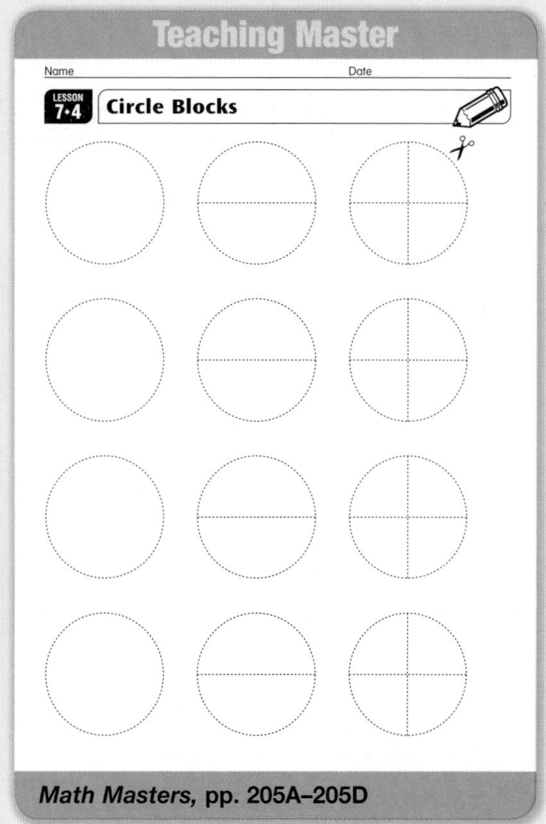

Math Masters, pp. 205A–205D

NOTE You may wish to repeat the stick-on note procedure for finding the middle value taught in Lesson 6-12. Additional practice with this skill will be helpful to children in future units.

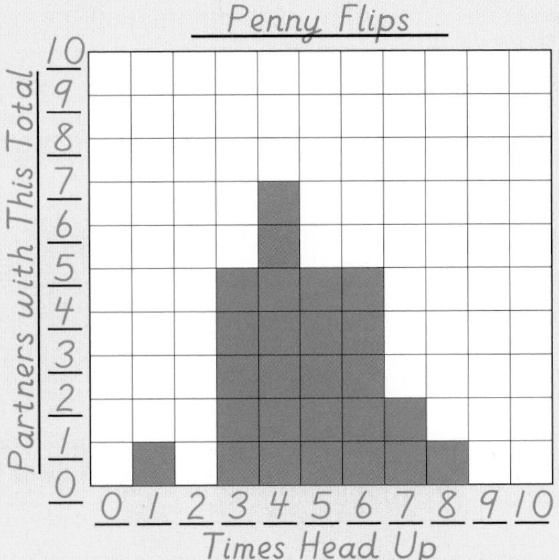

Teaching Master

Name Date

LESSON 7·4 **Name-Collection Boxes**

For each name-collection box, fill in the label. Add 5 names.

1. 12
6 + 6 16 − 4
Answers vary.

2. 16
4 + 4 + 4 + 4
Answers vary.

3. 10
19 − 9
Answers vary.

4. Your choice
Answers vary.

Math Masters, p. 206

2 Ongoing Learning & Practice

▶ Investigating Flipping Pennies

PARTNER ACTIVITY

(*Math Masters,* p. 329)

Children work with a partner. Each child flips a penny 10 times while the partner records in a tally chart how many times the penny landed head-side up and how many times it landed tail-side up.

When children have finished collecting their data, draw a tally chart on the Class Data Pad, showing the class results for the number of times that each partnership flipped the coin head-side up. Then make a bar graph of the results on the Class Data Pad or on an overhead transparency of *Math Masters,* page 329.

0	
1	/
2	
3	HHT
4	HHT //
5	HHT
6	HHT
7	//
8	/
9	
10	

NOTE *Everyday Mathematics* does not draw a distinction between histograms and bar graphs. For a discussion of how some people contrast them, see Section 12.2.3: Organizing and Displaying Data in the *Teacher's Reference Manual.*

▶ Practicing with Name-Collection Boxes

INDEPENDENT ACTIVITY

(*Math Masters,* p. 206)

Use *Math Masters,* page 206 to provide more practice with name-collection boxes.

▶ Math Boxes 7·4

INDEPENDENT ACTIVITY

(*Math Journal 2,* p. 144)

Mixed Practice Math Boxes in this lesson are linked to Math Boxes in Lessons 7-2 and 7-6. The skills in Problem 4 preview Unit 8 content.

▶ Home Link 7·4

INDEPENDENT ACTIVITY

(*Math Masters,* p. 207)

Home Connection Children use characteristics of a polygon to identify polygons.

3 Differentiation Options

READINESS

SMALL-GROUP ACTIVITY

▶ Finding 2-Dimensional Shapes

15–30 Min

To provide experience with basic polygons, have children cut out pictures from magazines to match specified polygons. Display the large shapes you have prepared. Review the name of each shape and discuss its attributes. Have children cut out pictures from magazines that match each of those shapes. Have children glue their pictures onto the appropriate shapes. Children can add their own drawings if they wish.

ENRICHMENT

PARTNER ACTIVITY

▶ Comparing Polygons and Other Figures

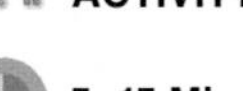

5–15 Min

(*Math Masters,* pp. 208 and 209)

To further explore attributes of polygons, have children compare polygons to figures that are not polygons. Explain to children how to complete a Venn diagram. Have children write attributes for each shape, with common attributes listed in the intersection of the two circles. Encourage partnerships to share their completed Venn diagrams.

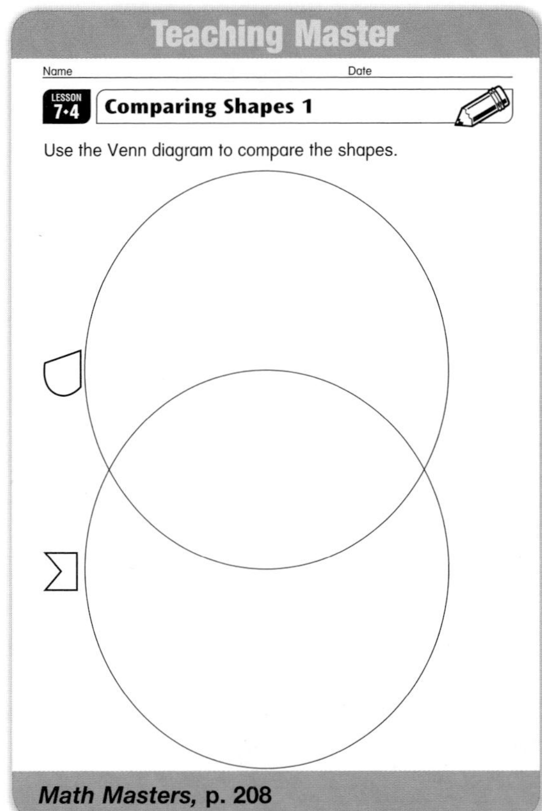

Teaching Master

Name Date

LESSON 7·4 **Comparing Shapes 1**

Use the Venn diagram to compare the shapes.

Math Masters, p. 208

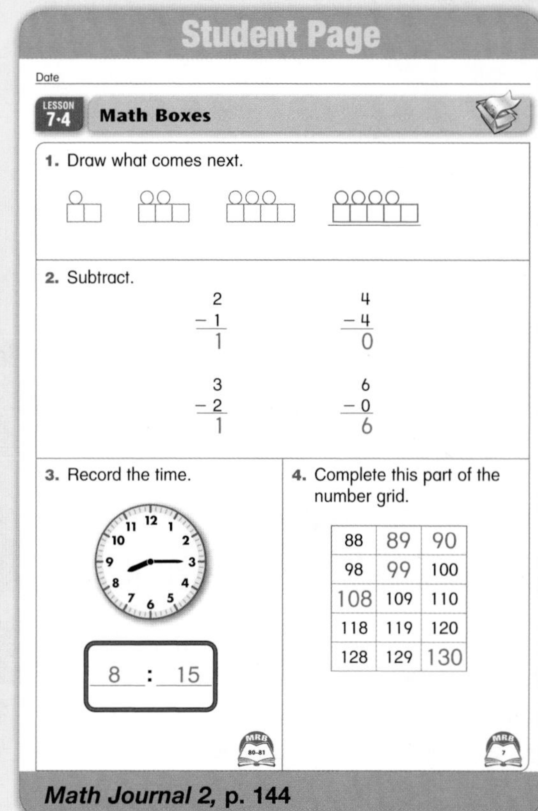

Student Page

Date

LESSON 7·4 **Math Boxes**

1. Draw what comes next.

2. Subtract.

2 − 1 = 1	4 − 4 = 0
3 − 2 = 1	6 − 0 = 6

3. Record the time.

8 : 15

4. Complete this part of the number grid.

88	89	90
98	99	100
108	109	110
118	119	120
128	129	130

Math Journal 2, p. 144

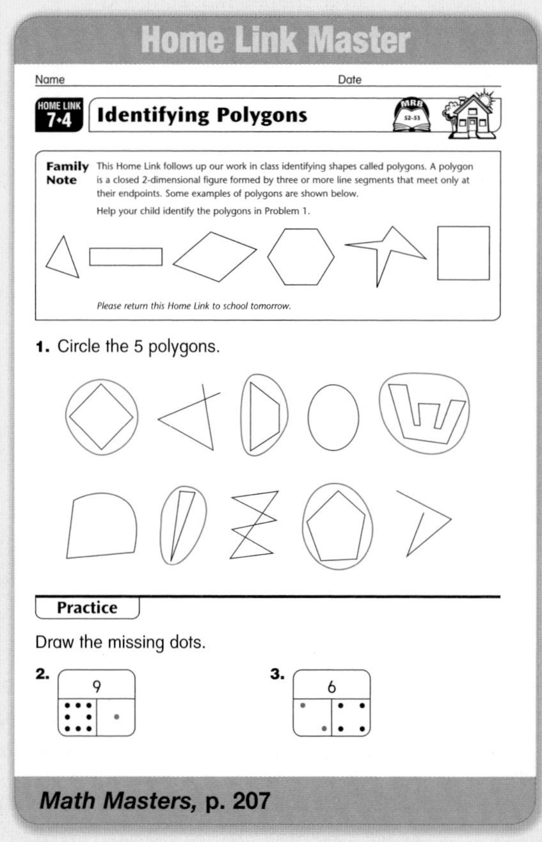

Home Link Master

Name Date

HOME LINK 7·4 **Identifying Polygons**

Family Note This Home Link follows up our work in class identifying shapes called polygons. A polygon is a closed 2-dimensional figure formed by three or more line segments that meet only at their endpoints. Some examples of polygons are shown below.

Help your child identify the polygons in Problem 1.

Please return this Home Link to school tomorrow.

1. Circle the 5 polygons.

Practice

Draw the missing dots.

2. 9

3. 6

Math Masters, p. 207

7•5 Spheres, Cylinders, and Rectangular Prisms

Objectives To guide the identification of spheres, cylinders, and rectangular prisms; and to facilitate the investigation of their characteristics.

Technology Resources www.everydaymathonline.com

ePresentations

eToolkit

Algorithms Practice

EM Facts Workshop Game™

Family Letters

Assessment Management

Common Core State Standards

Curriculum Focal Points

Interactive Teacher's Lesson Guide

1 Teaching the Lesson

Key Concepts and Skills

- Count the flat faces and corners on solid figures. [Number and Numeration Goal 2]
- Identify and describe solid figures; identify the flat faces and corners on solid figures. [Geometry Goal 1]
- Compose solid shapes. [Geometry Goal 1]

Key Activities

Children learn the names of three 3-dimensional shapes—*sphere, cylinder,* and *rectangular prism*—and discuss their characteristics. Children classify items brought from home to start a Shapes Museum and construct cylinders and rectangular prisms.

Ongoing Assessment: Recognizing Student Achievement Use Mental Math and Reflexes. [Number and Numeration Goal 3]

Key Vocabulary

sphere ◆ cylinder ◆ rectangular prism ◆ surface ◆ face

Materials

Home Link 7•4
Math Masters, p. 210 (optional); p. 212A
base-10 blocks (longs and cubes) ◆ slate ◆ ball, can, and box ◆ 3" by 5" index cards ◆ items for the Shapes Museum ◆ scissors ◆ tape ◆ per small group: 20 twist-ties and 4 each of 8" straws, 6" straws, and 4" straws

2 Ongoing Learning & Practice

Playing *Coin Exchange*
My Reference Book, pp. 128 and 129
per partnership: tool-kit coins, 2 dice
Children practice exchanging coins with equivalent values.

Math Boxes 7•5
Math Journal 2, p. 145
Children practice and maintain skills through Math Box problems.

Home Link 7•5
Math Masters, p. 211
Children practice and maintain skills through Home Link activities.

3 Differentiation Options

READINESS

Comparing Plane Shapes and Solid Figures
per partnership: 3-dimensional shapes, rectangular prism, cylinder
Children compare 2- and 3-dimensional shapes.

ENRICHMENT

Sorting Shapes by Their Faces
Math Masters, p. 212
3-dimensional shapes
Children sort 3-dimensional objects by the shapes of their faces.

ELL SUPPORT

Describing Shapes
Children describe shapes in the Shapes Museum.

Advance Preparation

Place a ball (sphere), a can (cylinder), and a box (rectangular prism) near the Math Message. For Part 1, write the words *sphere, cylinder, rectangular prism,* and *other* on index cards. Display models of a sphere, a cylinder, and a rectangular prism and label each with its name. Be prepared to add some of your objects to the Shapes Museum. For the optional Enrichment activity in Part 3, gather a variety of 3-dimensional shapes. You may wish to make a poster by enlarging and laminating *Math Masters,* page 210.

***Teacher's Reference Manual,* Grades 1–3** pp. 14, 141–146, 152

Getting Started

Mental Math and Reflexes ★

Display sets of base-10 blocks on the overhead or draw them on the board. Have children write the value of each set on their slates.

Suggestions:

●○○ 3 longs and 5 cubes 35

●●○ 4 longs and 11 cubes 51

●●● 1 flat, 2 longs, and 16 cubes 136

Math Message

Which of these objects can roll?

Home Link 7•4 Follow-Up

Review polygons. Briefly discuss what is necessary for a shape to be a polygon.

Ongoing Assessment: Recognizing Student Achievement

Mental Math and Reflexes ★

Use **Mental Math and Reflexes** to assess children's ability to name numbers represented by base-10 blocks. Children are making adequate progress if they are able to answer the first and second questions correctly. Some children may be able to correctly answer the third question, as well.

[Number and Numeration Goal 3]

1 Teaching the Lesson

▶ Math Message Follow-Up

WHOLE-CLASS ACTIVITY

Ask a child to try to roll the ball, the can, and the box. Have children share their observations.

Tell children that today they will learn about the shapes of objects in their world.

▶ Discussing the Characteristics of Spheres, Cylinders, and Rectangular Prisms

WHOLE-CLASS DISCUSSION

Ask children how they would describe the ball, the can, and the box. Expect answers such as the following:

- The ball is round and smooth.
- The ball has no flat sides.
- The can has a curved side and two flat sides.
- The flat sides of the can are circles.
- The can will sit on either of its flat sides.
- All of the sides of the box are flat.

Representations of 3-dimensional Figures

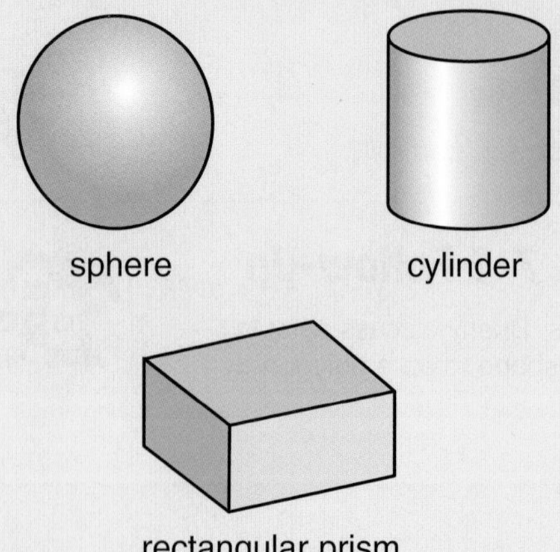

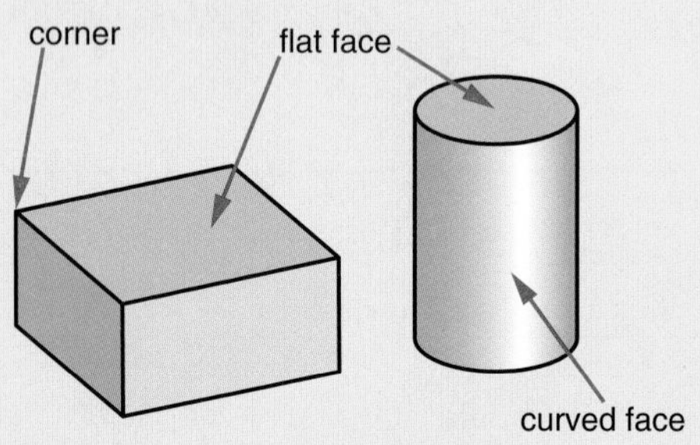

NOTE Two-dimensional shapes, such as squares and circles, have length and width. They exist entirely in a plane, such as a flat sheet of paper. Three-dimensional shapes are often represented in 2-dimensional drawings, but actual 3-dimensional objects always extend out of the plane because they have length, width, and height. Furthermore, 2-dimensional shapes are the faces of 3-dimensional shapes.

Children sort objects into categories to create a Shapes Museum.

Begin to use formal names for these shapes. Tell children that the ball is an example of a **sphere,** the can is an example of a **cylinder,** and the box is an example of a **rectangular prism.** Explain that the outside or "skin" of any of these 3-dimensional shapes is called its **surface.**

Ask someone to point to the flat sides of the rectangular prism and the cylinder. Say that these sides are sometimes called **faces.**

NOTE For most children, it will take repeated exposures before these geometric terms become part of their working vocabulary.

How many flat faces does each shape have? The sphere has 0 flat faces; the rectangular prism has 6; the cylinder has 2. Point to each face as the class counts them together. What are the shapes of the flat faces? All of the flat faces of the rectangular prism are rectangles. (Squares are special rectangles.) The flat faces of the cylinder are circles.

Point to a corner of the rectangular prism. Explain that a corner is a point at which at least three flat faces meet. A cylinder does not have any corners because its flat faces do not meet. How many corners does the rectangular prism have? 8 corners Point to each corner as the class counts.

Adjusting the Activity

ELL

Have children model the words *curve* and *flat* as attributes of surfaces. They model the word *curve* by holding their arms in front of them as though they were holding a large ball. They model the word *flat* by placing their hands on a table or desk.

AUDITORY ◆ KINESTHETIC ◆ TACTILE ◆ VISUAL

Art Link Show children pictures of uniquely shaped skyscrapers. Have them use solid figures to make models of those skyscrapers. Then ask children to identify and label the different solid figures that they used.

▶ Starting a Shapes Museum with a Display of 3-Dimensional Objects

WHOLE-CLASS ACTIVITY

Review museums as places to collect, organize, and label objects.

Tell children that they are going to start a Shapes Museum. Help children place objects they brought from home in the museum next to the correct labels. For now, have children put all shapes that are not spheres, cylinders, or rectangular prisms into the "other" category. Add some of your own items to the museum.

Children will have fun looking for other shapes that approximate spheres, cylinders, and rectangular prisms. Actual shapes are often "close, but not quite" the ideal 3-dimensional shapes; for example, books are "almost" rectangular prisms. Encourage children to notice the shapes of objects they see at school and at home. Tell them that they will continue to add to the Shapes Museum tomorrow.

▶ Making Cylinders and Rectangular Prisms

SMALL-GROUP ACTIVITY

(*Math Masters,* p. 212A)

Tell children that they will be making cylinders and rectangular prisms. For the cylinders, give each group scissors, tape, and one copy of *Math Masters*, page 212A on construction paper. For the rectangular prisms, provide straws and twist-ties. Begin by modeling how to make a cylinder:

1. Cut out the cylinder template from *Math Masters*, page 212A. Make sure the circles remain connected to the rectangle.
2. Fold the rectangle into a tube. The circles should be at the top and the bottom of the tube.
3. Tape the tube together by taping the tab on one edge of the rectangle to the inside of the other edge of the rectangle.
4. Fold the tabs on each circle and tape them to the top and bottom of the tube to make a cylinder.

Next demonstrate how to make a rectangular prism, reminding children how they constructed polygons in Lesson 7-4.

1. Make two rectangles using the 4" and 6" straws and twist-ties.
2. Have two children hold the rectangles while you anchor a new twist-tie around each corner of each rectangle.
3. Connect a corner of one rectangle to a corner of the other by inserting the anchor twist-ties into both ends of an 8" straw. Continue until four 8" straws connect all four corners of the two rectangles, making a rectangular prism.

Assist children as they construct these solids. When children are finished, have them add their shapes to the Shapes Museum.

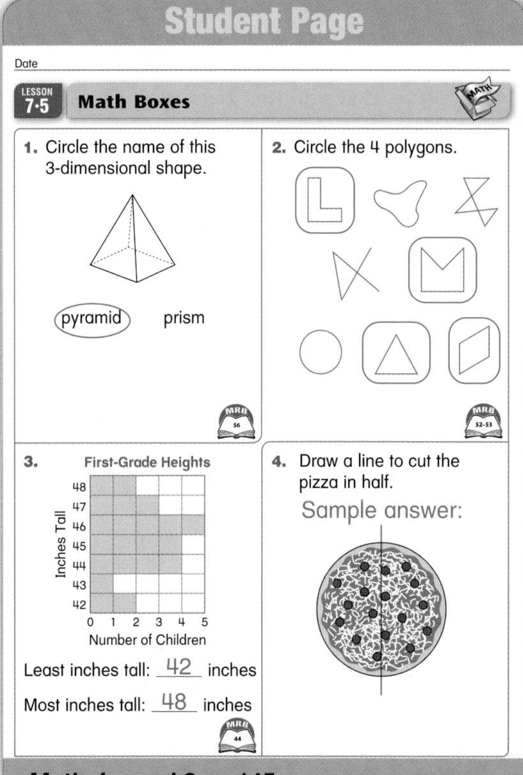
Student Page

Date

LESSON 7·5 **Math Boxes**

1. Circle the name of this 3-dimensional shape.

(pyramid) prism

2. Circle the 4 polygons.

3. First-Grade Heights

Least inches tall: 42 inches

Most inches tall: 48 inches

4. Draw a line to cut the pizza in half.

Sample answer:

Math Journal 2, p. 145

NOTE You may wish to cut out some cylinder templates before the lesson (1 per small group) in case children have trouble cutting the templates.

2 Ongoing Learning & Practice

▶ Playing *Coin Exchange*

PARTNER ACTIVITY

(*My Reference Book,* pp. 128 and 129)

Children make coin exchanges. For instructions, see Lesson 6-10.

▶ Math Boxes 7·5

INDEPENDENT ACTIVITY

(*Math Journal 2,* p. 145)

Mixed Practice Math Boxes in this lesson are paired with Math Boxes in Lesson 7-7. The skills in Problem 4 preview Unit 8 content.

Portfolio Ideas

Writing/Reasoning Have children write, draw, or verbalize an answer to this question: *What is a polygon?* A reasonable answer should include features of a polygon: straight sides, corners, and a closed shape.

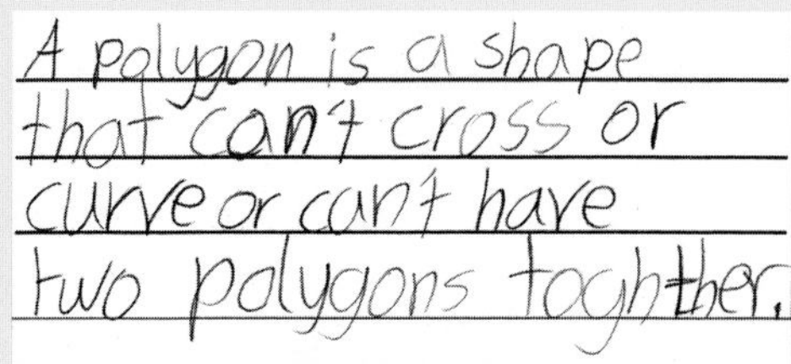

One child's work in response to the Writing/Reasoning prompt

Home Link Master

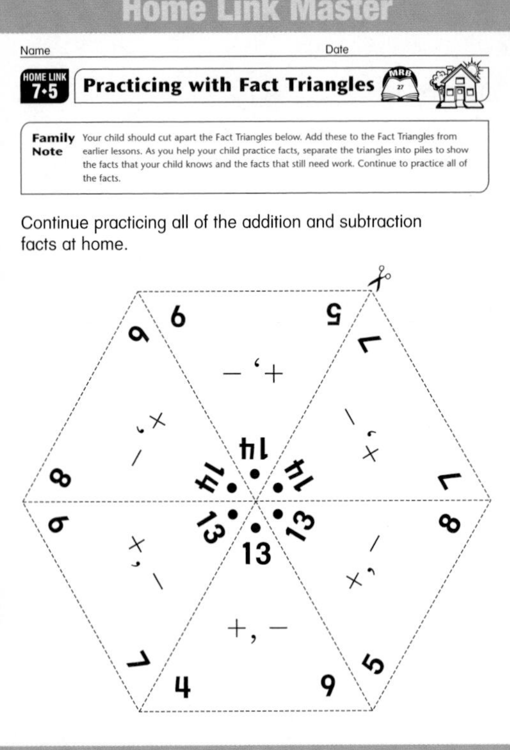

Name Date

HOME LINK 7•5 **Practicing with Fact Triangles**

Family Note Your child should cut apart the Fact Triangles below. Add these to the Fact Triangles from earlier lessons. As you help your child practice facts, separate the triangles into piles to show the facts that your child knows and the facts that still need work. Continue to practice all of the facts.

Continue practicing all of the addition and subtraction facts at home.

Math Masters, p. 211

NOTE The shapes for this activity can come from the Shapes Museum or from a set of geometric solids.

Teaching Master

Name Date

LESSON 7•5 **Sorting Shapes by Their Faces**

1. Find a 3-dimensional shape.
2. Write the name or draw the shape.
3. Match the shape to its face. Put an X in the box.

3-Dimensional Shape	○ Face	△ Face	□ Face	Other

Math Masters, p. 212

▶ Home Link 7•5

INDEPENDENT ACTIVITY

(*Math Masters,* p. 211)

Home Connection Children cut out a fifth set of Fact Triangles to continue their fact practice at home.

3 Differentiation Options

READINESS

PARTNER ACTIVITY

▶ Comparing Plane Shapes and Solid Figures

5–15 Min

To explore the relationships between plane shapes and solid figures, children trace faces of selected geometric solids. Have children label one side of a sheet of paper "Rectangular Prism" and the other side "Cylinder." They work with a partner to trace the flat surfaces, or *faces,* of both shapes on the appropriate side of the paper. They do not have to trace identical faces more than once. Have them discuss the results of their tracing. For example: *I traced rectangles when I drew the sides of the box.*

ENRICHMENT

INDEPENDENT ACTIVITY

▶ Sorting Shapes by Their Faces

5–15 Min

(*Math Masters,* p. 212)

To explore the characteristics of solid figures, have children record the faces of shapes from the Shapes Museum. They name or draw the shape they have chosen and write an *X* in the table corresponding to the shape of the faces.

When children have completed *Math Masters*, page 212, have them sort the objects into 3 groups by the shapes of the objects' faces.

ELL SUPPORT

SMALL-GROUP ACTIVITY

▶ Describing Shapes

5–15 Min

To provide language support for geometry, have children look at the Shapes Museum and describe some of the shapes. Encourage children to use vocabulary related to plane shapes and solid figures such as *side, corner, surface, flat, face, circle, triangle, square, sphere, cylinder,* and *rectangular prism*.

7·6 Pyramids, Cones, and Cubes

Objectives To guide the identification of pyramids, cones, and cubes; and to facilitate the investigation of their characteristics.

www.everydaymathonline.com

ePresentations

eToolkit

Algorithms Practice

EM Facts Workshop Game™

Family Letters

Assessment Management

Common Core State Standards

Curriculum Focal Points

Interactive Teacher's Lesson Guide

1 Teaching the Lesson

Key Concepts and Skills

- Count the flat faces and corners on solid figures. [Number and Numeration Goal 2]
- Identify and describe solid figures. [Geometry Goal 1]
- Compare and contrast solid figures. [Geometry Goal 1]
- Compose solid shapes. [Geometry Goal 1]

Key Activities

Children learn the names of three more 3-dimensional shapes—*pyramid, cone,* and *cube*—and discuss their characteristics. They move some of the "other" items in the Shapes Museum to the appropriate categories and construct cubes and cones.

Ongoing Assessment: Informing Instruction See page 652.

Key Vocabulary

pyramid ◆ cone ◆ cube

Materials

Math Journal 2, pp. 146 and 147
Home Link 7•5
Math Masters, p. 210 (optional); p. 212B
slate ◆ models of a pyramid, a cone, and a cube ◆ 3" by 5" index cards ◆ items for the Shapes Museum ◆ scissors ◆ tape ◆ per small group: 20 twist-ties and 12 straws (each 4" in length)

2 Ongoing Learning & Practice

Playing the *Attribute Train Game*
per partnership: pattern blocks, attribute blocks, folder
Children practice identifying attributes of shapes.

Ongoing Assessment: Recognizing Student Achievement
Use an Exit Slip (*Math Masters,* page 305).
[Geometry Goal 1]

Math Boxes 7·6
Math Journal 2, p. 148
Children practice and maintain skills through Math Box problems.

Home Link 7·6
Math Masters, p. 213
Children practice and maintain skills through Home Link activities.

Minute Math+
Minute Math®+, p. 59
Children practice identifying plane shapes and solid figures.

3 Differentiation Options

READINESS

Identifying Shapes Using Touch
Math Journal 2, p. 146
per group: several paper bags each filled with a different 3-dimensional shape
Children identify 3-dimensional shapes by touch.

ENRICHMENT

Comparing Prisms and Pyramids
Math Masters, p. 214
prisms and pyramids from the Shapes Museum
Children compare prisms and pyramids.

EXTRA PRACTICE

Reading About Geometry
Math Masters, p. 305
Children read *Cubes, Cones, Cylinders, & Spheres* to practice geometry skills.

Advance Preparation

For Part 1, write the words *pyramid, cone,* and *cube* on index cards. Display models of a pyramid and a cube, each with its name. Place a model of a cone with its name near the Math Message. Be prepared to add more objects to the Shapes Museum.

For the optional Extra Practice activity in Part 3, obtain a copy of ***Cubes, Cones, Cylinders, & Spheres*** by Tana Hoban (Greenwillow Books, 2000).

Getting Started

Mental Math and Reflexes

Children solve problems like the ones below, recording their answers on slates.

●○○ Write the number that comes before 30. Circle the digit in the tens place. (2)9

●●○ Write the number that comes before 100. Circle the digit in the tens place. (9)9

●●● Write the number that comes after 149. Circle the digit in the tens place. 1(5)0

Math Message

Name an object that is shaped like a cone.

Home Link 7·5 Follow-Up

Discuss which facts children think they know. They should be making progress on +1, +0, and doubles facts.

NOTE You may wish to cut out some cone templates before the lesson (1 per small group) in case children have trouble cutting the templates.

Links to the Future

Children are introduced to the geometric terms used to identify, describe, and compare solid figures. The Grade 3 Goal is for children to appropriately use geometric language including the terms *face*, *edge*, and *base* to identify, describe, and compare spheres, cylinders, rectangular prisms, pyramids, cones, and cubes.

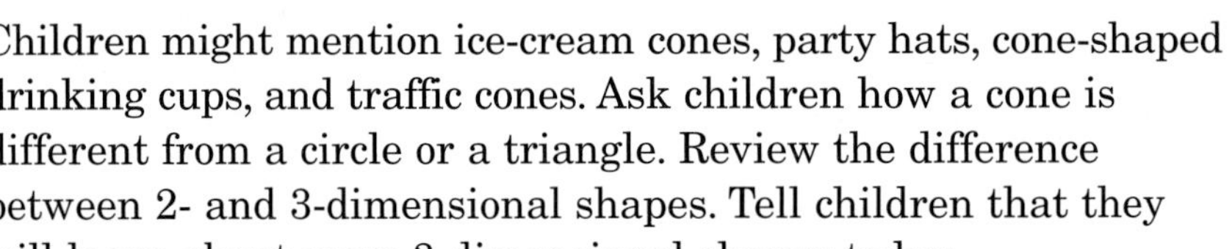

1 Teaching the Lesson

▶ Math Message Follow-Up

WHOLE-CLASS DISCUSSION

Children might mention ice-cream cones, party hats, cone-shaped drinking cups, and traffic cones. Ask children how a cone is different from a circle or a triangle. Review the difference between 2- and 3-dimensional shapes. Tell children that they will learn about more 3-dimensional shapes today.

▶ Discussing the Characteristics of Pyramids, Cones, and Cubes

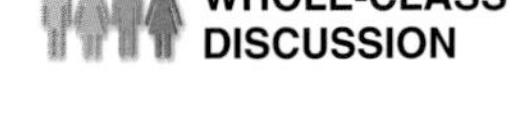

WHOLE-CLASS DISCUSSION

Ask children to describe the **pyramid, cone,** and **cube.** Expect answers such as the following:

- The pyramid has all flat faces (or sides).
- The flat faces of the pyramid that come to a point are all triangles.
- The pyramid has the same number of flat faces as corners.
- The cone has one flat face shaped like a circle and one curved surface.
- The curved surface of the cone comes to a point.
- The cube has 6 flat square faces. It has 8 corners.

Mention that a cube is a special rectangular prism whose faces are all squares of the same size.

Help children move all objects shaped like pyramids, cones, and cubes out of the "other" category of the Shapes Museum and into the appropriate categories. Ask them to name objects in the classroom that approximate those shapes.

Social Studies Link Show children images of the pyramids in Egypt. Discuss the purposes of the pyramids and how they were built.

Reviewing the Six 3-Dimensional Shapes

WHOLE-CLASS DISCUSSION

(*Math Journal 2,* p. 146)

Direct children's attention to the 3-Dimensional Shapes Poster on journal page 146. Ask questions such as the following:

- Which shapes come to a point? Cone and pyramid
- Which shapes have only flat surfaces? Pyramid, rectangular prism, and cube
- Which shape has no flat surfaces? sphere
- Which shapes have both flat and curved surfaces? Cylinder and cone

Adjusting the Activity

Have geometric models available for children to hold up in response to the above questions. Continue with questions like the following:

- What do a cone and a pyramid have in common? They both have at least one flat face, and they both come to a point.
- How are a cone and a pyramid different? A cone has a curved surface and one flat face; a pyramid has several flat faces but no curved surface.

AUDITORY ◆ KINESTHETIC ◆ TACTILE ◆ VISUAL

Identifying the Shapes of Various Objects

INDEPENDENT ACTIVITY

(*Math Journal 2,* pp. 146 and 147)

Children refer to the 3-Dimensional Shapes Poster on journal page 146 as they identify the shapes of the objects shown on journal page 147 and record their names.

Making Cubes and Cones

SMALL-GROUP ACTIVITY

(*Math Masters,* p. 212B)

Tell children that they will be making cubes and cones. For the cones, give each group scissors, tape, and one copy of *Math Masters*, page 212B on construction paper. For the cubes, provide straws and twist-ties. Begin by modeling for children how to make a cone:

1. Cut out the cone template from *Math Masters*, page 212B. This consists of two pieces: the circle and the half-circle.
2. Fold the half-circle so that the tab on one edge of the half-circle can be taped to the inside of the other edge.
3. Fold the tabs on the circle. Tape the tabs to the outside of the folded half-circle to secure the circle at the base of the cone.

Next model for children how to make a cube:

1. Remind children how they used twist-ties and straws to make a rectangular prism in Lesson 7-5.

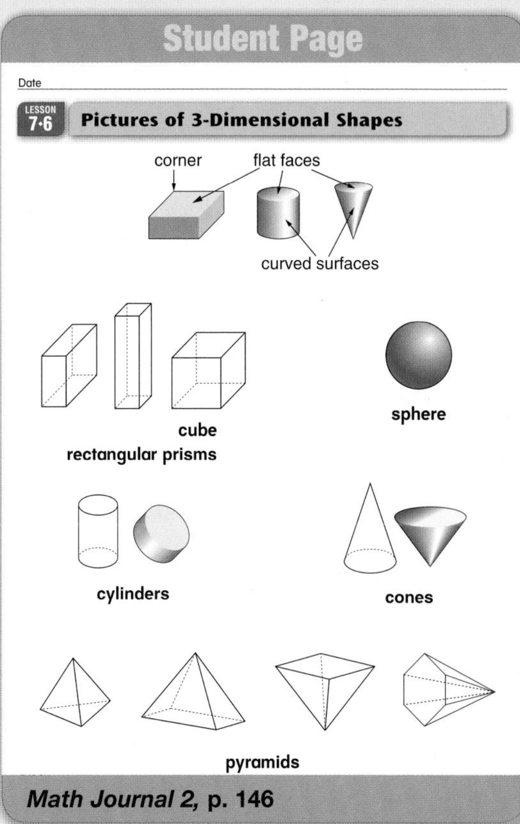

Math Journal 2, p. 146

NOTE You may want to enlarge journal page 146 to poster size. Display the poster for easy reference.

NOTE In geometry, a cone is defined as a closed 3-dimensional shape. It has a flat face (a lid) shaped like a circle. You need not mention this to the class at this time.

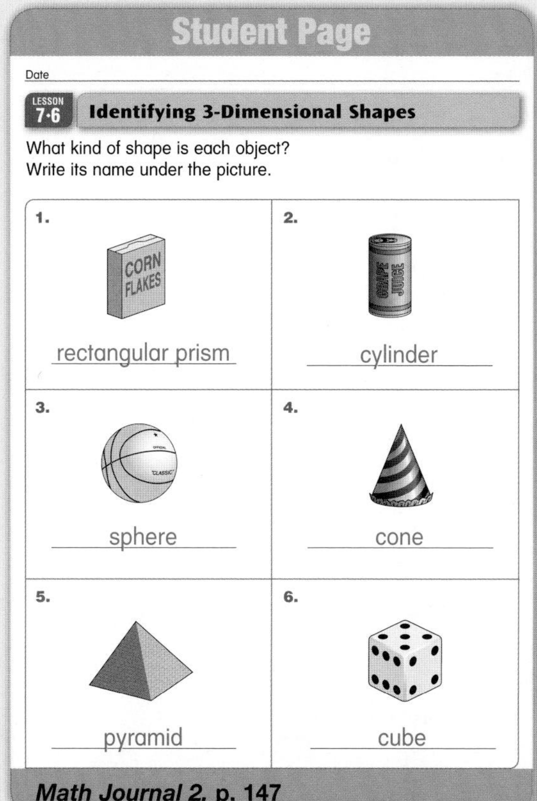

Math Journal 2, p. 147

Ongoing Assessment: Informing Instruction

Watch for children who have difficulty recognizing a 3-dimensional shape given its 2-dimensional representation. Direct children to the Shapes Museum to find 3-dimensional shapes that correspond to those shown on journal page 147.

Art Link Children can work in small groups to construct creatures out of boxes and paper-towel tubes. They cut 2-dimensional shapes out of construction paper and glue them on the boxes as eyes, noses, ears, and other features.

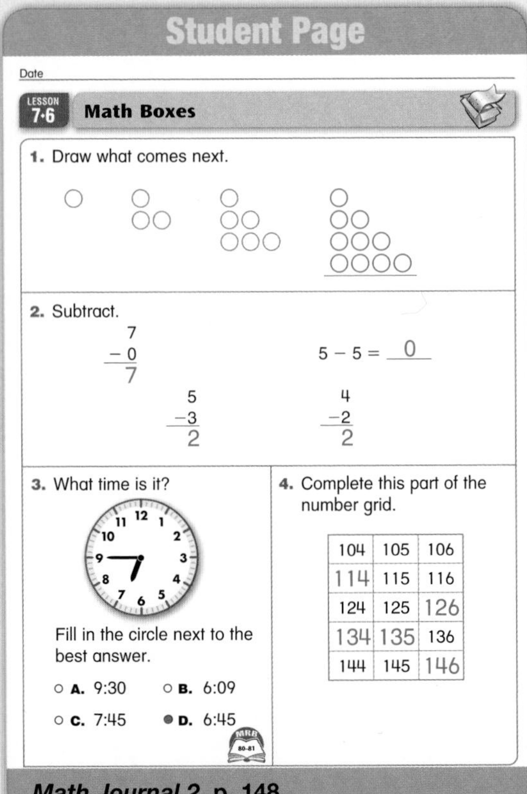

Student Page

Date

LESSON 7·6 **Math Boxes**

1. Draw what comes next.

2. Subtract.

7 − 0 = 7

5 − 5 = 0

5 − 3 = 2

4 − 2 = 2

3. What time is it?

Fill in the circle next to the best answer.

○ A. 9:30 ○ B. 6:09
○ C. 7:45 ● D. 6:45

4. Complete this part of the number grid.

104	105	106
114	115	116
124	125	126
134	135	136
144	145	146

Math Journal 2, p. 148

2. Illustrate the same directions (see page 647) used for the rectangular prism, using only 4" straws this time. First make two squares from 4" straws. Then connect them together with four 4" straws.
3. When you are finished constructing the cube, ask children how the cube you made and rectangular prism you made are different. Sample answer: The cube's faces are all squares of the same size; the rectangular prism's faces are all rectangles but not all squares.

Assist children as they construct these shapes. When children are finished, have them add their shapes to the Shapes Museum.

2 Ongoing Learning & Practice

▶ Playing the *Attribute Train Game*

PARTNER ACTIVITY

Algebraic Thinking Children identify attributes of shapes by playing the *Attribute Train Game.* For instructions, see Lesson 7-2.

Ongoing Assessment: Recognizing Student Achievement — **Exit Slip**

Use an **Exit Slip** to assess children's ability to recognize attributes of attribute blocks. Have each child draw and color at least three shapes from his or her train on the Exit Slip (*Math Masters,* page 305). Children are making adequate progress if their shape train follows the rules of the game.

[Geometry Goal 1]

▶ Math Boxes 7·6

INDEPENDENT ACTIVITY

(*Math Journal 2,* p. 148)

Mixed Practice Math Boxes in this lesson are linked to Math Boxes in Lessons 7-2 and 7-4. The skills in Problem 4 preview Unit 8 content.

Writing/Reasoning Have children write, draw, or verbalize an answer to the following question: *What patterns do you see on the number grid?* A reasonable answer should describe place-value patterns in rows and columns. Sample answer: Going across the ones place changes by one. Going down the tens place changes too.

▶ Home Link 7·6

INDEPENDENT ACTIVITY

(*Math Masters,* p. 213)

Home Connection Children trace flat faces of 3-dimensional objects and identify the shapes they have drawn. A Word List containing the names of shapes is provided on the Home Link page.

▶ *Minute Math+*

WHOLE-CLASS ACTIVITY

Use *Minute Math+*, page 59, to provide more practice identifying plane shapes and solid figures.

3 Differentiation Options

READINESS

SMALL-GROUP ACTIVITY

▶ Identifying Shapes Using Touch

5–15 Min

(*Math Journal 2,* p. 146)

To explore the attributes of solid figures, have children describe 3-dimensional shapes. Each group takes a paper bag containing a 3-dimensional shape. Without looking in the bag, each child takes a turn reaching into the bag and feeling the object. Once all of the children have described the object, they can remove it from the bag and compare it to the shapes pictured on journal page 146.

ENRICHMENT

INDEPENDENT ACTIVITY

▶ Comparing Prisms and Pyramids

5–15 Min

(*Math Masters,* p. 214)

To compare and contrast the attributes of prisms and pyramids, have children construct a Venn diagram. Children take the pyramids and prisms from the Shapes Museum and sort them into the two groups. They list the common attributes in the overlapping section of the Venn diagram and the distinct attributes in the appropriate sections of the diagram. Have children discuss the similarities and differences they have listed in their diagrams.

EXTRA PRACTICE

SMALL-GROUP ACTIVITY

▶ Reading About Geometry

5–15 Min

(*Math Masters,* p. 305)

Literature Link To provide practice with geometry skills, read ***Cubes, Cones, Cylinders, & Spheres*** by Tana Hoban (Greenwillow Books, 2000). On an Exit Slip (*Math Masters,* page 305), have children draw something shaped like a cube that is in their classroom.

Home Link Master

Name ______ Date ______

HOME LINK 7·6 **Tracing Shapes** MRB 54–58

Family Note The class has been working with 2-dimensional and 3-dimensional shapes. For today's Home Link, help your child find 3-dimensional objects and then trace around one face of each object. Some examples are the bottom of a box, the bottom of a can, and the bottom of a cup. Use the back of this sheet and other sheets if you want. For each tracing, help your child find the name for the shape in the Word List and write the name on the tracing.

Please return this Home Link to school tomorrow.

1. Find 3-dimensional shapes with flat faces (sides).

On the back of this page, trace around one face of each shape.

Write the name of the shape on each tracing.

Word List		
square	circle	hexagon
trapezoid	rhombus	triangle
not a polygon	rectangle	other polygon

Practice

2. Fill in the blanks.

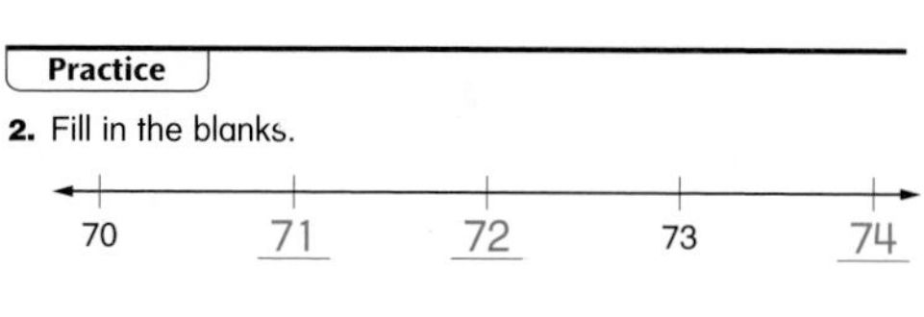

Math Masters, p. 213

NOTE The shapes that are placed in the paper bags can come from the Shape Museum or from a set of geometric solids.

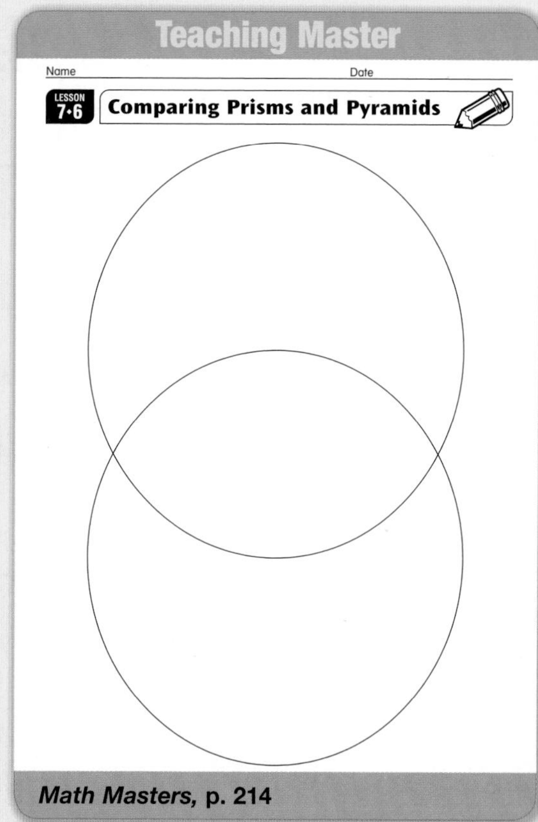

Math Masters, p. 214

7•7 Symmetry

Objective To facilitate the exploration of symmetrical shapes.

Technology Resources www.everydaymathonline.com

ePresentations

eToolkit

Algorithms Practice

EM Facts Workshop Game™

Family Letters

Assessment Management

Common Core State Standards

Curriculum Focal Points

Interactive Teacher's Lesson Guide

1 Teaching the Lesson

Key Concepts and Skills

- Identify shapes having line symmetry. [Geometry Goal 2]
- Create line-symmetric shapes. [Geometry Goal 2]

Key Activities

Children cut and fold symmetrical shapes so that the two halves match. The teacher demonstrates making symmetrical shapes by folding and cutting.

Ongoing Assessment: Informing Instruction See page 656.

Key Vocabulary

symmetrical ◆ symmetry

Materials

Home Link 7•6

Math Masters, p. 215

slate ◆ scissors ◆ number grid (optional)

2 Ongoing Learning & Practice

Playing *Addition Top-It*

My Reference Book, pp. 122 and 123

per partnership: 4 each of number cards 0–10 (from the Everything Math Deck, if available)

Children practice solving addition problems.

Math Boxes 7•7

Math Journal 2, p. 149

Children practice and maintain skills through Math Box problems.

Ongoing Assessment: Recognizing Student Achievement

Use Math Boxes, Problem 1.

[Geometry Goal 1]

Home Link 7•7

Math Masters, p. 216

Children practice and maintain skills through Home Link activities.

Minute Math+

Minute Math®+, pp. 14, 21, and 37

Children practice place-value and measurement skills.

3 Differentiation Options

ENRICHMENT

Making Symmetry Cards

small mirror ◆ magazines to cut up ◆ glue or tape ◆ scissors

Children make symmetry cards.

ELL SUPPORT

Playing *Make My Design*

Math Journal 2, p. 137

per partnership: pattern blocks, folder

Children practice naming and describing geometric designs and spatial relationships.

Advance Preparation

Place copies of *Math Masters,* page 215 near the Math Message, one per child.

For the optional Enrichment activity in Part 3, make "symmetry cards" using index cards. Draw pictures or glue pictures from magazines of halves of symmetrical objects. Each picture should stop at the line of symmetry.

***Teacher's Reference Manual,* Grades 1–3** pp. 149, 150

Getting Started

Mental Math and Reflexes

Review how to determine if a number is closer to one number or another by counting spaces on a number grid. Encourage children to use this method if it helps them. Also point out that they can look at the ones digit to help them find the answer. If the ones digit is less than 5, the number is closer to the smaller number. If the number is more than 5, the number is closer to the larger number. If the number is 5, the number is halfway between the two numbers. Have children write their answers on their slates.

●○○ Is 3 closer to 0 or 10? 0 Is 9 closer to 0 or 10? 10

●●○ Is 26 closer to 20 or 30? 30 Is 12 closer to 10 or 20? 10

●●● Is 45 closer to 40 or 50? Halfway between Is 97 closer to 90 or 100? 100

Math Message

Take a sheet of paper with a picture of a heart. Carefully cut out the paper heart.

Home Link 7·6 Follow-Up

Have volunteers describe some of the shapes they found and where they found them.

1 Teaching the Lesson

▶ Math Message Follow-Up

Have children fold their paper hearts in half so that the two halves match. Then ask them to give other examples of pictures or things that can be folded in half so that the two halves match. Sample answers: Butterfly, bell, vase, double-4 domino Tell children that such shapes are said to be ***symmetrical,*** or to have ***symmetry.***

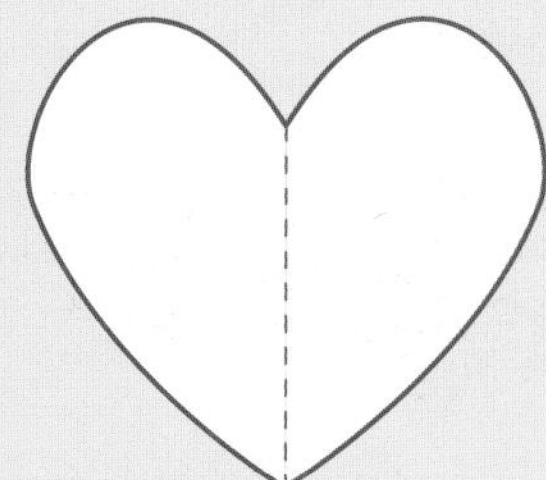

▶ Making Symmetrical Shapes

Have children do as many of the following activities as time allows.

Activity 1

Fold a half-sheet of paper in half. Cut out an irregular shape that contains part of the fold. Unfold the cut-out piece. *Is it symmetrical?* yes *How do you know?* The two halves match. *How many ways can you fold the shape so the two halves match?* 1

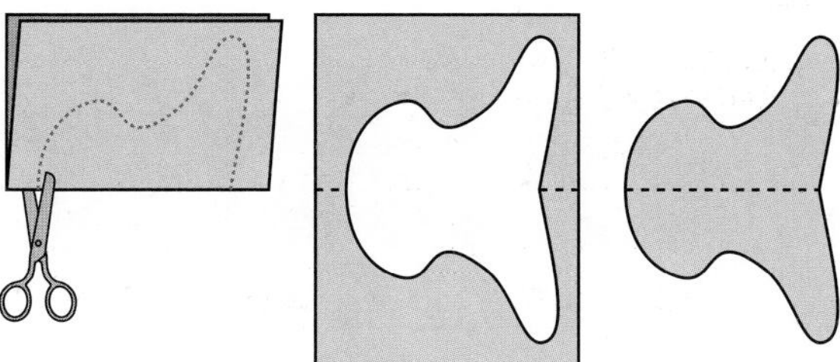

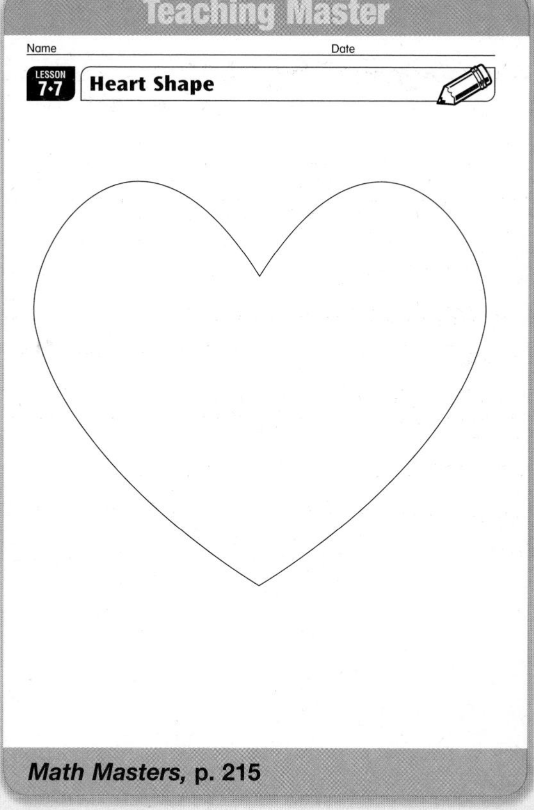

Math Masters, p. 215

Activity 2

Fold a half-sheet of paper in half, and then in half again. Cut out an irregular shape at the folded corner. Unfold the cut-out piece. *Is it symmetrical?* yes *How do you know?* The two halves match. *How many ways can you fold the shape so that the two halves match?* 2

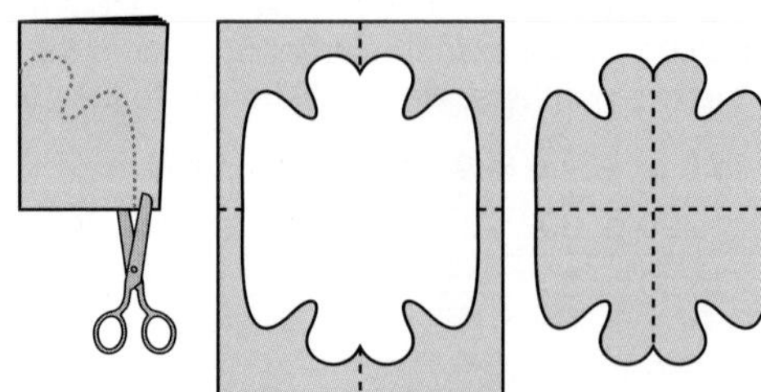

Activity 3

Fold a half-sheet of paper in half, and then in half again. Cut out the folded corner with a straight cut. Unfold the cut-out piece. *Is it symmetrical?* yes *How do you know?* The two halves match. *What kind of shape is it?* In most cases, it is a rhombus. It could be a square.

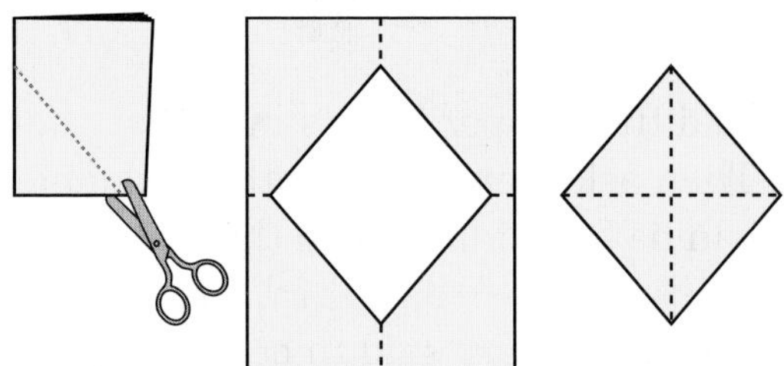

NOTE Symmetry is intuitively related to congruency. Point out to children that when the symmetrical shapes are divided, *congruent* shapes, shapes that are the same size and shape, are created.

You may wish to use commercial software to further explore.

Ongoing Assessment: Informing Instruction

Watch for children who cut the fold and end up with two shapes rather than one symmetrical shape.

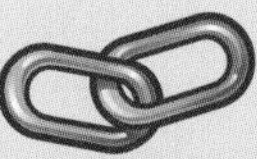

Links to the Future

This is children's first exposure to symmetry. Children should be able to identify shapes having a line of symmetry. The Grade 2 Goal is for children to create two-dimensional symmetric shapes. The Grade 3 Goal is for children to locate multiple lines of symmetry in two-dimensional shapes.

Teaching Master

Games

Addition Top-It

Materials ❑ number cards 0–10 (4 of each)

Players 2 to 4

Skill Addition facts 0 to 10

Object of the game To collect the most cards.

Directions

1. Shuffle the cards. Place the deck number-side down on the table.
2. Each player turns over 2 cards and calls out the sum of the numbers.
3. The player with the largest sum wins the round and takes all the cards.
4. In case of a tie for the largest sum, each tied player turns over 2 more cards and calls out the sum of the numbers. The player with the largest sum then takes all the cards from both plays.
5. The game ends when not enough cards are left for each player to have another turn.
6. The player with the most cards wins.

one hundred twenty-two

***My Reference Book,* pp. 122 and 123**

2 Ongoing Learning & Practice

▶ Playing *Addition Top-It*

(*My Reference Book,* pp. 122 and 123)

Children practice solving addition problems and comparing sums by playing *Addition Top-It.* For detailed instructions, see Lesson 6-1.

▶ Math Boxes 7•7

INDEPENDENT ACTIVITY

(*Math Journal 2,* p. 149)

Mixed Practice Math Boxes in this lesson are paired with Math Boxes in Lesson 7-5. The skills in Problem 4 preview Unit 8 content.

Ongoing Assessment: Recognizing Student Achievement

Math Boxes Problem 1 

Use **Math Boxes, Problem 1** to assess children's ability to identify cylinders. Children are making adequate progress if they are able to draw one cylindrical object. Some children may be able to draw more than one.

[Geometry Goal 1]

▶ Home Link 7•7

(*Math Masters,* p. 216)

Home Connection Children look for pictures that show examples of symmetry in nature. Pictures may include butterflies, flowers, snowflakes, and so on.

▶ *Minute Math+*

Use *Minute Math+,* pages 14, 21, and 37, to provide more practice with place value and measurements.

3 Differentiation Options

ENRICHMENT

▶ Making Symmetry Cards

To further explore the concept of symmetry, have children use mirrors to "complete" the pictures on the symmetry cards you made. Then have them create their own symmetry cards, using the same methods (drawing or cutting and gluing). Encourage children to use mirrors, especially when they are first trying to decide where the axis of symmetry is located.

EXTRA PRACTICE

▶ Playing *Make My Design*

(*Math Journal 2,* p. 137)

Children practice naming and describing geometric figures and spatial relationships by playing *Make My Design.* For detailed instructions, see Lesson 7-1.

Student Page

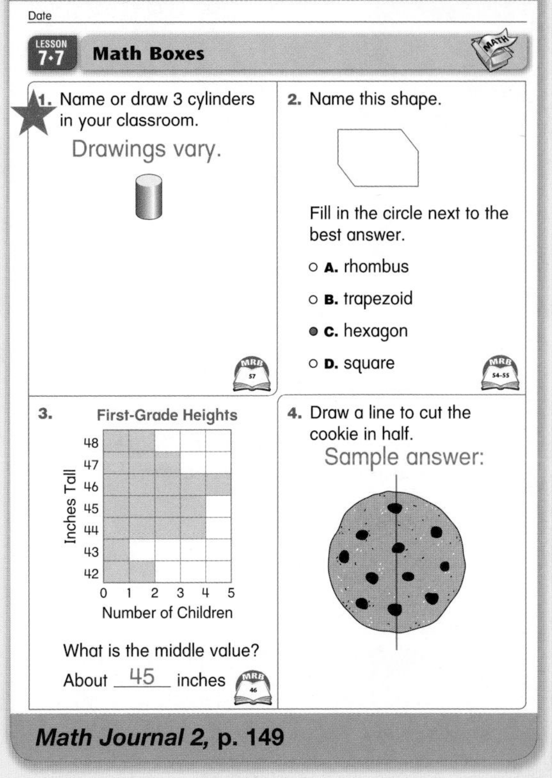

Date

LESSON 7•7 **Math Boxes**

1. Name or draw 3 cylinders in your classroom.
Drawings vary.

2. Name this shape.
Fill in the circle next to the best answer.
○ **A.** rhombus
○ **B.** trapezoid
● **C.** hexagon
○ **D.** square

3. First-Grade Heights
(Bar graph: Inches Tall 42–48; Number of Children 0–5)
What is the middle value?
About 45 inches

4. Draw a line to cut the cookie in half.
Sample answer:

Math Journal 2, p. 149

Home Link Master

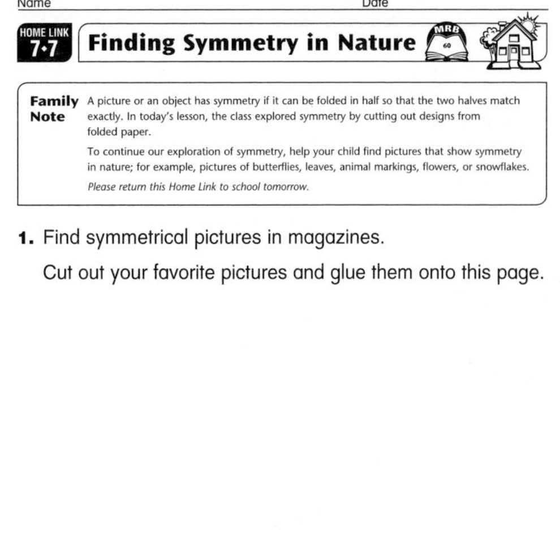

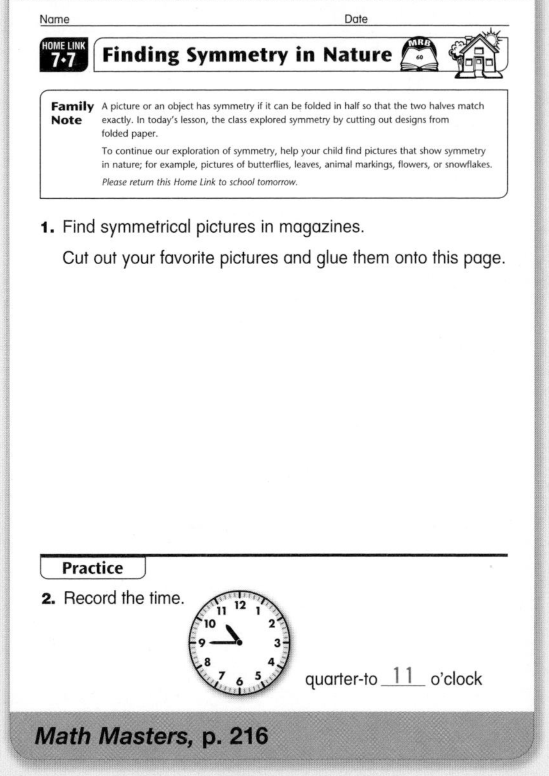

Name Date

HOME LINK 7•7 **Finding Symmetry in Nature**

Family Note A picture or an object has symmetry if it can be folded in half so that the two halves match exactly. In today's lesson, the class explored symmetry by cutting out designs from folded paper.
To continue our exploration of symmetry, help your child find pictures that show symmetry in nature; for example, pictures of butterflies, leaves, animal markings, flowers, or snowflakes.
Please return this Home Link to school tomorrow.

1. Find symmetrical pictures in magazines.
Cut out your favorite pictures and glue them onto this page.

Practice

2. Record the time.
quarter-to 11 o'clock

Math Masters, p. 216

7•8 Progress Check 7

Objective To assess children's progress on mathematical content through the end of Unit 7.

1 Looking Back: Cumulative Assessment

Input children's data from Progress Check 7 into the **Assessment Management Spreadsheets**.

Materials
- Home Link 7•7
- *Assessment Handbook,* pp. 102–109, 161–164, 183, and 224–227
- slate; Pattern-Block Template

CONTENT ASSESSED	LESSON(S)	ASSESSMENT ITEMS				
		SELF	ORAL/SLATE	WRITTEN PART A	WRITTEN PART B	OPEN RESPONSE
Read, write, and represent whole numbers through hundreds; identify digits and express their values in such numbers. [Number and Numeration Goal 3]	7•2, 7•4–7•7			1, 4		
Know addition and subtraction facts. [Operations and Computation Goal 1]	7•1–7•4, 7•6, 7•7		3, 4	2		
Calculate the values of combinations of coins. [Operations and Computation Goal 2]	7•1, 7•3, 7•5	5			9	
Ask and answer questions and draw conclusions based on data representations. [Data and Chance Goal 2]	7•4, 7•5, 7•7	2		6		
Make exchanges between coins. [Measurement and Reference Frames Goal 2]					9	
Show and tell time to the nearest half-hour. [Measurement and Reference Frames Goal 4]	7•2, 7•4, 7•6	6	2	3	8	
Identify and describe plane and solid figures. [Geometry Goal 1]	7•1–7•7	1	1	5		✓
Solve problems involving simple functions and rules. [Patterns, Functions, and Algebra Goal 1]	7•2	3			7	✓
Write number sentences using symbols. [Patterns, Functions, and Algebra Goal 2]			3			
Use the properties of addition. [Patterns, Functions, and Algebra Goal 3]	7•2, 7•3	4	4	2		

2 Looking Ahead: Preparing for Unit 8

Math Boxes 7•8

Home Link 7•8: Unit 8 Family Letter

Materials
- *Math Journal 2,* p. 150
- *Math Masters,* pp. 217–220

Getting Started

Math Message • Self Assessment

Complete the Self Assessment (Assessment Handbook, page 161).

Home Link 7·7 Follow-Up

Have volunteers describe the symmetrical pictures they found. If time allows, have children use mirrors to find the lines of symmetry in the pictures.

1 Looking Back: Cumulative Assessment

▶ Math Message Follow-Up

(Self Assessment, *Assessment Handbook,* p. 161)

The Self Assessment offers children the opportunity to reflect upon their progress.

▶ Oral and Slate Assessments

Problems 3 and 4 provide summative information and can be used for grading purposes. Problems 1 and 2 provide formative information that can be useful in planning future instruction.

Oral Assessment

1. Ask children to look around the classroom and find and point to a triangle, a square, a rectangle, a hexagon, a circle, a trapezoid, and a rhombus.
2. Show times on the demonstration clock. Have children tell the times shown.
   - 4:45
   - 1:15
   - 11:45

Slate Assessment

3. Read the following phrases. Ask children to write a number model for each phrase and solve it. Sample answers shown.
   - 9 plus 1 $9 + 1 = 10$
   - 7 minus 0 $7 - 0 = 7$
   - 6 and 6 more $6 + 6 = 12$
   - 4 plus 10 $4 + 10 = 14$
   - 10 take away 4 $10 - 4 = 6$
   - 9 plus 5 $9 + 5 = 14$
   - 8 and 3 more $8 + 3 = 11$

Assessment Master

Name Date

LESSON 7·8 **Self Assessment** Progress Check 7

Put a check in the box that tells how you do each skill.

	I can do this by myself. I can explain how to do this.	I can do this by myself.	I can do this with help.
1. Name shapes.			
2. Answer questions about data.			
3. Find the rule in function machines.			
4. Write fact families.			
5. Show amounts of money with coins.			
6. Draw hands on an analog clock.			

Assessment Handbook, **p. 161**

Assessment Master

Name Date

LESSON 7·8 **Written Assessment** Progress Check 7

Part A

1. Use □ | •.
   Show 124. □ | | • • • •
   Show 49. | | | | • • • • • • • • •
2. Write the fact family.
   10, 2, 8, +, −
   8 + 2 = 10
   2 + 8 = 10
   10 − 2 = 8
   10 − 8 = 2
3. Write the time.
   12 : 30
4. Circle the tens place.
   45 92 77 56 161 29
5. Color the triangle red. Color the square yellow. Color the circle blue. Color the rhombus green.
   blue yellow red green

Assessment Handbook, **p. 162**

Assessment Master

Name Date

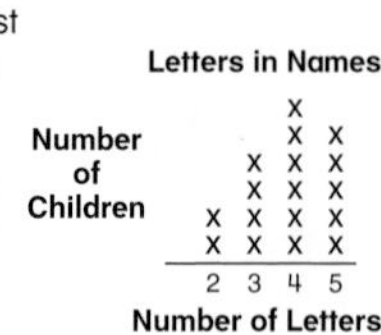

LESSON 7·8 Written Assessment *continued*

6. How many letters do the greatest number of children have in their names? 4

How many letters do the fewest number of children have in their names? 2

Letters in Names

Number of Letters	2	3	4	5
Number of Children	X X	X X X X	X X X X X X	X X X X X

Part B

7. Complete the table. Fill in the missing rule.

in	out
4	8
7	11
13	17
20	24

Rule: Add 4

8. Draw the hands.

11:15

9. Show 68¢ in two ways. Use Ⓠ, Ⓓ, Ⓝ, and Ⓟ.
Sample answers:
ⓆⓆⒹⓃⓅⓅⓅ ⒹⒹⒹⒹⒹⓃⓃⓃⓅⓅⓅ

Assessment Handbook, p. 163

Assessment Master

Name Date

LESSON 7·8 **Open Response** Progress Check 7

Shapes That Belong in a Group

Think: Which shapes from your Pattern-Block Template belong together in a group?

Use your template to draw 3 shapes that go together in the box "Shapes That Belong in the Group." In the other box, draw 3 shapes that do not belong in the group.

Shapes That Belong in the Group	Shapes That Do Not Belong in the Group

Explain or show how you know if a shape belongs in the group.

Assessment Handbook, p. 164

4. Tell children that you have 2 green marbles, 4 red marbles, and 6 blue marbles. You wanted to find the total so you added 2 and 4 and then added 6. Then write on the board:

$2 + 4 = \mathbf{6}$

$\mathbf{6} + 6 = 12$

Ask children how else you could have found the total. Have them write their number models. Sample answers: $2 + 6 = \mathbf{8}$, $\mathbf{8} + 4 = 12$; $4 + 6 = \mathbf{10}$, $\mathbf{10} + 2 = 12$

Written Assessment

INDEPENDENT ACTIVITY

(*Assessment Handbook*, pp. 162 and 163)

Part A Recognizing Student Achievement

Problems 1–6 provide summative information and may be used for grading purposes.

Problem(s)	**Description**
1, 4	Read, write, and represent whole numbers with base-10 blocks; identify digits.
2	Use the Commutative Property of Addition.
3	Tell time on an analog clock.
5	Identify and describe plane figures.
6	Answer questions based on data representations.

Part B Informing Instruction

Problems 7–9 provide formative information that can be useful in planning future instruction.

Problem(s)	**Description**
7	Solve problems involving Function Machines.
8	Show time on an analog clock.
9	Calculate the values of combinations of coins.

Use the checklists on pages 221 and 223 of the *Assessment Handbook* to record results. Then input the data into the **Assessment Management Spreadsheets** to keep an ongoing record of children's progress toward Grade-Level Goals.

▶ Open Response

INDEPENDENT ACTIVITY

(*Assessment Handbook*, p. 164)

Shapes That Belong in a Group

The open-response item requires children to apply skills and concepts from Unit 7 to solve a multistep problem. See *Assessment Handbook,* pages 105–109 for rubrics and children's work samples for this problem.

Children begin by working independently (or with a partner) to solve the multistep problem on *Assessment Handbook,* page 164. Take this time to circulate throughout the classroom.

After children have had a chance to complete the multistep problem, invite individual children to explain their solution strategies. Encourage them to use words and drawings to explain their strategies as you list them on the board. Be sure to discuss both successful and unsuccessful strategies.

NOTE You should set out a pile of pattern blocks for children to use when making their designs.

2 Looking Ahead: Preparing for Unit 8

▶ Math Boxes 7·8

INDEPENDENT ACTIVITY

(*Math Journal 2,* p. 150)

Mixed Practice This Math Boxes page previews Unit 8 content.

▶ Home Link 7·8: Unit 8 Family Letter

(*Math Masters*, pp. 217–220)

Home Connection The Unit 8 Family Letter provides families with information and activities related to Unit 8 topics.

Student Page

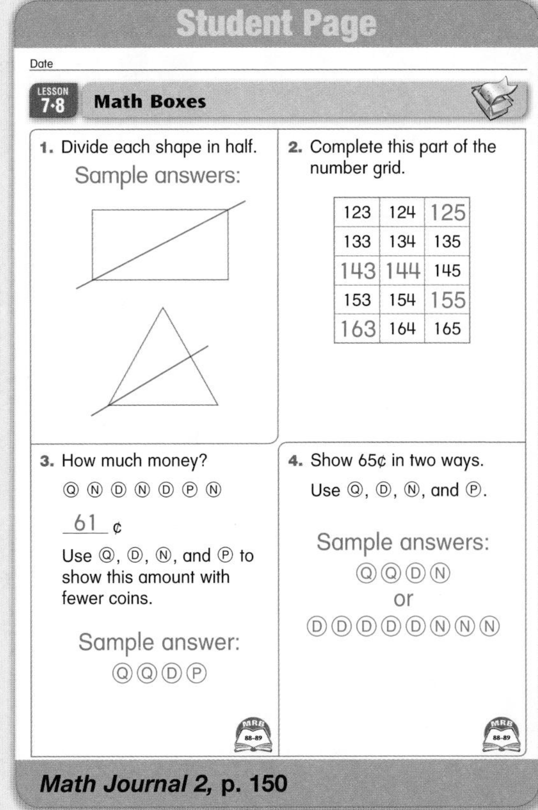

Date

LESSON 7·8 **Math Boxes**

1. Divide each shape in half.
Sample answers:

2. Complete this part of the number grid.

123	124	125
133	134	135
143	144	145
153	154	155
163	164	165

3. How much money?
Ⓠ Ⓝ Ⓓ Ⓝ Ⓓ Ⓟ Ⓝ
61 ¢
Use Ⓠ, Ⓓ, Ⓝ, and Ⓟ to show this amount with fewer coins.
Sample answer:
ⓆⓆⒹⓅ

4. Show 65¢ in two ways.
Use Ⓠ, Ⓓ, Ⓝ, and Ⓟ.
Sample answers:
ⓆⓆⒹⓃ
or
ⒹⒹⒹⒹⒹⓃⓃⓃ

Math Journal 2, p. 150

Home Link Masters

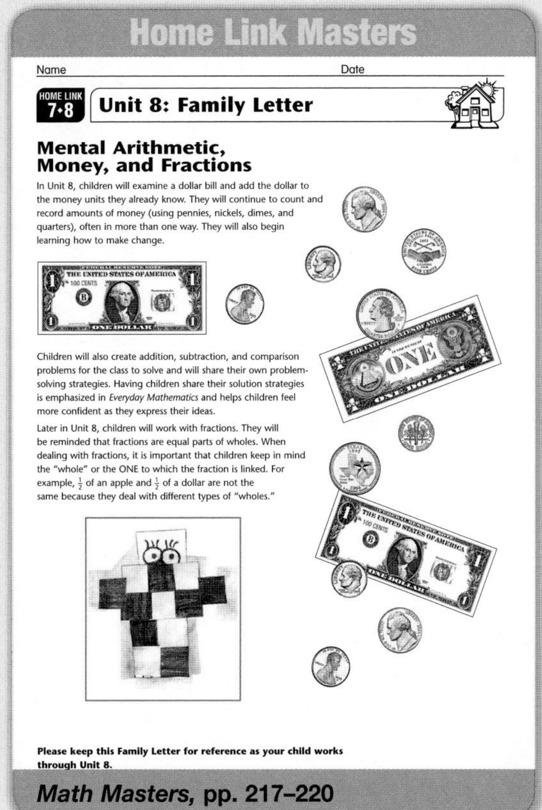

Name Date

HOME LINK 7·8 **Unit 8: Family Letter**

Mental Arithmetic, Money, and Fractions

In Unit 8, children will examine a dollar bill and add the dollar to the money units they already know. They will continue to count and record amounts of money (using pennies, nickels, dimes, and quarters), often in more than one way. They will also begin learning how to make change.

Children will also create addition, subtraction, and comparison problems for the class to solve and will share their own problem-solving strategies. Having children share their solution strategies is emphasized in *Everyday Mathematics* and helps children feel more confident as they express their ideas.

Later in Unit 8, children will work with fractions. They will be reminded that fractions are equal parts of wholes. When dealing with fractions, it is important that children keep in mind the "whole" or the ONE to which the fraction is linked. For example, $\frac{1}{2}$ of an apple and $\frac{1}{2}$ of a dollar are not the same because they deal with different types of "wholes."

Please keep this Family Letter for reference as your child works through Unit 8.

Math Masters, pp. 217–220

Unit 8 Organizer

Mental Arithmetic, Money, and Fractions

Overview

The first five lessons in this unit review money and place-value concepts that were introduced earlier and then take those concepts another step forward. The rest of the unit deals with fractions, expanding upon informal work introduced in *Kindergarten Everyday Mathematics.* The lessons here and in Unit 9 begin formally to introduce concepts of fractions, to teach fraction notation, and to teach some of the vocabulary of fractions. Unit 8 has three main areas of focus:

- To extend work with money to include dollars,
- To extend place-value concepts to hundreds, and
- To continue to develop an understanding of fractional parts of a whole.

CCSS Linking to the Common Core State Standards

The content of Unit 8 addresses the Common Core State Standards for Mathematics in *Number and Operations in Base Ten.* The correlation of the Common Core State Standards to the *Everyday Mathematics* Grade 1 lessons begins on page CS1.

Contents

Learning In Perspective

	Lesson Objectives	Links to the Past	Links to the Future
8•1	To review, reinforce, and assess skills associated with counting and exchanging coins.	In Units 2–6, children are introduced to dollars-and-cents notation and make exchanges between coins. Earlier in Grade 1 and in Kindergarten, children are introduced to coins, and find the values of coin combinations.	In Unit 10, children calculate combinations of coins and dollar bills. In Grades 2–6, they count money and exchange coins.
8•2	To reinforce an understanding of money; to introduce dollars; and to facilitate the use of money to explore place value.	Earlier in Grade 1 and in Kindergarten, children are introduced to coins, and find the values of coin combinations.	In Units 9 and 10, children calculate combinations of coins and dollar bills and use manipulatives to represent whole numbers.
8•3	To extend place-value concepts to hundreds.	In Units 1, 4, and 5, children use base-10 blocks to explore place-value concepts. In Kindergarten, children explore place value using manipulatives.	In Grades 1–3, children learn to read, write, and model with manipulatives whole numbers.
8•4	To provide practice solving number stories that involve addition and subtraction.	In Units 1–5, children tell and solve number stories and are introduced to situation diagrams. Children begin telling number stories in Kindergarten.	In Unit 10, children solve number stories using situation diagrams. In Grade 2, children solve number stories.
8•5	To develop the use of counting up as a strategy for making change.	In Units 1–6, children practice counting up on the number line, number grid, and calculator. They practice counting up in Kindergarten.	In Unit 10 and in Grades 2 and 3, children will practice counting up to make change.
8•6	To guide exploration of dividing regions into equal parts.	In Units 3 and 5–7 and in Kindergarten, children covered shapes with pattern blocks. In Kindergarten, children are introduced to the concept of $\frac{1}{2}$.	Throughout Grades 1 and 2, children use manipulatives to model fractions, compare fractions, and explore equivalent fractions and non-unit fractions.
8•7	To guide further understanding of fractional parts of a whole; and to introduce unit fraction notation.	In Units 3 and 5–7 and in Kindergarten, children cover shapes with pattern blocks. In Kindergarten, children are introduced to the concept of $\frac{1}{2}$.	Throughout Grades 1 and 2, children use manipulatives to model fractions, compare fractions, and explore equivalent fractions and non-unit fractions.
8•8	To introduce finding fractional parts of collections.	In Units 3 and 5–7 and in Kindergarten, children cover shapes with pattern blocks. In Kindergarten, children are introduced to the concept of $\frac{1}{2}$.	Throughout Grades 1 and 2, children use manipulatives to model fractions, compare fractions, and explore equivalent fractions and non-unit fractions.
8•9	To guide exploration of the relationship between multiples and fractions; to reinforce naming fractional parts of regions; and to provide practice with addition facts.	In Units 3–7, children practice addition facts. In Kindergarten, children are introduced to the concept of $\frac{1}{2}$.	Throughout Grades 1 and 2, children use manipulatives to work with fractions. In these grades, children also practice all basic addition and subtraction facts.

Lesson	Key Concepts and Skills	Grade 1 Goals*
8•1	Express the value of combinations of coins.	Operations and Computation Goal 2
	Show amounts of money with the fewest number of coins.	Measurement and Reference Frames Goal 2
	Write number sentences using the symbols +, −, and =.	Patterns, Functions, and Algebra Goal 2
8•2	Express amounts of money using dollars-and-cents notation.	Number and Numeration Goal 3
	Identify a dollar and know its value.	Measurement and Reference Frames Goal 2
	Make exchanges between coins.	Measurement and Reference Frames Goal 2
8•3	Count collections of objects.	Number and Numeration Goal 2
	Read and write whole numbers modeled with base-10 blocks.	Number and Numeration Goal 3
8•4	Express amounts of money using dollars-and-cents notation.	Number and Numeration Goal 3
	Use a variety of strategies to add and subtract with 2-digit numbers.	Operations and Computation Goal 2
	Make up, solve, and record money number stories and discuss solution strategies.	Operations and Computation Goal 4
	Show amounts of money with the fewest number of coins.	Measurement and Reference Frames Goal 2
	Write number sentences to match solution strategies.	Patterns, Functions, and Algebra Goal 2
8•5	Make change by counting up.	Operations and Computation Goal 2
	Make up and solve number stories.	Operations and Computation Goal 4
	Identify the values of coins.	Measurement and Reference Frames Goal 2
8•6	Count equal parts of wholes.	Number and Numeration Goal 2
	Divide shapes into halves, thirds, and fourths.	Number and Numeration Goal 4
	Find objects divided into equal parts.	Number and Numeration Goal 4
8•7	Count equal parts of wholes.	Number and Numeration Goal 2
	Identify shapes divided into halves, thirds, and fourths.	Number and Numeration Goal 4
	Record the number of equal parts in a whole and label each part with a corresponding fraction.	Number and Numeration Goal 4
8•8	Count by halves, thirds, fourths, and sixths to 1.	Number and Numeration Goal 1
	Find fractional parts of sets.	Number and Numeration Goal 4
8•9	Use fractions to relate smaller shapes to larger shapes.	Number and Numeration Goal 4
	Divide shapes into equal parts and label the parts.	Number and Numeration Goal 4
	Recognize and sort doubles facts and near-doubles facts.	Operations and Computation Goal 1

*See the Appendix for a complete list of Grade 1 Goals.

A Balanced Curriculum

Ongoing Practice

Everyday Mathematics provides numerous opportunities for ongoing practice. These activities are embedded throughout the lessons:

Mental Math and Reflexes activities promote speed and accuracy in mental computation.

Math Boxes offer mixed practice and are paired across lessons as shown in the brackets below. This makes them useful as assessment tools. The last one or two boxes on each page preview the next unit's content.

Mixed practice	[8•1, 8•3], [8•2, 8•4], [8•5, 8•7, 8•9], [8•6, 8•8]
Mixed practice with multiple choice	8•3, 8•4, 8•6, 8•9
Mixed practice with writing/reasoning opportunity	8•1, 8•2, 8•6, 8•7

Home Links are daily homework assignments that review the content of the lesson and often contain ongoing facts practice.

Minute Math+ problems are offered for additional practice in Lessons 8•2, 8•7, and 8•8.

EM Facts Workshop Game provides online practice of basic facts and computation.

EXTRA PRACTICE **Extra Practice** activities are included in Lessons 8•1, 8•2, 8•3, 8•8, and 8•9.

Practice through Games

Games are an essential component of practice in the *Everyday Mathematics* program. Games offer skills practice and promote strategic thinking. See the *Differentiation Handbook* for ways to adapt games to meet children's needs.

Lesson	Game	Skill Practiced
8•1	*Coin Exchange*	Counting and exchanging coins [MRF Goal 2]
8•1	*Coin Top-It*	Calculating and comparing the values of combinations of coins [OC Goal 2]
8•2, 8•7	*One-Dollar Exchange*	Exchanging coins and bills [MRF Goal 2]
8•3	*Beat the Calculator*	Addition facts [OC Goal 2]
8•3	*Tric-Trac*	Addition facts [OC Goal 2]
8•4	*Base-10 Exchange*	Place value [NN Goal 3]
8•5, 8•9	*3, 2, 1 Game*	Subtraction [OC Goal 2]
8•5	*Difference Game*	Subtraction [OC Goal 2]
8•8	*Addition Top-It*	Finding and comparing sums [NN Goal 7 and OC Goal 2]

[NN] Number and Numeration
[MRF] Measurement and Reference Frames
[OC] Operations and Computation
[GEO] Geometry
[DC] Data and Chance
[PFA] Patterns, Functions, and Algebra

Problem Solving 

Good problem solvers use a variety of strategies, including the following:

- Draw a picture.
- Act out the problem.
- Make a table, chart, or list.
- Look for a pattern.
- Try a simpler version of the problem.
- Make a guess and try it out.

The table below lists some of the opportunities in this unit for children to practice these strategies.

Lessons that teach *through* problem solving, not just *about* problem solving

Lesson	Activity
8•2	Solve Broken Calculator puzzles.
8•4	Make up and solve number stories involving money.
8•5	Play the role of a shopkeeper and a shopper.
8•5, 8•9	Find a winning strategy for the *3, 2, 1 Game.*
8•6	Divide crackers equally among different numbers of people.
8•6	Solve "What's My Rule?" problems.
8•8	Solve problems involving the equal sharing of pennies.

See Chapter 18: Problem Solving in the *Teacher's Reference Manual* for more information.

The Language of Mathematics

Everyday Mathematics provides lesson-specific suggestions to help all children acquire, process, and express mathematical ideas. Throughout Unit 8, there are lesson-specific language development notes that address the needs of English language learners, indicated by ELL.

ELL SUPPORT Activities to support English language learners are in Part 3 of Lessons 8•2, 8•6, and 8•8.

The *English Learners Handbook* and the *Differentiation Handbook* have suggestions for promoting language development and acquisition of mathematics vocabulary. See Unit 8 in each handbook.

Unit 8 Vocabulary

decimal point
equal parts
fourths
fraction
fractional part
halves
hundreds
hundreds place
near doubles
ones
ones place
tens
tens place
thirds
to make change
whole

Literacy Connection

Lesson 8•2 *Follow the Money,* by Loreen Leedy, Holiday House, Inc., 2003

Lesson 8•6 *Ed Emberley's Picture Pie: A Cut and Paste Drawing Book,* by Ed Emberley, Little Brown & Co., 2006

For more literacy connections, see the *Home Connection Handbook,* Grades 1–3.

Cross-Curricular Links 

Social Studies

Lesson 8•1 Children explore foreign coins.

Lesson 8•5 Children discuss different types of stores and what they sell.

Art

Lesson 8•6 Children identify fractions on quilts.

Balanced Assessment

Daily Assessments

- **Recognizing Student Achievement** – A daily assessment that is included in every lesson to evaluate children's progress toward the Grade 1 Grade-Level Goals.
- **Informing Instruction** – Notes that appear throughout the unit to help anticipate children's common errors and suggest appropriate problem-solving strategies.

Lesson	Recognizing Student Achievement	Informing Instruction
8•1	Count money. [OC Goal 2]	
8•2	Write accurate number models using <, >, and =. [PFA Goal 2]	Exchange coins using a Place-Value Mat.
8•3	Model numbers with base-10 blocks. [NN Goal 3]	Name numbers shown with base-10 blocks.
8•4	Solve addition and subtraction facts. [OC Goal 1]	
8•5	Identify the tens digit in numbers. [NN Goal 3]	Make change by counting up.
8•6	Show equal parts. [NN Goal 4]	
8•7	Complete a symmetric shape. [GEO Goal 2]	Label fractional parts of geometric figures.
8•8	Determine the likelihood of spinning a certain number. [DC Goal 3]	
8•9	Name 2-dimensional shapes. [GEO Goal 1]	Create symmetric shapes on geoboards.

[NN] Number and Numeration
[MRF] Measurement and Reference Frames
[OC] Operations and Computation
[GEO] Geometry
[DC] Data and Chance
[PFA] Patterns, Functions, and Algebra

Portfolio Opportunities

The following lessons provide opportunities to gather samples of children's mathematical writings, drawings, and creations to add balance to the assessment process: Lessons 8•1, 8•2, 8•6, 8•7, 8•8, 8•9, and 8•10.

See pages 16 and 17 in the *Assessment Handbook* for more information about portfolios and how to use them.

Unit Assessment

Progress Check 8 – A cumulative assessment of concepts and skills taught in Unit 8 and in previous units, providing information for evaluating children's progress and planning for future instruction. These assessments include oral/slate, written, and open-response activities, as shown below in the sample Progress Check lesson opener.

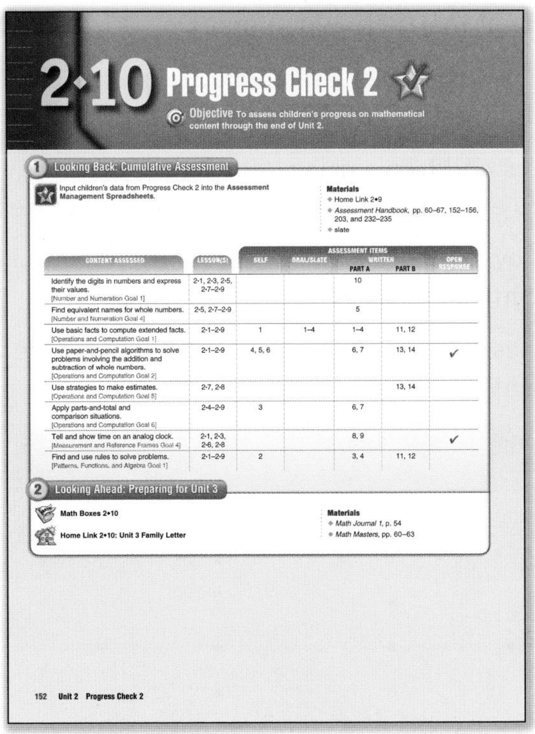

2·10 Progress Check 2

Objective To assess children's progress on mathematical content through the end of Unit 2.

1 Looking Back: Cumulative Assessment

Input children's data from Progress Check 2 into the **Assessment Management Spreadsheets.**

Materials
- Home Link 2•9
- *Assessment Handbook,* pp. 60–67, 152–156, 203, and 232–235
- slate

CONTENT ASSESSED	LESSON(S)	ASSESSMENT ITEMS				
		SELF	ORAL/SLATE	WRITTEN PART A	WRITTEN PART B	OPEN RESPONSE
Identify the digits in numbers and express their values. [Number and Numeration Goal 1]	2·1, 2·3, 2·5, 2·7–2·9			10		
Find equivalent names for whole numbers. [Number and Numeration Goal 4]	2·5, 2·7–2·9			5		
Use basic facts to compute extended facts. [Operations and Computation Goal 1]	2·1–2·9	1	1–4	1–4	11, 12	
Use paper-and-pencil algorithms to solve problems involving the addition and subtraction of whole numbers. [Operations and Computation Goal 2]	2·1–2·9	4, 5, 6		6, 7	13, 14	✓
Use strategies to make estimates. [Operations and Computation Goal 5]	2·7, 2·8				13, 14	
Apply parts-and-total and comparison situations. [Operations and Computation Goal 6]	2·4–2·9	3		6, 7		
Tell and show time on an analog clock. [Measurement and Reference Frames Goal 4]	2·1, 2·3, 2·6, 2·8			8, 9		✓
Find and use rules to solve problems. [Patterns, Functions, and Algebra Goal 1]	2·1–2·9	2		3, 4	11, 12	

2 Looking Ahead: Preparing for Unit 3

Math Boxes 2•10

Home Link 2•10: Unit 3 Family Letter

Materials
- *Math Journal 1,* p. 54
- *Math Masters,* pp. 60–63

152 Unit 2 Progress Check 2

Core Assessment Resources

Assessment Handbook

- **Unit 8 Assessment Overview,** pages 110–117
- **Unit 8 Assessment Masters,** pages 165–168
- **Unit 8 Individual Profiles of Progress,** pages 228, 229, and 248
- **Unit 8 Class Checklists,** pages 230, 231, and 249
- **Quarterly Checklist: Quarter 3,** pages 244 and 245
- **Math Logs,** pages 254–256
- **Exit Slip,** page 251
- **Other Student Assessment Forms,** pages 252, 253, 257, and 258

Assessment Management Spreadsheets

The Assessment Management Spreadsheets consist of the Digital Class Checklists and Individual Profile of Progress Checklists. Use them to monitor, record, and report children's progress.

Addressing All Needs

Differentiated Instruction

Adjusting the Activity – suggests adaptations that target advanced learners, English language learners, or learners who need additional instructional support.

ELL SUPPORT / **ELL** – provides lesson-specific suggestions to help English language learners understand and process the mathematical content.

READINESS – accesses children's prior knowledge or previews content that prepares children to engage in the lesson's Part 1 activities.

EXTRA PRACTICE – provides additional opportunities to apply the mathematical content of the lesson.

ENRICHMENT – enables children to apply or further explore the mathematical content of the lesson.

Lesson	Adjusting the Activity	ELL Support/ ELL	Readiness	Extra Practice	Enrichment
8•1	•		•	•	•
8•2		•	•	•	•
8•3	•	•	•	•	•
8•4	•	•	•		•
8•5	•	•	•		•
8•6	•	•			•
8•7	•	•	•		•
8•8	•	•		•	•
8•9	•	•	•	•	

Additional Resources

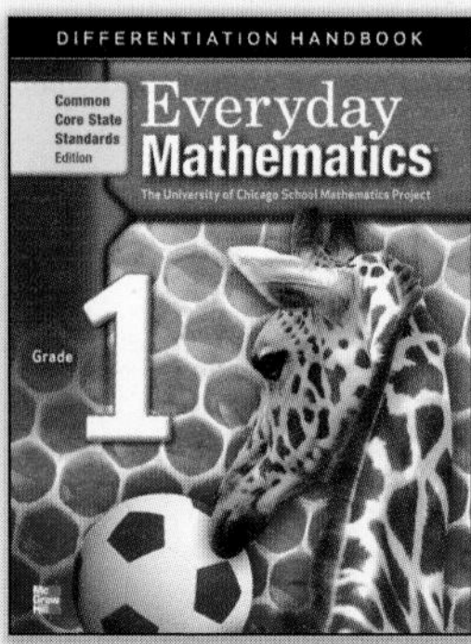

Differentiation Handbook
Provides ideas and strategies for differentiating instruction.
Pages 99–105

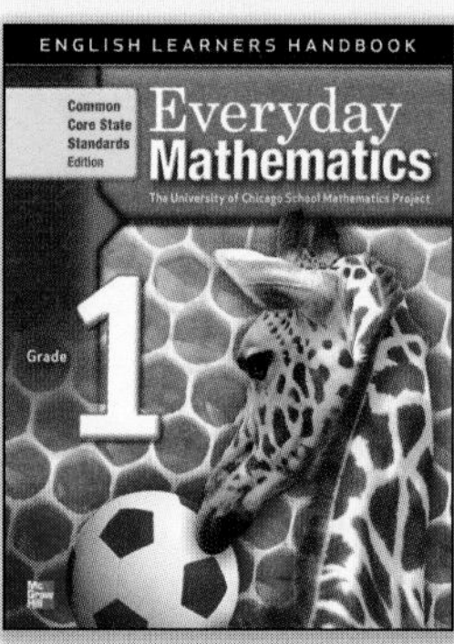

English Learners Handbook
Contains lesson-specific comprehension strategies.
Pages 85–93

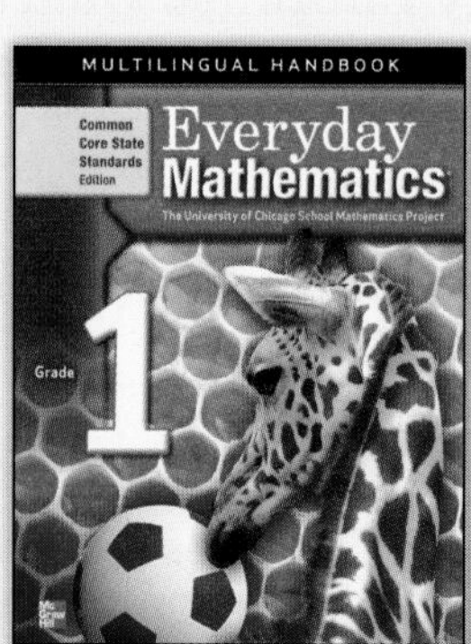

Multilingual Handbook
Previews concepts and vocabulary. It is written in six languages.
Pages 169–186

Planning Tips

Multiage Classroom

Companion Lessons from Grades K and 2 can help you meet instructional needs of a multiage classroom. The full Scope and Sequence can be found in the Appendix.

Grade K	6•1, 6•2, 6•7, 7•5, 8•7, 8•16	8•7, 8•8	7•5, 8•1	8•8	6•8, 8•8	6•11, 6•16	6•11, 6•16	6•1, 6•11	6•11, 6•16, 7•6
Grade 1	**8•1**	**8•2**	**8•3**	**8•4**	**8•5**	**8•6**	**8•7**	**8•8**	**8•9**
Grade 2	3•2, 3•8, 10•1	10•1, 10•6	3•1, 10•8–10•10	3•7, 11•1, 11•2	3•7, 3•8, 10•6	8•1, 8•2, 10•7	8•1, 8•2	7•5, 8•3	2•2, 2•3, 8•1–8•3

Pacing for Success

Pacing depends on a number of factors, such as children's individual needs and how long your school has been using *Everyday Mathematics*. At the beginning of Unit 8, you may want to use tools available at www.everydaymathonline.com to help you set your pace.

Home Support

Unit 8 Family Letter (English/Spanish) provides families with an overview, Do-Anytime Activities, Building Skills through Games, a list of vocabulary, and answers to the daily homework (Home Links). Family Letters in English, Spanish, and seven other languages are also available online.

Home Links are the daily homework assignments. They consist of active projects and ongoing review problems.

Home Support Resources

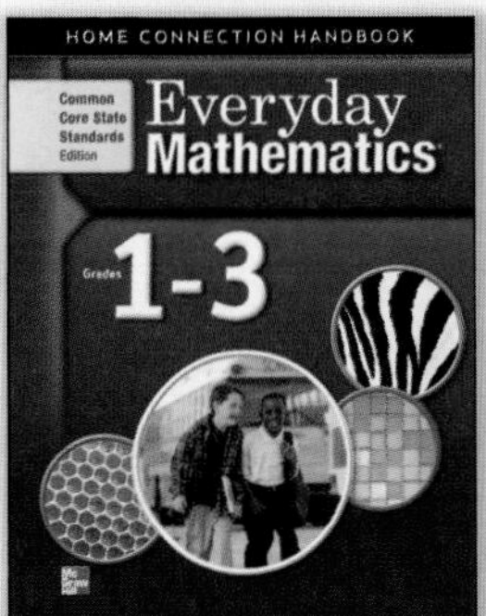

Home Connection Handbook
Offers ideas and reproducible masters for communicating with families. See Table of Contents for unit information.

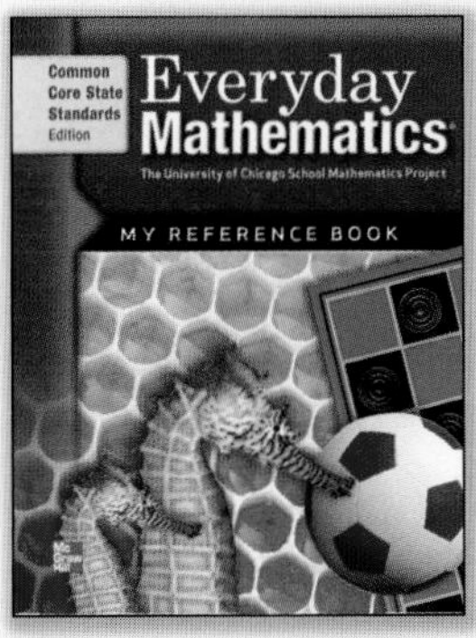

My Reference Book
Provides a resource for children and parents.
Pages 144, 145, 150, 151, 156–158

Technology Resources

Materials

Technology Resources www.everydaymathonline.com

ePresentations

eToolkit

Algorithms Practice

EM Facts Workshop Game™

Family Letters

Assessment Management

Common Core State Standards

Curriculum Focal Points

Interactive Teacher's Lesson Guide

Lesson	Masters	Manipulative Kit	Other Items
8•1	Home Link Masters, pp. 221 and 222 Teaching Aid Master, p. 328 Transparency of *Math Masters,* p. 329* Teaching Master, p. 223	base-10 blocks (flats, longs, and cubes); tool-kit coins; per partnership: 2 dice; polyhedral dice*; slate	Story of Money Poster; overhead coins*; Class Data Pad; stick-on notes; modified deck of *Coin Top-It* cards from Lesson 6•9; calculator
8•2	Teaching Masters, pp. 224 and 226 Teaching Aid Masters, pp. 331 and 332 Home Link Master, p. 225	tool-kit coins; per partnership: 2 dice; coin stamps*; slate	scissors; dollar bills; Story of Money Poster; enlarged copy of both sides of a dollar bill; calculator; per group: 1 magnifying lens
8•3	Teaching Master, p. 224 Transparency of *Math Masters,* p. 224* Home Link Master, p. 227 Game Master, p. 360	base-10 blocks; per partnership: 2 dice; 6 each of number cards 0–9	overhead base-10 blocks*; per partnership: 20 pennies; 3" by 5" index cards; calculator
8•4	Transparencies of *Math Masters,* pp. 228 and 229* Teaching Master, p. 224 Home Link Master, p. 230	tool-kit coins; base-10 blocks (flats, longs, and cubes); per partnership: 2 dice; slate; counters	overhead coins*; advertisements from discount stores; calculator
8•5	Transparencies of *Math Masters,* pp. 228, 229, and 231* Home Link Master, p. 232 Teaching Master, p. 233	tool-kit coins and bills; per partnership: 4 each of number cards 1–10; slate; counters*	calculator
8•6	Teaching Masters, pp. 234*, 235, and 237 Transparency of *Math Masters,* p. 231* Home Link Master, p. 236 *Differentiation Handbook,* p. 127	slate	fruit bars; scissors; glue or transparent tape; 2" by 2" color squares (two of each color per partnership: purple, red, and orange; three of each color per partnership: yellow and brown); per child: 1 measuring cup of dry cereal in a large bowl; measuring cups: $\frac{1}{2}$ cup, $\frac{1}{3}$ cup, and $\frac{1}{4}$ cup
8•7	Home Link Master, p. 238 Teaching Masters, pp. 226 and 239	per partnership: 2 dice	per partnership: 1 dollar, 20 dimes, and 20 pennies; paper shapes; calculator
8•8	Home Link Master, p. 240 *Differentiation Handbook,* p. 126	base-10 blocks; tool-kit pennies; 4 each of number cards 0–10	Pattern-Block Template*; per child: 12 one-inch paper squares in two colors; scissors*; glue
8•9	Teaching Masters, pp. 151, 241–243 Teaching Aid Masters, pp. 315 and 316 Home Link Master, p. 244	pattern blocks; geoboard; rubber bands (colored, if possible); slate	Pattern-Block Template; Fact Triangles; scissors; drawing paper
8•10	Assessment Masters, pp. 165–168 Home Link Masters, pp. 245–248	slate	

*Denotes optional materials

Mathematical Background

The discussion below highlights the major content ideas presented in Unit 8 and helps establish instructional priorities.

Counting Money and Exchanges

(Lessons 8◆1 and 8◆2)

In Units 2, 3, and 6, children became familiar with the coins we use, learned how to find the value of collections of coins, and learned how to represent amounts of money with different but equivalent combinations of coins. These skills are reviewed in Lesson 8-1 and extended to include dollars in Lesson 8-2. Children conduct a detailed examination of dollar bills and complete the Story of Money Poster.

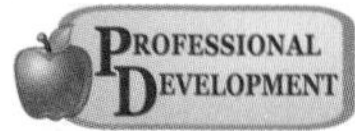

See Section 14.9 in the *Teacher's Reference Manual* for more information about money.

Place Value to Hundreds

(Lessons 8◆2–8◆4)

Formal study of place-value concepts was begun in Unit 5, when children used base-10 blocks to represent 1- and 2-digit numbers. In Lesson 8-2, children play *One-Dollar Exchange*—a game that involves exchanges with pennies, dimes, and dollars. In Lesson 8-3, they add flats (10-by-10 square blocks) to their collections of base-10 blocks and use flats, longs, and cubes to represent 3-digit numbers. Finally, in Lesson 8-4, they play the *Base-10 Exchange* game, which is played exactly like *One-Dollar Exchange,* except that base-10 blocks are used instead of money. This serves to reinforce the idea that the relationship between pennies, dimes, and dollars is the same as the relationship between ones, tens, and hundreds.

Working with money is an important part of the first-grade curriculum, since the ability to use money securely and efficiently is an important life skill. In *Everyday Mathematics,* money is also used as a meaningful aid to understanding place value. The relationship between money and place value will be revisited in later grades, when the digit in the tenths place in a decimal will be viewed as a certain number of dimes and the digit in the hundredths place as a number of pennies.

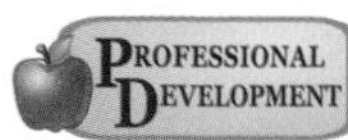

For more information about place-value concepts, see Section 9.2.1 in the *Teacher's Reference Manual.*

Money and Mental Arithmetic

(Lessons 8◆4 and 8◆5)

Children use School Store Mini-Posters and a Museum Store Mini-Poster as catalysts for posing number stories for the whole class to solve. The following routine for developing mental arithmetic skills with posters was introduced in Unit 2 and can be continued in this unit:

1. Children make up problems for the class to solve.
2. With a partner or individually, they devise solution strategies to solve the problems.
3. Children share their strategies. As they discuss their strategies, they record their procedures on the board, write a label in a unit box, and write a number model.
4. When appropriate, you can summarize problems with situation diagrams.

The children's strategies are "mental" strategies in the sense that they have not yet developed algorithmic methods for adding and subtracting multi-digit numbers. However, the strategies are not totally "mental" because children will use a variety of aids—counters, base-10 blocks, number lines and number grids, pictures, doodles, counting on fingers, and so on.

Sharing solution strategies is an important aspect of *Everyday Mathematics*. Sharing strategies in a friendly setting helps children become more comfortable verbalizing their thoughts and taking risks in expressing their own ideas. The strategies thus developed and expressed are often precursors for developing reliable procedures (algorithms) for adding and subtracting multidigit numbers, which is a main focus of *Second Grade Everyday Mathematics*.

Please encourage children to vary the types of number stories they tell. If the children get into a pattern of telling only one type of story, intervene and model some different types (change, parts-and-total, comparison) of addition and subtraction stories.

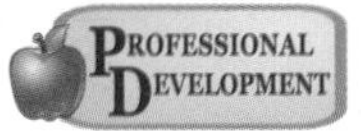

Consult Section 16.3 in the *Teacher's Reference Manual* for more about mental arithmetic strategies.

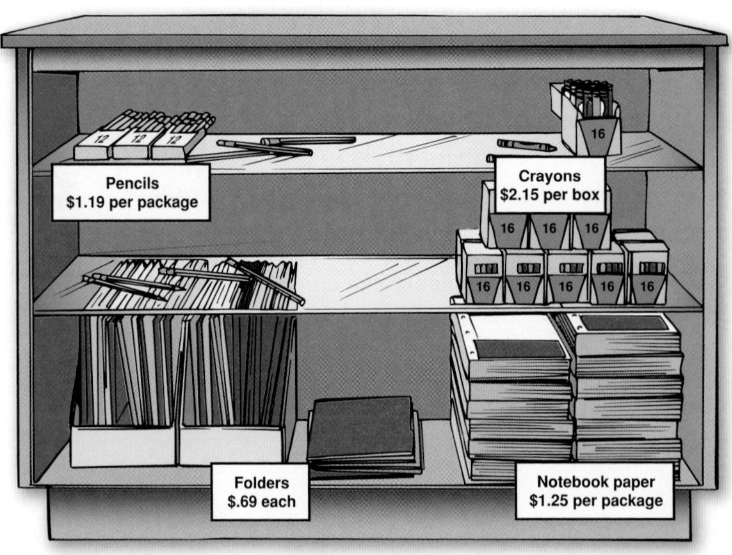

Making Change in Money Transactions (Lesson 8◆5)

Project Note

Use Project 8, A Flea Market, to provide opportunities for children to participate in buying-and-selling situations using coins.

In this lesson, children use one of the School Store Mini-Posters or the Museum Store Mini-Poster to practice counting up to make change while role-playing shopper and storekeeper.

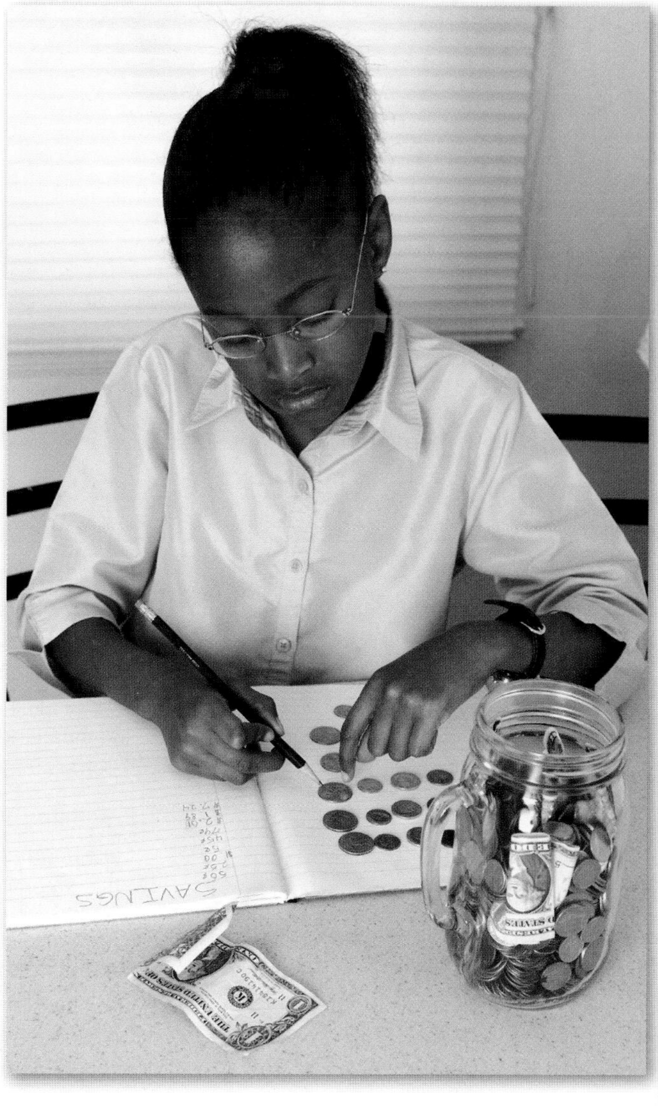

Making or getting change is a mysterious concept to many young children, and also to many adolescents and adults, as you may notice when making purchases in restaurants and stores. Indeed, because it is such a problem for so many people, most modern cash registers automatically calculate and display the change due the customer. But making change or checking whether you receive the correct change should not become a lost art, even apart from being a very useful school exercise in teaching the meanings of, and links between, addition and subtraction.

Fraction Concepts and Notation (Lessons 8◆6–8◆9)

In these lessons, children are reminded that fractions are equal parts of wholes. It is quite important for them to understand that fractions are usually meaningless without knowing the "whole" to which the fraction is linked. Examples make this obvious: A half-dollar and a half-million dollars are very different; half a doughnut doesn't have much to do with half a mile, and so on. This idea requires constant reminders and repeated experience before it can become thoroughly absorbed and utilized. Examples such as those just given can be used as Mental Math and Reflexes exercises on many occasions to foster this basic understanding.

These lessons remind children of some of the vocabulary associated with fractions, and of the links between written fraction notation and the vocabulary of fractions. In interviews with 4- to 9-year-old children, the authors were surprised both with how many young children responded correctly when asked to give us "half" of something and with how few children, younger or older, linked that understanding with the numeral "$\frac{1}{2}$." Just as learning to read involves associating words in the spoken language with marks on a page, we believe there are many mathematical ideas (including fractions) that also eventually need to be associated with the written symbols that express them.

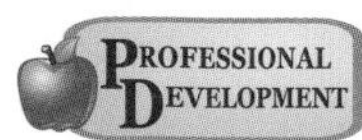

See Section 9.3 in the *Teacher's Reference Manual* for more information about fraction concepts.

8•1 Review Money

Objective To review, reinforce, and assess skills associated with counting and exchanging coins.

www.everydaymathonline.com

ePresentations

eToolkit

Algorithms Practice

EM Facts Workshop Game™

Family Letters

Assessment Management

Common Core State Standards

Curriculum Focal Points

Interactive Teacher's Lesson Guide

1 Teaching the Lesson

Key Concepts and Skills

- Express the value of combinations of coins. [Operations and Computation Goal 2]
- Show amounts of money with the fewest number of coins. [Measurement and Reference Frames Goal 2]
- Write number sentences using the symbols +, −, and =. [Patterns, Functions, and Algebra Goal 2]

Key Activities

Children count collections of quarters, dimes, nickels, and pennies and use them to show amounts of money. Children play *Coin Exchange.*

Ongoing Assessment: Recognizing Student Achievement
Use journal page 151.
[Operations and Computation Goal 2]

Materials

Math Journal 2, p. 151
base-10 blocks (flats, longs, and cubes) ◆ Story of Money Poster ◆ slate ◆ tool-kit coins ◆ per partnership: 2 dice ◆ overhead coins (optional) ◆ polyhedral dice (optional)

2 Ongoing Learning & Practice

Investigating Spinning Colors
Math Masters, p. 328; transparency of p. 329 (optional)
Class Data Pad ◆ stick-on notes
Children tally spinner results and find data landmarks based on their recorded information.

Practicing Telling Time
Math Journal 2, p. 152
Children practice telling time using analog and digital clocks.

Math Boxes 8•1
Math Journal 2, p. 153
Children practice and maintain skills through Math Box problems.

Home Link 8•1
Math Masters, pp. 221 and 222
Children practice and maintain skills through Home Link activities.

3 Differentiation Options

READINESS

Counting Coins with a Calculator
per partnership: calculator, tool-kit coins
Children count coins using a calculator.

ENRICHMENT

Solving Coin Riddles
Math Masters, p. 223
tool-kit coins
Children show amounts of money using specified numbers of coins.

EXTRA PRACTICE

Playing *Coin Top-It*
per partnership: modified deck of *Coin Top-It* cards from Lesson 6•9
Children practice comparing money amounts.

Advance Preparation

For the Investigating Spinning Colors activity in Part 2, make one spinner for each partnership using *Math Masters,* page 328. Use heavy paper or glue the spinner to a paper plate. Divide the spinner as follows: $\frac{1}{2}$ green, $\frac{1}{8}$ yellow, and $\frac{3}{8}$ red.

Getting Started

Mental Math and Reflexes

Display combinations of base-10 blocks on the overhead or on the board. On their slates, children write the number represented by the blocks. Begin with longs and cubes to represent 2-digit numbers, and then add flats for 3-digit numbers.

Option: Display two sets of base-10 blocks. Children write the numbers for each set on their slates and insert a < or > symbol. *For example:*

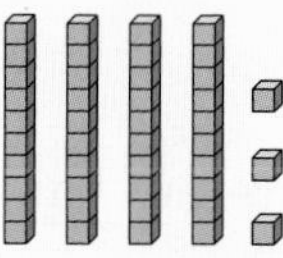
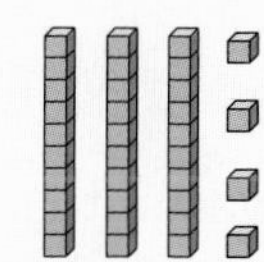

Children write 43 > 34.

Math Message

1 nickel = 5 *pennies*

1 dime = 10 *pennies*

1 quarter = 25 *pennies*

1 dime = 2 *nickels*

1 quarter = 5 *nickels*

1 Teaching the Lesson

▶ Math Message Follow-Up

WHOLE-CLASS DISCUSSION

Briefly go over the answers.

▶ Review Counting Combinations of Coins

WHOLE-CLASS ACTIVITY

Review the Story of Money Poster. Remind children to use it as a reference when counting coins.

Use overhead pennies, nickels, dimes, and quarters, or draw coin symbols on the board. Children count their own coins and write the total value using cents or dollar notation on their slates.

Suggestions:

▷ 2 dimes and 2 nickels 30¢ or \$0.30

▷ 1 quarter and 3 nickels 40¢ or \$0.40

▷ 2 quarters and 3 dimes 80¢ or \$0.80

▷ 3 quarters, 1 dime, and 3 nickels 100¢ or \$1.00

Do more problems as needed.

Adjusting the Activity

Suggest arranging the coins into groups of like coins. Then have children count the coins, starting with the coins of the greatest value.

AUDITORY ◆ KINESTHETIC ◆ TACTILE ◆ VISUAL

Interactive whiteboard-ready ePresentations are available at www.everydaymathonline.com to help you teach the lesson.

▶ Showing an Amount of Money

Write an amount such as 38¢ on the board. Have children show that amount with coins. List their solutions on the board. For 38¢, there are many possibilities, including the following:

- ▷ Ⓓ Ⓓ Ⓓ Ⓝ Ⓟ Ⓟ Ⓟ
- ▷ Ⓓ Ⓓ Ⓝ Ⓝ Ⓝ Ⓟ Ⓟ Ⓟ
- ▷ Ⓓ Ⓝ Ⓝ Ⓝ Ⓝ Ⓝ Ⓟ Ⓟ Ⓟ
- ▷ Ⓝ Ⓝ Ⓝ Ⓝ Ⓝ Ⓝ Ⓝ Ⓟ Ⓟ Ⓟ

If no one suggests it, ask children to show the amount using the fewest number of coins. 38¢: Ⓠ Ⓓ Ⓟ Ⓟ Ⓟ

▶ Playing *Coin Exchange*

Children practice counting and exchanging coins by playing *Coin Exchange*. For detailed instructions, see Lesson 6-10. To extend this activity, have children play with a larger bank and two polyhedral dice.

▶ Finding Values of Sets of Coins

(*Math Journal 2,* p. 151)

Partners complete the journal page.

Ongoing Assessment: Recognizing Student Achievement

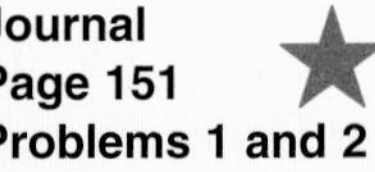

Journal Page 151 Problems 1 and 2

Use **journal page 151, Problems 1 and 2** to assess children's ability to count money. Children are making adequate progress if they are able to correctly answer the first two problems. Some children may have success with the remaining problems.

[Operations and Computation Goal 2]

Social Studies Link Invite children to bring foreign coins to school. Use a newspaper or Web site to find the approximate exchange rate between U.S. currency and a foreign currency. Determine how many foreign coins are about equal to one dollar.

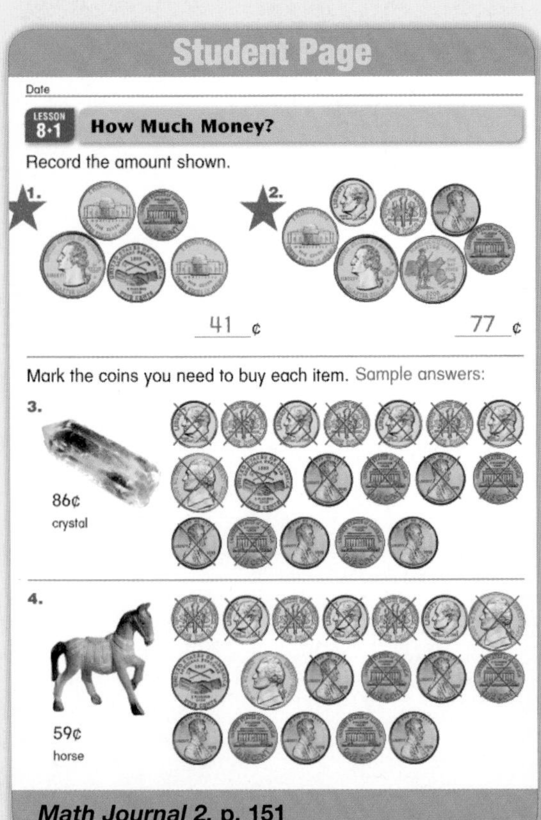

Math Journal 2, p. 151

2 Ongoing Learning & Practice

▶ Investigating Spinning Colors

 PARTNER ACTIVITY

(*Math Masters,* pp. 328 and 329)

Partnerships spin the green, yellow, and red spinner 25 times, recording in a tally chart how many times the spinner lands on each color.

When children have finished collecting their data, draw a class tally chart on the Class Data Pad showing how many times the spinner landed on green. Once the tally chart is complete, make a bar graph of the class results on the Class Data Pad or on an overhead transparency of *Math Masters,* page 329. Discuss the data landmarks for the graph. Ask: *What are the maximum and minimum numbers of times the spinner landed on green? What is the range? The middle value?* Use stick-on notes, as taught in Lesson 6-12, for finding the middle value.

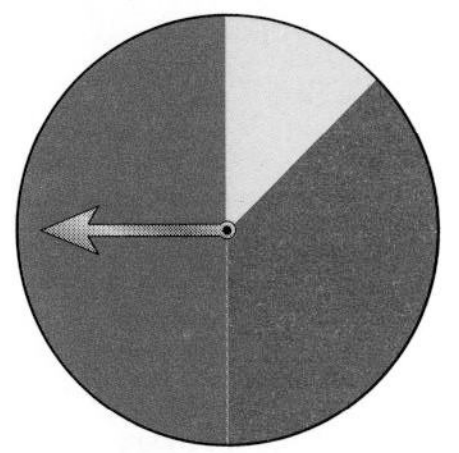

Green	~~////~~ ~~////~~ ///
Red	~~////~~ ///
Yellow	////

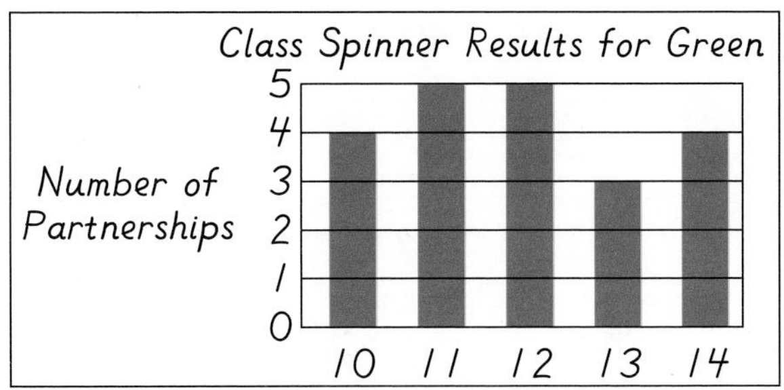

Adjusting the Activity

Divide the class into two groups. Have one group collect data about how many times each partnership landed on yellow. Then ask them to make a tally chart and a bar graph and to find the data landmarks for the information they gathered. Have the other group do the same for red spins.

AUDITORY ◆ KINESTHETIC ◆ TACTILE ◆ VISUAL

NOTE While this activity focuses on finding data landmarks, you may wish to discuss with children the probability of landing on each color.

Teaching Aid Master

Name Date

Spinner

1. Copy and cut out the spinner. Use heavy paper or glue the spinner to cardboard.
2. Divide the spinner into 2 or more regions.
3. Point a pencil to the dot in the center of the spinner.
4. Spin a paper clip around the pencil.

Math Masters, **p. 328**

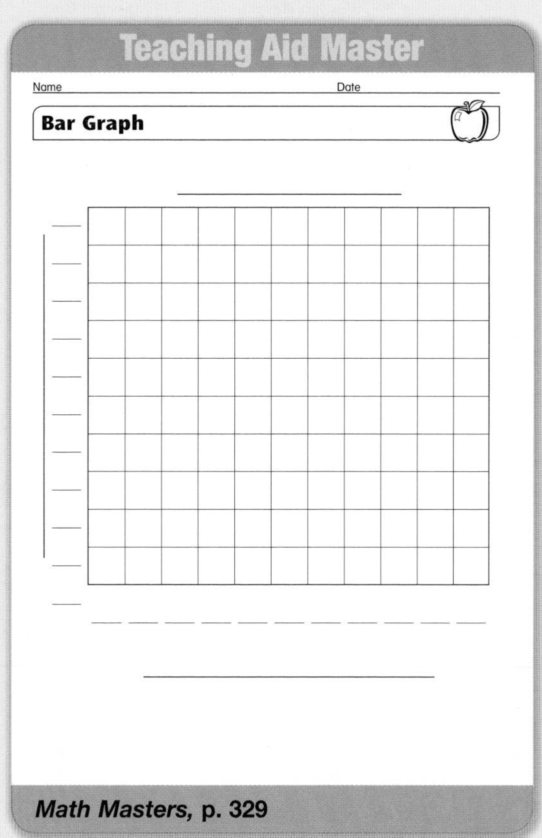

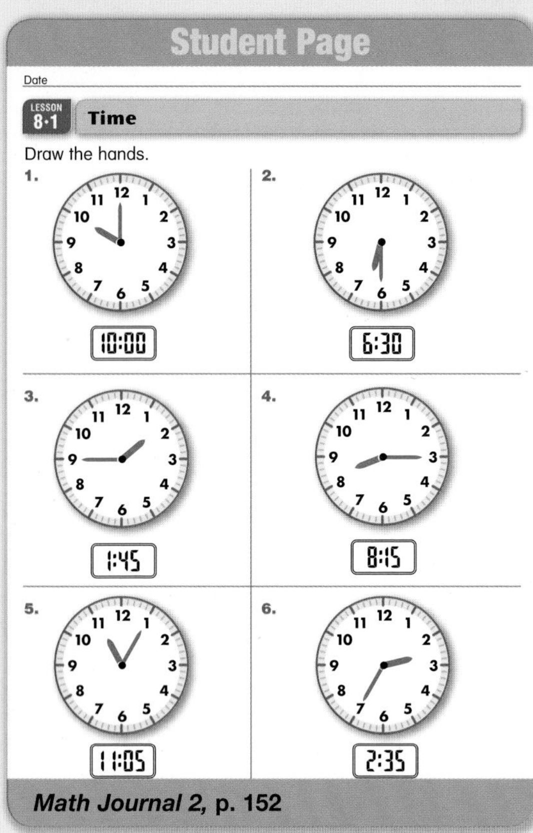
Student Page

Date

LESSON 8·1 Time

Draw the hands.

1. 10:00
2. 6:30
3. 1:45
4. 8:15
5. 11:05
6. 2:35

Math Journal 2, p. 152

▶ Practicing Telling Time

INDEPENDENT ACTIVITY

(*Math Journal 2,* p. 152)

Use journal page 152 to provide practice telling time on analog and digital clocks.

▶ Math Boxes 8·1

INDEPENDENT ACTIVITY

(*Math Journal 2,* p. 153)

Mixed Practice Math Boxes in this lesson are paired with Math Boxes in Lesson 8-3. The skills in Problem 4 preview Unit 9 content.

Writing/Reasoning Have children draw, write, or verbalize an answer to the following question: *Why is it important to know addition facts?* A reasonable answer should discuss solving addition problems with speed and accuracy. Sample answer: Addition problems are basic. To do them you need fact power.

▶ Home Link 8·1

INDEPENDENT ACTIVITY

(*Math Masters,* pp. 221 and 222)

Home Connection Children practice finding the values of combinations of coins in preparation for counting amounts of money that include dollars.

NOTE Point out to children the different nickel heads shown on *Math Masters,* page 221. Explain that they are both pictures of Thomas Jefferson and that both kinds of nickels are worth 5 cents.

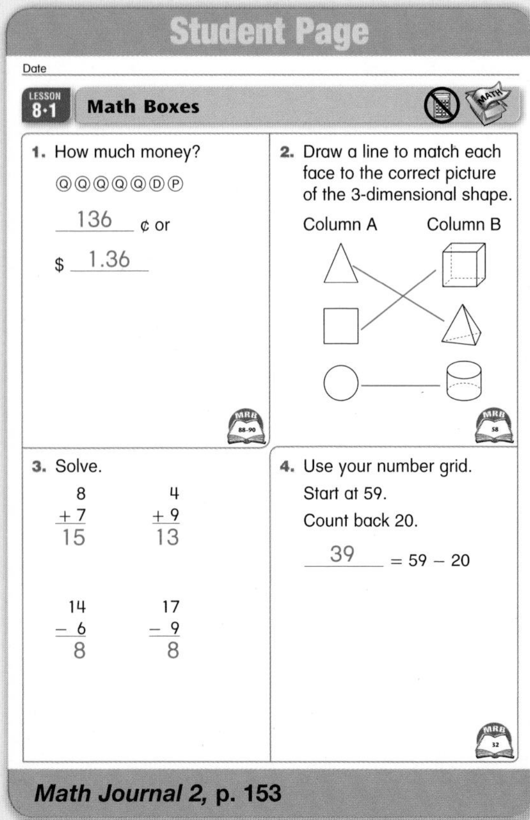
Student Page

Date

LESSON 8·1 Math Boxes

1. How much money?
Ⓠ Ⓠ Ⓠ Ⓠ Ⓠ Ⓓ Ⓟ
136 ¢ or
\$ 1.36

2. Draw a line to match each face to the correct picture of the 3-dimensional shape.
Column A Column B

3. Solve.
8 + 7 = 15
4 + 9 = 13
14 − 6 = 8
17 − 9 = 8

4. Use your number grid.
Start at 59.
Count back 20.
39 = 59 − 20

Math Journal 2, p. 153

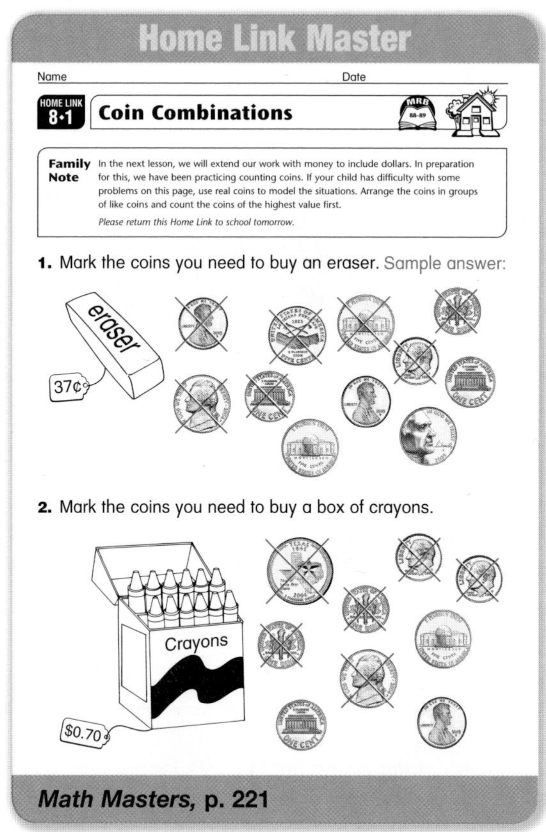
Home Link Master

Name Date

HOME LINK 8·1 Coin Combinations

Family Note In the next lesson, we will extend our work with money to include dollars. In preparation for this, we have been practicing counting coins. If your child has difficulty with some problems on this page, use real coins to model the situations. Arrange the coins in groups of like coins and count the coins of the highest value first.

Please return this Home Link to school tomorrow.

1. Mark the coins you need to buy an eraser. Sample answer:

2. Mark the coins you need to buy a box of crayons.

Math Masters, p. 221

3 Differentiation Options

READINESS

PARTNER ACTIVITY

5–15 Min

Counting Coins with a Calculator

To provide experience counting coin combinations, have children find the values of groups of coins using a calculator. Children take a small collection of pennies. They program their calculators to count by 1s. As one partner counts each penny, the other child counts on the calculator at the same time. Repeat using nickels, dimes, and quarters, having partners switch roles. The calculator must be reprogrammed each time to count by the correct amount.

ENRICHMENT

INDEPENDENT ACTIVITY

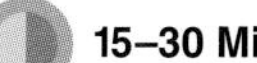

15–30 Min

Solving Coin Riddles

(*Math Masters,* p. 223)

To apply children's knowledge of counting coin combinations, have them solve coin riddles and make up their own riddles for classmates to solve. Children may use their tool-kit coins to help solve the problems.

EXTRA PRACTICE

PARTNER ACTIVITY

5–15 Min

Playing *Coin Top-It*

Children play *Coin Top-It* to practice comparing money amounts. For detailed instructions, see Lesson 2-13.

Planning Ahead

You will need several dollar bills for Lesson 8-2.

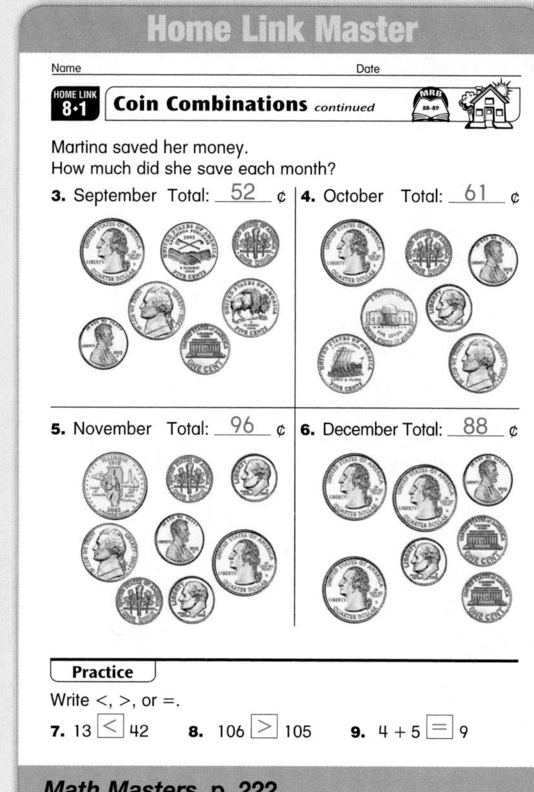

Home Link Master

Name Date

HOME LINK 8•1 **Coin Combinations** *continued*

Martina saved her money.
How much did she save each month?

3. September Total: 52 ¢
4. October Total: 61 ¢
5. November Total: 96 ¢
6. December Total: 88 ¢

Practice

Write <, >, or =.

7. 13 < 42
8. 106 > 105
9. 4 + 5 = 9

Math Masters, p. 222

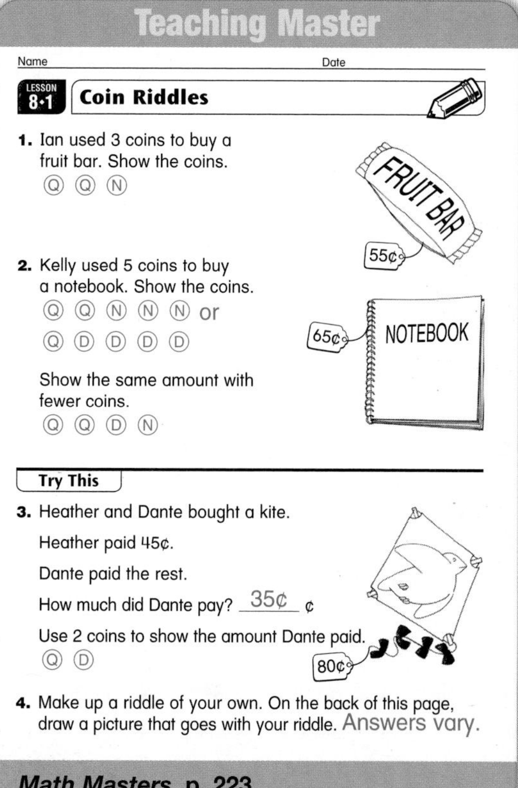

Teaching Master

Name Date

LESSON 8•1 **Coin Riddles**

1. Ian used 3 coins to buy a fruit bar. Show the coins.
Ⓠ Ⓠ Ⓝ

2. Kelly used 5 coins to buy a notebook. Show the coins.
Ⓠ Ⓠ Ⓝ Ⓝ Ⓝ or
Ⓠ Ⓓ Ⓓ Ⓓ Ⓓ

Show the same amount with fewer coins.
Ⓠ Ⓠ Ⓓ Ⓝ

Try This

3. Heather and Dante bought a kite.
Heather paid 45¢.
Dante paid the rest.
How much did Dante pay? 35¢ ¢
Use 2 coins to show the amount Dante paid.
Ⓠ Ⓓ

4. Make up a riddle of your own. On the back of this page, draw a picture that goes with your riddle. Answers vary.

Math Masters, p. 223

8•2 Dollars

Objectives To reinforce an understanding of money; to introduce dollars; and to facilitate the use of money to explore place value.

www.everydaymathonline.com

ePresentations

eToolkit

Algorithms Practice

EM Facts Workshop Game™

Family Letters

Assessment Management

Common Core State Standards

Curriculum Focal Points

Interactive Teacher's Lesson Guide

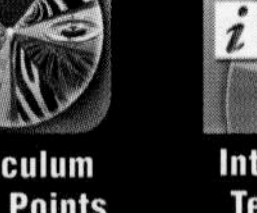

1 Teaching the Lesson

Key Concepts and Skills

- Express amounts of money using dollars-and-cents notation.
  [Number and Numeration Goal 3]
- Identify a dollar and know its value.
  [Measurement and Reference Frames Goal 2]
- Make exchanges between coins.
  [Measurement and Reference Frames Goal 2]

Key Activities

Children examine a dollar bill. They review dollars-and-cents notation. Then they show various amounts of money with dollar bills and coins. They play *One-Dollar Exchange* to practice exchanging pennies for a dime and dimes for a dollar.

Ongoing Assessment: Recognizing Student Achievement Use Mental Math and Reflexes.
[Patterns, Functions, and Algebra Goal 2]

Ongoing Assessment: Informing Instruction See page 685.

Key Vocabulary

decimal point

Materials

Math Masters, pp. 224, 331, and 332
Home Link 8•1
My Reference Book, pp. 144 and 145
slate ◆ scissors ◆ dollar bills ◆ Story of Money Poster ◆ tool-kit coins ◆ per group: magnifying lens ◆ per partnership: 2 dice

2 Ongoing Learning & Practice

Solving Broken Calculator Puzzles

calculator
Children solve Broken Calculator puzzles.

Practicing Comparing Money Amounts

Math Journal 2, p. 154
Children practice comparing money amounts.

Math Boxes 8•2

Math Journal 2, p. 155
Children practice and maintain skills through Math Box problems.

Home Link 8•2

Math Masters, p. 225
Children practice and maintain skills through Home Link activities.

3 Differentiation Options

READINESS

Exchanging Coins

Math Masters, p. 226
Children explore relationships with coin values.

ENRICHMENT

Making a Dollar Book

tool-kit coins ◆ coin stamps (optional)
Children make a Dollar Book.

EXTRA PRACTICE

Minute Math+

Minute Math®+, p. 68
Children practice counting money.

ELL SUPPORT

Examining a Dollar Bill

enlarged copy of both sides of a dollar bill ◆ poster board (optional) ◆ transparency (optional)
Children discuss features of a dollar bill.

Advance Preparation

For Part 1, children need to cut out the dollar bills from *Math Masters,* pages 331 and 332. You may wish to obtain the book ***Follow the Money*** by Loreen Leedy (Holiday House, Inc., 2003) as it relates to lesson content.

***Teacher's Reference Manual,* Grades 1–3** pp. 59, 60, 165

Getting Started

Mental Math and Reflexes ★

Dictate pairs of numbers. Children write the numbers on their slates and then write <, >, or = between them.

Suggestions:

●○○ 25, 30 25 < 30; 49, 49 49 = 49; 54, 62 54 < 62

●●○ 77, 87 77 < 87; 90, 89 90 > 89; 95, 100 95 < 100

●●● 102, 120 102 < 120; 135, 140 135 < 140; 162, 126 162 > 126

Math Message

(Place the class bank near the Math Message.)

Cut out the dollar bills from Math Masters, *pages 331 and 332. Put 5 bills in your money holder and the rest in the class bank.*

Home Link 8•1 Follow-Up

Go over the answers to Problems 1–6.

Ongoing Assessment: Recognizing Student Achievement

Mental Math and Reflexes ★

Use **Mental Math and Reflexes** to assess children's ability to compare numbers using <, >, and =. Children are making adequate progress if they are able to write accurate number models using <, >, and =.

[Patterns, Functions, and Algebra Goal 2]

1 Teaching the Lesson

▶ Math Message Follow-Up

WHOLE-CLASS DISCUSSION

Check that each child has 5 one-dollar bills. *How many pennies equal $1.00?* 100 *How many pennies equal $5.00?* 500

▶ Examining a Dollar Bill

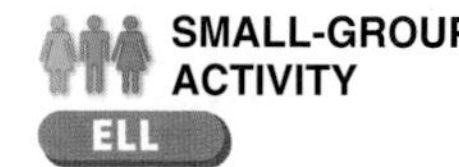

SMALL-GROUP ACTIVITY

ELL

Discuss what children know about a dollar bill. Then distribute a real dollar bill to each small group to examine closely with a magnifying lens as you discuss details. Record that information on the Story of Money poster, begun in Lesson 2-8. Make sure that each child has the opportunity to handle a real bill.

Mention the following information about the dollar. As you discuss it, write it on the board to support English language learners.

▷ The front of the bill shows a picture of George Washington. *Which coin shows George Washington?* quarter

▷ Each dollar bill has its own serial number.

▷ The seal to the left of the picture of George Washington identifies the branch of the Federal Reserve Bank that issued that particular dollar.

▷ On the right is the seal of the Treasury Department.

Teaching Aid Master

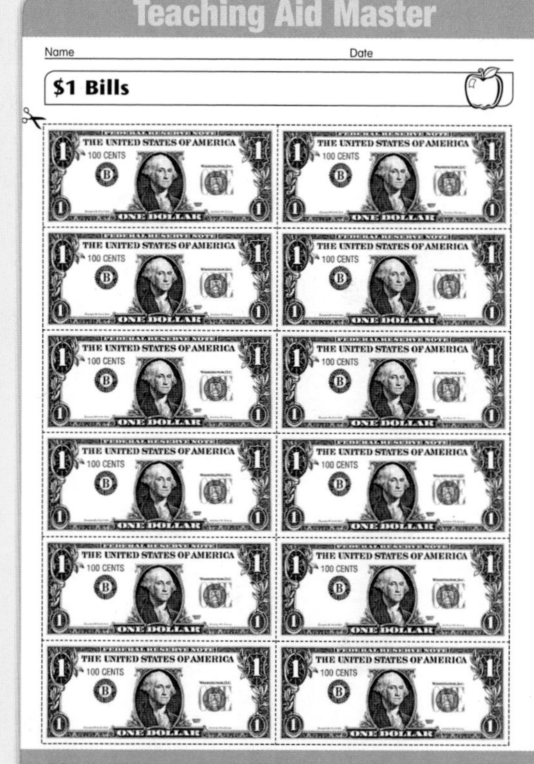

Math Masters, p. 331

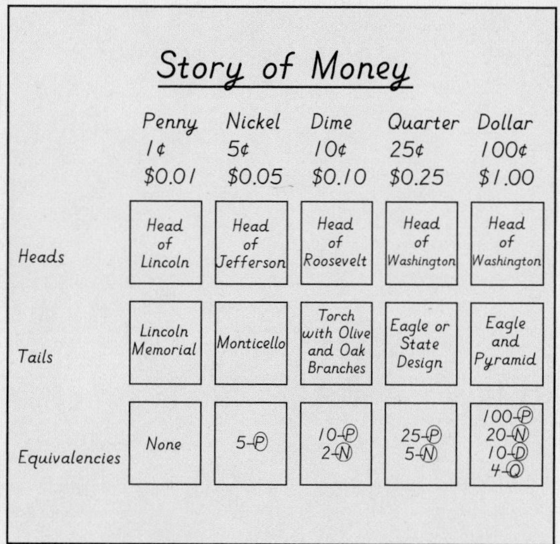

Story of Money

	Penny	Nickel	Dime	Quarter	Dollar
	1¢	5¢	10¢	25¢	100¢
	$0.01	$0.05	$0.10	$0.25	$1.00
Heads	Head of Lincoln	Head of Jefferson	Head of Roosevelt	Head of Washington	Head of Washington
Tails	Lincoln Memorial	Monticello	Torch with Olive and Oak Branches	Eagle or State Design	Eagle and Pyramid
Equivalencies	None	5-Ⓟ	10-Ⓟ 2-Ⓝ	25-Ⓟ 5-Ⓝ	100-Ⓟ 20-Ⓝ 10-Ⓓ 4-Ⓠ

The Story of Money Poster

- ▷ The reverse side shows both sides of the great seal of the United States. The front of the seal (on the right) shows an eagle clutching 13 arrows and an olive branch. The arrows stand for the preparedness of the original colonies to fight for their independence, and the olive branch represents their desire for peace. The back of the seal (on the left) shows a 13-step pyramid. The Roman numeral MDCCLXXVI (1776) is displayed on the base.

▶ Discussing the Purchasing Power of a Dollar

Ask children to name things they think can be bought for one dollar. Expect considerable variation in their responses due to the differences in their experiences with money.

Make sure each child has one dollar. Have children count the total number of dollars for the whole class. Write the amount on the board. *What do you think we could buy for that amount?*

Next, review how many coins of each type are equivalent to a dollar. To support English language learners, write each question and its answer on the board. *How many pennies [nickels, dimes, quarters] are equal to a dollar?* 100; 20; 10; 4

▶ Using Money Notation and Vocabulary

Review dollars-and-cents notation. Write $1.25 on the board and label it with the following:

- ▷ The symbol "$" stands for the word *dollar.*
- ▷ The period before the last two numbers is called a **decimal point.**
- ▷ The numbers that come before the decimal point are dollar amounts. The numbers that come after the decimal point are numbers of cents.
- ▷ $1.25 is read as "one dollar and 25 cents." Mention commonly used alternatives like "a dollar twenty-five" or "a dollar and a quarter." Write all three on the board to support English language learners. Emphasize that $1.25 is greater than 1 dollar.

Mention that an amount with zero before the decimal point, such as \$0.62, is less than one dollar. It can be written with a cent symbol as 62¢.

Write various amounts on the board. Have children use their play dollar bills and coins to show the amounts. Ask them to say each amount. *Suggestions:* \$5.43; \$2.26; \$1.10; \$1.01; \$0.57; \$0.08; \$1.36.

Encourage children to say the amounts as "one dollar and ten cents," "five dollars and forty-three cents," and so on, with the word *and* indicating the decimal point. Ask: *Why do people use paper money as well as coins?* Paper money takes up less space. If people used only coins, larger numbers of coins would be very heavy and would take up a lot of space.

▶ Introducing *One-Dollar Exchange*

PARTNER ACTIVITY

(*Math Masters,* p. 224; *My Reference Book,* pp. 144 and 145)

Ask children to look at the Place-Value Mat on *Math Masters*, p. 224. Point out that it is the same as the Place-Value Mat they used before, except that money units have been added in the headings. Discuss how the relationship of flats to longs to cubes is the same as the relationship of dollars to dimes to pennies.

Introduce *One-Dollar Exchange*. For directions, see the *My Reference Book,* pages 144 and 145.

Ongoing Assessment: Informing Instruction

Watch for children who make errors exchanging coins on their Place-Value Mats. You may want to prepare multiple copies of a Place-Value Mat with 10 circles in each of the pennies and dimes columns. Tell children to cover the circles with coins from the bank. When they have covered 10 circles in a column, they should exchange the coins for the next higher coin or bill.

Links to the Future

Children are gaining additional exposure to dollars-and-cents notation in this lesson. The Grade 2 Goals include making exchanges between coins and bills and reading and writing numbers in dollars-and-cents notation.

Teaching Master

Name Date

LESSON 8·2 **Place-Value Mat**

\$1.00 100¢ Dollars 100s Flats	\$0.10 10¢ Dimes 10s Longs	\$0.01 1¢ Pennies 1s Cubes

Math Masters, p. 224

Student Page

Games

One-Dollar Exchange

Materials ❑ 1 dollar, 20 dimes, 20 pennies
❑ 1 Place-Value Mat per player
❑ 2 six-sided dice
❑ 1 sheet of paper labeled "Bank"

Players 2

Skill Coin and bill equivalencies

Object of the game To make the exchange for a dollar.

Directions

1. Place all of the money in the "Bank."
2. Players take turns. When it is your turn.
   - Roll the dice and find the total number of dots.
   - Take that number of cents from the bank and place the coins on the Place-Value Mat.
   - If there are 10 or more pennies in the Pennies column, exchange 10 pennies for 1 dime. Place the dime in the Dimes column.
   - If there are 10 or more dimes in the Dimes column, exchange 10 dimes for 1 dollar.

My Reference Book, pp. 144 and 145

Date

LESSON 8·2 Comparing Money Amounts

Write <, >, or =.

< is less than
= is equal to
> is greater than

1. 2 dimes < $0.25
2. 50¢ > 5 pennies
3. 4 quarters = 100¢
4. 100¢ = 20 nickels
5. $1.25 > 120¢
6. $1.75 = 7 quarters
7. 200¢ > 10 dimes and 10 nickels
8. $1.44 = 1 dollar, 4 dimes, and 4 pennies

Math Journal 2, p. 154

NOTE Remember to use the Dice-Roll Activity on a regular basis to practice fact strategies. See Lesson 5-10 for detailed instructions. When your class is ready, you may wish to try some of the variations listed in Lesson 5-10.

Student Page

Date

LESSON 8·2 Math Boxes

1. Use [$1], Ⓠ, Ⓓ, Ⓝ, and Ⓟ to show this amount.
$3.49
Sample answer.
[$1] [$1] [$1] Ⓠ Ⓓ Ⓝ Ⓝ Ⓟ Ⓟ Ⓟ Ⓟ

2. This is a picture of a shape. Circle the name of the shape.
(prism) pyramid

3. Subtract.

18	12
− 9	− 8
9	4

15	10
− 7	− 7
8	3

4. Add.
57

Math Journal 2, p. 155

2 Ongoing Learning & Practice

▶ Solving Broken Calculator Puzzles

Have children imagine that the 4-key on their calculator is broken—when they press 4, nothing happens. Ask them to try to get the number 14 to appear in the calculator display without pressing the "broken" 4-key. Begin by having children press the 11 [+] 3 [=] keys to show one way to make 14 appear in the calculator display.

Have children share their strategies.

Possible solutions:

- ▷ 5 [+] 9 [=]
- ▷ 12 [−] 6 [+] 8 [=]
- ▷ 2 [+] 2 [+] 2 [+] 2 [+] 2 [+] 2 [+] 2 [=]

Continue to pose other Broken Calculator puzzles.

▶ Practicing Comparing Money Amounts

INDEPENDENT ACTIVITY

(*Math Journal 2,* p. 154)

Use journal page 154 to provide practice comparing money amounts.

▶ Math Boxes 8·2

INDEPENDENT ACTIVITY

(*Math Journal 2,* p. 155)

Mixed Practice Math Boxes in this lesson are paired with Math Boxes in Lesson 8-4. The skills in Problem 4 preview Unit 9 content.

Writing/Reasoning Have children draw, write, or verbalize an answer to the following question: *What is a prism?* A reasonable answer should mention that a prism is a shape with flat faces.

▶ Home Link 8•2

INDEPENDENT ACTIVITY

(*Math Masters,* p. 225)

Home Connection Children show how to pay for various items with combinations of dollar bills and/or coins.

3 Differentiation Options

READINESS

PARTNER ACTIVITY

▶ Exchanging Coins

5–15 Min

(*Math Masters,* p. 226)

To explore the relationships between the values of coins, have children work with a partner to make and record coin exchanges. As children are completing *Math Masters,* page 226, encourage them to model the statements with coins.

ENRICHMENT

INDEPENDENT ACTIVITY

▶ Making a Dollar Book

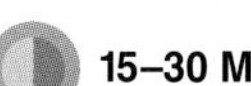

15–30 Min

Portfolio Ideas

To further explore the value of a dollar, have children show combinations of coins that total one dollar. On quarter-sheets of paper, they use coin stamps or draw Ⓟs, Ⓝs, Ⓓs, and Ⓠs. Each quarter-sheet of paper should show a different combination of coins equaling one dollar. Assemble the quarter-sheets into a Dollar Book.

EXTRA PRACTICE

SMALL-GROUP ACTIVITY

▶ *Minute Math+*

5–15 Min

Use *Minute Math+*, page 68, to provide practice finding money amounts over time and with different coins.

ELL SUPPORT

SMALL-GROUP ACTIVITY

▶ Examining a Dollar Bill

5–15 Min

To provide language support for money, discuss features of the dollar bill. Make enlarged copies of both sides of a dollar bill and display them on a poster or on an overhead transparency. Discuss different features of the dollar bill, such as the serial number and the seals. Point to each feature, talk about it, and label the poster or transparency. Include in the discussion the following facts: George Washington was the first president of the United States, the year 1776 was significant in our country's history, and the United States had colonies prior to states.

Home Link Master

Name Date

HOME LINK 8•2 **Dollars and More**

Family Note Today we took a close look at a dollar bill. Since we have only begun to work with dollars, some of the problems on this page may be difficult for your child. If possible, use real money to model the problems. Start by counting the bills and coins in the example with your child.

Please return this Home Link to school tomorrow.

Show how you would pay for each item. Use $1, Ⓠ, Ⓓ, Ⓝ, or Ⓟ.

Example: $1.95 MYSTERY — $1 Ⓠ Ⓠ Ⓠ Ⓓ Ⓓ

1. $2.85 — Sample answer: $1 $1 Ⓠ Ⓠ Ⓠ Ⓓ

2. $3.24 — Sample answer: $1 $1 $1 Ⓓ Ⓓ Ⓟ Ⓟ Ⓟ Ⓟ

3. Write this amount in two ways.

Ⓠ Ⓠ Ⓝ Ⓓ Ⓝ Ⓓ Ⓟ Ⓓ Ⓓ Ⓓ

Total: 111 ¢ $ 1.11

Show this amount using fewer coins.

Sample answer: Ⓠ Ⓠ Ⓠ Ⓠ Ⓓ Ⓟ

Practice

4. Circle the tens place. Is the number odd or even?

86 even

***Math Masters,* p. 225**

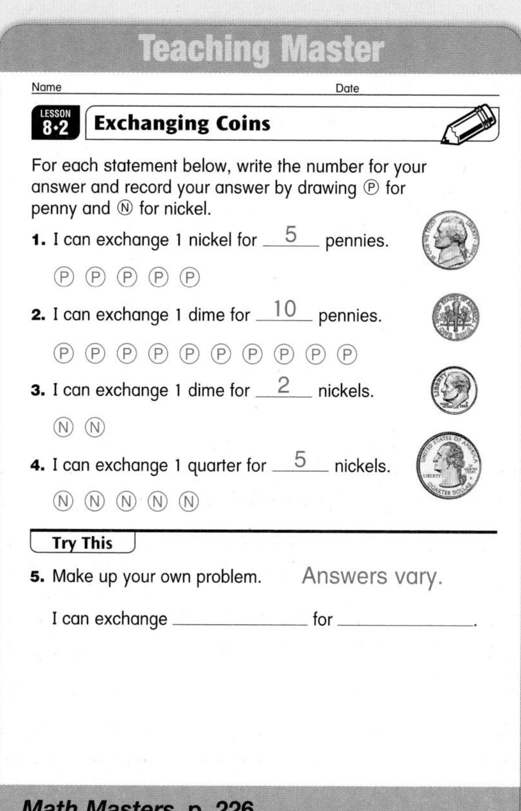

Teaching Master

Name Date

LESSON 8•2 **Exchanging Coins**

For each statement below, write the number for your answer and record your answer by drawing Ⓟ for penny and Ⓝ for nickel.

1. I can exchange 1 nickel for 5 pennies.

Ⓟ Ⓟ Ⓟ Ⓟ Ⓟ

2. I can exchange 1 dime for 10 pennies.

Ⓟ Ⓟ Ⓟ Ⓟ Ⓟ Ⓟ Ⓟ Ⓟ Ⓟ Ⓟ

3. I can exchange 1 dime for 2 nickels.

Ⓝ Ⓝ

4. I can exchange 1 quarter for 5 nickels.

Ⓝ Ⓝ Ⓝ Ⓝ Ⓝ

Try This

5. Make up your own problem. Answers vary.

I can exchange ________ for ________.

***Math Masters,* p. 226**

8•3 Place Value: Hundreds, Tens, and Ones

Objective To extend place-value concepts to hundreds.

Technology Resources www.everydaymathonline.com

ePresentations

eToolkit

Algorithms Practice

EM Facts Workshop Game™

Family Letters

Assessment Management

Common Core State Standards

Curriculum Focal Points

Interactive Teacher's Lesson Guide

1 Teaching the Lesson

Key Concepts and Skills

- Count collections of objects. [Number and Numeration Goal 2]
- Read and write whole numbers modeled with base-10 blocks. [Number and Numeration Goal 3]

Key Activities

Children practice naming 3-digit numbers represented by base-10 blocks. They exchange cubes for longs or longs for flats.

Ongoing Assessment: Recognizing Student Achievement Use the Math Message. [Number and Numeration Goal 3]

Ongoing Assessment: Informing Instruction See page 690.

Key Vocabulary

hundreds ◆ tens ◆ ones ◆ hundreds place ◆ tens place ◆ ones place

Materials

Math Journal 2, p. 156
Math Journal 2, Activity Sheets 13 and 14
Math Masters, pp. 224 and 360
Home Link 8•2
transparency of *Math Masters,* p. 224 (optional) ◆ calculator ◆ base-10 blocks ◆ overhead base-10 blocks (optional)

2 Ongoing Learning & Practice

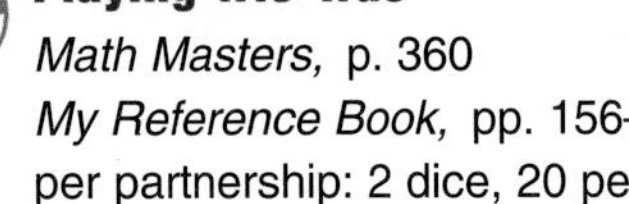

Playing *Tric-Trac*
Math Masters, p. 360
My Reference Book, pp. 156–158
per partnership: 2 dice, 20 pennies
Children practice addition facts.

Math Boxes 8•3
Math Journal 2, p. 157
Children practice and maintain skills through Math Box problems.

Home Link 8•3
Math Masters, p. 227
Children practice and maintain skills through Home Link activities.

3 Differentiation Options

READINESS

Counting Base-10 Blocks with a Calculator
per partnership: base-10 blocks (longs and cubes), calculator
Children count base-10 blocks with a calculator.

ENRICHMENT

Making and Comparing 3-Digit Numbers
per partnership: 6 each of number cards 0–9 (from the Everything Math Deck, if available)
Children make and compare 3-digit numbers.

EXTRA PRACTICE

Ordering Numbers with Base-10 Blocks
3" by 5" index cards ◆ per group: base-10 blocks (longs and cubes); optional
Children draw and order base-10 longs and cubes.

Advance Preparation

For Part 1, children use base-10 blocks or those cut from Activity Sheets 13 and 14. You may want to make a transparency of the Place-Value Mat (*Math Masters,* page 224) to use with base-10 blocks, or draw a mat on the board and use the notation ■ | • to represent flats, longs, and cubes.

***Teacher's Reference Manual,* Grades 1–3** pp. 69, 70

Getting Started

Mental Math and Reflexes  

Play a round of *Beat the Calculator.* See Lesson 6-4 for directions.

Math Message 

Show 53 with base-10 blocks.

Home Link 8·2 Follow-Up 

Go over the answers to Problems 1–4.

1 Teaching the Lesson

▶ Math Message Follow-Up

WHOLE-CLASS ACTIVITY

Most, if not all, children will represent the number 53 with 5-longs and 3 cubes. Encourage them to show 53 in another way, such as 4 longs and 13 cubes.

Discuss why these are equivalent. Illustrate with pictures on the board or with base-10 blocks on the overhead.

Ask children how many cubes would need to be added to 53 to make an exchange for 1 more long. 7 cubes Model the exchange and emphasize that you are composing a ten from ones. Tell them that today they will be making exchanges between cubes and longs, and longs and flats.

Ongoing Assessment: Recognizing Student Achievement

Math Message 

Use the **Math Message** to assess children's ability to model numbers with base-10 blocks. Children are making adequate progress if they are able to show 53 with base-10 blocks.

[Number and Numeration Goal 3]

▶ Naming Numbers Shown with Base-10 Blocks

WHOLE-CLASS ACTIVITY

(*Math Masters,* p. 224)

Use the following routine:

Display 2 flats, 4 longs, and 3 cubes on your Place-Value Mat. Children do the same on their mats. Discuss the following and write the main ideas on the board to support English language learners.

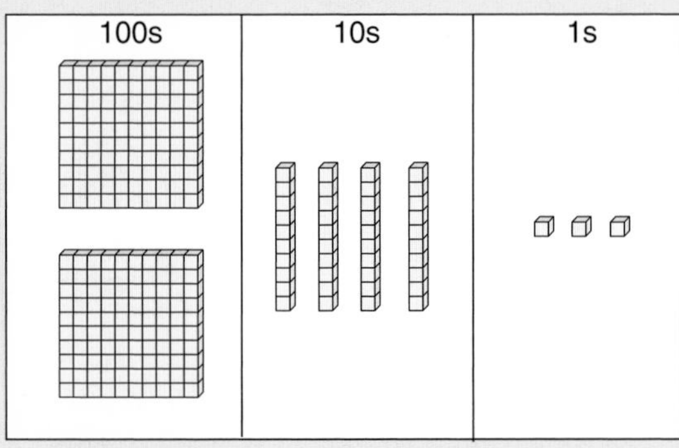

Ask children to show 2 flats, 4 longs, and 3 cubes on their Place-Value Mats on *Math Masters,* page 224.

NOTE To help children better understand place value, have children write numbers in expanded form. For example, for 226, they would write 2 hundreds + 2 tens + 6 ones.

- What number do these base-10 blocks show? 243

Write the number on your mat. Review place-value terminology:

- The 2 flats stand for 2 **hundreds,** the 4 longs stand for 4 **tens,** and the 3 cubes stand for 3 **ones.**
- The 2 in 243 is in the **hundreds place,** the 4 is in the **tens place,** and the 3 is in the **ones place.**

Repeat this routine with other numbers as needed. *Suggestions:*

▷ 1 flat, 4 longs, and 6 cubes 146

▷ 2 flats and 6 cubes 206

▷ 2 flats and 7 longs 270

▶ Making Exchanges with Base-10 Blocks

(*Math Masters,* p. 224)

Display 1 flat, 12 longs, and 6 cubes on your Place-Value Mat. Children do the same on the mat from *Math Masters,* page 224. Ask what number is shown. Discuss how to obtain the answer. If no one brings it up, demonstrate the following exchange: Trade 10 of the longs for 1 flat and place the flat in the hundreds column. There are now 2 flats, 2 longs, and 6 cubes. Ask: *What number is shown?* 226

Ongoing Assessment: Informing Instruction

Watch for children:

▷ who do not choose the correct base-10 blocks to represent 1s, 10s, and 100s.

▷ who make a trade, such as 10 cubes for 1 long, but do not remove the 10-cubes from the total amount of blocks.

▷ who make counting errors when trading blocks.

▷ who do not use zero as a place holder when needed.

Adjusting the Activity

You may wish to have children cover a flat with 10 longs to ascertain that a flat is the same as 10 longs. Then replace the 10 longs with 1 flat.

AUDITORY ◆ KINESTHETIC ◆ TACTILE ◆ VISUAL

Repeat this routine with other combinations of longs and cubes that require an exchange. *Suggestions:*

- ▷ 2 flats, 15 longs, and 2 cubes 352
- ▷ 1 flat, 3 longs, and 16 cubes 146
- ▷ 3 flats and 12 cubes 312
- ▷ 1 flat and 12 longs 220
- ▷ 3 flats, 4 longs, and 10 cubes 350
- ▷ 2 flats, 10 longs, and 5 cubes 305

Ask children what number can be represented by 2 flats, 13 longs, and 15 cubes. 345 Have them demonstrate their solution strategies with blocks. If children are able to do so, have them figure out the numbers without making the exchanges.

▶ Writing Numbers for Base-10-Block Riddles

INDEPENDENT ACTIVITY

(*Math Journal 2,* p. 156)

Encourage children to use base-10 blocks to help them solve the riddles. When they are finished, have them share their riddles and have the other children work together to solve them.

2 Ongoing Learning & Practice

▶ Playing *Tric-Trac*

PARTNER ACTIVITY

(*Math Masters,* p. 360; *My Reference Book,* pp. 156–158)

Children practice addition facts by playing *Tric-Trac.* For detailed instructions, see Lesson 6-8.

▶ Math Boxes 8•3

INDEPENDENT ACTIVITY

(*Math Journal 2,* p. 157)

Mixed Practice Math Boxes in this lesson are paired with Math Boxes in Lesson 8-1. The skills in Problem 4 preview Unit 9 content.

▶ Home Link 8•3

INDEPENDENT ACTIVITY

(*Math Masters,* p. 227)

Home Connection Children write 3-digit numbers represented by flats, longs, and cubes.

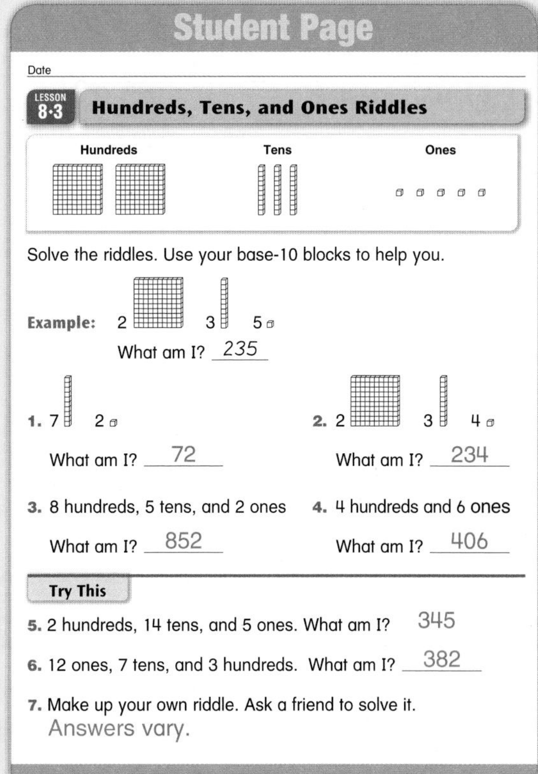

Student Page

Date

LESSON 8•3 **Hundreds, Tens, and Ones Riddles**

Hundreds | Tens | Ones

Solve the riddles. Use your base-10 blocks to help you.

Example: 2 [flats] 3 [longs] 5 [cubes] What am I? 235

1. 7 [longs] 2 [cubes] What am I? 72
2. 2 [flats] 3 [longs] 4 [cubes] What am I? 234
3. 8 hundreds, 5 tens, and 2 ones What am I? 852
4. 4 hundreds and 6 ones What am I? 406

Try This

5. 2 hundreds, 14 tens, and 5 ones. What am I? 345
6. 12 ones, 7 tens, and 3 hundreds. What am I? 382
7. Make up your own riddle. Ask a friend to solve it. Answers vary.

Math Journal 2, **p. 156**

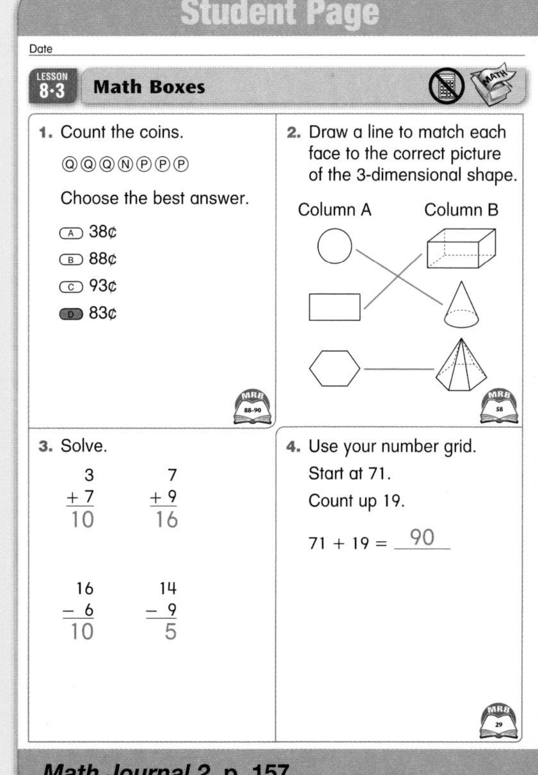

Student Page

Date

LESSON 8•3 **Math Boxes**

1. Count the coins. Ⓠ Ⓠ Ⓠ Ⓝ Ⓟ Ⓟ Ⓟ
   Choose the best answer.
   - Ⓐ 38¢
   - Ⓑ 88¢
   - Ⓒ 93¢
   - Ⓓ 83¢
2. Draw a line to match each face to the correct picture of the 3-dimensional shape.
   Column A | Column B
3. Solve.
   $3 + 7 = 10$, $7 + 9 = 16$, $16 - 6 = 10$, $14 - 9 = 5$
4. Use your number grid. Start at 71. Count up 19.
   $71 + 19 =$ 90

Math Journal 2, **p. 157**

Getting Started

Mental Math and Reflexes

To practice place-value and rounding skills, have children write answers on their slates to the following:

- ●○○ Is 14 closer to 10 or 20? 10 Is 16 closer to 10 or 20? 20
- ●●○ Is 39 closer to 30 or 40? 40 Is 21 closer to 20 or 30? 20
- ●●● Is 83 closer to 80 or 90? 80 Is 77 closer to 70 or 80? 80

Math Message

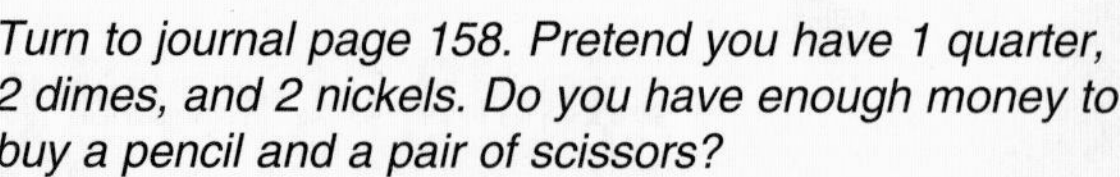

Turn to journal page 158. Pretend you have 1 quarter, 2 dimes, and 2 nickels. Do you have enough money to buy a pencil and a pair of scissors?

Home Link 8◆3 Follow-Up

Briefly go over the answers.

1 Teaching the Lesson

▶ Math Message Follow-Up

Ask children to describe how they found the answer. Model (or have a volunteer model) the solution with overhead coins, or draw the coins on the board. They can buy either the pencil or the scissors, but not both.

▶ Making Up and Solving Number Stories

(*Math Journal 2,* pp. 158 and 159)

Tell children that they will be making up and solving each other's number stories. Explain the importance of listening carefully to the stories.

Children will use the School Store Mini-Posters on journal pages 158 and 159 as a source for number stories. If children are having difficulty making up number stories, model several stories before asking them to invent their own (see page 695 for suggestions). You can use transparencies of the posters (*Math Masters,* pages 228 and 229) for this activity.

Adjusting the Activity

ELL

As a story is read, write it on the board.

AUDITORY ◆ KINESTHETIC ◆ TACTILE ◆ VISUAL

Use the following procedure:

1. All children try to solve the stories using whichever strategy they choose. Encourage children to use concrete models, such as tool-kit coins, base-10 blocks, and number grids or lines, and to use drawings, such as base-10 shorthand or tallies. Some children may compute entirely in their heads. The goal is to have children learn to use mental calculations to solve problems.

Student Page

Date

LESSON 8·4 **School Store Mini-Poster 2**

Math Journal 2, p. 158

Repeat this routine with other combinations of longs and cubes that require an exchange. *Suggestions:*

- ▷ 2 flats, 15 longs, and 2 cubes 352
- ▷ 1 flat, 3 longs, and 16 cubes 146
- ▷ 3 flats and 12 cubes 312
- ▷ 1 flat and 12 longs 220
- ▷ 3 flats, 4 longs, and 10 cubes 350
- ▷ 2 flats, 10 longs, and 5 cubes 305

Ask children what number can be represented by 2 flats, 13 longs, and 15 cubes. 345 Have them demonstrate their solution strategies with blocks. If children are able to do so, have them figure out the numbers without making the exchanges.

▶ Writing Numbers for Base-10-Block Riddles

(*Math Journal 2,* p. 156)

Encourage children to use base-10 blocks to help them solve the riddles. When they are finished, have them share their riddles and have the other children work together to solve them.

2 Ongoing Learning & Practice

▶ Playing *Tric-Trac*

(*Math Masters,* p. 360; *My Reference Book,* pp. 156–158)

Children practice addition facts by playing *Tric-Trac.* For detailed instructions, see Lesson 6-8.

▶ Math Boxes 8•3

INDEPENDENT ACTIVITY

(*Math Journal 2,* p. 157)

Mixed Practice Math Boxes in this lesson are paired with Math Boxes in Lesson 8-1. The skills in Problem 4 preview Unit 9 content.

▶ Home Link 8•3

(*Math Masters,* p. 227)

Home Connection Children write 3-digit numbers represented by flats, longs, and cubes.

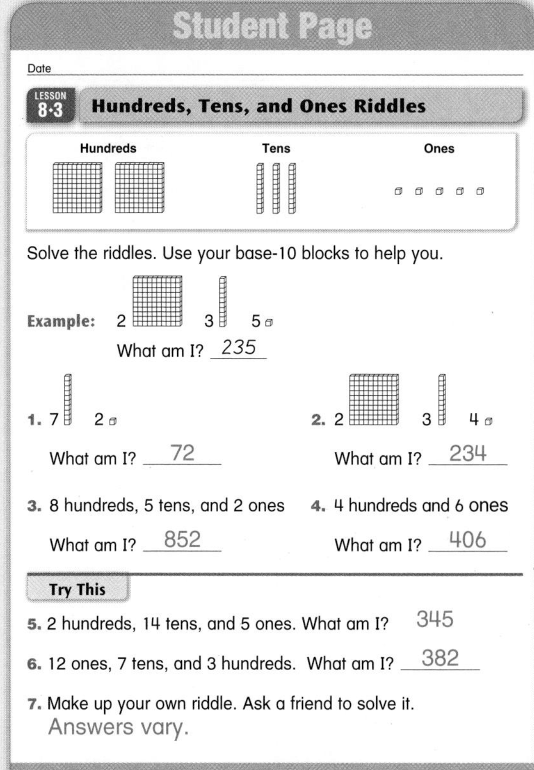

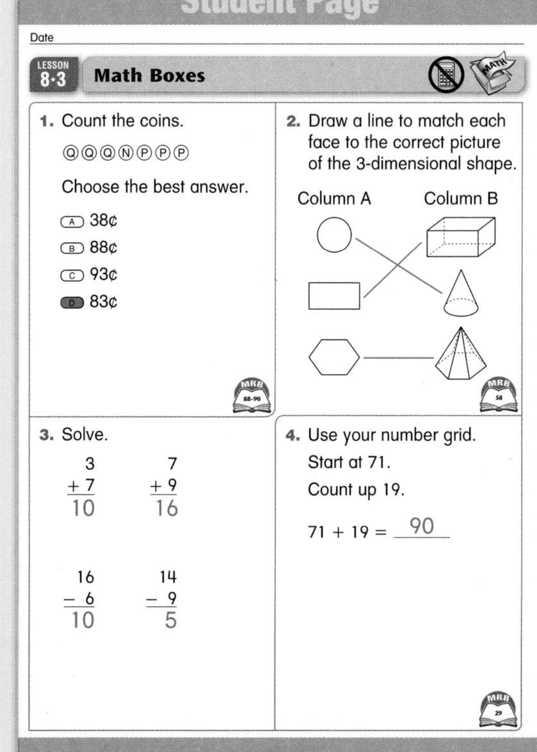

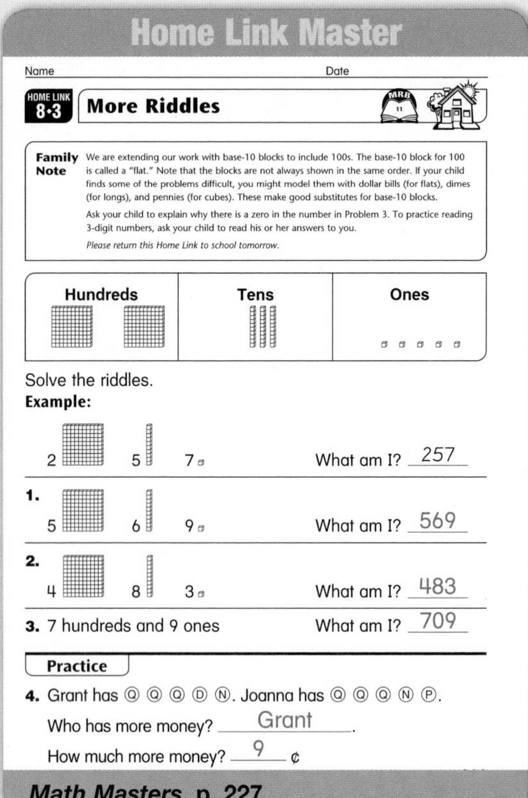
Home Link Master

Name Date

HOME LINK 8·3 More Riddles

Family Note: We are extending our work with base-10 blocks to include 100s. The base-10 block for 100 is called a "flat." Note that the blocks are not always shown in the same order. If your child finds some of the problems difficult, you might model them with dollar bills (for flats), dimes (for longs), and pennies (for cubes). These make good substitutes for base-10 blocks.
Ask your child to explain why there is a zero in the number in Problem 3. To practice reading 3-digit numbers, ask your child to read his or her answers to you.
Please return this Home Link to school tomorrow.

Hundreds	Tens	Ones

Solve the riddles.
Example: What am I? 257
1. What am I? 569
2. What am I? 483
3. 7 hundreds and 9 ones What am I? 709

Practice
4. Grant has Ⓠ Ⓠ Ⓠ Ⓓ Ⓝ. Joanna has Ⓠ Ⓠ Ⓠ Ⓝ Ⓟ.
Who has more money? Grant.
How much more money? 9 ¢

Math Masters, p. 227

3 Differentiation Options

READINESS

PARTNER ACTIVITY

5–15 Min

▶ Counting Base-10 Blocks with a Calculator

To explore place-value concepts, have children count base-10 blocks using their calculators. Children take a small collection of cubes. They program their calculators to count by 1s. As one partner counts each cube, the other partner counts on the calculator at the same time. Guide children to understand that the ones place in the number that is displayed on their calculator changes each time a cube is added. Ask them to make note of when the tens place changes. Have children discuss why the tens place changes and ask them to predict when the tens place will change again. They should continue counting cubes as time permits. Consider having children count longs by programming their calculator to count by 10s. Ask children to explain why the ones place does not change and what they think will happen when they have 10 longs.

ENRICHMENT

PARTNER ACTIVITY

5–15 Min

▶ Making and Comparing 3-Digit Numbers

To apply children's understanding of place-value concepts, have them play a variation of the *Digit Game*. Each partner takes three number cards and creates the largest 3-digit number he or she can. The partner with the larger number takes all of the cards. See Lesson 5-1 for detailed instructions.

EXTRA PRACTICE

SMALL-GROUP ACTIVITY

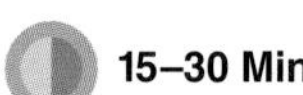
15–30 Min

▶ Ordering Numbers with Base-10 Blocks

To provide practice with place value, have children work in small groups. Each child in the group takes two index cards and draws base-10 blocks (using | and • notation) on each card to represent a 2-digit number. When all children in the group have finished their cards, they work together to order the cards by figuring out the number represented on each card.

Children may use more than 10 cubes to represent a number, so it will be necessary to trade cubes for longs to compose a ten to figure out what number is represented. They can model the numbers with base-10 blocks to help them figure out the totals.

8•4 Application: Shopping at the School Store

Objective To provide practice solving number stories that involve addition and subtraction.

www.everydaymathonline.com

ePresentations

eToolkit

Algorithms Practice

EM Facts Workshop Game™

Family Letters

Assessment Management

Common Core State Standards

Curriculum Focal Points

Interactive Teacher's Lesson Guide

1 Teaching the Lesson

Key Concepts and Skills

- Express amounts of money using dollars-and-cents notation.
  [Number and Numeration Goal 3]
- Use a variety of strategies to add and subtract with 2-digit numbers.
  [Operations and Computation Goal 2]
- Make up, solve, and record money number stories and discuss solution strategies.
  [Operations and Computation Goal 4]
- Show amounts of money with the fewest number of coins.
  [Measurement and Reference Frames Goal 2]
- Write number sentences to match solution strategies.
  [Patterns, Functions, and Algebra Goal 2]

Key Activities

Children make up, solve, and record number stories based on the cost of items that might be available in a school store.

Materials

Math Journal 2, pp. 158–160
Home Link 8•3
transparencies of *Math Masters,* pp. 228 and 229 (optional) ◆ slate ◆ tool-kit coins ◆ base-10 blocks ◆ overhead coins (optional)

2 Ongoing Learning & Practice

Playing *Base-10 Exchange*
Math Masters, p. 224
per partnership: base-10 blocks (flats, longs, and cubes), 2 dice
Children practice exchanging 10 cubes for 1 long and 10 longs for 1 flat.

Math Boxes 8•4
Math Journal 2, p. 161
Children practice and maintain skills through Math Box problems.

Ongoing Assessment: Recognizing Student Achievement
Use Math Boxes, Problem 3.
[Operations and Computation Goal 1]

Home Link 8•4
Math Masters, p. 230
Children practice and maintain skills through Home Link activities.

3 Differentiation Options

READINESS

Using Counters to Model Number Stories
slate ◆ counters
Children use counters to model number stories.

ENRICHMENT

Spending Ten Dollars
advertisements from discount stores ◆ calculator
Children shop for ten-dollars worth of items.

Getting Started

Mental Math and Reflexes

To practice place-value and rounding skills, have children write answers on their slates to the following:

●○○ Is 14 closer to 10 or 20? 10 Is 16 closer to 10 or 20? 20

●●○ Is 39 closer to 30 or 40? 40 Is 21 closer to 20 or 30? 20

●●● Is 83 closer to 80 or 90? 80 Is 77 closer to 70 or 80? 80

Math Message

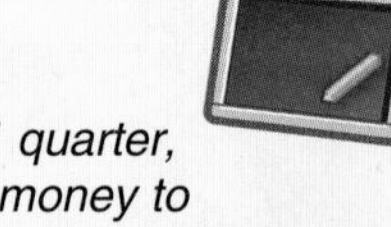

Turn to journal page 158. Pretend you have 1 quarter, 2 dimes, and 2 nickels. Do you have enough money to buy a pencil and a pair of scissors?

Home Link 8•3 Follow-Up

Briefly go over the answers.

1 Teaching the Lesson

▶ Math Message Follow-Up

WHOLE-CLASS ACTIVITY

Ask children to describe how they found the answer. Model (or have a volunteer model) the solution with overhead coins, or draw the coins on the board. They can buy either the pencil or the scissors, but not both.

▶ Making Up and Solving Number Stories

WHOLE-CLASS ACTIVITY

(*Math Journal 2,* pp. 158 and 159)

Tell children that they will be making up and solving each other's number stories. Explain the importance of listening carefully to the stories.

Children will use the School Store Mini-Posters on journal pages 158 and 159 as a source for number stories. If children are having difficulty making up number stories, model several stories before asking them to invent their own (see page 695 for suggestions). You can use transparencies of the posters (*Math Masters,* pages 228 and 229) for this activity.

Adjusting the Activity

ELL

As a story is read, write it on the board.

AUDITORY ◆ KINESTHETIC ◆ TACTILE ◆ VISUAL

Use the following procedure:

1. All children try to solve the stories using whichever strategy they choose. Encourage children to use concrete models, such as tool-kit coins, base-10 blocks, and number grids or lines, and to use drawings, such as base-10 shorthand or tallies. Some children may compute entirely in their heads. The goal is to have children learn to use mental calculations to solve problems.

Student Page

Date

LESSON 8·4 School Store Mini-Poster 2

Math Journal 2, p. 158

2. When most children are finished, have volunteers share their answers and solution strategies. As children explain their reasoning, draw or write the strategies, including writing number models. Have children suggest their own number models to represent the strategies as well.

3. As children present new strategies, reinforce the strategies by asking them to solve new number stories using each one. In particular, you may pose the following number stories to emphasize these common strategies:

   Making ten: Use base-10 blocks to find how much the pencil and eraser would cost together. Add tens to tens and ones to ones, and compose a new 10 to find the price.

   Counting on from the larger addend: Liz needs a ruler and a crayon for an art project. Starting with the larger price (55¢), count up the amount of the smaller price (6¢) to find the total.

   Counting up to subtract: Chen has 18¢ and wants to buy a pencil. Count up to the price of the pencil (28¢) to find the difference between the amount of money Chen has and the amount he needs.

   Using the number grid to subtract: Find how much more it would cost to buy the crayons rather than the bookmark. On the number grid, start with the price of the crayons (72¢). Stay in the same column and count down by tens to the price of the bookmark (12¢).

4. Summarize proposed solutions with situation diagrams. You may wish to use some of the following sample number stories.

   Parts-and-total: Malcolm bought candy and a ball. How much did he pay? Candy: 8¢; ball: 35¢; total: 43¢

   Parts-and-total (3 addends): What is the cost of a pencil, a crayon, and an eraser? Pencil: 28¢; crayon: 6¢; eraser: 17¢; total: 51¢

   Parts-and-total (part missing): Lisa spent 49¢ total. She bought an eraser and something else. What else did she buy? Eraser: 17¢; total: 49¢. The missing part is 32¢, the price of the scissors.

   Comparison: Scissors cost how much more than gum? Scissors: 32¢; gum: 2¢; difference: 30¢

   Comparison (quantity missing): Kate and Marissa each bought one item. Kate spent 22¢ more than Marissa. Kate bought a 28¢ pencil. What did Marissa buy? Pencil: 28¢; difference: 22¢. The missing quantity is 6¢, so Marissa bought a crayon.

   Change-to-more (change missing): Riva has 20 cents. How much more does she need to buy a ball? Ball: 35¢; amount needed: 15¢

   Change-to-more (start missing): Doug borrowed 10¢ so he could buy 32¢ scissors. How much money did he start with? Amount borrowed: 10¢; scissors: 32¢. Doug started with 22¢.

NOTE If there is disagreement about answers, tally how many children arrived at various answers as you list them on the board. Encourage children to come to a consensus. If they settle on an incorrect answer, examine the reasoning that led to that answer. Then guide the class toward a sound strategy.

Tally how many children arrived at various answers.

Parts-and-total (part missing)

Total	
49¢	
Part	Part
17¢	?

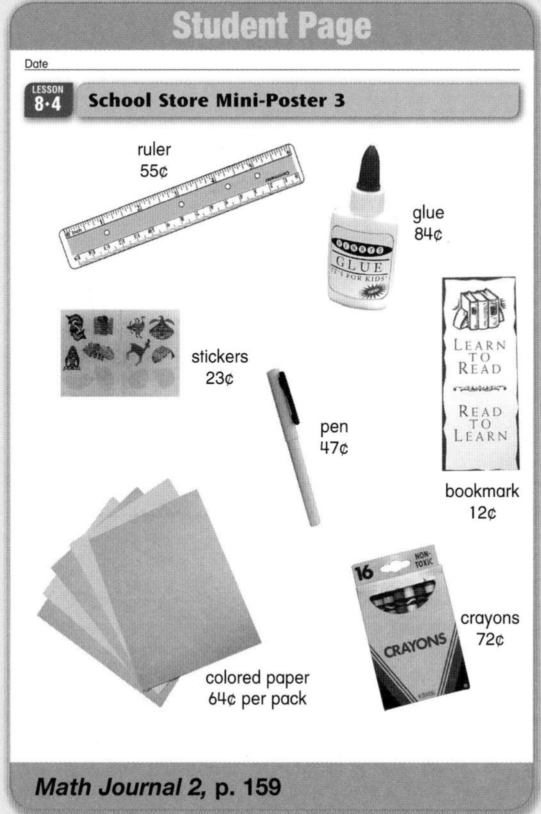

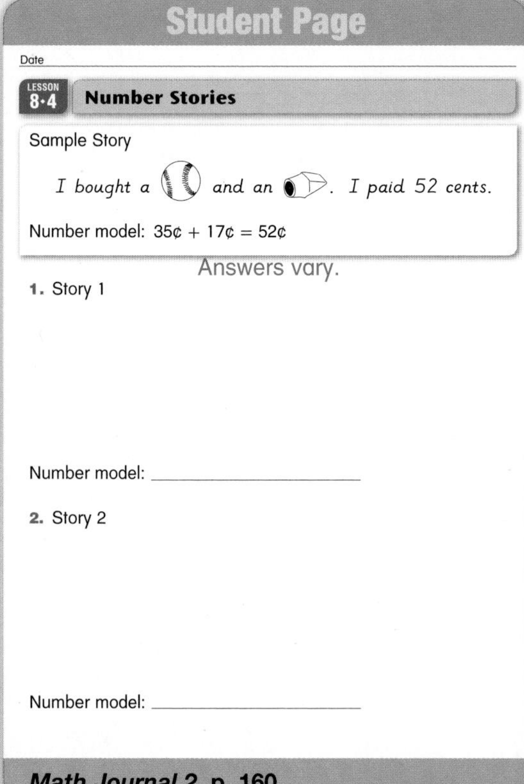

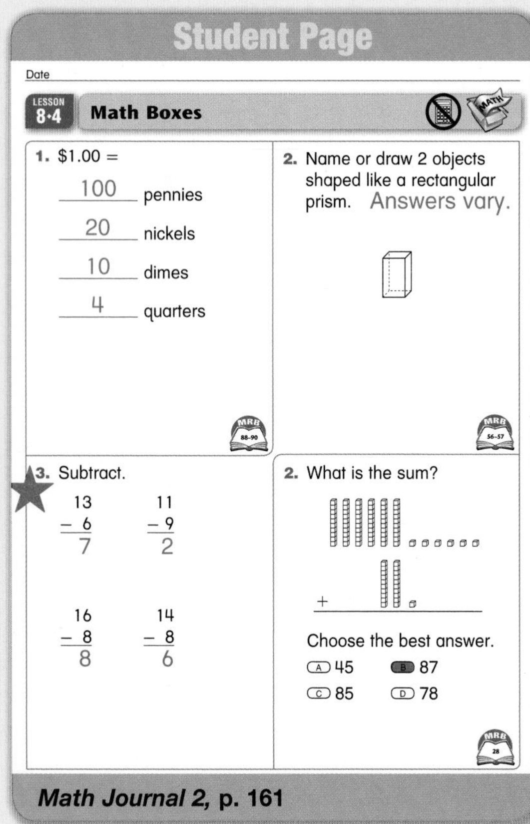

Change-to-less: A ball that I want to buy costs 10 cents less than the baseball. How much does the ball that I want cost? Baseball: 35¢; other ball: 25¢

Change-to-less (start missing): I bought an item on sale at the store for 7¢. The sale price was 10 cents less than its regular price. What item did I buy? Change in price: 10¢; sale price: 7¢. The item was originally 17¢, so it was the eraser.

Multiples: How much money will I need to buy 2 crayons? How much money will I need for 4 crayons? 1 crayon: 6¢; 2 crayons: 12¢; 4 crayons: 24¢

Two-step problem: How much money will I need to buy 4 pieces of gum and one candy? Gum: 2¢; 4 pieces of gum: 8¢; candy: 8¢; total: 16¢

▶ Recording Number Stories

PARTNER ACTIVITY

(*Math Journal 2,* p. 160)

Partners record two number stories in words or by drawing pictures on journal page 160. They can use stories that came up in the whole-class activity or make up new ones. Have them write a number model to show how they solved each number story.

2 Ongoing Learning & Practice

▶ Playing *Base-10 Exchange*

(*Math Masters,* p. 224)

Children practice base-10 exchanges by playing an extension of the *Base-10 Exchange* game they learned in Lesson 5-3. To extend the game, players use the Place-Value Mat on *Math Masters,* page 224. This will allow them to exchange 10 longs for a flat.

Players take turns putting base-10 blocks on their Place-Value Mats according to the roll of the dice. Whenever possible, they exchange 10 cubes for 1 long and 10 longs for 1 flat. The first player to get 3 flats wins.

▶ Math Boxes 8·4

INDEPENDENT ACTIVITY

(*Math Journal 2,* p. 161)

Mixed Practice Math Boxes in this lesson are paired with Math Boxes in Lesson 8-2. The skills in Problem 4 preview Unit 9 content.

Math Boxes Problem 3

Use **Math Boxes, Problem 3** to assess children's knowledge of addition and subtraction facts. Children are making adequate progress if they are able to correctly answer the problems. [Operations and Computation Goal 1]

▶ Home Link 8·4

INDEPENDENT ACTIVITY

(*Math Masters,* p. 230)

Home Connection Children find pictures in a magazine, newspaper, or catalog. They make up a number story and write a number model to go with the pictures.

3 Differentiation Options

READINESS

SMALL-GROUP ACTIVITY

▶ Using Counters to Model Number Stories

15–30 Min

To explore number stories, children use counters to model the stories and review their solutions by drawing situation diagrams. Have children suggest number models to go with the stories. *Suggestions:*

- Brandi had 3 red crayons and 4 blue crayons. How many crayons did she have altogether? Children draw a line to divide their slates in half. They place 3 counters on one side and 4 on the other. Then they erase the line to get 7. Draw a parts-and-total diagram to record the answer.
- Ricardo has 5 cookies. Renee has 7 cookies. How many more cookies does Renee have than Ricardo? Children take 5 counters and 7 counters and line them up one-to-one next to each other. Two of Renee's "cookies" will not have a match, so Renee has 2 more cookies than Ricardo. Draw a comparison diagram to record the answer.
- The snow was 2 inches deep in the morning. By lunch, 3 more inches of snow had fallen. How much snow had fallen by lunch time? Sample answer: Children start with 2 counters on their slates. They add 3 more counters. This could be a parts-and-total diagram or a change-to-more diagram, depending on how children view it.

ENRICHMENT

PARTNER ACTIVITY

▶ Spending Ten Dollars

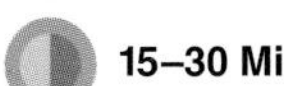

15–30 Min

To apply children's understanding of money concepts, have them create a shopping list of items that cost about ten dollars in all. Distribute advertisements from discount stores. Tell children to pretend they have ten dollars to go shopping at the advertised store. They work with a partner to come up with a list of at least five items they can buy for a total of about ten dollars. Children record the name of each item (or draw a picture of it) and list its cost in dollars-and-cents notation. They write a number model for finding the exact total cost of their items and then use a calculator to find the total.

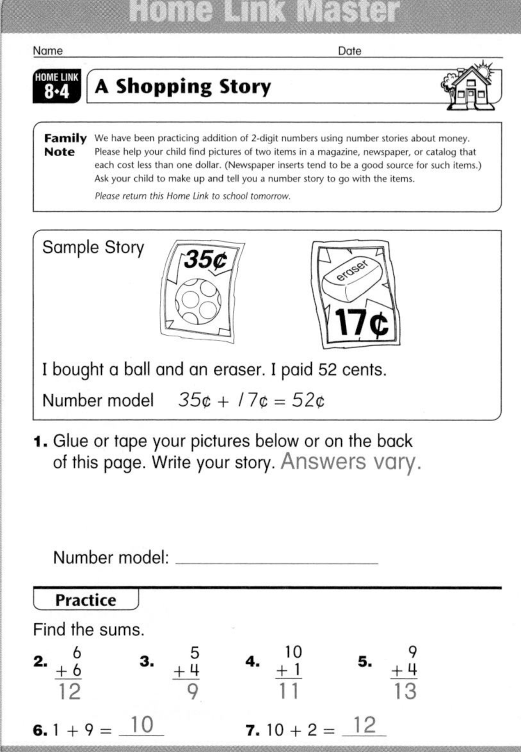

Home Link Master

Name ____ Date ____

HOME LINK 8·4 **A Shopping Story**

Family Note We have been practicing addition of 2-digit numbers using number stories about money. Please help your child find pictures of two items in a magazine, newspaper, or catalog that each cost less than one dollar. (Newspaper inserts tend to be a good source for such items.) Ask your child to make up and tell you a number story to go with the items.

Please return this Home Link to school tomorrow.

Sample Story

35¢ eraser 17¢

I bought a ball and an eraser. I paid 52 cents.

Number model 35¢ + 17¢ = 52¢

1. Glue or tape your pictures below or on the back of this page. Write your story. Answers vary.

Number model: ____

Practice

Find the sums.

2. 6 + 6 = 12
3. 5 + 4 = 9
4. 10 + 1 = 11
5. 9 + 4 = 13
6. 1 + 9 = 10
7. 10 + 2 = 12

Math Masters, p. 230

8•5 Making Change

Objective To develop the use of counting up as a strategy for making change.

Technology Resources www.everydaymathonline.com

ePresentations

eToolkit

Algorithms Practice

EM Facts Workshop Game™

Family Letters

Assessment Management

Common Core State Standards

Curriculum Focal Points

Interactive Teacher's Lesson Guide

1 Teaching the Lesson

Key Concepts and Skills

- Make change by counting up.
  [Operations and Computation Goal 2]
- Make up and solve number stories.
  [Operations and Computation Goal 4]
- Identify the values of coins.
  [Measurement and Reference Frames Goal 2]

Key Activities

Children practice making change by pretending they are paying for items with too much money.

Ongoing Assessment: Recognizing Student Achievement Use Mental Math and Reflexes.
[Number and Numeration Goal 3]

Ongoing Assessment: Informing Instruction See page 700.

Key Vocabulary

to make change

Materials

Math Journal 2, pp. 158, 159, 162, and 163
Home Link 8•4
transparencies of *Math Masters,* pp. 228, 229, and 231 (optional) ◆ slate ◆ tool-kit coins ◆ calculator (optional)

2 Ongoing Learning & Practice

Introducing the *3, 2, 1 Game*
My Reference Book, pp. 150 and 151
per partnership: slate, calculator (optional)
Children practice subtracting 1, 2, or 3 from a number.

Math Boxes 8•5
Math Journal 2, p. 164
Children practice and maintain skills through Math Box problems.

Home Link 8•5
Math Masters, p. 232
Children practice and maintain skills through Home Link activities.

3 Differentiation Options

READINESS

Counting Up to Find the Difference
per partnership: 4 each of number cards 1–10 (from the Everything Math Deck, if available), tool-kit pennies
Children practice counting up as a strategy for solving addition and subtraction problems.

ENRICHMENT

Paying with Dollar Bills
Math Masters, p. 233 (at least 1 quarter-sheet per child)
tool-kit coins and bills
Children pretend to pay for an item with dollar bills and then make correct change.

Advance Preparation

For the optional Enrichment activity in Part 3, make copies of *Math Masters,* page 233 and cut them apart into quarter-sheets.

***Teacher's Reference Manual,* Grades 1–3** pp. 105–107

Getting Started

Mental Math and Reflexes 

On your slate, write the number that is

●○○ 10 more than 34. Circle the tens digit. ④4
10 less than 41. Circle the tens digit. ③1
10 more than 52. Circle the tens digit. ⑥2

●●○ 10 more than 67. Circle the tens digit. ⑦7
10 less than 89. Circle the tens digit. ⑦9
10 more than 90. Circle the hundreds digit. ①00

●●● 10 more than 105. Circle the hundreds digit. ①15
10 less than 103. Circle the tens digit. ⑨3
10 more than 190. Circle the hundreds digit. ②00

Math Message

You buy a toy elephant that costs 72¢. You pay with 3 quarters. How much money will you get back?

Home Link 8•4 Follow-Up

Children share their number stories.

Ongoing Assessment: Recognizing Student Achievement

Mental Math and Reflexes

Use **Mental Math and Reflexes** to assess children's knowledge of place-value concepts. Children are making adequate progress if they are able to answer the first set of questions. Some children may be able to answer all of the sets of questions.

[Number and Numeration Goal 3]

1 Teaching the Lesson

▶ Math Message Follow-Up

Children share solution strategies. To support English language learners, write the strategies on the board. If no one suggests it, use a counting-up strategy to find the difference between the cost of the elephant, 72¢, and what was paid, 75¢. *Three quarters is 75¢. Count up, starting from 72: 73 (1 penny), 74 (2 pennies), 75 (3 pennies). It took 3 pennies to go from 72 cents to 75 cents. You should get back 3 cents.*

Adjusting the Activity

Show how this action can be expressed as a number model: 72¢ + 3¢ = 75¢. The 72¢ represents what was bought and the 75¢ represents the amount given. The 3¢ is the change. An alternate number model is 75¢ − 72¢ = 3¢; this represents the difference between the amount paid and the actual cost.

AUDITORY ♦ KINESTHETIC ♦ TACTILE ♦ VISUAL

▶ Making Change by Counting Up

Discuss what happens when someone goes to the store and pays for an item with coins and/or bills that add up to more than the cost of the item. Pose a question such as the following: *I want to buy an 18-cent ring. I have 2 dimes. How much money will the salesperson give back?* 2¢ The amount you get back is called the *change.* To support English language learners, discuss the everyday and mathematical usage of the word *change.* You may also want to discuss the difference between the statements *I have change in my pocket* and *The cashier gave me 5 cents in change.*

Demonstrate counting up **to make change:**

1. Select two children.
2. One child pays 3 dimes to buy a 27¢ airplane.
3. The other child says, "The airplane costs 27¢. Here is your change," and then counts out the change, "28, 29, 30 cents" while handing over the 3 pennies.
4. Summarize by saying that the change is 3¢.

Ongoing Assessment: Informing Instruction

Watch for children who include the price of an object when counting back change. For the example above, they would count 27, 28, 29, 30, and give their partner 4 cents change. Have children check their answers on a calculator to see if they are making this mistake.

Adjusting the Activity

Have children use the number line to count up from the price to the amount paid when they make change.

AUDITORY ◆ KINESTHETIC ◆ TACTILE ◆ VISUAL

NOTE Depending on your children's abilities, use one or both of the School Store Mini-Posters (*Math Masters,* pages 228 and 229) and/or the Museum Store Mini-Poster (*Math Masters,* page 231) for this activity. You may wish to make transparencies of the masters.

▶ Role-Playing Shopping and Making Change

(*Math Journal 2,* pp. 158, 159, 162, and 163)

Using real coins and one of the store posters, partners take turns playing storekeeper and shopper. Shoppers make selections and pay too much; storekeepers count out change. Both children record three transactions on journal page 163.

At first, shoppers should pay for the items using only dimes. Storekeepers give change in pennies, making change by counting up to the next multiple of 10 cents. As children gain confidence in making change with pennies, add nickels (or dimes or quarters) to the storekeeper's money so that children can count on by 1s and 5s (or 10s or 25s) to make change.

Social Studies Link Discuss other kinds of stores and their products. You may want to create additional store posters that children can use to role-play shopping and making change.

Adjusting the Activity

Encourage children to use only as many dimes as necessary. Children should look at the tens digit in the price and pay one dime more than that digit.

AUDITORY ◆ KINESTHETIC ◆ TACTILE ◆ VISUAL

Circulate to offer assistance and to assess counting-up skills used to make change. Show and encourage exchanges for other coins whenever five or more pennies are counted out as change.

Student Page

Date

LESSON 8·5 **Making Change**

Record what you bought. Record how much change you got.

Example:

I bought a plane for 27 cents.

I gave ⒹⒹⒹ to the clerk.

I got ⓅⓅⓅ in change.

Answers vary.

1. I bought ______ for ______ cents.
   I gave ______ to the clerk.
   I got ______ in change.
2. I bought ______ for ______ cents.
   I gave ______ to the clerk.
   I got ______ in change.
3. I bought ______ for ______ cents.
   I gave ______ to the clerk.
   I got ______ in change.

Math Journal 2, p. 163

2 Ongoing Learning & Practice

▶ Introducing the *3, 2, 1 Game*

(*My Reference Book,* pp. 150 and 151)

Partners play the *3, 2, 1 Game.* The object of the game is to be the first player to reach exactly 0 by subtracting 1, 2, or 3 from a given number. Children will need to play several times before they start noticing patterns that will help them form winning strategies. You can vary the game by using a calculator or by choosing different starting numbers. For directions to play the *3, 2, 1 Game*, see *My Reference Book*, pages 150 and 151.

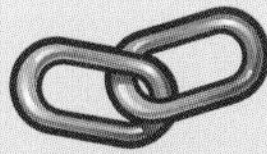

Links to the Future

In first grade, one way that children practice subtraction is by playing the *3, 2, 1 Game*. Automaticity with all addition and subtraction facts through 10 + 10 is a Grade 2 Goal.

Adjusting the Activity

Have children use counters to play the game.

AUDITORY ◆ KINESTHETIC ◆ TACTILE ◆ VISUAL

▶ Math Boxes 8•5

INDEPENDENT ACTIVITY

(*Math Journal 2,* p. 164)

Mixed Practice Note that starting with this page, there will be six Math Boxes. Math Boxes in this lesson are linked to Math Boxes in Lessons 8-7 and 8-9. The skills in Problem 6 preview Unit 9 content.

▶ Home Link 8•5

INDEPENDENT ACTIVITY

(*Math Masters,* p. 232)

Home Connection Children continue to practice making change for purchases made with dimes.

Student Page

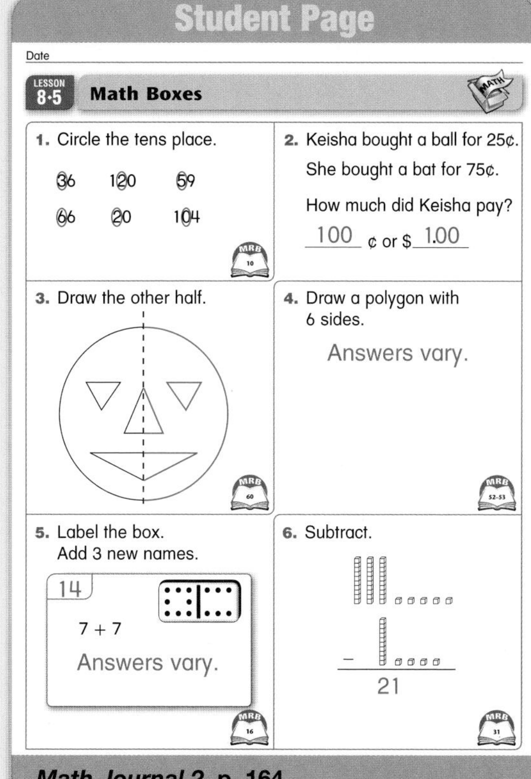

Date

LESSON 8•5 **Math Boxes**

1. Circle the tens place.
36 120 59
66 20 104

2. Keisha bought a ball for 25¢. She bought a bat for 75¢.
How much did Keisha pay?
100 ¢ or $ 1.00

3. Draw the other half.

4. Draw a polygon with 6 sides.
Answers vary.

5. Label the box. Add 3 new names.
14
7 + 7
Answers vary.

6. Subtract.
21

Math Journal 2, p. 164

Home Link Master

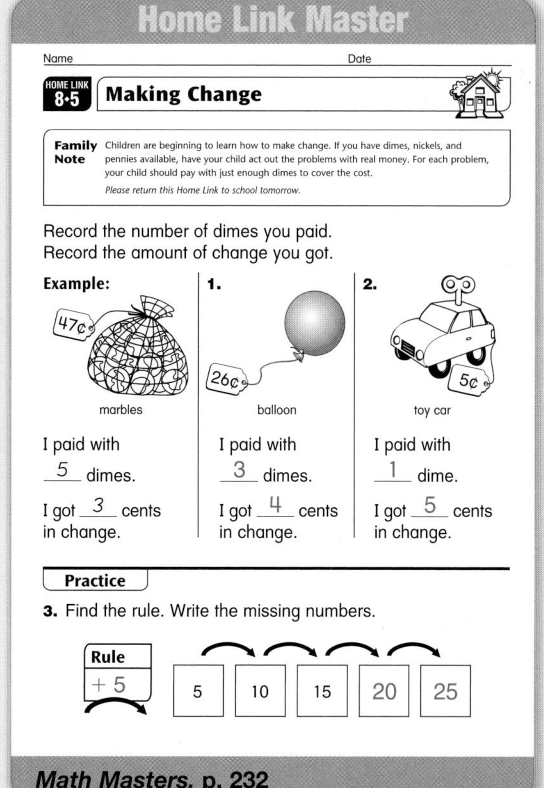

Name Date

HOME LINK 8•5 **Making Change**

Family Note Children are beginning to learn how to make change. If you have dimes, nickels, and pennies available, have your child act out the problems with real money. For each problem, your child should pay with just enough dimes to cover the cost.
Please return this Home Link to school tomorrow.

Record the number of dimes you paid.
Record the amount of change you got.

Example: 47¢ marbles
I paid with 5 dimes.
I got 3 cents in change.

1. 26¢ balloon
I paid with 3 dimes.
I got 4 cents in change.

2. 5¢ toy car
I paid with 1 dime.
I got 5 cents in change.

Practice

3. Find the rule. Write the missing numbers.

Rule: + 5

5, 10, 15, 20, 25

Math Masters, p. 232

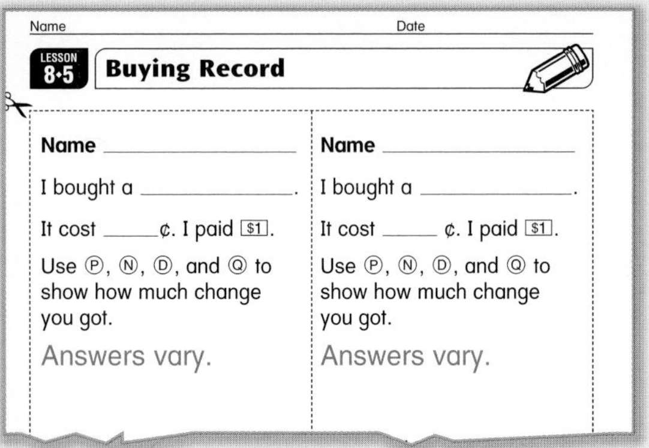
Name Date

LESSON 8·5 **Buying Record**

Name ______	Name ______
I bought a ______.	I bought a ______.
It cost ____¢. I paid $1.	It cost ____¢. I paid $1.
Use Ⓟ, Ⓝ, Ⓓ, and Ⓠ to show how much change you got.	Use Ⓟ, Ⓝ, Ⓓ, and Ⓠ to show how much change you got.
Answers vary.	Answers vary.

Math Masters, page 233

3 Differentiation Options

READINESS

▶ Counting Up to Find the Difference

To explore counting up as a strategy for solving addition and subtraction problems, have children play the *Difference Game.* For detailed instructions, see Lesson 5-7. To extend the game, increase the number of coins children use to play the game.

ENRICHMENT

▶ Paying with Dollar Bills

(*Math Masters,* p. 233)

To apply children's understanding of making change, have them shop at the museum store and use a dollar bill to pay for each item. The shopkeeper counts out the change by counting up. Children record their transactions.

Planning Ahead

For Lesson 8-6, you may want to use two different-sized candy bars that are scored for breaking into sections.

8•6 Equal Shares

Objective To guide exploration of dividing regions into equal parts.

www.everydaymathonline.com

ePresentations

eToolkit

Algorithms Practice

EM Facts Workshop Game™

Family Letters

Assessment Management

Common Core State Standards

Curriculum Focal Points

Interactive Teacher's Lesson Guide

1 Teaching the Lesson

Key Concepts and Skills

- Count equal parts of wholes.
  [Number and Numeration Goal 2]
- Divide shapes into halves, thirds, and fourths.
  [Number and Numeration Goal 4]
- Find objects divided into equal parts.
  [Number and Numeration Goal 4]

Key Activities

Children divide regions into halves, thirds, and fourths, using slates and paper "crackers." Children identify and describe objects divided into equal regions.

Ongoing Assessment: Recognizing Student Achievement
Use journal page 165.
[Number and Numeration Goal 4]

Key Vocabulary

whole ◆ equal parts ◆ halves ◆ fourths ◆ thirds

Materials

Math Journal 2, pp. 162 and 165
Home Link 8•5
Math Masters, p. 234 (optional)
transparency of *Math Masters,* p. 231 (optional) ◆ fruit bars ◆ slate ◆ scissors ◆ glue or transparent tape

2 Ongoing Learning & Practice

Making Jam Sandwiches

Math Masters, p. 235
per partnership: 2" by 2" colored squares (two each of purple, red, and orange; three each of yellow and brown)
Children count possible outcomes of an event.

Solving "What's My Rule?" Problems

Math Journal 2, p. 166
Children practice "What's My Rule?" problems.

Math Boxes 8•6

Math Journal 2, p. 167
Children practice and maintain skills through Math Box problems.

Home Link 8•6

Math Masters, p. 236
Children practice and maintain skills through Home Link activities.

3 Differentiation Options

Dividing Cereal with Standard Measuring Cups

Math Masters, p. 237
per child: 1 measuring cup of dry cereal in a large bowl ◆ per group: measuring cups ($\frac{1}{2}$ cup; $\frac{1}{3}$ cup; $\frac{1}{4}$ cup)
Children divide cereal into equal portions.

ELL SUPPORT

Building a Math Word Bank

Differentiation Handbook, p. 127
Children add the terms *whole, equal parts,* and *one half* to their Math Word Banks.

Advance Preparation

For the Math Message discussion in Part 1, use a small and a large fruit bar. For the optional Enrichment activity in Part 3, label the respective measuring cups *small, medium,* and *large.* You may wish to obtain ***Picture Pie: A Circle Drawing Book*** by Ed Emberley (Little, Brown, 2006) as it relates to lesson content.

***Teacher's Reference Manual,* Grades 1–3** pp. 61, 62, 159–161

Getting Started

Mental Math and Reflexes

Display a transparency of the Museum Store Mini-Poster (*Math Masters,* page 231) or have children turn to journal page 162. Name two or three items and ask children to estimate whether the total cost of the items is more than or less than one dollar. Children show "thumbs-up" if they estimate that it is more than one dollar and "thumbs-down" if they estimate that it is less. Children share estimation strategies.

Math Message

Draw a tally chart with the headings *fruit bar, half of a fruit bar,* and *don't know.* Ask: *Which would you want, a fruit bar or half a fruit bar? Make a tally mark to show your vote.*

Home Link 8·5 Follow-Up

Briefly go over the answers.

1 Teaching the Lesson

▶ Math Message Follow-Up

NOTE Continue to stress the importance of the unit whenever there is an opportunity; for example, a sixth of a window is different from a sixth of a bookshelf; and half of a dollar is different from half of a hundred dollars.

Encourage children to explain their votes. Some children might prefer half of a fruit bar for various reasons. Someone may observe that half of some fruit bars is more than the whole bar of some others. Point out to children that the size of a "half" depends on the size of the unit with which you start.

Make a list of items children have divided in half in order to share with someone. Examples may include a cookie, a sandwich, a piece of gum, and a piece of paper. Again, point out that the size of a half is dependent on the size of the whole.

▶ Dividing Slates into Equal Parts

NOTE For these exercises, draw rectangles on the board to simulate slates and mark the rectangles in various ways as you discuss children's slate responses to your requests.

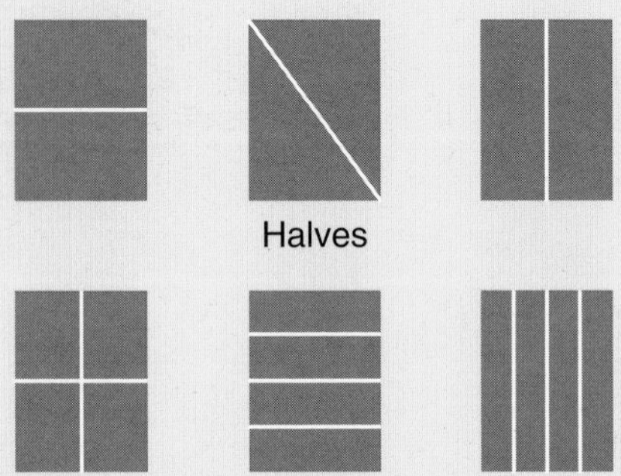

Have each child divide a slate, the **whole,** into 2 approximately **equal parts** with a chalk mark. Encourage children to make their divisions as equal as they can. Observe that each part is one of two equal parts.

As children display their slates, discuss different ways slates can be divided in half. Most children probably divided their slates vertically or horizontally. Ask if anyone divided the slate diagonally.

Count **halves.** Children draw an X in one part of their slates as they say "one half of a slate," then an X in the other part as they say "two halves of a slate." To support English language learners, write *1 half* and *2 halves* on the board. Discuss the spelling of the plural form of the word *half.*

NOTE Children are decomposing shapes when they divide larger shapes (their slates) into smaller shapes. After each division of the slate, ask: *Into what shapes did you divide your slate?*

Children erase their chalk marks and then divide their slates into 4 approximately equal parts. Explain that each part is one-fourth of the slate. Discuss different solutions as children display their divided slates.

Count and write **fourths.** Children shade one part and say "one-fourth," shade another part and say "two-fourths," and continue for "three-fourths" and "four-fourths."

Repeat this procedure for **thirds.**

▶ Looking for Objects That Are Divided into Equal Parts

Children look around the room for objects that are divided into equal parts. They name each object and report the number of equal parts. Objects may include glass panes in windows, shelves in bookcases or storage units, sections of some Math Boxes, board sections, light fixtures, and/or drawers in filing cabinets.

▶ Folding and Cutting Whole Crackers into Equal Parts

(*Math Masters,* p. 234 and *Math Journal 2,* p. 165)

Have children cut out the crackers on *Math Masters,* page 234. Discuss ways to share one whole cracker equally between two people. Children fold and cut one of their whole crackers into two equal parts. They glue each part in the space under "Halves" on journal page 165. Partners follow the same routine for sharing one cracker equally among four people and among three people.

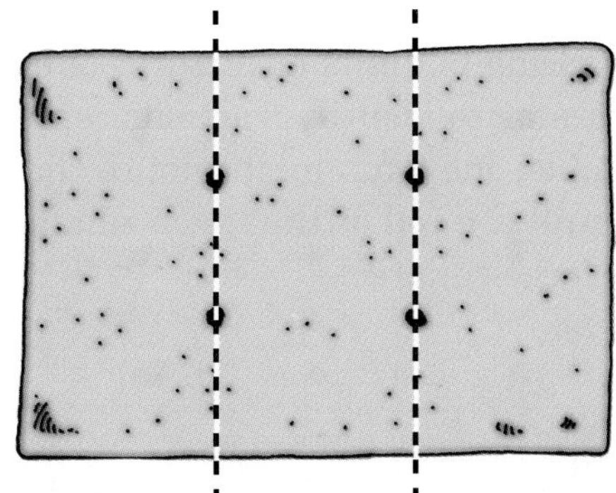

Sharing one cracker equally among three people

Ongoing Assessment: Recognizing Student Achievement

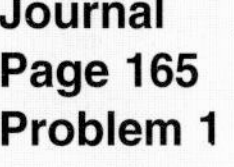

Journal Page 165 Problem 1

Use **journal page 165, Problem 1** to assess children's competency with fractions. Children are making adequate progress if they are able to correctly answer the first problem. Some children may be successful with all of the problems.

[Number and Numeration Goal 4]

Teaching Master

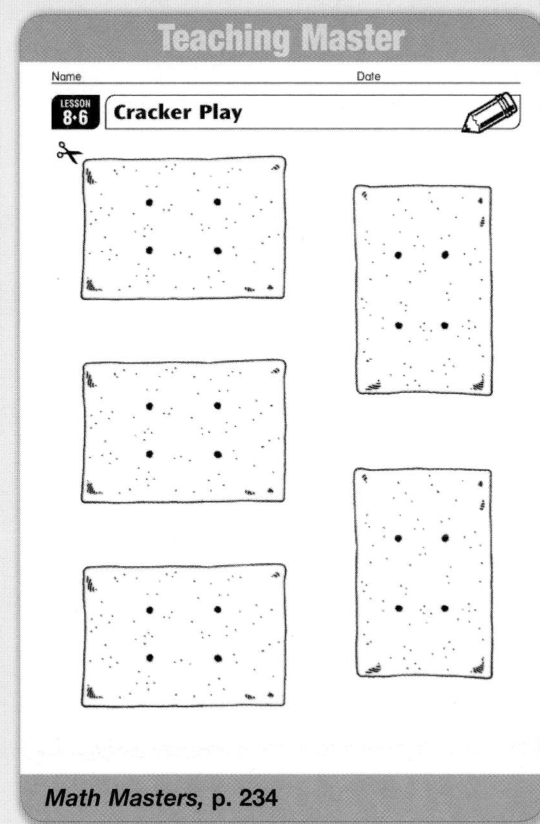

Name Date

LESSON 8·6 Cracker Play

Math Masters, p. 234

Student Page

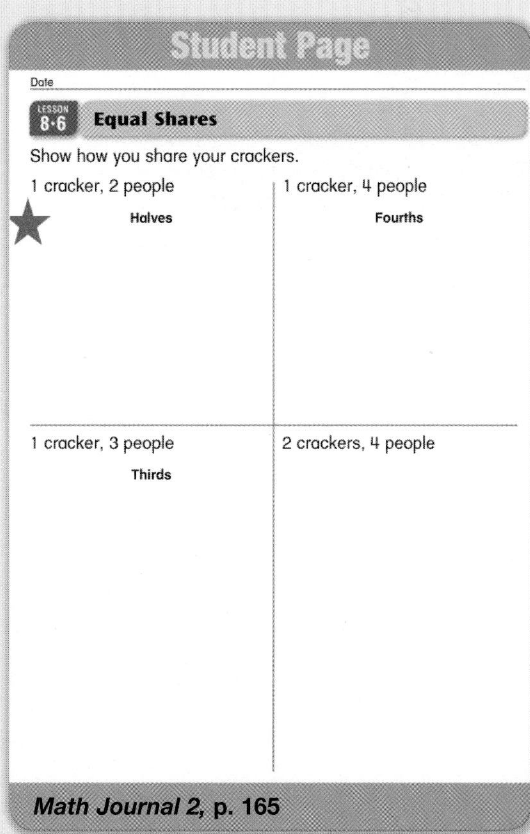

Date

LESSON 8·6 Equal Shares

Show how you share your crackers.

1 cracker, 2 people Halves	1 cracker, 4 people Fourths
1 cracker, 3 people Thirds	2 crackers, 4 people

Math Journal 2, p. 165

Adjusting the Activity

Suggest that children use the dots to help divide the crackers.

AUDITORY ◆ KINESTHETIC ◆ TACTILE ◆ VISUAL

When children have glued their pieces of crackers for fourths and thirds, ask: *When we cut the cracker into more parts, do the parts get bigger or smaller?* smaller *Which is more, one-fourth or one-half of a cracker?* one-half *If we cut the cracker into eight parts, would each part (one-eighth) be bigger or smaller than one-fourth of the cracker?* smaller

Challenge children with the following problem: *If you want to share two crackers equally among four people, how much would each person get?* Half of a cracker

Children use the two remaining crackers to solve the problem and paste the pieces at the bottom of the page.

▷ Ask children to explain how they got their answers. One strategy: Divide each cracker into two equal parts. Each person gets one part, or half of a cracker. Another strategy: Divide each cracker into four equal parts. Each person gets two parts, or two-fourths of a cracker.

▷ When children are finished, ask: *Which is more, two-fourths or one-half of a cracker?* They are equal. Encourage children to justify their answers using the crackers or by drawing pictures on the board.

Art Link Bring in quilts or pictures of quilts. Have children work in teams to identify fractions represented on the quilts. For example, one team might notice that one-half of the triangles on a quilt are red or that each small square represents one-fourth of a large square.

2 Ongoing Learning & Practice

▶ Making Jam Sandwiches

PARTNER ACTIVITY

(*Math Masters,* p. 235)

Give each partnership colored squares. Explain that purple represents grape jam, red represents strawberry jam, orange represents peach jam, yellow represents a cracker, and brown represents a slice of bread. Write each of these representations on the board. Tell children that they are going to "make" jam sandwiches using one kind of jam and either the bread or the cracker. Have children record all of the possible kinds of sandwiches on *Math Masters,* page 235. When they are finished, discuss their work.

Teaching Master

Name Date

LESSON 8·6 **Making Jam Sandwiches**

Use crayons. Color the squares in the table to show the jam and the bread or cracker.

Sandwich 1	Sandwich 2	Sandwich 3
Sandwich 4	**Sandwich 5**	**Sandwich 6**

Math Masters, p. 235

Adjusting the Activity

Ask children some of the following questions. Give them time to make the variations of sandwiches.

- How many sandwiches can you make if you run out of strawberry jam? 4 sandwiches
- How many sandwiches can you make if you only use bread? 3 sandwiches
- How many sandwiches can you make in all if you use four kinds of jam instead of just three kinds of jam? 8 sandwiches

AUDITORY ◆ KINESTHETIC ◆ TACTILE ◆ VISUAL

▶ Solving "What's My Rule?" Problems

PROBLEM SOLVING

(*Math Journal 2,* p. 166)

Algebraic Thinking Use journal page 166 to provide practice solving "What's My Rule?" problems.

▶ Math Boxes 8·6

(*Math Journal 2,* p. 167)

Mixed Practice Math Boxes in this lesson are paired with Math Boxes in Lesson 8-8. The skills in Problem 6 preview Unit 9 content.

Writing/Reasoning Have children draw, write, or verbalize an answer to the following question: *How do you make change?* A reasonable answer should include a strategy for finding the difference between the cost of the item and the amount paid.

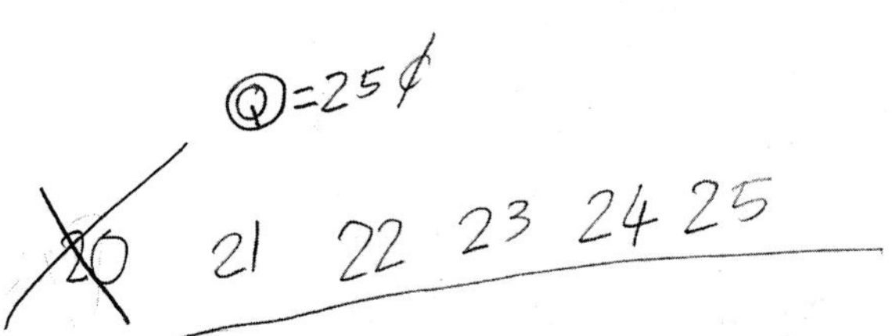

One child's work in response to the Writing/Reasoning prompt

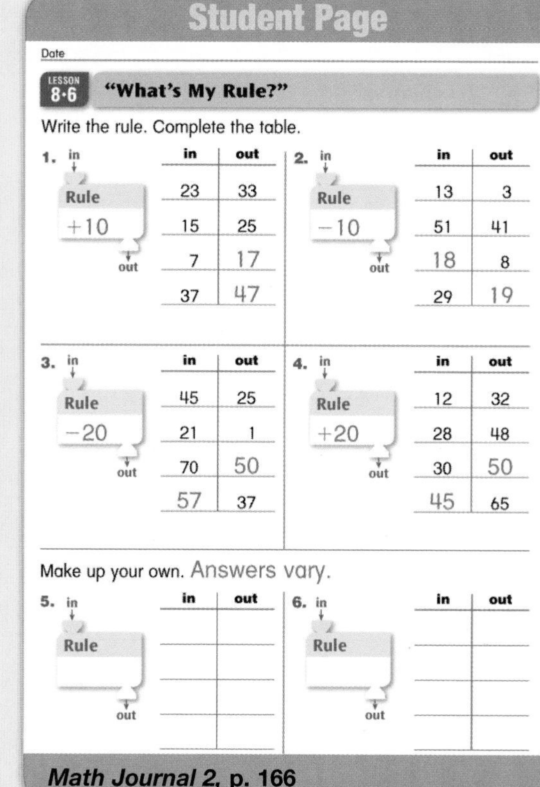

Student Page

Date

LESSON 8·6 **"What's My Rule?"**

Write the rule. Complete the table.

1. Rule: +10

in	out
23	33
15	25
7	17
37	47

2. Rule: −10

in	out
13	3
51	41
18	8
29	19

3. Rule: −20

in	out
45	25
21	1
70	50
57	37

4. Rule: +20

in	out
12	32
28	48
30	50
45	65

Make up your own. Answers vary.

5. Rule

in	out

6. Rule

in	out

Math Journal 2, **p. 166**

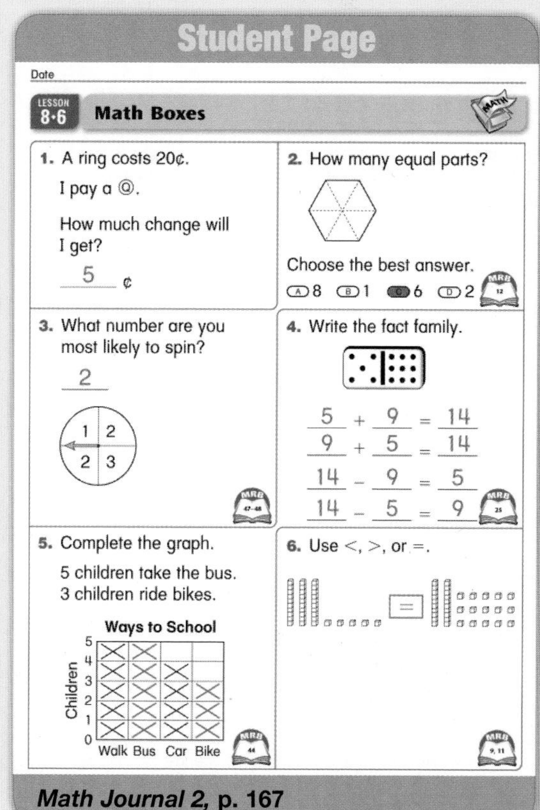

Student Page

Date

LESSON 8·6 **Math Boxes**

1. A ring costs 20¢. I pay a Ⓠ. How much change will I get? 5 ¢
2. How many equal parts? Choose the best answer. (A) 8 (B) 1 (C) 6 (D) 2
3. What number are you most likely to spin? 2
4. Write the fact family. 5 + 9 = 14; 9 + 5 = 14; 14 − 9 = 5; 14 − 5 = 9
5. Complete the graph. 5 children take the bus. 3 children ride bikes. Ways to School (Children; Walk, Bus, Car, Bike)
6. Use <, >, or =. =

Math Journal 2, **p. 167**

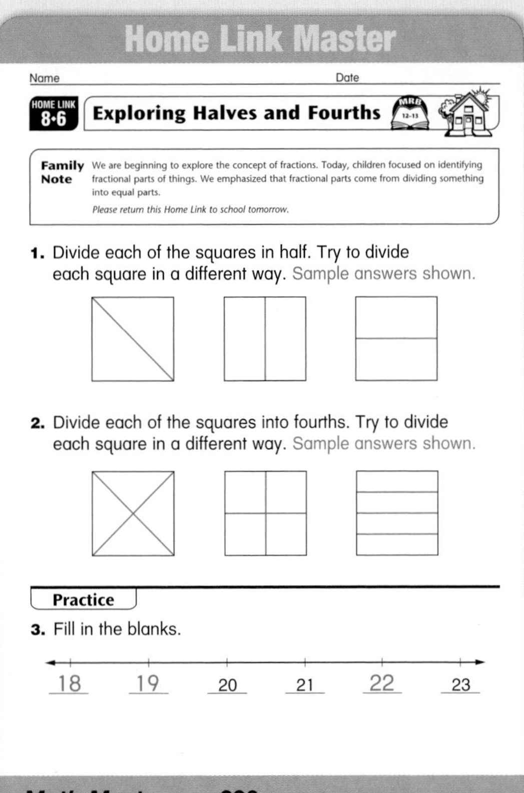
Home Link Master

Name Date

HOME LINK 8•6 **Exploring Halves and Fourths**

Family Note We are beginning to explore the concept of fractions. Today, children focused on identifying fractional parts of things. We emphasized that fractional parts come from dividing something into equal parts.

Please return this Home Link to school tomorrow.

1. Divide each of the squares in half. Try to divide each square in a different way. Sample answers shown.

2. Divide each of the squares into fourths. Try to divide each square in a different way. Sample answers shown.

Practice

3. Fill in the blanks.

18 19 20 21 22 23

Math Masters, p. 236

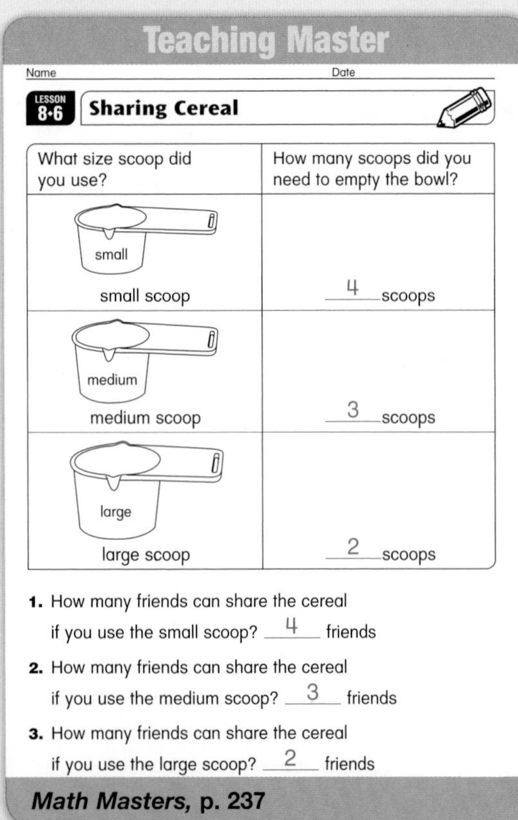
Teaching Master

Name Date

LESSON 8•6 **Sharing Cereal**

What size scoop did you use?	How many scoops did you need to empty the bowl?
small scoop	4 scoops
medium scoop	3 scoops
large scoop	2 scoops

1. How many friends can share the cereal if you use the small scoop? 4 friends
2. How many friends can share the cereal if you use the medium scoop? 3 friends
3. How many friends can share the cereal if you use the large scoop? 2 friends

Math Masters, p. 237

▶ Home Link 8•6

INDEPENDENT ACTIVITY

(*Math Masters,* p. 236)

Home Connection Children divide squares into halves and fourths in several different ways.

3 Differentiation Options

ENRICHMENT

INDEPENDENT ACTIVITY

15–30 Min

▶ Dividing Cereal with Standard Measuring Cups

(*Math Masters,* p. 237)

To explore the concept of sharing a quantity equally, have children measure equal portions of cereal. Give each child measuring cups labeled *small, medium,* and *large,* and a bowl with 1 cup of cereal in it. Have the child use the small measuring cup to scoop out all the cereal—they can pour each scoop onto a separate piece of paper. Remind them that the measuring cup must be full or level to be considered a scoop. Children record on *Math Masters,* page 237 how many small scoops it takes to empty the bowl. Refill the bowl and repeat the activity with the medium and the large scoops. Then have children answer the questions. Encourage them to think about how the size of the scoop determines the number of individual portions or the number of friends who can share the cereal.

ELL SUPPORT

SMALL-GROUP ACTIVITY

5–15 Min

▶ Building a Math Word Bank

(*Differentiation Handbook,* p. 127)

To provide language support for equal shares, have children use the Word Bank Template found on *Differentiation Handbook,* page 127. Ask children to write the terms *whole, equal parts,* and *one half,* draw pictures representing the terms, and write other words that describe them. See the *Differentiation Handbook* for more information.

8·7 Fractions

Objectives To guide further understanding of fractional parts of a whole; and to introduce unit fraction notation.

www.everydaymathonline.com

ePresentations

eToolkit

Algorithms Practice

EM Facts Workshop Game™

Family Letters

Assessment Management

Common Core State Standards

Curriculum Focal Points

Interactive Teacher's Lesson Guide

1 Teaching the Lesson

Key Concepts and Skills

- Count equal parts of wholes. [Number and Numeration Goal 2]
- Identify shapes divided into halves, thirds, and fourths. [Number and Numeration Goal 4]
- Record the number of equal parts in a whole and label each part with a corresponding fraction. [Number and Numeration Goal 4]

Key Activities

Children explore the idea that fractional parts of a whole must be equal. They are introduced to fraction notation for unit fractions. They label fractional parts of figures.

Ongoing Assessment: Informing Instruction See page 711.

Key Vocabulary

fraction ◆ fractional part

Materials

Math Journal 2, pp. 165, 168, and 169
Home Link 8•6
calculator

2 Ongoing Learning & Practice

Playing *One-Dollar Exchange*
Math Masters, p. 226
My Reference Book, pp. 144 and 145
per partnership: 2 dice, 1 dollar, 20 dimes, and 20 pennies
Children practice exchanging pennies for a dime and dimes for a dollar.

Math Boxes 8•7
Math Journal 2, p. 170
Children practice and maintain skills through Math Box problems.

Ongoing Assessment: Recognizing Student Achievement
Use Math Boxes, Problem 3.
[Geometry Goal 2]

Home Link 8•7
Math Masters, p. 238
Children practice and maintain skills through Home Link activities.

Minute Math+
Minute Math®+, pp. 30, 49, and 102
Children practice with counting, fractions, and number stories.

3 Differentiation Options

READINESS

Folding Paper Pizzas
per child: 1 large circle, square, triangle, and semicircle cut from $8\frac{1}{2}$" by 11" sheets of paper
Children explore equal parts by folding paper "pizzas."

ENRICHMENT

Making a Fraction Book
Math Masters, p. 239
Children make fraction books showing objects that are divided into equal parts.

Advance Preparation

For the optional Readiness activity in Part 3, cut a large circle, square, triangle, and semicircle out of an $8\frac{1}{2}$" by 11" piece of paper for each child. For the optional Enrichment activity in Part 3, make several copies of *Math Masters,* page 239 for each child. Cut each in half.

***Teacher's Reference Manual,* Grades 1–3** pp. 60, 61

Getting Started

Mental Math and Reflexes

Play *Beat the Calculator.* See Lesson 6-4 for directions.

Math Message

Look at the drinking glasses on journal page 168. Which glass is half full?

Home Link 8·6 Follow-Up

Briefly review answers. Ask volunteers to show how they divided squares into halves and fourths.

NOTE A fraction with the number 1 in the numerator is called a *unit fraction.* Notation for non-unit fractions (fractions with numerators other than 1) will be discussed in Lesson 9-7.

Student Page

Date

LESSON 8·7 **Equal Parts of Wholes**

Which glass is half full? Circle it.

Which rectangles are divided into thirds? Circle them.

A B C

D E F

Math Journal 2, p. 168

1 Teaching the Lesson

▶ Math Message Follow-Up

WHOLE-CLASS DISCUSSION

Children share answers. Some suggestions for discussion:

- How can you tell that the third glass is half full? The filled part takes up the same amount of space as the empty part. (Emphasize that for the glass to be half full, the parts must be equal.) Can we say that the glass is half empty? yes
- Does a glass that is half full have more water than a same-sized glass that is half empty? No. The amounts of water are the same.
- How can you tell that the other two glasses are not half full? The filled part and the empty part are not equal.
- Which glass is less than half full? The first glass Which is more than half full? The second glass

Discuss with children the idea that just because something is divided into two parts does not necessarily mean that each part is one-half of the whole.

▶ Introducing Fraction Notation

WHOLE-CLASS ACTIVITY

ELL

(*Math Journal 2,* pp. 165 and 168)

1. Hold up a quarter-sheet of paper and fold it into two equal parts. Unfold it. Draw a sketch of the piece of paper on the board. Label each part $\frac{1}{2}$. Explain that each part is one-half of the whole piece of paper. One-half is written as $\frac{1}{2}$, where the 1 is written above the line and the 2 below the line. On the board, write the following: $\frac{1}{2}$ is an example of a **fraction.** The 2 tells into how many equal parts the whole has been divided. The 1 tells how many of the equal parts we are talking about. Write $\frac{1}{2}$ in each half of your unfolded quarter-sheet of paper.

2. Ask children to write $\frac{1}{2}$ in each half of the half-full drinking glass on journal page 168.

3. Distribute quarter-sheets of paper. Ask children to fold them into four equal parts. Mention that each part is one-fourth of the sheet. Have children color each fourth in a different color or mark each with a different pattern such as dots or Xs. Then ask children to describe their sheets; for example, "One-fourth of my paper is red; one-fourth has dots on it."

NOTE Call children's attention to the fact that $\frac{1}{4}$ is read as "one-fourth;" not "one-fours."

Ask a volunteer to write the fraction $\frac{1}{4}$ on the board. Children then label each part $\frac{1}{4}$. Remind them that each part is one of four equal parts.

Tell children that the word *quarter* is another way of saying *one-fourth.* A 25-cent coin is called a quarter because it is one-fourth of a dollar. (There are four quarters in a dollar.) Ask for other examples where the word *quarter* means one-fourth. Sample answers: A quarter hour; a quart of milk is a quarter of a gallon; a quarter in a football game Write the children's answers on the board to support English language learners.

4. Ask children to turn to journal page 165 and to write the fraction $\frac{1}{2}$ in one of the half crackers. Also, have them label one of the fourths and one of the thirds of a cracker.

   Emphasize that a fraction always represents a **fractional part** of a whole thing; for example, one-half of a *whole* drinking glass, one-third of a *whole* sheet of paper, one-fourth of a *whole* cracker.

5. Ask children to circle the rectangles on journal page 168 that are divided into thirds. Rectangles C and E Discuss why the others are not divided into thirds. Rectangle A is divided into fourths. Rectangle B is divided in half. Rectangles D and F are divided into 3 parts, but the parts are not equal.

Labeling Fractional Parts of Geometric Figures

INDEPENDENT ACTIVITY

(*Math Journal 2,* p. 169)

Do Problem 1 with children to make sure that everyone understands what to do. As they work on Problems 2–4 independently, circulate to offer assistance and assess children's understanding of fractions.

Ongoing Assessment: Informing Instruction

Watch for children who do not label each part of a shape with the same fraction. Check children's work to be sure that the number under the fraction bar is the number of equal parts in the shape.

Adjusting the Activity

Remind children to count the total number of parts into which the shape is divided. Each part is 1 out of the total (x) number of parts, that is, $\frac{1}{x}$ of the figure.

AUDITORY ♦ KINESTHETIC ♦ TACTILE ♦ VISUAL

Student Page

Date

LESSON 8•7 **Fractions**

1. How many equal parts are there? 3

   Write a fraction in each part of the circle.

   Color $\frac{1}{3}$ of the circle.

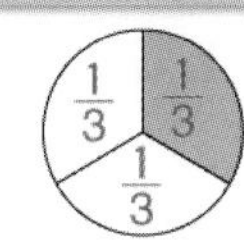

2. How many equal parts are there? 4

   Write a fraction in each part of the square.

   Color $\frac{1}{4}$ of the square.

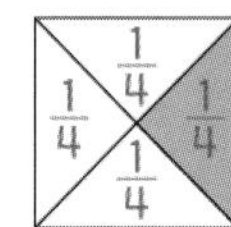

3. How many equal parts are there? 6

   Write a fraction in each part of the hexagon.

   Color $\frac{1}{6}$ of the hexagon.

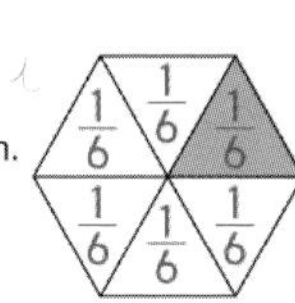

4. How many equal parts are there? 8

   Write a fraction in each part of the rectangle.

   Color $\frac{1}{8}$ of the rectangle.

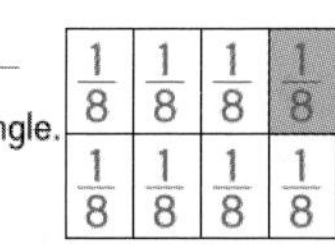

Math Journal 2, p. 169

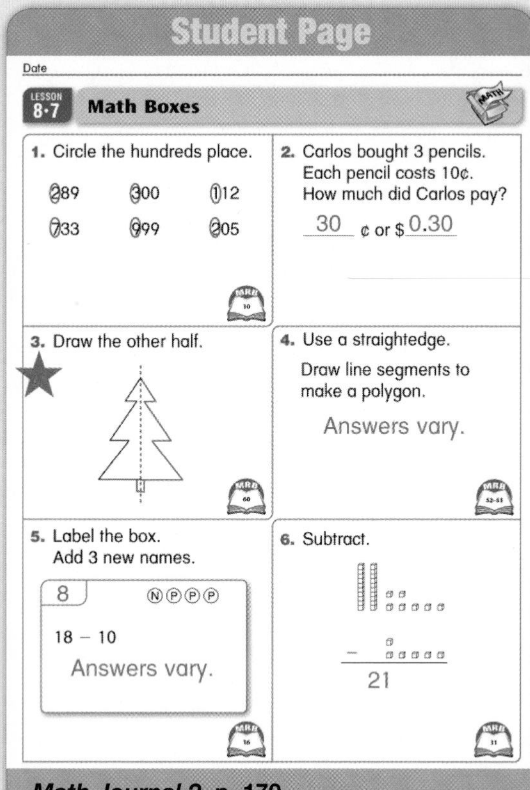
Student Page

Date

LESSON 8·7 **Math Boxes**

1. Circle the hundreds place.
289 300 012
733 999 205

2. Carlos bought 3 pencils. Each pencil costs 10¢. How much did Carlos pay?
30 ¢ or $ 0.30

3. Draw the other half.

4. Use a straightedge. Draw line segments to make a polygon.
Answers vary.

5. Label the box. Add 3 new names.
8
18 − 10
Answers vary.

6. Subtract.
21

Math Journal 2, p. 170

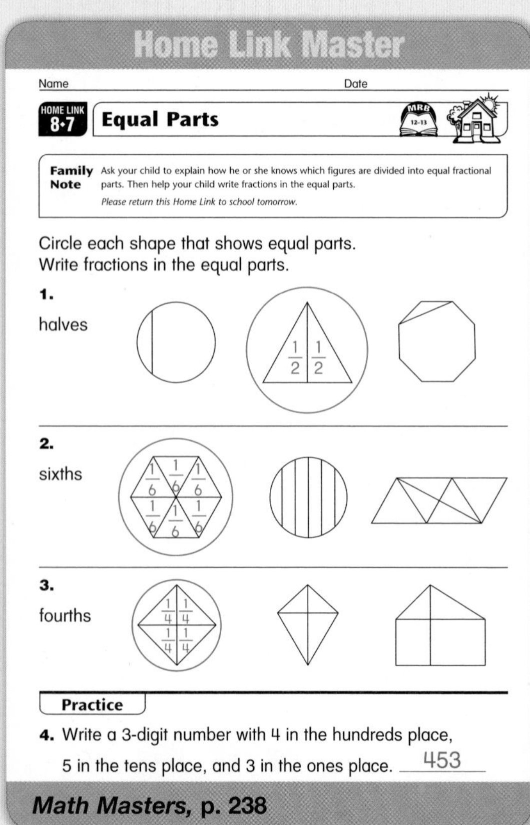
Home Link Master

Name Date

HOME LINK 8·7 **Equal Parts**

Family Note Ask your child to explain how he or she knows which figures are divided into equal fractional parts. Then help your child write fractions in the equal parts.
Please return this Home Link to school tomorrow.

Circle each shape that shows equal parts.
Write fractions in the equal parts.

1. halves

2. sixths

3. fourths

Practice

4. Write a 3-digit number with 4 in the hundreds place, 5 in the tens place, and 3 in the ones place. 453

Math Masters, p. 238

2 Ongoing Learning & Practice

▶ Playing *One-Dollar Exchange*

PARTNER ACTIVITY

(*Math Masters,* p. 226; *My Reference Book,* pp. 144 and 145)

Children practice money skills by playing *One-Dollar Exchange.* For detailed instructions, see Lesson 8-2.

▶ Math Boxes 8·7

INDEPENDENT ACTIVITY

(*Math Journal 2,* p. 170)

Mixed Practice Math Boxes in this lesson are linked to Math Boxes in Lessons 8-5 and 8-9. The skills in Problem 6 preview Unit 9 content.

Ongoing Assessment: Recognizing Student Achievement

Math Boxes Problem 3

Use **Math Boxes, Problem 3** to assess children's understanding of symmetry. Children are making adequate progress if they are able to draw the other half of the pine tree.

[Geometry Goal 2]

Writing/Reasoning Have children draw, write, or verbalize an answer to the following question: *How do you know how many hundreds are in a number?* A reasonable answer should point to the hundreds place of a number. Sample answer: If it is a 3-digit number, the first number is the number that tells how many hundreds are in the number.

▶ Home Link 8·7

INDEPENDENT ACTIVITY

(*Math Masters,* p. 238)

Home Connection Children decide which of a set of figures is divided into equal parts. They label the equal parts with the appropriate fraction.

▶ *Minute Math+*

WHOLE-CLASS ACTIVITY

Use *Minute Math+*, pages 30, 49, and 102, to provide practice with counting, fractions, and number stories.

3 Differentiation Options

READINESS

PARTNER ACTIVITY

▶ Folding Paper Pizzas

5–15 Min

To explore dividing shapes into halves using a concrete model, have children fold circles, squares, triangles, and semi-circles into two equal parts. Give each child the four different paper shapes. Children will work in pairs to divide "pizza" shapes into two equal parts. Have children decorate their pizzas by putting different ingredients in each of the equal parts; for example, it might be half sausage and half mushroom. Emphasize that the two parts must be equal for the pizza to be divided into halves. Discuss how the halves of different shapes are different in size. Have children describe their pizzas and share their strategies for dividing the shapes into two equal parts. *Sample Strategies:*

- ▷ "I folded the paper until the edges met all the way around."
- ▷ "I measured across and figured out what half of that would be."
- ▷ "I looked at it and guessed and folded to check my answer."

ENRICHMENT

INDEPENDENT ACTIVITY

▶ Making a Fraction Book

30+ Min

(*Math Masters,* p. 239)

To apply children's understanding of fraction concepts, have them make a fraction book. Plan to have children work on this activity for several days.

Distribute several Fraction Book pages (*Math Masters,* page 239). Children look for objects that are divided into equal parts. They draw one object on each half-sheet, shade a fraction of the equal parts, and complete the sentences on *Math Masters,* page 239. At first, have children shade one of the equal parts to make a unit fraction. Then children can go beyond unit fractions by coloring more than one equal part of the object. Have children describe the objects they drew and name the fractional parts they shaded and labeled.

Collect children's drawings and assemble into a Fraction Book.

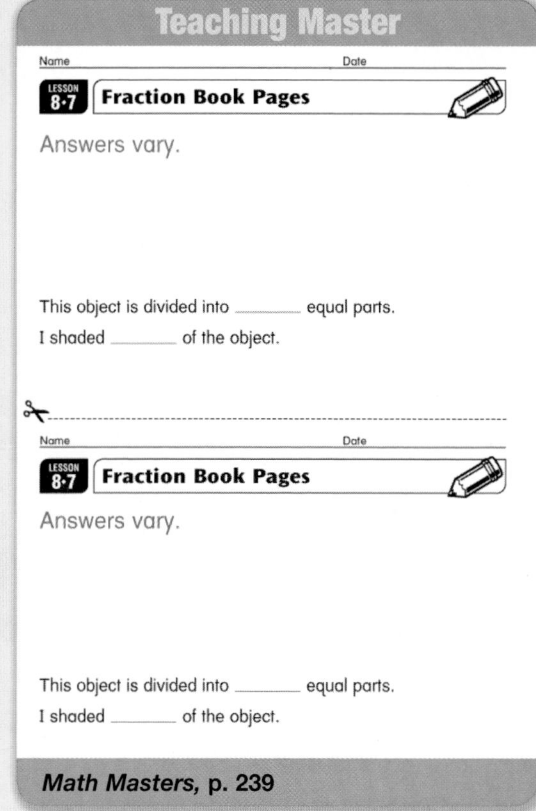
Teaching Master

Name Date

LESSON 8·7 **Fraction Book Pages**

Answers vary.

This object is divided into ______ equal parts.

I shaded ______ of the object.

Name Date

LESSON 8·7 **Fraction Book Pages**

Answers vary.

This object is divided into ______ equal parts.

I shaded ______ of the object.

Math Masters, p. 239

8•8 Sharing Pennies

Objective To introduce finding fractional parts of collections.

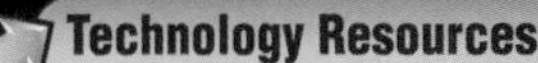

www.everydaymathonline.com

ePresentations

eToolkit

Algorithms Practice

EM Facts Workshop Game™

Family Letters

Assessment Management

Common Core State Standards

Curriculum Focal Points

Interactive Teacher's Lesson Guide

1 Teaching the Lesson

Key Concepts and Skills

- Count by halves, thirds, fourths, and sixths to 1.
  [Number and Numeration Goal 1]
- Find fractional parts of sets.
  [Number and Numeration Goal 4]

Key Activities

Children find fractional parts of collections of pennies.

Materials

Math Journal 2, pp. 171 and 172
Home Link 8•7
base-10 blocks ◆ tool-kit pennies

2 Ongoing Learning & Practice

Playing *Addition Top-It*

My Reference Book, pp. 122 and 123
per partnership: 4 each of number cards 0–10 (from the Everything Math Deck, if available)
Children practice addition skills.

Math Boxes 8•8

Math Journal 2, p. 173
Children practice and maintain skills through Math Box problems.

Ongoing Assessment: Recognizing Student Achievement

Use Math Boxes, Problem 5.
[Data and Chance Goal 3]

Home Link 8•8

Math Masters, p. 240
Children practice and maintain skills through Home Link activities.

3 Differentiation Options

ENRICHMENT

Making Fraction Creatures

per child: 12 one-inch paper squares in two different colors ◆ glue ◆ Pattern-Block Template and/or scissors (optional)
Children make "fraction creatures" out of equal-sized squares and write fractions to describe them.

EXTRA PRACTICE

Minute Math+

Minute Math®+, p. 40
Children practice finding parts in a whole.

ELL SUPPORT

Building a Math Word Bank

Differentiation Handbook, p. 126
Children add the terms *equal parts* and *fraction* to their Math Word Banks.

Getting Started

Mental Math and Reflexes

Set the following numbers of base-10 blocks on the overhead. Turn on the overhead for about 3–5 seconds and then turn it off. Ask children to estimate the number that the blocks represent. Count the blocks to check the accuracy of their estimates.

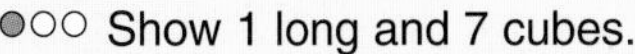

●○○ Show 1 long and 7 cubes.
●●○ Show 2 longs and 14 cubes.
●●● Show 3 longs and 20 cubes.

Math Message

Take 14 pennies. If you share them equally with a friend, how many pennies will each of you have?

Home Link 8·7 Follow-Up

Children discuss their choices in each of the problems. Ask children to show how they wrote fractions for the shapes with equal parts.

1 Teaching the Lesson

▶ Math Message Follow-Up

WHOLE-CLASS ACTIVITY

Ask a volunteer to act out sharing 14 pennies with a friend. One possible strategy is to distribute the pennies into two piles, as if you were dealing playing cards: One for you, one for me, one for you, one for me, and so on, until you run out of pennies.

Tell children that they are going to practice sharing pennies equally.

NOTE In this lesson, children divide a group of pennies into equal groups. At later grades, equal groups will be used to write repeated addition sentences such as 4 + 4 + 4 = 12. Repeated addition and rectangular arrays will be used as a basis to teach multiplication. For more information about these topics, see *My Reference Book,* pages 36–38.

▶ Sharing 12 Pennies

WHOLE-CLASS ACTIVITY

PROBLEM SOLVING

1. Ask children to count out 12 pennies and act out the following problem: *If you shared your pennies equally with a friend, how many pennies would each of you get?* 6 pennies

Draw a picture demonstrating that each share represents one-half of the total number of pennies, that is, one-half of 12 pennies.

Count halves. Children point to their piles of pennies as they count: "One half, two halves."

To summarize, write the following on the board:

$$\frac{1}{2} \textit{ of 12 pennies} = \textit{6 pennies}$$

2. Have children act out sharing 12 pennies equally among 3 people. Mention that each pile represents one-third of 12 pennies.

Count thirds. Children point to their piles as they count: "One third, two thirds, three thirds."

To summarize, write the following on the board:

$$\frac{1}{3} \textit{ of 12 pennies} = \textit{4 pennies}$$

- *How many pennies will 2 of the 3 people get in all?* 8 pennies

Children act out sharing 12 pennies among 3 people.

NOTE Throughout this activity, emphasize that the shares must be equal.

Student Page

Date

Sharing Pennies

Use your pennies to help you solve the problems.
Circle each person's share.

1. Halves: 2 people share 8 pennies equally.

   How many pennies does each person get? 4 pennies

2. Thirds: 3 people share 9 pennies equally.

   How many pennies does each person get? 3 pennies

   How many pennies do 2 of the 3 people get in all?

   6 pennies

Math Journal 2, **p. 171**

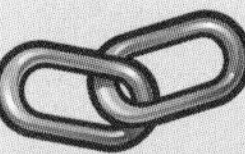

Links to the Future

This is children's first exposure to finding fractions of a set. Most children should be able to model half of a set of objects. Finding fractions of a set with numerators greater than 1, such as $\frac{2}{3}$, is a Grade 2 Goal.

3. Repeat the above routine for equal shares among 4 people.
   - How many pennies will 2 people get in all? 6 pennies
   - How many pennies will 3 people get in all? 9 pennies
4. Repeat the above routine for 6 people and 12 people.
5. Have children try to divide 11 pennies into two equal shares. Discuss what happens. One-half of 11 is $5\frac{1}{2}$. Since a penny cannot be cut in half, 11 pennies cannot be divided into two equal shares.

NOTE You may wish to have children share a group of pennies among 5 people.

▶ Practicing Sharing Pennies

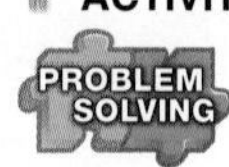

(*Math Journal 2,* pp. 171 and 172)

Children show equal shares of various numbers of pennies among various numbers of people. They use pennies to act out the solutions to the problems and record their solutions by circling groups of pennies on journal pages 171 and 172.

Adjusting the Activity

Have children use one quarter-sheet of paper to represent each person with whom the pennies will be shared. They can then distribute the pennies onto the quarter-sheets of paper to form equal groups. Ask children who are able to solve the problems without manipulatives to share their mental strategies with the class.

AUDITORY ◆ KINESTHETIC ◆ TACTILE ◆ VISUAL

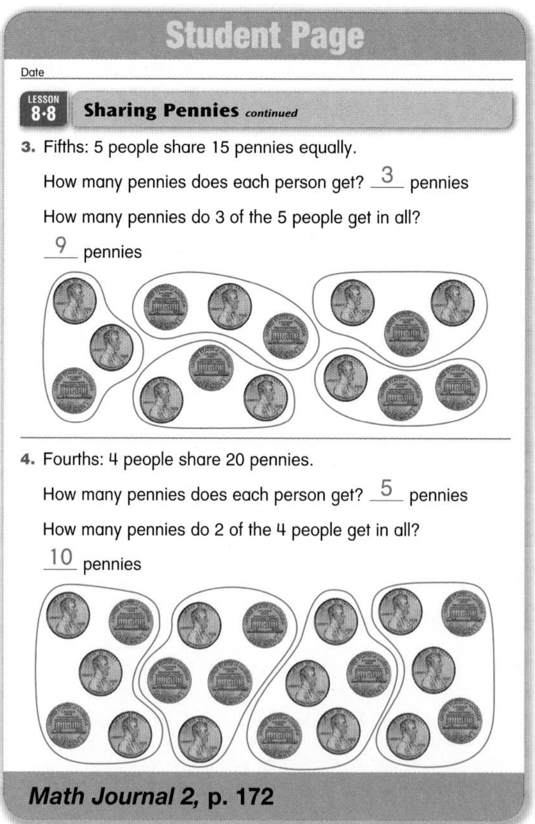

Student Page

Date

LESSON 8·8 **Sharing Pennies** *continued*

3. Fifths: 5 people share 15 pennies equally.

   How many pennies does each person get? 3 pennies

   How many pennies do 3 of the 5 people get in all?

   9 pennies

4. Fourths: 4 people share 20 pennies.

   How many pennies does each person get? 5 pennies

   How many pennies do 2 of the 4 people get in all?

   10 pennies

Math Journal 2, **p. 172**

2 Ongoing Learning & Practice

▶ Playing *Addition Top-It*

(*My Reference Book,* pp. 122 and 123)

Children practice addition skills by playing *Addition Top-It*. For detailed instructions, see Lesson 6-1.

▶ Math Boxes 8·8

INDEPENDENT ACTIVITY

(*Math Journal 2,* p. 173)

Mixed Practice Math Boxes in this lesson are paired with Math Boxes in Lesson 8-6. The skills in Problem 6 preview Unit 9 content.

▶ Home Link 8·8

INDEPENDENT ACTIVITY

(*Math Masters,* p. 240)

Home Connection Children find equal shares of a set of objects shared among a number of people.

Home Link Master

Name Date

HOME LINK 8·8 **Sharing Sets of Objects**

Family Note Today we extended our work with fractions to finding fractional parts of collections of objects. Help your child act out the problems below with pennies or counters. When sharing things equally, one strategy is to distribute the things just as you would deal cards in a card game and then count the things in one share.

Please return this Home Link to school tomorrow.

Use pennies to help you solve the problems.

1. Halves: 2 people share 10 pennies equally.
   Circle each person's share.

   Ⓟ Ⓟ Ⓟ Ⓟ Ⓟ Ⓟ Ⓟ Ⓟ Ⓟ Ⓟ

   How many pennies does each person get? 5 pennies
2. Thirds: 3 children share 12 balloons equally.
   Draw the balloons that each child gets.

   How many balloons does each child get? 4 balloons
3. Fourths: 4 children share 16 flowers equally.
   How many flowers does each child get? 4 flowers

Practice

4. How old will you be in 20 years? Answers vary.
   Is the number odd or even? Answers vary.

Math Masters, p. 240

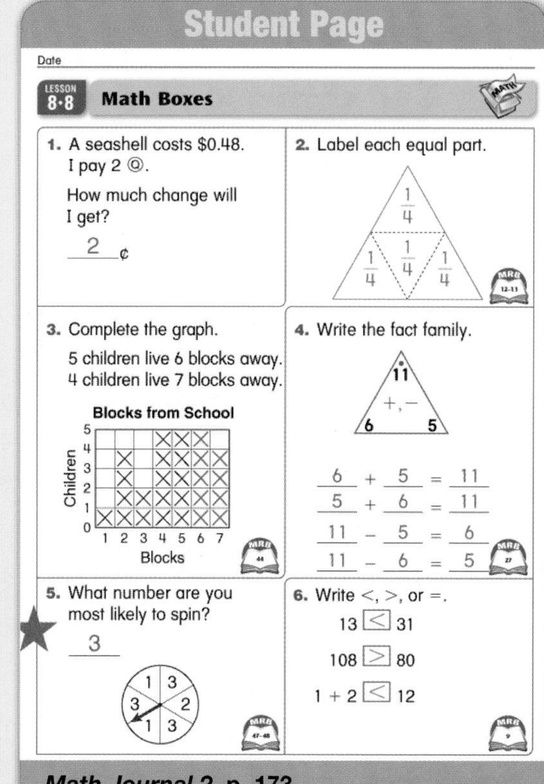

Student Page

Date

LESSON 8·8 **Math Boxes**

1. A seashell costs \$0.48. I pay 2 Ⓠ. How much change will I get? 2 ¢
2. Label each equal part. $\frac{1}{4}$ $\frac{1}{4}$ $\frac{1}{4}$ $\frac{1}{4}$
3. Complete the graph.
   5 children live 6 blocks away.
   4 children live 7 blocks away.

   Blocks from School (Children; Blocks 1 2 3 4 5 6 7)
4. Write the fact family. 11, 6, 5 (+, −)

   6 + 5 = 11
   5 + 6 = 11
   11 − 5 = 6
   11 − 6 = 5
5. What number are you most likely to spin? 3
6. Write $<$, $>$, or $=$.

   13 $<$ 31

   108 $>$ 80

   1 + 2 $<$ 12

Math Journal 2, p. 173

Ongoing Assessment: Recognizing Student Achievement

Math Boxes Problem 5

Use **Math Boxes, Problem 5** to assess children's proficiency with probability. Children are making adequate progress if they are able to tell that they are more likely to spin a 3.

[Data and Chance Goal 3]

My creature is $\frac{7}{12}$ blue and $\frac{5}{12}$ yellow.

NOTE You can make the squares yourself out of construction paper, or children can use their Pattern-Block Templates to draw and color the squares on a sheet of paper and then cut them out. Or they may use their templates to draw their creatures directly on paper.

3 Differentiation Options

ENRICHMENT

INDEPENDENT ACTIVITY

Making Fraction Creatures

30+ Min

To apply children's understanding of fractions of a set, have them use 12 one-inch squares in two different colors to make a "fraction creature." Children paste their creatures on a sheet of paper and write fractions that describe their creatures.

SMALL-GROUP ACTIVITY

Minute Math+

5–15 Min

Use *Minute Math+,* page 40 to provide practice with fractions by finding parts of a whole.

ELL SUPPORT

SMALL-GROUP ACTIVITY

Building a Math Word Bank

5–15 Min

(*Differentiation Handbook,* p. 126)

To provide language support for fractions, have children use the Word Bank Template found on *Differentiation Handbook,* page 126. Ask children to write the terms *equal parts* and *fraction,* draw pictures representing the terms, and write other words that describe them. See the *Differentiation Handbook* for more information.

8•9 Exploring Fractional Parts and Addition Facts

Explorations

Objectives To guide exploration of the relationship between multiples and fractions; to reinforce naming fractional parts of regions; and to provide practice with addition facts.

Technology Resources www.everydaymathonline.com

ePresentations

eToolkit

Algorithms Practice

EM Facts Workshop Game™

Family Letters

Assessment Management

Common Core State Standards

Curriculum Focal Points

Interactive Teacher's Lesson Guide

1 Teaching the Lesson

Key Concepts and Skills

- Use fractions to relate smaller shapes to larger shapes. [Number and Numeration Goal 4]
- Divide shapes into equal parts and label the parts. [Number and Numeration Goal 4]
- Recognize and sort doubles facts and near-doubles facts. [Operations and Computation Goal 1]

Key Activities

Exploration A: Children solve and design pattern-block puzzles involving fractional parts. They label the fractional parts of each figure.

Exploration B: Children divide geoboard shapes into 2, 3, or 4 equal parts.

Exploration C: Children sort Fact Triangles into doubles, near doubles, and sums of 10, and then practice the facts.

Ongoing Assessment: Recognizing Student Achievement Use the Math Message. [Geometry Goal 1]

Ongoing Assessment: Informing Instruction See page 721.

Key Vocabulary

near doubles

Materials

Home Link 8•8
Pattern-Block Template

Exploration A: Per group:
Math Masters, pp. 241 and 242
pattern blocks ◆ Pattern-Block Template

Exploration B: Per partnership:
Math Masters, pp. 315 and 316
geoboard ◆ rubber bands (colored, if possible)

Exploration C: Per partnership:
Math Masters, p. 243
Fact Triangles

2 Ongoing Learning & Practice

Playing the *3, 2, 1 Game*
My Reference Book, pp. 150 and 151
per partnership: slate

Math Boxes 8•9
Math Journal 2, p. 174

Home Link 8•9
Math Masters, p. 244

3 Differentiation Options

READINESS

Cutting Symmetrical Shapes
scissors ◆ drawing paper

EXTRA PRACTICE

Two-Fisted Penny Addition for 17 and 18
Math Masters, p. 151

Advance Preparation

Put pieces of paper near the Math Message.

Getting Started

Mental Math and Reflexes

Do stop and start counts. Give the following directions:

●○○ Begin at 0. Count by 10s to 60. Stop. Continue counting by 5s to 75. Stop. Continue counting by 1s to 78.

●●○ Begin at 0. Count by 25s to 50. Stop. Continue counting by 10s to 100. Stop. Continue counting by 5s to 115. Stop. Continue counting by 1s to 117.

●●● Begin at 25. Count by 25s to 100. Stop. Continue counting by 10s to 150. Stop. Continue counting by 5s to 195. Stop. Continue counting by 1s to 199.

Math Message 

Take a piece of paper. Use your Pattern-Block Template to draw each pattern-block shape. Write the name of each shape.

Home Link 8·8 Follow-Up

Briefly go over the answers to Problems 1–4.

1 Teaching the Lesson

▶ Math Message Follow-Up

WHOLE-CLASS ACTIVITY

Go over the answers. You may want to collect the children's papers to assess their progress.

Ongoing Assessment: Recognizing Student Achievement

Math Message 

Use the **Math Message** to assess children's knowledge of the names of 2-dimensional shapes. Children are making adequate progress if they are able to name triangles, squares, and circles.

[Geometry Goal 1]

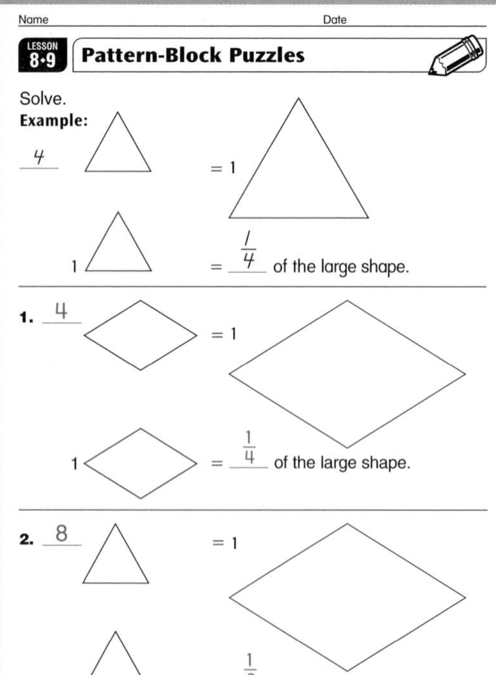

Teaching Master

Name Date

LESSON 8·9 **Pattern-Block Puzzles**

Solve.

Example: 4 (triangles) = 1 (large triangle)

1 (triangle) = 1/4 of the large shape.

1. 4 (rhombuses) = 1 (large rhombus)

1 (rhombus) = 1/4 of the large shape.

2. 8 (triangles) = 1 (large rhombus)

1 (triangle) = 1/8 of the large shape.

Math Masters, p. 241

▶ Exploration A: Finding Relationships Involving Pattern Blocks

SMALL-GROUP ACTIVITY

(*Math Masters*, pp. 241 and 242)

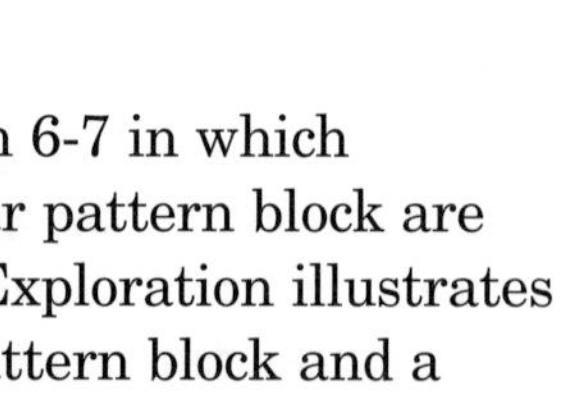

This is a follow-up to Exploration A in Lesson 6-7 in which children determined how many of a particular pattern block are needed to cover a larger pattern block. This Exploration illustrates how the relationship between the size of a pattern block and a larger shape can be expressed as a multiple of the smaller block or as a fraction of the larger block.

Draw a rhombus on the board. Ask children to use two triangle pattern blocks to make a rhombus. Ask a child to show where to draw a line to divide the rhombus into two triangles. Ask: *How many triangles make the whole rhombus?* 2 Explain that this whole can be described as two triangles, or two of the shares. Ask: *What fraction of the rhombus is each triangle?* one-half

Do the example on *Math Masters,* page 241 together.

1. Have children cover the larger shape with one kind of pattern block. In this case, cover the large triangle with small triangle pattern blocks.
2. Use the Pattern-Block Template to draw the arrangement of the pattern blocks on the larger shape.
3. Fill in the numbers that express the relationship between the pattern block and the larger shape. For the example, ask: *How many small triangles make up the large triangle?* 4 Point out that you can describe the whole as four, or all, of the shares. Ask: *What fraction of the whole large triangle is each small triangle?* one-fourth Tell children that another way to say "one-fourth" is "one-quarter."

Following the same steps, children complete *Math Masters* pages 241 and 242. They may work together, but children make their own records.

▶ Exploration B: Naming Fractional Parts of Regions

PARTNER ACTIVITY

(*Math Masters,* pp. 315 and 316)

Each partnership starts with a geoboard and several rubber bands. One partner makes a symmetrical shape with a rubber band. The other partner uses more rubber bands to try to divide the shape into 2 (or 3 or 4) equal parts. On their record sheets, each partner records four of the shapes that can be divided into equal parts and shows how they were divided. Encourage children to begin with a variety of symmetric shapes, including rectangles, squares, and triangles.

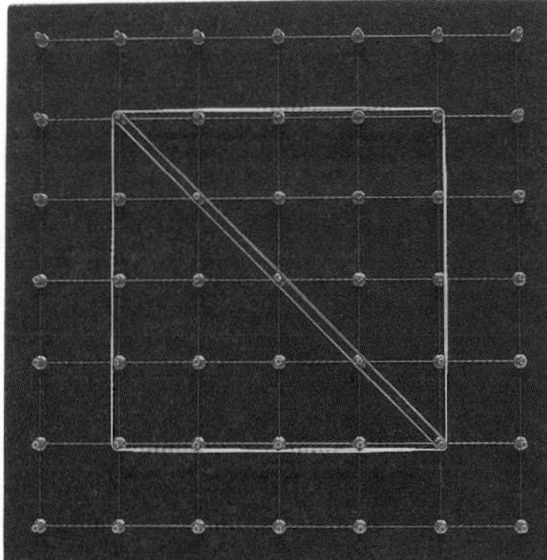

Ongoing Assessment: Informing Instruction

Watch for children who make irregular shapes on their geoboards. Remind them to create symmetrical shapes that can be divided equally.

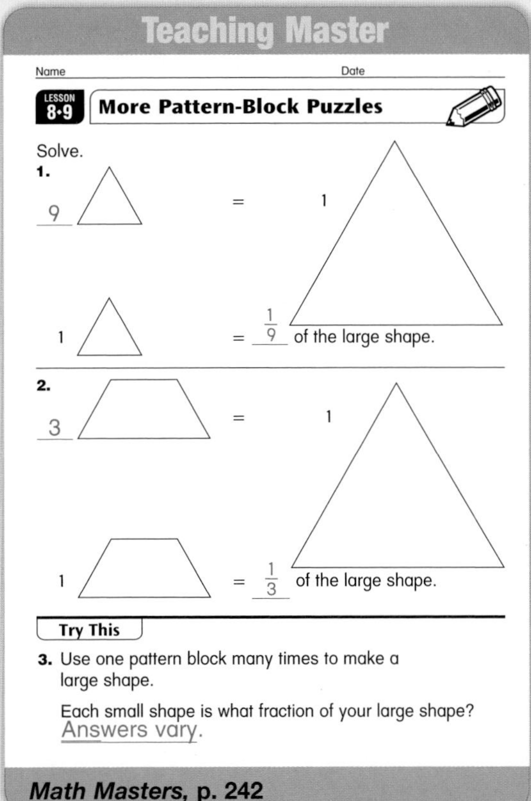

Teaching Master

Name Date

LESSON 8•9 **More Pattern-Block Puzzles**

Solve.

1. 9 (small triangle) = 1 (large triangle)

1 (small triangle) = $\frac{1}{9}$ of the large shape.

2. 3 (trapezoid) = 1 (large triangle)

1 (trapezoid) = $\frac{1}{3}$ of the large shape.

Try This

3. Use one pattern block many times to make a large shape.

Each small shape is what fraction of your large shape?
Answers vary.

Math Masters, p. 242

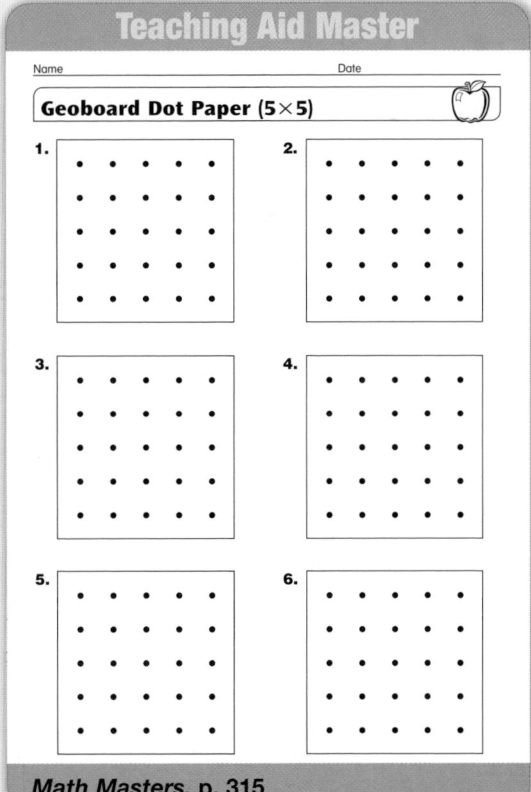

Teaching Aid Master

Name Date

Geoboard Dot Paper (5×5)

1. 2. 3. 4. 5. 6.

Math Masters, p. 315

Teaching Master

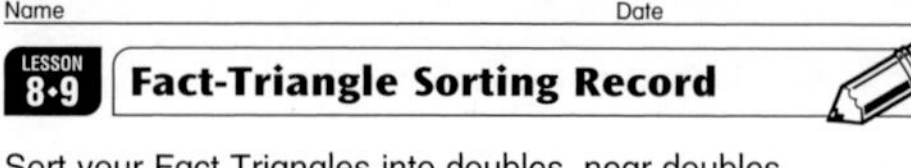

Name Date

LESSON 8·9 **Fact-Triangle Sorting Record**

Sort your Fact Triangles into doubles, near doubles, and 10 sums. Record each kind below.

Doubles

2 + 2 = 4	5 + 5 = 10	8 + 8 = 16
3 + 3 = 6	6 + 6 = 12	9 + 9 = 18
4 + 4 = 8	7 + 7 = 14	

Near Doubles

2 + 3 = 5	5 + 4 = 9	7 + 8 = 15
3 + 2 = 5	5 + 6 = 11	8 + 7 = 15
3 + 4 = 7	6 + 5 = 11	8 + 9 = 17
4 + 3 = 7	6 + 7 = 13	9 + 8 = 17
4 + 5 = 9	7 + 6 = 13	2 + 1 = 3
		1 + 2 = 3

10 Sums

2 + 8 = 10	7 + 3 = 10	6 + 4 = 10
8 + 2 = 10	4 + 6 = 10	5 + 5 = 10
3 + 7 = 10	1 + 9 = 10	9 + 1 = 10

Math Masters, p. 243

▶ Exploration C: Sorting Fact Triangles

PARTNER ACTIVITY

FACTS PRACTICE

(*Math Masters,* p. 243)

Before children begin this Exploration, make sure they understand the meaning of **near doubles** (also known as doubles plus-1).

Partners sort one set of Fact Triangles into doubles, near doubles, 10 sums, and other facts and then record them on *Math Masters,* page 243. Then have children practice the facts, either by category or in random order.

Adjusting the Activity

List a doubles fact on the board and label it "doubles fact." Then record a related near-doubles fact. Label this "near-doubles fact."

AUDITORY ◆ KINESTHETIC ◆ TACTILE ◆ VISUAL

2 Ongoing Learning & Practice

▶ Playing the *3, 2, 1 Game*

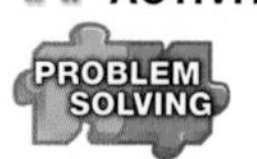

(*My Reference Book,* pp. 150 and 151)

Children practice subtraction playing the *3, 2, 1 Game.* For detailed instructions, see *My Reference Book,* pages 150 and 151.

▶ Math Boxes 8·9

(*Math Journal 2,* p. 174)

Mixed Practice Math Boxes in this lesson are linked to Math Boxes in Lessons 8-5 and 8-7. The skills in Problem 6 preview Unit 9 content.

Student Page

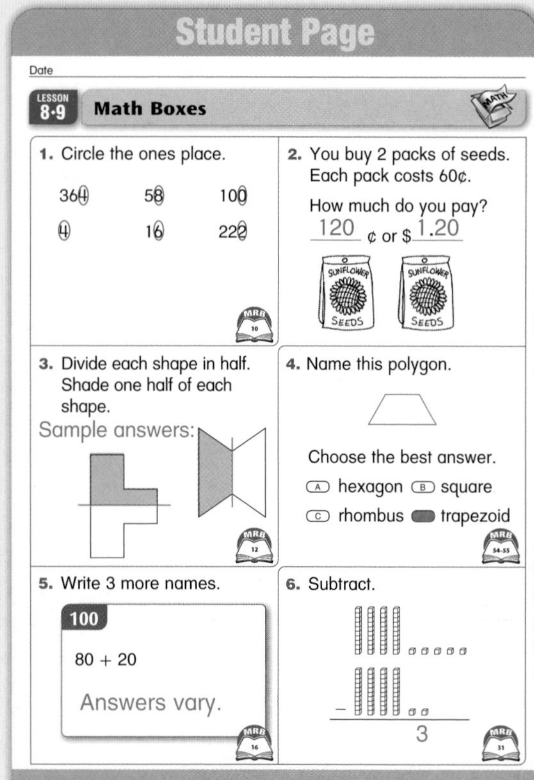

Date

LESSON 8·9 **Math Boxes**

1. Circle the ones place.
   364 58 100
   4 16 222

2. You buy 2 packs of seeds. Each pack costs 60¢.
   How much do you pay?
   120 ¢ or $ 1.20

3. Divide each shape in half. Shade one half of each shape.
   Sample answers:

4. Name this polygon.
   Choose the best answer.
   (A) hexagon (B) square
   (C) rhombus (D) trapezoid

5. Write 3 more names.
   100
   80 + 20
   Answers vary.

6. Subtract.
   3

Math Journal 2, p. 174

▶ Home Link 8•9

(*Math Masters,* p. 244)

Home Connection Children practice addition and subtraction facts. The goal is for children to have memorized the +0, +1, doubles facts, and 10 sums by the end of this school year.

3 Differentiation Options

READINESS

▶ Cutting Symmetrical Shapes

Portfolio Ideas

To explore the concept of equal parts using a concrete model, have children test circles, squares, and triangles for symmetry. Have children attempt to cut a circle, triangle, and square from drawing paper. Guide children to fold paper shapes in half to test for symmetry. Encourage them to trim shapes as necessary to make them symmetrical. If no one suggests it, share the strategy of folding the paper first and then cutting half the shape.

EXTRA PRACTICE

▶ Two-Fisted Penny Addition for 17 and 18

(*Math Masters,* p. 151)

Children complete Two-Fisted Penny Addition to provide practice finding complements for the numbers 17 and 18. See Lesson 2-3 for detailed instructions.

Home Link Master

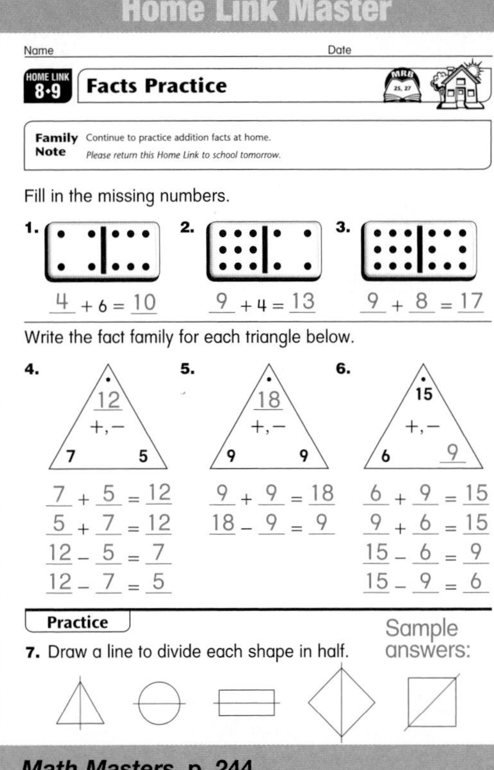

Name Date

HOME LINK 8•9 **Facts Practice**

Family Note Continue to practice addition facts at home. *Please return this Home Link to school tomorrow.*

Fill in the missing numbers.

1. 4 + 6 = 10
2. 9 + 4 = 13
3. 9 + 8 = 17

Write the fact family for each triangle below.

4. 12, 7, 5 (+, −)
7 + 5 = 12
5 + 7 = 12
12 − 5 = 7
12 − 7 = 5

5. 18, 9, 9 (+, −)
9 + 9 = 18
18 − 9 = 9

6. 15, 6, 9 (+, −)
6 + 9 = 15
9 + 6 = 15
15 − 6 = 9
15 − 9 = 6

Practice

7. Draw a line to divide each shape in half. Sample answers:

***Math Masters,* p. 244**

Teaching Master

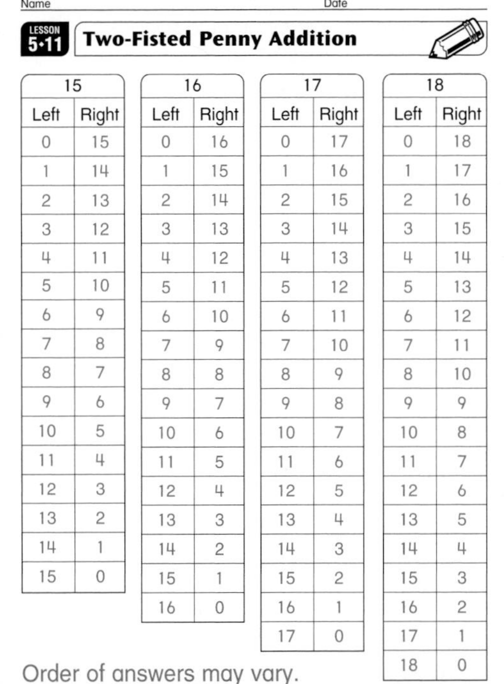

Name Date

LESSON 5•11 **Two-Fisted Penny Addition**

15		16		17		18	
Left	Right	Left	Right	Left	Right	Left	Right
0	15	0	16	0	17	0	18
1	14	1	15	1	16	1	17
2	13	2	14	2	15	2	16
3	12	3	13	3	14	3	15
4	11	4	12	4	13	4	14
5	10	5	11	5	12	5	13
6	9	6	10	6	11	6	12
7	8	7	9	7	10	7	11
8	7	8	8	8	9	8	10
9	6	9	7	9	8	9	9
10	5	10	6	10	7	10	8
11	4	11	5	11	6	11	7
12	3	12	4	12	5	12	6
13	2	13	3	13	4	13	5
14	1	14	2	14	3	14	4
15	0	15	1	15	2	15	3
		16	0	16	1	16	2
				17	0	17	1
						18	0

Order of answers may vary.

***Math Masters,* p. 151**

8•10 Progress Check 8

Objective To assess children's progress on mathematical content through the end of Unit 8.

1 Looking Back: Cumulative Assessment

Input children's data from Progress Check 8 into the **Assessment Management Spreadsheets**.

Materials
- Home Link 8•9
- *Assessment Handbook,* pp. 110–117, 165–168, 184, and 228–231
- slate

CONTENT ASSESSED	LESSON(S)	ASSESSMENT ITEMS				
		SELF	ORAL/SLATE	WRITTEN PART A	WRITTEN PART B	OPEN RESPONSE
Count collections of objects. [Number and Numeration Goal 2]	8•3					✓
Read, write, and represent whole numbers; identify digits and express their values. [Number and Numeration Goal 3]	8•1, 8•3, 8•4, 8•5, 8•7, 8•9		4	4		
Use drawings to represent and explain fractions. [Number and Numeration Goal 4]	8•6–8•9	2	2, 3	1, 2	7	✓
Represent equivalent names for numbers. [Number and Numeration Goal 6]	8•2, 8•5, 8•7, 8•9	3	1	3		
Know addition and subtraction facts. [Operations and Computation Goal 1]	8•1–8•4, 8•9	4		5	9	
Use and explain strategies for solving number stories; calculate and compare the values of combinations of coins. [Operations and Computation Goal 2]	8•1–8•9	6		6		
Identify and describe solid figures. [Geometry Goal 1]	8•1–8•4	5			8	
Complete simple symmetric shapes or designs. [Geometry Goal 2]	8•5, 8•7, 8•9	1		2		
Use +, −, and = and explain what they mean. [Patterns, Functions, and Algebra Goal 2]	8•1, 8•3, 8•4, 8•6, 8•8				9	
Use the Commutative and Associative Properties of Addition. [Patterns, Functions, and Algebra Goal 3]	8•6, 8•8			5	9	

2 Looking Ahead: Preparing for Unit 9

Math Boxes 8•10

Home Link 8•10: Unit 9 Family Letter

Materials
- *Math Journal 2,* p. 175
- *Math Masters,* pp. 245–248

Getting Started

Math Message • Self Assessment

Complete the Self Assessment (Assessment Handbook, page 165).

Home Link 8·9 Follow-Up

Briefly go over the answers.

1 Looking Back: Cumulative Assessment

▶ Math Message Follow-Up

INDEPENDENT ACTIVITY

(Self Assessment, *Assessment Handbook*, p. 165)

The Self Assessment offers children the opportunity to reflect upon their progress.

▶ Oral and Slate Assessments

WHOLE-CLASS ACTIVITY

Problems 1 and 2 provide summative information and can be used for grading purposes. Problems 3 and 4 provide formative information that can be useful in planning future instruction.

Oral Assessment

1. State a number. Ask children to state an equivalent of that number. Give them an example such as "14." An equivalent would be 1 long and 4 cubes or 7 + 7. *Suggestions:*
   - 7
   - 29
   - 35
   - 40
   - 56
   - 75
2. Draw each of these shapes on the board with a dotted line. Ask: *Does the dotted line divide the shape into two equal parts?*

- 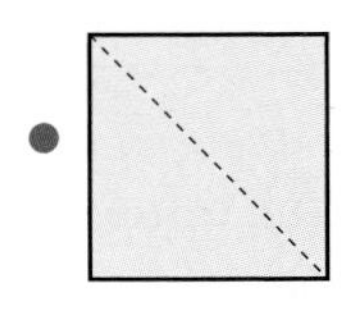 yes
- 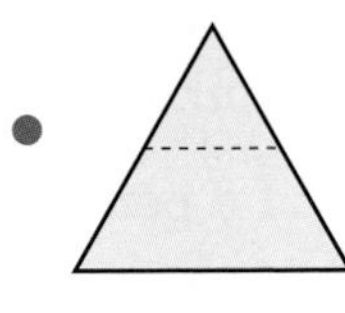 no
- 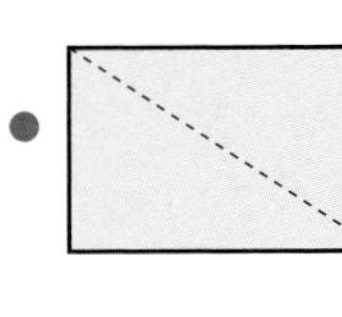 yes
- yes

Slate Assessment

3. Ask children to draw the stated shape using their Pattern-Block Templates. Then tell them into how many equal parts they should divide the shape. Ask them to label the equal parts with fractions.
   - square; four equal parts
     labels: $\frac{1}{4}$
   - circle; two equal parts
     labels: $\frac{1}{2}$
   - rectangle; three equal parts
     labels: $\frac{1}{3}$
   - rhombus; two equal parts
     labels: $\frac{1}{2}$

Assessment Master

Name Date

LESSON 8·10 **Self Assessment** Progress Check 8

Put a check in the box that tells how you do each skill.

Skills	I can do this by myself. I can explain how to do this.	I can do this by myself.	I can do this with help.
1. Complete symmetrical shapes.			
2. Find fractions.			
3. Fill name-collection boxes.			
4. Know math facts.			
5. Identify 3-dimensional shapes.			
6. Solve number stories.			

***Assessment Handbook,* p. 165**

Assessment Master

Name Date

LESSON 8·10 **Written Assessment** Progress Check 8

Part A

1. Divide each shape in half. Shade one half of each shape.

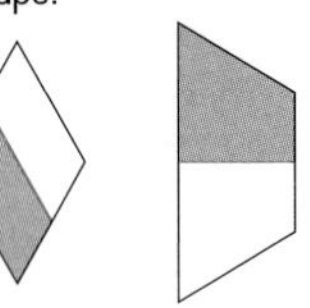

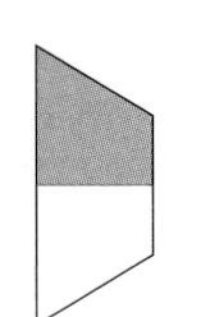

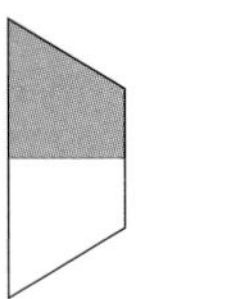

2. Draw the other half.

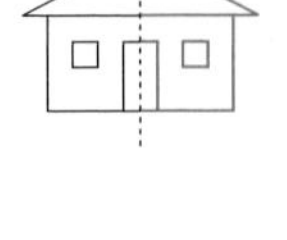

3. Label the box. Add 3 new names.

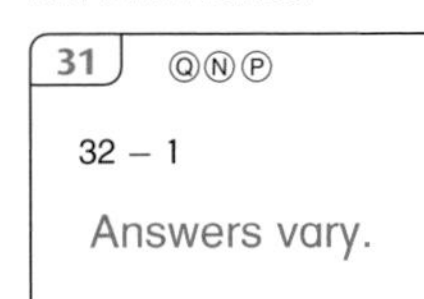

4. Write the number. Circle the number in the ones place.

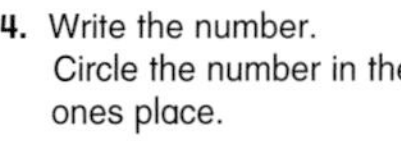

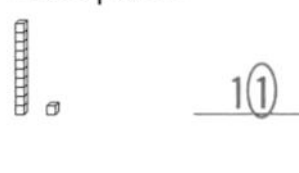

5. Add. Tell which numbers you added first.

4 + 7 + 6 = 17

Answers vary. Sample answer: I know 4 + 6 = 10, so I added them first. Then I added 10 + 7.

***Assessment Handbook,* p. 166**

Assessment Master

Name ______ Date ______

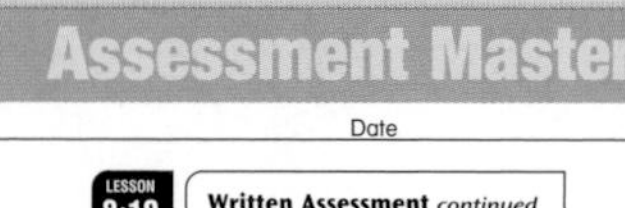

6. Kimi bought 5 lollipops. Each lollipop costs 5¢. How much did Kimi pay?
   25 ¢ or $ 0 . 25

Part B

7. Label each equal part.

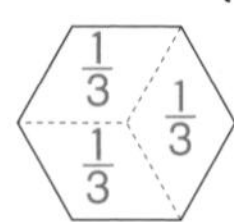

8. Draw a line to match each face to the correct picture of the 3-dimensional shape.

   Column A   Column B

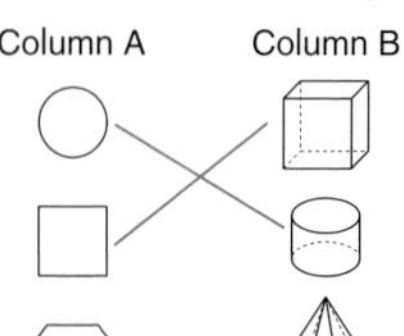

9. Fill in the fact triangle. Write the fact family.
   Answers vary.

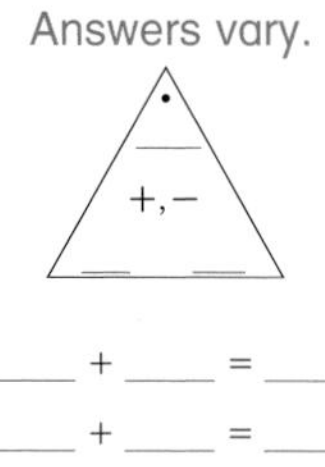

___ + ___ = ___
___ + ___ = ___
___ − ___ = ___
___ − ___ = ___

Assessment Handbook, **p. 167**

Use the checklists on pages 221 and 223 of the *Assessment Handbook* to record results. Then input the data into the **Assessment Management Spreadsheets** to keep an ongoing record of children's progress toward Grade-Level Goals.

Assessment Master

Name ______ Date ______

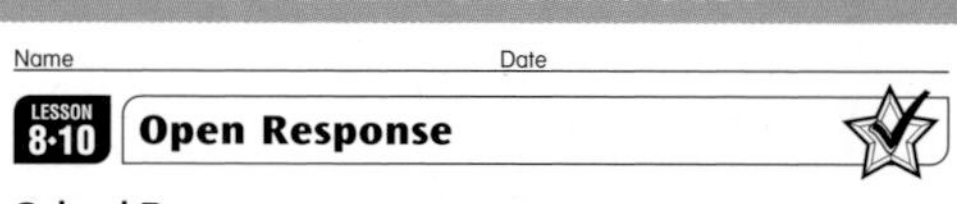

School Box

1. Draw different color crayons in the school box on this page. Use the clues to help you draw the crayons:
   $\frac{1}{2}$ of the crayons in the school box are blue.
   $\frac{1}{4}$ of the crayons in the school box are red.
   $\frac{1}{4}$ of the crayons in the school box are yellow.

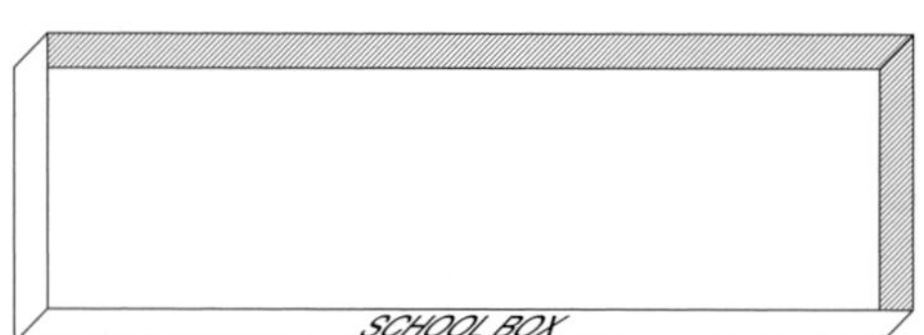

2. How many blue crayons did you draw? ____ crayons
   How many red crayons did you draw? ____ crayons
   How many yellow crayons did you draw? ____ crayons
3. Explain how you know that half of the crayons you drew are blue. You may use words, numbers, and pictures to help you explain.

Assessment Handbook, **p. 168**

4. Dictate a number. Children write it on their slates and circle the digit in the specified place.
   - twenty, circle the number in the tens place (2)0
   - ninety-nine, circle the number in the ones place 9(9)
   - one hundred, circle the number in the tens place 1(0)0
   - one hundred twenty one, circle the number in the hundreds place (1)21

▶ Written Assessment

(*Assessment Handbook*, pp. 166 and 167)

Part A Recognizing Student Achievement

Problems 1–6 provide summative information and may be used for grading purposes.

Problem(s)	Description
1, 2	Use drawings to represent and explain simple fractions (halves) as equal parts of a region.
2	Complete simple two-dimensional symmetric shapes or designs.
3	Use pictures to find equivalent names for numbers; use tally marks and numerical expressions involving addition and subtraction of 1-digit and 2-digit whole numbers to represent equivalent names for numbers.
4	Read, write, and represent whole numbers through hundreds with base-10 blocks; identify digits and express their values in such numbers.
5	Know addition and subtraction facts.
5	Use +, −, and = to write number sentences.
5	Use the properties of addition to find the sum of three 1-digit numbers.
6	Know the value of a penny, nickel, dime, quarter. Calculate and compare the values of combinations of coins.
6	Solve number stories.

Part B Informing Instruction

Problems 7–9 provide formative information that can be useful in planning future instruction.

Problem(s)	Description
7	Use drawings to represent and explain simple fractions (thirds) as equal parts of a region.
8	Identify and describe solid figures such as pyramids, cubes, and cylinders.

9	Know addition and subtraction facts.
9	Use +, −, and = to write number sentences.
9	Use the Commutative Property of Addition (the "turn-around rule") to solve basic addition facts.

▶ Open Response

INDEPENDENT ACTIVITY

(*Assessment Handbook,* p. 168)

School Box

The open-response item requires children to apply concepts and skills from Unit 8 to solve a multistep problem. See *Assessment Handbook,* pages 114–117 for rubrics and children's work samples for this problem.

Distribute *Assessment Handbook,* page 168. Read the problem aloud to children. Allow children to solve the problem and record their solutions on the page.

After children have had a chance to complete the page, invite individual children to use words and drawings to explain their strategies as you record them on the board. Be sure to discuss both successful and unsuccessful strategies.

2 Looking Ahead: Preparing for Unit 9

▶ Math Boxes 8•10

INDEPENDENT ACTIVITY

(*Math Journal 2,* p. 175)

Mixed Practice This Math Boxes page previews Unit 9 content.

▶ Home Link 8•10: Unit 9 Family Letter

INDEPENDENT ACTIVITY

(*Math Masters,* pp. 245–248)

Home Connection The Unit 9 Family Letter provides families with information and activities related to Unit 9 topics.

Student Page

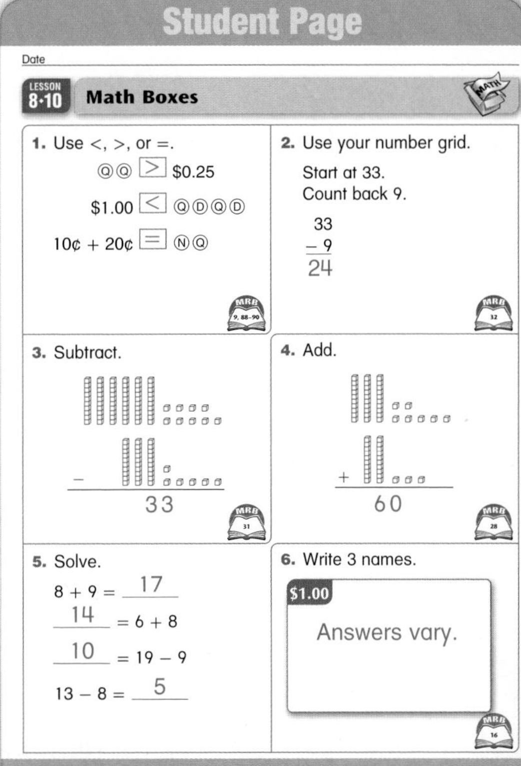

Date

LESSON 8•10 **Math Boxes**

1. Use <, >, or =.
   Ⓠ Ⓠ > $0.25
   $1.00 < Ⓠ Ⓓ Ⓠ Ⓓ
   10¢ + 20¢ = Ⓝ Ⓠ
2. Use your number grid.
   Start at 33.
   Count back 9.
   33
   − 9
   24
3. Subtract.
   33
4. Add.
   60
5. Solve.
   8 + 9 = 17
   14 = 6 + 8
   10 = 19 − 9
   13 − 8 = 5
6. Write 3 names.
   $1.00
   Answers vary.

Math Journal 2, p. 175

NOTE Make crayons available to children when solving this open-response problem.

Home Link Masters

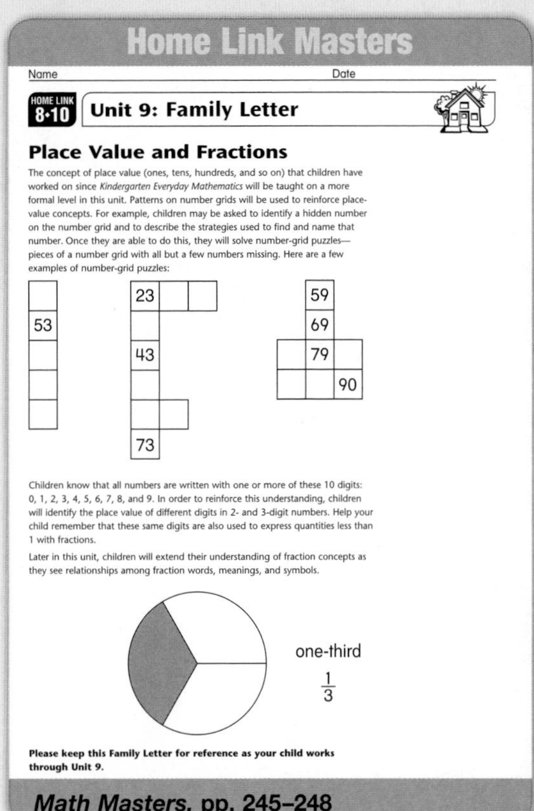

Name Date

HOME LINK 8•10 **Unit 9: Family Letter**

Place Value and Fractions

The concept of place value (ones, tens, hundreds, and so on) that children have worked on since *Kindergarten Everyday Mathematics* will be taught on a more formal level in this unit. Patterns on number grids will be used to reinforce place-value concepts. For example, children may be asked to identify a hidden number on the number grid and to describe the strategies used to find and name that number. Once they are able to do this, they will solve number-grid puzzles—pieces of a number grid with all but a few numbers missing. Here are a few examples of number-grid puzzles:

Children know that all numbers are written with one or more of these 10 digits: 0, 1, 2, 3, 4, 5, 6, 7, 8, and 9. In order to reinforce this understanding, children will identify the place value of different digits in 2- and 3-digit numbers. Help your child remember that these same digits are also used to express quantities less than 1 with fractions.

Later in this unit, children will extend their understanding of fraction concepts as they see relationships among fraction words, meanings, and symbols.

Please keep this Family Letter for reference as your child works through Unit 9.

Math Masters, pp. 245–248

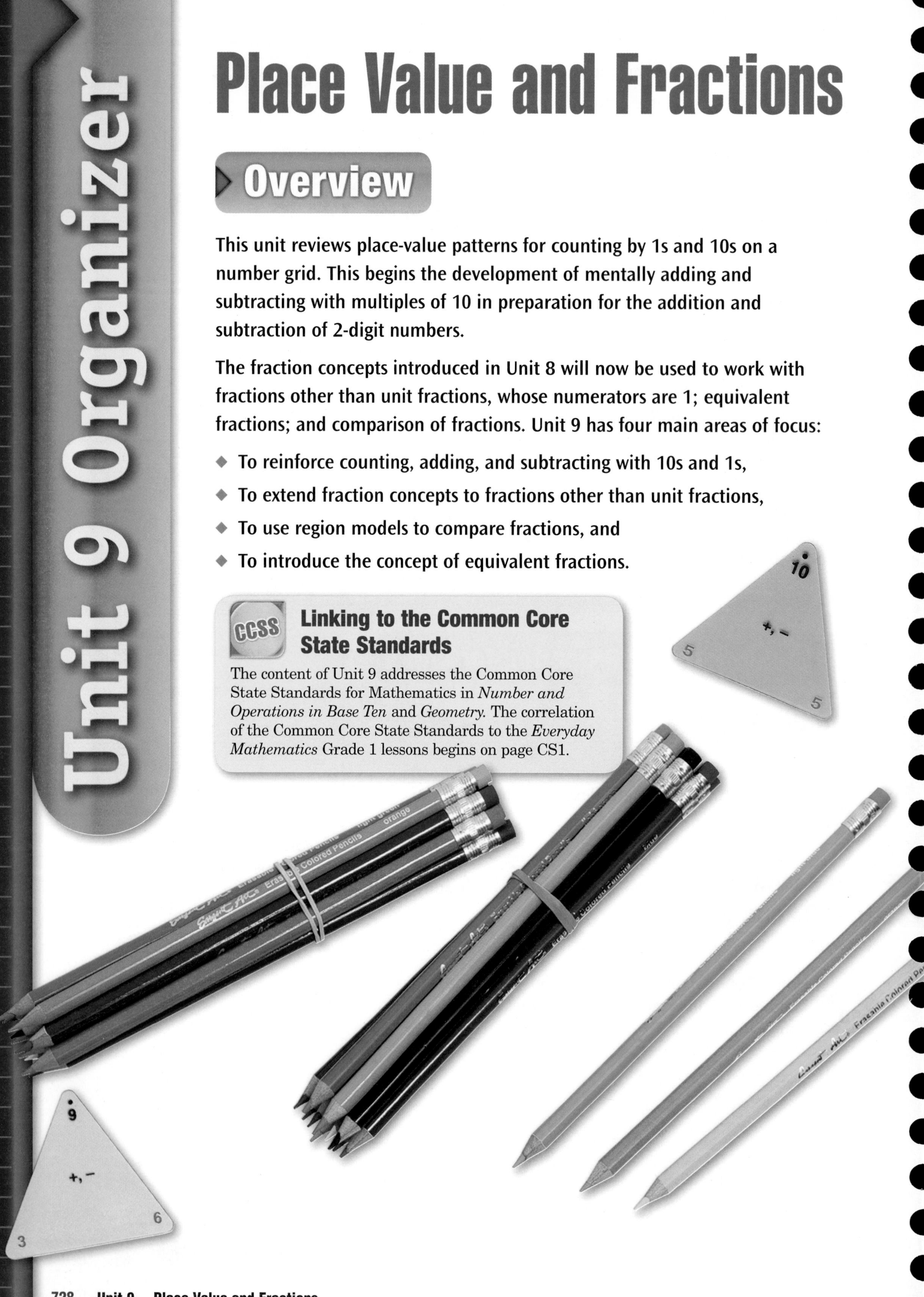

Unit 9 Organizer

Place Value and Fractions

Overview

This unit reviews place-value patterns for counting by 1s and 10s on a number grid. This begins the development of mentally adding and subtracting with multiples of 10 in preparation for the addition and subtraction of 2-digit numbers.

The fraction concepts introduced in Unit 8 will now be used to work with fractions other than unit fractions, whose numerators are 1; equivalent fractions; and comparison of fractions. Unit 9 has four main areas of focus:

- To reinforce counting, adding, and subtracting with 10s and 1s,
- To extend fraction concepts to fractions other than unit fractions,
- To use region models to compare fractions, and
- To introduce the concept of equivalent fractions.

CCSS Linking to the Common Core State Standards

The content of Unit 9 addresses the Common Core State Standards for Mathematics in *Number and Operations in Base Ten* and *Geometry.* The correlation of the Common Core State Standards to the *Everyday Mathematics* Grade 1 lessons begins on page CS1.

Contents

Learning In Perspective

	Lesson Objectives	Links to the Past	Links to the Future
9•1	To provide experiences counting by 1s and 10s on the number grid in preparation for adding and subtracting on the number grid.	In Units 1–6 and 8, children are introduced to addition and subtraction. They also use a number grid for place value, skip counting, and patterns.	Children use a number grid to solve addition and subtraction problems throughout Grades 1–3.
9•2	To provide opportunities to develop proficiency in adding and subtracting 10s.	In Units 1–8, children are introduced to addition and subtraction. They also use a number grid for place value, skip counting, and addition and subtraction facts.	In Unit 10, children develop skills for adding and subtracting 2-digit whole numbers, develop fact power, and review place value through hundreds.
9•3	To reinforce counting, adding, and subtracting with 10s and 1s using number-grid patterns.	In Units 1–8, children are introduced to addition and subtraction. They also use a number grid for place value, skip counting, and addition and subtraction facts.	In Unit 10, children develop skills for adding and subtracting 2-digit whole numbers, develop fact power, and review place value through hundreds.
9•4	To provide practice adding and subtracting 2-digit numbers.	In Units 1–8, children are introduced to addition and subtraction; practice addition and subtraction facts; and are introduced to addition and subtraction of 2-digit numbers.	In Unit 10, children develop skills for adding and subtracting 2-digit whole numbers. In Grade 2, children solve similar problems.
9•5	To provide experiences comparing capacities of containers; creating a symmetrical design; and making a second height measurement.	In Units 4, 6, and 7, children use both nonstandard and standard units to compare and measure lengths. They also explore symmetry.	In Grade 2, children measure and compare length using standard and nonstandard units, and create and complete 2-dimensional symmetric shapes or designs.
9•6	To extend fraction concepts to fractions other than unit fractions.	In Units 5–8, children cover shapes with pattern blocks and divide regions into equal parts. They are also introduced to unit fraction notation and fractional parts of collections.	In Grade 2, children use manipulatives to model fractions as equal parts, compare fractions, and investigate equivalent fractions and non-unit fractions.
9•7	To review fraction concepts; and to provide experiences using region models to compare fractions.	In Units 5–8, children cover shapes with pattern blocks and divide regions into equal parts. They are introduced to unit fraction notation and fractional parts of collections.	In Grade 2, children use manipulatives to model fractions as equal parts, compare fractions, and investigate equivalent fractions and non-unit fractions.
9•8	To introduce the idea that fractional parts of a whole have many names (equivalent fractions).	In Units 5–8, children cover shapes with pattern blocks and divide regions into equal parts. They are introduced to unit fraction notation and fractional parts of collections.	In Grade 2, children use manipulatives to model fractions as equal parts, compare fractions, and investigate equivalent fractions and non-unit fractions.

	Key Concepts and Skills	Grade 1 Goals*
9•1	Count forward and backward by 1s and 10s using a number grid.	Number and Numeration Goal 1
	Name missing numbers on a number grid.	Number and Numeration Goal 7
	Extend patterns on a number grid.	Patterns, Functions, and Algebra Goal 1
9•2	Count forward and backward by 1s and 10s using a number grid.	Number and Numeration Goal 1
	Add and subtract 1s and 10s from 2-digit numbers.	Operations and Computation Goal 2
	Solve addition and subtraction problems with and without manipulatives and tools.	Operations and Computation Goal 2
	Use number-grid patterns to solve addition and subtraction problems.	Patterns, Functions, and Algebra Goal 1
9•3	Count forward and backward by 1s and 10s using a number grid.	Number and Numeration Goal 1
	Identify the values of digits in a 2-digit number.	Number and Numeration Goal 3
	Extend patterns on a number grid.	Patterns, Functions, and Algebra Goal 1
	Solve number-grid puzzles.	Patterns, Functions, and Algebra Goal 1
9•4	Explain strategies used to solve problems involving the addition and subtraction of 2-digit by 2-digit numbers.	Operations and Computation Goal 2
	Add and subtract 2-digit numbers using strategies based on place value and the relationship between addition and subtraction.	Operations and Computation Goal 2
	Tell, write, and solve number stories.	Operations and Computation Goal 4
	Write addition and subtraction number sentences using +, −, and =.	Patterns, Functions, and Algebra Goal 2
	Use the properties of operations to add and subtract 2-digit numbers.	Patterns, Functions, and Algebra Goal 3
9•5	Use standard measuring tools to measure length to the nearest inch.	Measurement and Reference Frames Goal 1
	Use non-standard tools to estimate capacity.	Measurement and Reference Frames Goal 1
	Draw plane shapes.	Geometry Goal 1
	Complete line-symmetric designs.	Geometry Goal 2
9•6	Divide shapes into fractional parts.	Number and Numeration Goal 4
	Model fractional parts of a region.	Number and Numeration Goal 4
	Identify halves and fourths.	Number and Numeration Goal 4
	Identify equivalent names for fractional parts of a region.	Number and Numeration Goal 4
9•7	Compare fractional parts.	Number and Numeration Goal 4
	Label fractional parts using fractional notation.	Number and Numeration Goal 4
	Identify halves, thirds, fourths, sixths, and eighths.	Number and Numeration Goal 4
	Identify and explain the meanings of *numerator* and *denominator*.	Number and Numeration Goal 4
9•8	Use manipulatives to model equivalent fractions.	Number and Numeration Goal 4
	Use = to describe the relationship between fractions.	Patterns, Functions, and Algebra Goal 2

*See the Appendix for a complete list of Grade 1 Goals.

A Balanced Curriculum

Ongoing Practice

Everyday Mathematics provides numerous opportunities for ongoing practice. These activities are embedded throughout the lessons:

Mental Math and Reflexes activities promote speed and accuracy in mental computation.

Math Boxes offer mixed practice and are paired across lessons as shown in the brackets below. This makes them useful as assessment tools. The last one or two boxes on each page preview the next unit's content.

Mixed practice	[9•1, 9•3], [9•2, 9•4], [9•5, 9•7], [9•6, 9•8]
Mixed practice with multiple choice	9•3, 9•4, 9•7, 9•8
Mixed practice with writing/reasoning opportunity	9•2, 9•3, 9•5, 9•8

Home Links are daily homework assignments that review the content of the lesson and often contain ongoing facts practice.

Minute Math+ problems are offered for additional practice in Lesson 9•2.

EM Facts Workshop Game provides online practice of basic facts and computation.

EXTRA PRACTICE **Extra Practice** activities are included in Lessons 9•1, 9•2, 9•5, and 9•8.

Practice through Games

Games are an essential component of practice in the *Everyday Mathematics* program. Games offer skills practice and promote strategic thinking. See the *Differentiation Handbook* for ways to adapt games to meet children's needs.

Lesson	Game	Skill Practiced
9•1	*Beat the Calculator*	Addition Facts [OC Goal 2]
9•2, 9•5	*Number-Grid Game*	Adding and subtracting on a number grid [OC Goal 2]
9•3	*Make My Design*	Describing geometric designs and spatial relationships [GEO Goal 1]
9•7	*Difference Game*	Subtraction [OC Goal 2]
9•8	*One-Dollar Exchange*	Exchanging coins and bills [MRF Goal 2]

[NN] Number and Numeration
[MRF] Measurement and Reference Frames
[OC] Operations and Computation
[GEO] Geometry
[DC] Data and Chance
[PFA] Patterns, Functions, and Algebra

Problem Solving 

Good problem solvers use a variety of strategies, including the following:

- Draw a picture.
- Act out the problem.
- Make a table, chart, or list.
- Look for a pattern.
- Try a simpler version of the problem.
- Make a guess and try it out.

The table below lists some of the opportunities in this unit for children to practice these strategies.

Lesson	Activity
9•1	Name hidden numbers on a number grid.
9•3	Solve number-grid puzzles.
9•4	Create and solve number stories.
9•6	Find the range and middle value of a set of data.
9•7	Compare pairs of fractions.
9•8	Name fractions in different ways.

Lessons that teach *through* problem solving, not just *about* problem solving

See Chapter 18: Problem Solving in the *Teacher's Reference Manual* for more information.

The Language of Mathematics

Everyday Mathematics provides lesson-specific suggestions to help all children acquire, process, and express mathematical ideas. Throughout Unit 9, there are lesson-specific language development notes that address the needs of English language learners, indicated by ELL.

ELL SUPPORT Activities to support English language learners are in Part 3 of Lessons 9•4, 9•5, and 9•6.

The *English Learners Handbook* and the *Differentiation Handbook* have suggestions for promoting language development and acquisition of mathematics vocabulary. See Unit 9 in each handbook.

Unit 9 Vocabulary

denominator
number-grid puzzle
numerator

Literacy Connection

Lesson 9•5 *Lulu's Lemonade,* by Barbara deRubertis, Kane Press, 2000

Lesson 9•6 *Fraction Action,* by Loreen Leedy, Holiday House, 1996

For more literacy connections, see the *Home Connection Handbook,* Grades 1–3.

Cross-Curricular Links 

Physical Education
Lesson 9•1 Children link number grid patterns to gross motor movements.

Music
Lesson 9•6 Children are introduced to whole, half, and quarter notes.

Social Studies
Lesson 9•5 Children locate tall buildings on a world map and make a bar graph of heights.

Balanced Assessment

Daily Assessments

- **Recognizing Student Achievement** – A daily assessment that is included in every lesson to evaluate children's progress toward the Grade 1 Grade-Level Goals.
- **Informing Instruction** – Notes that appear throughout the unit to help anticipate children's common errors and suggest appropriate problem-solving strategies.

Lesson	Recognizing Student Achievement	Informing Instruction
9•1	Order numbers to 110. [NN Goal 7]	
9•2	Use a number grid to add and subtract. [OC Goal 2]	
9•3	Name 2-dimensional shapes. [GEO Goal 1]	
9•4	Find fractions of a set. [NN Goal 4]	Solve number stories.
9•5	Create numbers using given digits. [NN Goal 3]	Find the capacity of containers.
9•6	Divide shapes into equal parts. [NN Goal 4]	Differentiate between *numerator* and *denominator*.
9•7	Solve number-grid puzzles. [PFA Goal 1]	
9•8	Estimate sums. [OC Goal 3]	Find names for fractional parts.

[NN] Number and Numeration
[MRF] Measurement and Reference Frames
[OC] Operations and Computation
[GEO] Geometry
[DC] Data and Chance
[PFA] Patterns, Functions, and Algebra

Portfolio Opportunities

The following lessons provide opportunities to gather samples of children's mathematical writings, drawings, and creations to add balance to the assessment process: Lessons 9•2, 9•3, 9•5, 9•6, 9•8, and 9•9.

See pages 16 and 17 in the *Assessment Handbook* for more information about portfolios and how to use them.

Unit Assessment

Progress Check 9 – A cumulative assessment of concepts and skills taught in Unit 9 and in previous units, providing information for evaluating children's progress and planning for future instruction. These assessments include oral/slate, written, and open-response activities, as shown below in the sample Progress Check lesson opener.

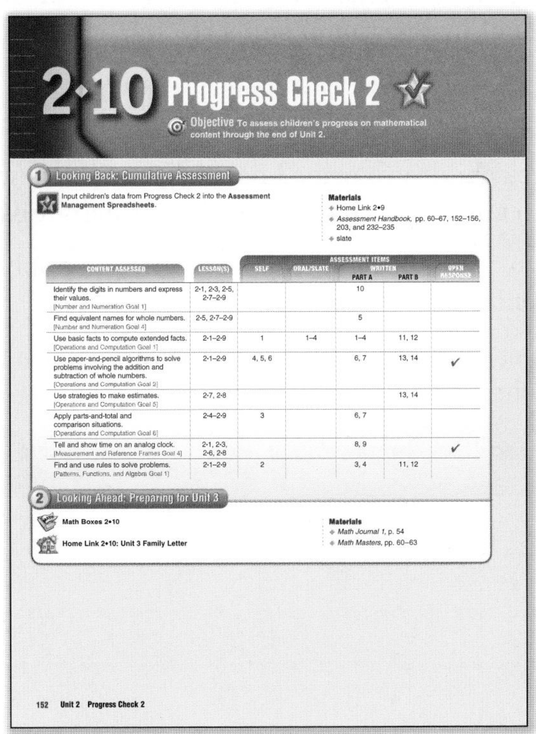

2·10 Progress Check 2

Objective To assess children's progress on mathematical content through the end of Unit 2.

1 Looking Back: Cumulative Assessment

Input children's data from Progress Check 2 into the **Assessment Management Spreadsheets**.

Materials
- Home Link 2•9
- *Assessment Handbook*, pp. 60–67, 152–156, 203, and 232–235
- slate

CONTENT ASSESSED	LESSON(S)	ASSESSMENT ITEMS				
		SELF	ORAL/SLATE	WRITTEN PART A	WRITTEN PART B	OPEN RESPONSE
Identify the digits in numbers and express their values. [Number and Numeration Goal 1]	2·1, 2·3, 2·5, 2·7–2·9			10		
Find equivalent names for whole numbers. [Number and Numeration Goal 4]	2·5, 2·7–2·9			5		
Use basic facts to compute extended facts. [Operations and Computation Goal 1]	2·1–2·9	1	1–4	1–4	11, 12	
Use paper-and-pencil algorithms to solve problems involving the addition and subtraction of whole numbers. [Operations and Computation Goal 2]	2·1–2·9	4, 5, 6		6, 7	13, 14	✓
Use strategies to make estimates. [Operations and Computation Goal 5]	2·7, 2·8				13, 14	
Apply parts-and-total and comparison situations. [Operations and Computation Goal 6]	2·4–2·9	3		6, 7		
Tell and show time on an analog clock. [Measurement and Reference Frames Goal 4]	2·1, 2·3, 2·6, 2·8			8, 9		✓
Find and use rules to solve problems. [Patterns, Functions, and Algebra Goal 1]	2·1–2·9	2		3, 4	11, 12	

2 Looking Ahead: Preparing for Unit 3

Math Boxes 2•10

Home Link 2•10: Unit 3 Family Letter

Materials
- *Math Journal 1*, p. 54
- *Math Masters*, pp. 60–63

152 Unit 2 Progress Check 2

Core Assessment Resources

Assessment Handbook

- **Unit 9 Assessment Overview,** pages 118–125
- **Unit 9 Assessment Masters,** pages 169–172
- **Unit 9 Individual Profiles of Progress,** pages 232, 233, and 248
- **Unit 9 Class Checklists,** pages 234, 235, and 249
- **Math Logs,** pages 254–256
- **Exit Slip,** page 251
- **Other Student Assessment Forms,** pages 252, 253, 257, and 258

Assessment Management Spreadsheets

The Assessment Management Spreadsheets consist of the Digital Class Checklists and Individual Profile of Progress Checklists. Use them to monitor, record, and report children's progress.

Addressing All Needs

Differentiated Instruction

Adjusting the Activity – suggests adaptations that target advanced learners, English language learners, or learners who need additional instructional support.

ELL SUPPORT / **ELL** – provides lesson-specific suggestions to help English language learners understand and process the mathematical content.

READINESS – accesses children's prior knowledge or previews content that prepares children to engage in the lesson's Part 1 activities.

EXTRA PRACTICE – provides additional opportunities to apply the mathematical content of the lesson.

ENRICHMENT – enables children to apply or further explore the mathematical content of the lesson.

Lesson	Adjusting the Activity	ELL Support/ ELL	Readiness	Extra Practice	Enrichment
9◆1	•		•	•	
9◆2	•		•	•	•
9◆3	•		•		•
9◆4	•	•	•		•
9◆5	•	•	•	•	•
9◆6	•	•	•		
9◆7		•	•		•
9◆8	•	•		•	•

Additional Resources

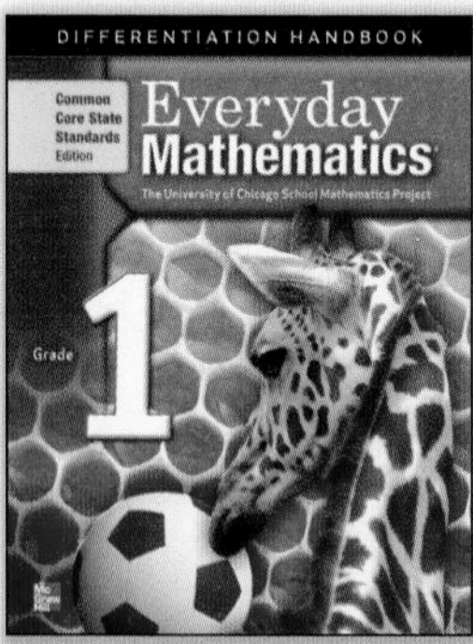

Differentiation Handbook
Provides ideas and strategies for differentiating instruction.
Pages 106–112

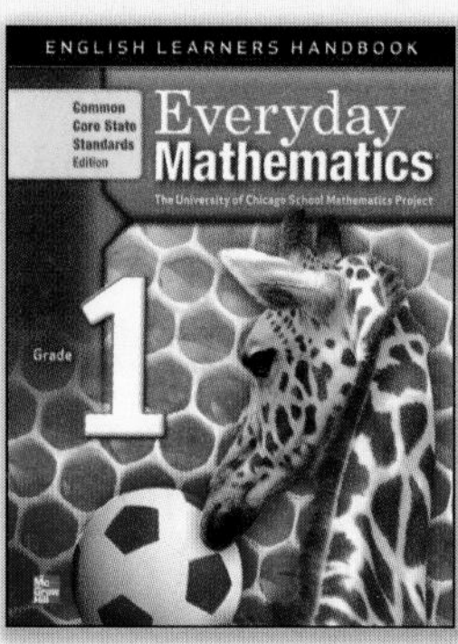

English Learners Handbook
Contains lesson-specific comprehension strategies.
Pages 94–101

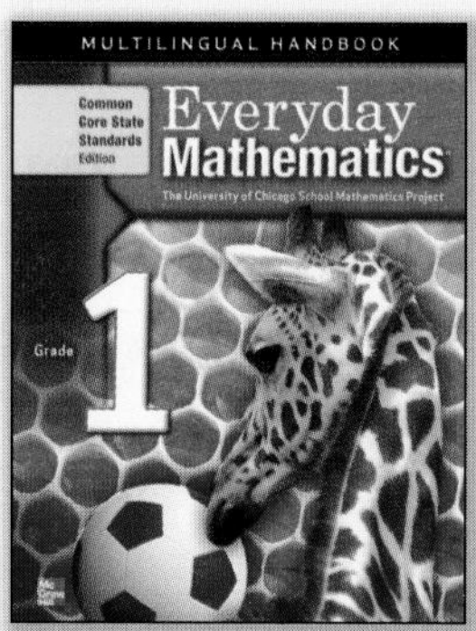

Multilingual Handbook
Previews concepts and vocabulary. It is written in six languages.
Pages 187–202

Planning Tips

Multiage Classroom

Companion Lessons from Grades K and 2 can help you meet instructional needs of a multiage classroom. The full Scope and Sequence can be found in the Appendix.

Grade K	5•15, 5•16	3•15, 4•4, 4•11	5•15, 5•16	4•4, 4•11, 4•16	2•15, 2•16, 5•12	6•11	6•11	6•11
Grade 1	**9•1**	**9•2**	**9•3**	**9•4**	**9•5**	**9•6**	**9•7**	**9•8**
Grade 2	1•8, 7•1	2•10, 7•2	1•8	4•8, 4•9, 6•5	6•6, 9•6	8•1	8•6	8•4, 8•5

Pacing for Success

Pacing depends on a number of factors, such as children's individual needs and how long your school has been using *Everyday Mathematics*. At the beginning of Unit 9, you may want to use tools available at www.everydaymathonline.com to help you set your pace.

Home Support

Unit 9 Family Letter (English/Spanish) provides families with an overview, Do-Anytime Activities, Building Skills through Games, a list of vocabulary, and answers to the daily homework (Home Links). Family Letters in English, Spanish, and seven other languages are also available online.

Home Links are the daily homework assignments. They consist of active projects and ongoing review problems.

Home Support Resources

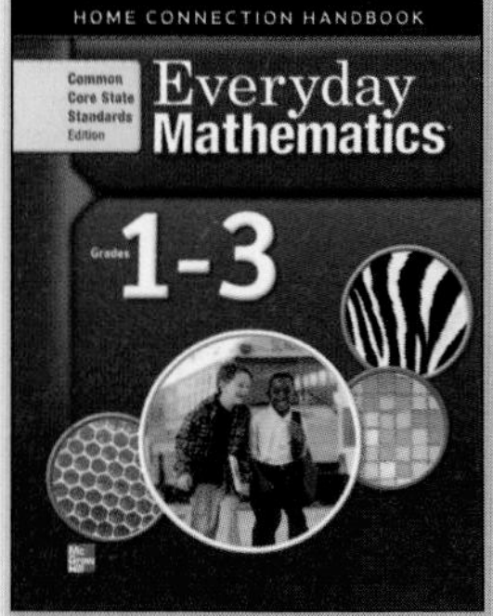

Home Connection Handbook
Offers ideas and reproducible masters for communicating with families. See Table of Contents for unit information.

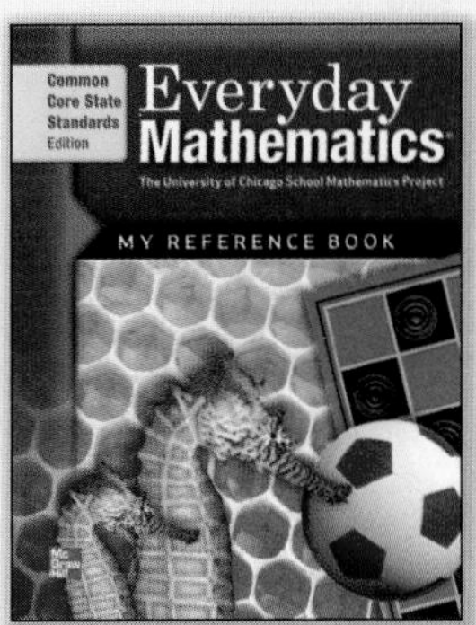

My Reference Book
Provides a resource for children and parents.

Pages 130, 131, 142–145

Technology Resources

Unit 9 Organizer

Materials

Technology Resources www.everydaymathonline.com

ePresentations

eToolkit

Algorithms Practice

EM Facts Workshop Game™

Family Letters

Assessment Management

Common Core State Standards

Curriculum Focal Points

Interactive Teacher's Lesson Guide

Lesson	Masters	Manipulative Kit	Other Items
9•1	Teaching Masters, pp. 110, 249, 251, and 252 Transparencies of *Math Masters,* pp. 249* and 250* Home Link Master, p. 253	slate; number cards 0–9	Number-Grid Poster*; scissors; tape or glue; envelopes; calculator
9•2	Teaching Masters, pp. 249, 254, 256, and 257 Transparency of *Math Masters,* p. 249* Home Link Master, p. 255	slate; per partnership: 1 die; base-10 blocks	Number-Grid Poster; game markers; stick-on notes; Class Data Pad
9•3	Teaching Masters, pp. 258, 259, and 261 Home Link Master, p. 260 Teaching Aid Master, p. 305	base-10 blocks (flats, longs, and cubes); slate; pattern blocks	Number-Grid Poster; scissors; per partnership: 1 folder; 3" by 3" stick-on notes
9•4	Home Link Master, p. 263 Teaching Master, p. 262	slate; base-10 blocks (longs and cubes); 2 each of number cards 0–9	animal cards from Unit 5; Number-Grid Poster; per partnership: 1 penny; bath scale; objects to weigh
9•5	Teaching Masters, pp. 264 and 265 Home Link Master, p. 266 *Differentiation Handbook,* p. 126	tape measure; pattern blocks; slate; per partnership: 1 die, geoboard, rubber bands	per group: 3 containers of different sizes and shapes labeled *A, B,* and *C,* a pourable substance (unpopped popcorn, rice, or dried beans) to fill all three containers, 6 paper cups (three of one size and three of another size); Pattern-Block Template*; height stick-on notes from Lesson 4◆7; book; 1 number grid; game markers; paint; small brushes; markers; measuring cups: cup, pint; beans, large bowl
9•6	Teaching Masters, pp. 267, 267A, 267B, and 268 Home Link Master, p. 269	tool-kit coins or counters*; slate; per partnership: pattern blocks	Pattern-Block Template; scissors; animal cards from Unit 5
9•7	Teaching Masters, pp. 270 and 272 Home Link Master, p. 271	slate; 4 each of number cards 1–10; tool-kit pennies	scissors; paper clip or envelope; 3" by 5" index cards
9•8	Teaching Masters, pp. 224, 270, 274, and 275 Home Link Master, p. 273 Teaching Aid Master, p. 325	per partnership: 2 dice	fraction strips from Lesson 9◆7; scissors; per partnership: 1 dollar, 20 dimes, and 20 pennies; fraction pieces from Part 1
9•9	Assessment Masters, pp. 169–172 Home Link Masters, pp. 276–279	slate; base-10 blocks (flats, longs, and cubes)	analog clock

*Denotes optional materials

Mathematical Background

The discussion below highlights the major content ideas presented in Unit 9 and helps establish instructional priorities.

Base-Ten and Place Value as Foundations of Our Numeration System (Lessons 9◆1–9◆4)

The basic arithmetic skills—counting, reading, writing, and computing with whole numbers and decimals—are based on our base-ten place-value system. The ten digits 0, 1, 2, 3, 4, 5, 6, 7, 8, and 9 are all that are required to name any whole number; the value of a digit depends on its position, or place, in a numeral. These place-value ideas have been in the background throughout *Kindergarten* and *First Grade Everyday Mathematics*. In Unit 9, formal consideration is given to some of these ideas with the help of base-ten blocks and number grids.

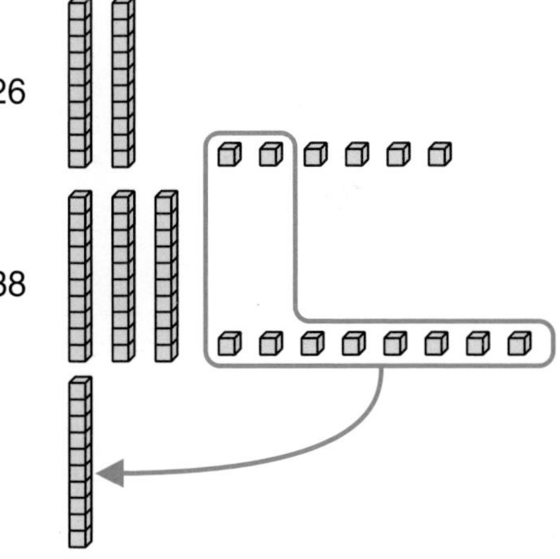

$26 + 38 = 64$

Base-10 blocks are used as concrete representations of the digits in a numeral. Flats represent hundreds, longs represent tens, and cubes represent ones. For example, 2 flats, 6 longs, and 8 cubes can be used to represent the number 268. Since the largest digit in the base-ten system is 9, children learn that if a number is represented by more than nine base-10 blocks of the same kind, they must exchange 10 of the blocks for 1 of the next higher-valued blocks. This idea is applied in modeling the solution of addition problems. For example, when base-10 blocks are combined to represent the solution of 26 + 38, you end up with 5 longs and 14 cubes. Since there are more than 9 cubes, you must exchange 10 cubes for 1 long, resulting in 6 longs and 4 cubes, or the sum 64.

Some subtraction problems with base-10 blocks call for skills that will be taken up formally in *Second Grade Everyday Mathematics.*

Certain patterns in number grids are analogous to the place-value patterns in base-ten numerals.

- The tens digit is the same for each number in a given row except for the last number in the row.
- The ones digit is the same for each number in a given column.

These patterns make it easy to add and subtract 2-digit numbers with the help of the number grid.

- To add 10 to a number, count down one row from the starting number. To subtract 10 from a number, count up one row from the starting number.
- To add a number less than 10 to another number, count that number of spaces to the right of the starting number. When the end of a row is reached, continue the count with the first number in the next row. To subtract another number less than 10 from another number, count that number of spaces to the left of the starting number.

When the beginning of a row is reached, continue the count with the last number in the previous row.

- To add or subtract a 2-digit number, combine the above steps. For example, to solve 26 + 38, start at 26 and add 30 by counting down 3 rows to 56. Then count 8 spaces from 56 to 64. To subtract 67 – 42, start at 67 and subtract 40 by counting up 4 rows to 27. Then count back 2 spaces to 25.

The authors recommend that children try a variety of strategies besides using the number grid to solve addition and subtraction problems. These strategies include modeling a problem with counters or with base-10 blocks, drawing pictures, or, for some problems, solving them mentally. Children should use the number grid as a last resort or to check answers obtained by other methods.

For more information about numeration and place value, see Section 9.2.1 in the *Teacher's Reference Manual.*

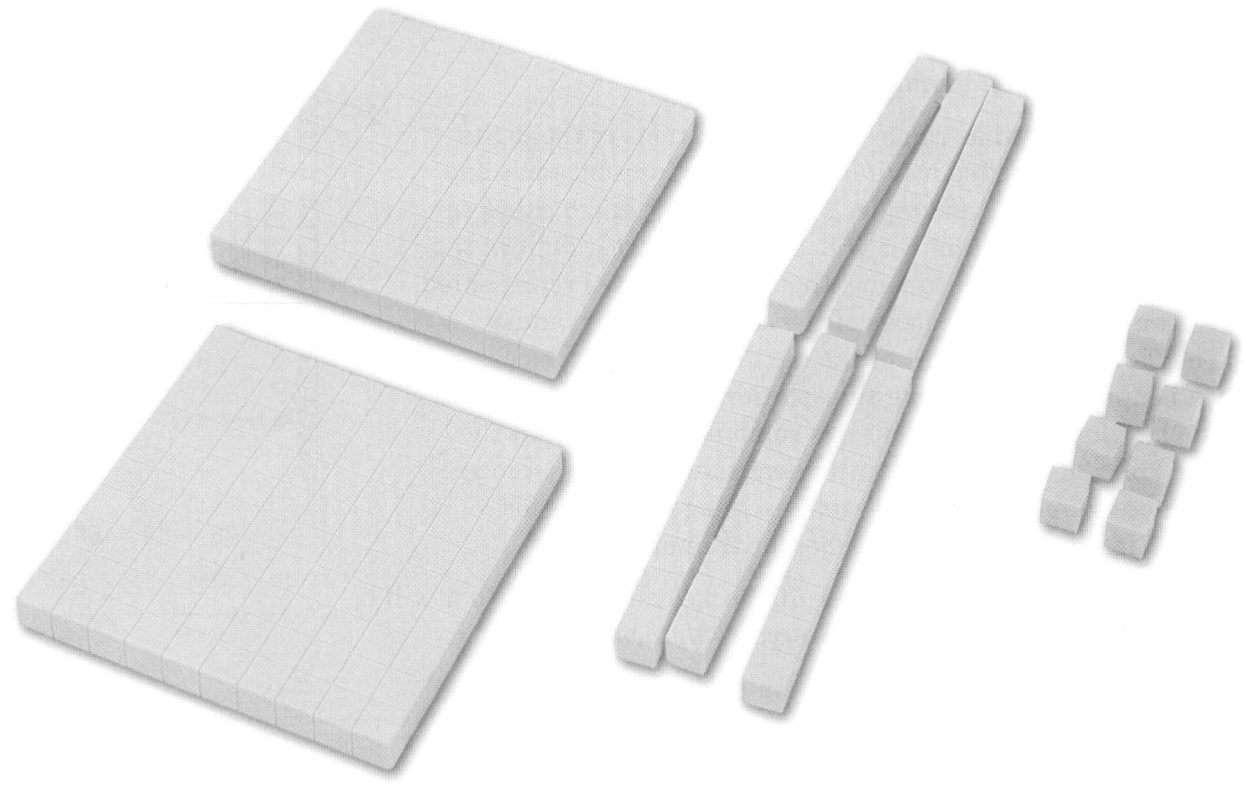

268

Number-Grid Puzzles (Lesson 9•3)

This new routine makes the structure of our number system (as represented on number grids) even more apparent. Each number-grid puzzle presents a fragment of the number grid with just one number filled in. Children use the number-grid patterns to figure out what the missing numbers are. Teachers are often surprised at the complexity of the puzzles that children make (and are able to solve).

You might want to make extra copies of blank number grids so that children can make pieces of the puzzles to fill in over the next several weeks.

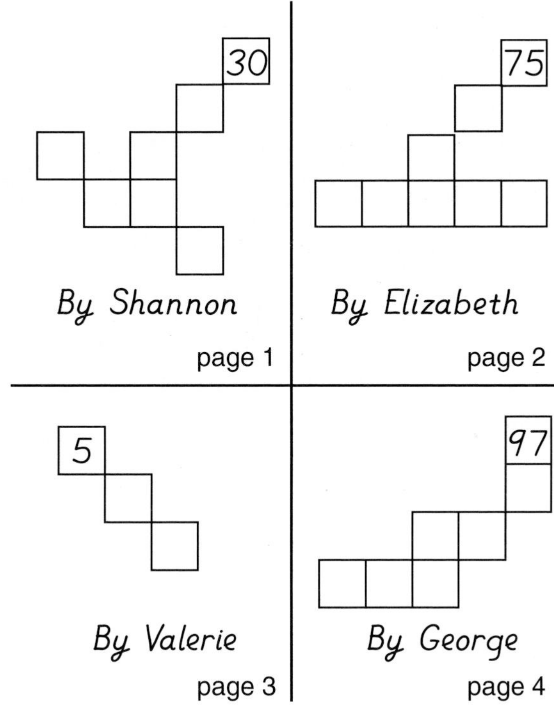

Review of Basic Fraction Concepts

(Lessons 9◆6–9◆8)

These lessons reinforce and extend fraction ideas that have been discussed in earlier units, including these basic concepts:

- Fractions always name a number of parts of a whole that has been divided into equal parts.
- The *denominator* (the number under the fraction bar) represents the total number of equal parts into which the whole has been divided. The *numerator* (the number above the fraction bar) tells how many of these parts the fraction represents.
- The larger the denominator, the smaller the parts (and vice versa).
- Two or more fractions that look different (such as $\frac{1}{2}$ and $\frac{2}{4}$) can represent the same amount.

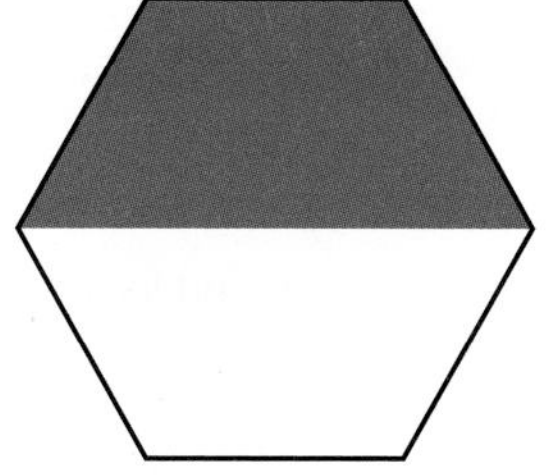

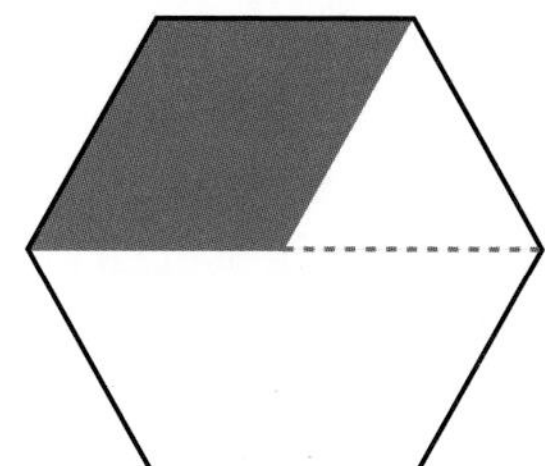

At this early stage of our work with fractions, it is important to support all work with fraction symbols with concrete representations—pictures, pattern blocks, counters, and so on. For example, children are not expected to be able to tell that $\frac{1}{2}$ is more than $\frac{1}{3}$ by looking at the fraction symbols only. But they should be able to do so by examining concrete models, one of which has been divided into three equal parts and the other in half, so that they may see that $\frac{1}{2}$ of the whole is more than $\frac{1}{3}$.

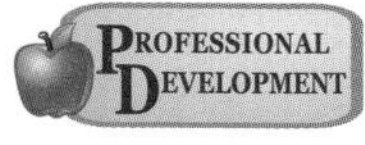

Section 9.3 of the *Teacher's Reference Manual* has more information about fractions.

9•1 Tens and Ones Patterns on the Number Grid

Objective To provide experiences counting by 1s and 10s on the number grid in preparation for adding and subtracting on the number grid.

www.everydaymathonline.com

ePresentations

eToolkit

Algorithms Practice

EM Facts Workshop Game™

Family Letters

Assessment Management

Common Core State Standards

Curriculum Focal Points

Interactive Teacher's Lesson Guide

1 Teaching the Lesson

Key Concepts and Skills

- Count forward and backward by 1s and 10s using a number grid. [Number and Numeration Goal 1]
- Name missing numbers on a number grid. [Number and Numeration Goal 7]
- Extend patterns on a number grid. [Patterns, Functions, and Algebra Goal 1]

Key Activities

Children review tens and ones patterns on the number grid and use them to solve number-grid problems.

Ongoing Assessment: Recognizing Student Achievement
Use journal page 176.
[Number and Numeration Goal 7]

Materials

Math Journal 2, p. 176 and inside back cover
Math Masters, p. 251
transparencies of *Math Masters,* pp. 249 and 250 (optional) ◆ calculator ◆ scissors ◆ tape or glue ◆ slate ◆ Number-Grid Poster (optional)

2 Ongoing Learning & Practice

Practicing Using Digits to Make Numbers

Math Masters, p. 252
number cards 0–9 (from the Everything Math Deck, if available)
Children practice using digits to make large and small numbers.

Math Boxes 9•1

Math Journal 2, p. 177
Children practice and maintain skills through Math Box problems.

Home Link 9•1

Math Masters, p. 253
Children practice and maintain skills through Home Link activities.

3 Differentiation Options

READINESS

Piecing Together a Number Grid

Math Journal 2, inside back cover
Math Masters, p. 249
per partnership: envelope
Children review the patterns on a number grid by putting together number-grid puzzles.

EXTRA PRACTICE

Writing Larger Numbers

Math Masters, p. 110
Children practice writing larger numbers by filling in number scrolls.

Advance Preparation

Children will be using a number grid in many of the activities in Unit 9. You may find it helpful to tape a copy of *Math Masters,* page 249 on each child's desk or have children keep a laminated copy of the master in their journals.

For the optional Readiness activity in Part 3, cut apart number grids (*Math Masters,* page 249) by columns, rows, and in other ways that are appropriate for your children. For each number-grid puzzle, mark all of the pieces with a colored dot so that they are easy to identify and sort, and put them in an envelope marked with the same colored dot.

***Teacher's Reference Manual,* Grades 1–3** pp. 56, 57

Getting Started

Mental Math and Reflexes

Play a round of *Beat the Calculator* to practice addition facts. Emphasize +0, +1, doubles, near doubles, and sums of 10 facts.

Math Message

Count to yourself by 10s, starting at 57. Write down how far you counted.

1 Teaching the Lesson

Interactive whiteboard-ready **ePresentations** are available at www.everydaymathonline.com to help you teach the lesson.

▶ Math Message Follow-Up

Children report the highest number to which they counted. Use this information to adjust the lesson to meet the needs of children.

As a group, have the class slowly count up by 10s from 57 past 100 and then back by 10s to 7. Record the resulting count in a column on the board for discussion later in the lesson.

Adjusting the Activity

Continue to count back by 10s past 0.

AUDITORY ◆ KINESTHETIC ◆ TACTILE ◆ VISUAL

ELL When you use the *Everyday Mathematics* posters with English language learners, display either the English version only or the English and Spanish versions simultaneously.

▶ Reviewing Number-Grid Patterns

(*Math Journal 2,* inside back cover; *Math Masters,* p. 249)

Have children look for patterns on the number grid located on the inside back cover of their journals. Use the Number-Grid Poster or a transparency of a number grid (*Math Masters,* page 249) to discuss the patterns they find. Make sure to include the following:

- The 1s digit is the same in each column.
- The 10s digit is the same in each row, except for the last number.

Physical Education Link Discuss a number pattern found on the number grid, such as 0s in the ones place. Use a pointer to count together on the Number-Grid Poster. Each time children say a number that has 0 in the ones place, have them perform a gross motor movement such as a jumping jack. Repeat this activity with different number patterns and different gross motor movements.

Teaching Master

Name Date

LESSON 9·1 **Number Grid**

−9	−8	−7	−6	−5	−4	−3	−2	−1	0
1	2	3	4	5	6	7	8	9	10
11	12	13	14	15	16	17	18	19	20
21	22	23	24	25	26	27	28	29	30
31	32	33	34	35	36	37	38	39	40
41	42	43	44	45	46	47	48	49	50
51	52	53	54	55	56	57	58	59	60
61	62	63	64	65	66	67	68	69	70
71	72	73	74	75	76	77	78	79	80
81	82	83	84	85	86	87	88	89	90
91	92	93	94	95	96	97	98	99	100
101	102	103	104	105	106	107	108	109	110

Math Masters, p. 249

Teaching Master

Name Date

LESSON 9•1 **Framed Number Grid**

−9	−8	−7	−6	−5	−4	−3	−2	−1	0
1	2	3	4	5	6	7	8	9	10
11									
21									
31									
41									
51									
61									
71									
81									
91									
101									

Math Masters, **p. 250**

NOTE If you are using a transparency of the number grid, you can cover a row or a column with a narrow strip of paper cut from *Math Masters,* page 251. If you are using the Number-Grid Poster, cut out the wider strips and tape or glue them together into one long strip consisting of 12 cells.

Teaching Master

Name Date

LESSON 9•1 **12-Cell Strip**

glue glue

Math Masters, **p. 251**

▶ Naming Hidden Numbers on the Number Grid

WHOLE-CLASS ACTIVITY

PROBLEM SOLVING

(*Math Masters,* pp. 249, 250, and 251)

Repeat each of the following activities with several numbers. As children figure out a method, have them use it on other problems.

1. Using *Math Masters,* page 251, cover a column on the Number-Grid Poster or on the transparency of the number grid. Point to a covered square and ask what the hidden number is. List children's responses on the board. Ask children to share how they arrived at their answers. Then reveal the hidden number.
2. Cover a row of the number grid and ask children to identify a hidden number.
3. On a transparency of the framed number grid, *Math Masters,* page 250, or on the teaching master itself, point to a square and ask which number belongs there, or ask questions like: *Where does 37 go?* Record the numbers on the grid.

Adjusting the Activity

Model one or more of the following methods:

▷ If 27 is the hidden number and the 7s column is covered, begin at 21 and go across the row counting up by 1s: "21, 22, 23, ..., 27." Or begin at 30 and count back by 1s across the row: "30, 29, 28, 27."

▷ If 27 is the hidden number and the 20s row is covered, begin at 7 and then go down the column as you count by 10s: "7, 17, 27."

Help children observe that the ones digit must be 7 as in all of the other numbers in that column and the tens digit must be 2 as in all of the other numbers in that row, except for the last number.

AUDITORY ◆ KINESTHETIC ◆ TACTILE ◆ VISUAL

▶ Completing a Number-Grid Hunt

PARTNER ACTIVITY

(*Math Journal 2,* p. 176)

Partners take turns. One partner writes a number on his or her slate; the other partner records it in the correct square on the number grid on journal page 176. After 10 turns each, partners check each other's work. Then they record the remaining missing numbers independently.

Ongoing Assessment: Recognizing Student Achievement

Journal Page 176

Use **journal page 176** to assess children's ability to order numbers to 110. Children are making adequate progress if they are able to correctly place all of the numbers on the number grid.

[Number and Numeration Goal 7]

2 Ongoing Learning & Practice

▶ Practicing Using Digits to Make Numbers

INDEPENDENT ACTIVITY

(*Math Masters,* p. 252)

Use *Math Masters,* page 252 to provide practice using digits to make large and small numbers. Remind children not to use 0 as the first digit.

▶ Math Boxes 9•1

INDEPENDENT ACTIVITY

(*Math Journal 2,* p. 177)

Mixed Practice Math Boxes in this lesson are paired with Math Boxes in Lesson 9-3. The skills in Problem 6 preview Unit 10 content.

▶ Home Link 9•1

INDEPENDENT ACTIVITY

(*Math Masters,* p. 253)

Home Connection Children complete a number grid for the numbers 101–200.

Teaching Master

Name Date

LESSON 9•1 **The Smallest and the Largest**

Use your 0–9 number cards. Choose two number cards. Make the smallest number you can. Make the largest number you can. Record the numbers.

	Digits Used	Smallest Number	Largest Number
Example	5, 3	35	53

Choose three number cards. Make the smallest number you can. Make the largest number you can. Record the numbers.

	Digits Used	Smallest Number	Largest Number
Example	8, 0, 2	208	820

Math Masters, **p. 252**

Student Page

Date

LESSON 9•1 **Number-Grid Hunt**

−9	−8	−7	−6	−5	−4	−3	−2	−1	0
1	2	3	4	5	6	7	8	9	10
11	12	13	14	15	16	17	18	19	20
21	22	23	24	25	26	27	28	29	30
31	32	33	34	35	36	37	38	39	40
41	42	43	44	45	46	47	48	49	50
51	52	53	54	55	56	57	58	59	60
61	62	63	64	65	66	67	68	69	70
71	72	73	74	75	76	77	78	79	80
81	82	83	84	85	86	87	88	89	90
91	92	93	94	95	96	97	98	99	100
101	102	103	104	105	106	107	108	109	110

Math Journal 2, **p. 176**

Student Page

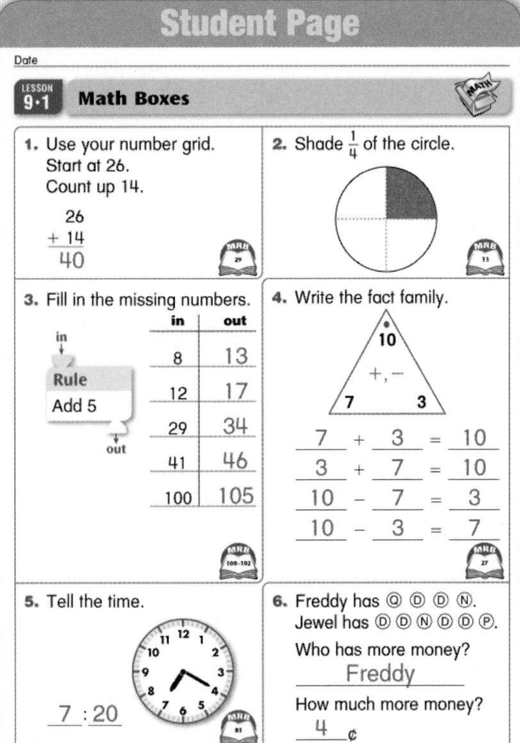
Date

LESSON 9·1 **Math Boxes**

1. Use your number grid. Start at 26. Count up 14.
   26
   + 14
   40

2. Shade $\frac{1}{4}$ of the circle.

3. Fill in the missing numbers.
   Rule: Add 5

in	out
8	13
12	17
29	34
41	46
100	105

4. Write the fact family.
   7 + 3 = 10
   3 + 7 = 10
   10 – 7 = 3
   10 – 3 = 7

5. Tell the time.
   7 : 20

6. Freddy has Ⓠ Ⓓ Ⓓ Ⓝ. Jewel has Ⓓ Ⓓ Ⓝ Ⓓ Ⓓ Ⓟ.
   Who has more money? Freddy
   How much more money? 4 ¢

Math Journal 2, p. 177

Home Link Master

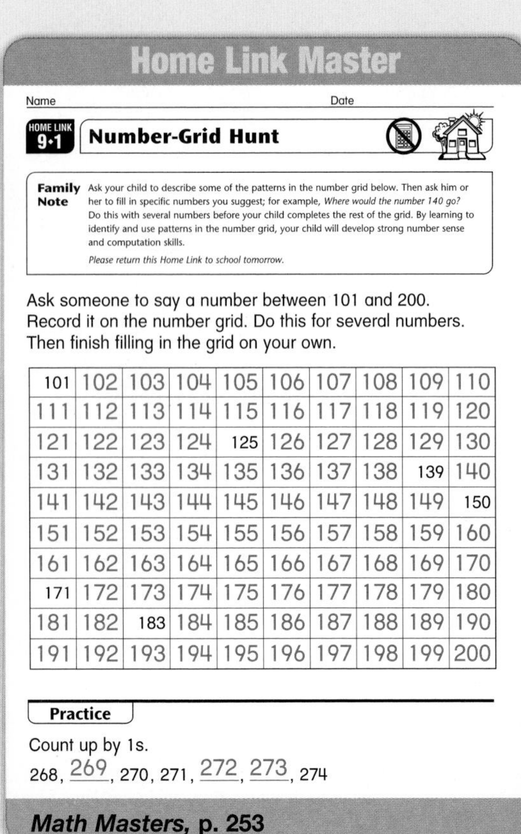
Name Date

HOME LINK 9·1 **Number-Grid Hunt**

Family Note Ask your child to describe some of the patterns in the number grid below. Then ask him or her to fill in specific numbers you suggest; for example, *Where would the number 140 go?* Do this with several numbers before your child completes the rest of the grid. By learning to identify and use patterns in the number grid, your child will develop strong number sense and computation skills.

Please return this Home Link to school tomorrow.

Ask someone to say a number between 101 and 200. Record it on the number grid. Do this for several numbers. Then finish filling in the grid on your own.

101	102	103	104	105	106	107	108	109	110
111	112	113	114	115	116	117	118	119	120
121	122	123	124	125	126	127	128	129	130
131	132	133	134	135	136	137	138	139	140
141	142	143	144	145	146	147	148	149	150
151	152	153	154	155	156	157	158	159	160
161	162	163	164	165	166	167	168	169	170
171	172	173	174	175	176	177	178	179	180
181	182	183	184	185	186	187	188	189	190
191	192	193	194	195	196	197	198	199	200

Practice

Count up by 1s.
268, 269, 270, 271, 272, 273, 274

Math Masters, p. 253

3 Differentiation Options

READINESS

PARTNER ACTIVITY

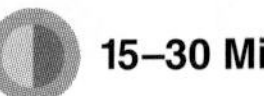
15–30 Min

▶ Piecing Together a Number Grid

(*Math Journal 2,* inside back cover; *Math Masters,* p. 249)

To explore using number-grid patterns to solve problems, have partners assemble a number grid from prepared pieces. Give each partnership an envelope containing the pieces needed to put together a complete number grid. Explain that you have cut the number grids apart and need help putting them back together. Encourage children to use the numbers on the pieces to determine how they fit together. When they are done, have them check their number grids against the number grid on the inside back cover of their journals. Have children describe how the patterns helped them assemble the grids.

EXTRA PRACTICE

INDEPENDENT ACTIVITY

15–30 Min

▶ Writing Larger Numbers

(*Math Masters,* p. 110)

Children practice writing larger numbers in order by filling in number scrolls on *Math Masters,* page 110.

Teaching Master

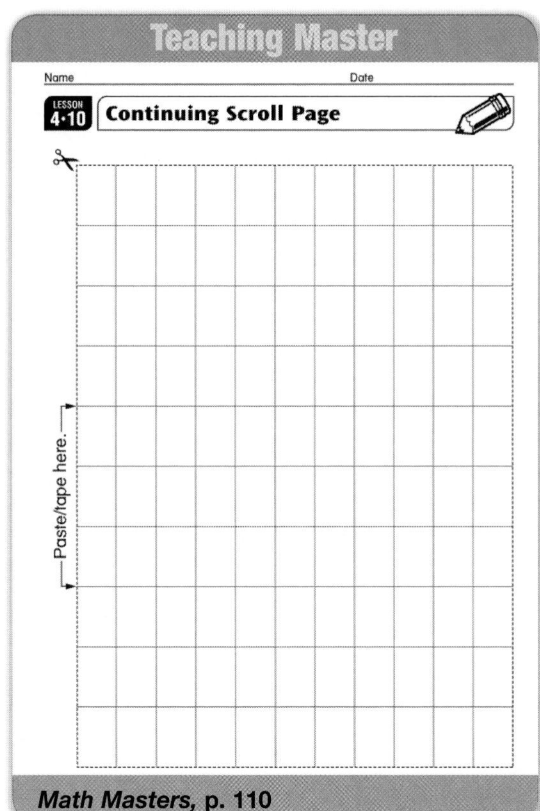
Name Date

LESSON 4·10 **Continuing Scroll Page**

Paste/tape here.

Math Masters, p. 110

9•2 Adding and Subtracting Tens

Objective To provide opportunities to develop proficiency in adding and subtracting 10s.

Technology Resources www.everydaymathonline.com

ePresentations

eToolkit

Algorithms Practice

EM Facts Workshop Game™

Family Letters

Assessment Management

Common Core State Standards

Curriculum Focal Points

Interactive Teacher's Lesson Guide

1 Teaching the Lesson

Key Concepts and Skills

- Count forward and backward by 1s and 10s using a number grid.
  [Number and Numeration Goal 1]
- Add and subtract 1s and 10s from 2-digit numbers.
  [Operations and Computation Goal 2]
- Solve addition and subtraction problems with and without manipulatives and tools.
  [Operations and Computation Goal 2]
- Use number-grid patterns to solve addition and subtraction problems.
  [Patterns, Functions, and Algebra Goal 1]

Key Activities

Children add and subtract 10s, first using a number grid, then using concrete models, drawings, and mental strategies. They play the *Number-Grid Game.*

Ongoing Assessment: Recognizing Student Achievement
Use the Math Message.
[Operations and Computation Goal 2]

Materials

Home Link 9•1
Math Masters, p. 249 per partnership
My Reference Book, pp. 142 and 143
transparency of *Math Masters,* p. 249 (optional) ◆ Number-Grid Poster ◆ base-10 blocks ◆ per group: 1 die, game markers, 2 dice (optional) ◆ slate

2 Ongoing Learning & Practice

Identifying How Many Letters are in Your First Name
Class Data Pad ◆ stick-on notes
Children create and analyze a line plot that identifies the number of letters in their first names.

Practicing with "What's My Rule?" and Frames-and-Arrows
Math Masters, p. 254
Children practice solving "What's My Rule?" and Frames-and-Arrows problems.

Math Boxes 9•2
Math Journal 2, p. 179
Children practice and maintain skills through Math Box problems.

Home Link 9•2
Math Masters, p. 255
Children practice and maintain skills through Home Link activities.

3 Differentiation Options

READINESS

Adding and Subtracting 10s
Math Masters, p. 256
base-10 blocks
Children model numbers with base-10 blocks.

ENRICHMENT

Finding a Pattern for 9s
Math Journal 2, inside back cover
Math Masters, p. 257
Children find a shortcut for 9s on the number grid.

EXTRA PRACTICE

Minute Math+
Minute Math®+, p. 42
Children practice solving problems with 10s.

Advance Preparation

***Teacher's Reference Manual,* Grades 1–3** pp. 177–182

Getting Started

Mental Math and Reflexes

Dictate one number at a time. Children write it on their slates and circle the digit in the tens place.

●○○ 12, 39, 55 ①2, ③9, ⑤5

●●○ 80, 101, 122 ⑧0, 1⓪1, 1②2

●●● 440, 591, 999 4④0, 5⑨1, 9⑨9

Math Message

Be ready to show how to use the number grid to solve these problems.

15 + 8 = _____

24 + 10 = _____

32 – 6 = _____

28 – 10 = _____

Home Link 9·1 Follow-Up

Ask a volunteer to explain how to find the number 132 on the number grid. Sample answer: Find the column that has 2s in the ones place and count down: 102, 112, 122, 132.

Ongoing Assessment: Recognizing Student Achievement

Math Message

Use the **Math Message** to assess children's ability to use a number grid to add and subtract. Children are making adequate progress if they are able to demonstrate their solutions on the number grid. Some children may use more sophisticated methods for solving the problems than others.

[Operations and Computation Goal 2]

1 Teaching the Lesson

▶ Math Message Follow-Up

WHOLE-CLASS ACTIVITY

Children use the Number-Grid Poster to show how they solved the problems. If some children were able to solve them mentally, without the help of the grid, ask them to use the grid to "prove" that their answers are correct. Recognize children who solved 24 + 10, not by counting up 10 spaces from 24, but by moving down one row from 24 to 34 (or those who solved 28 – 10 by moving up one row from 28 to 18).

▶ Adding and Subtracting 10s

WHOLE-CLASS ACTIVITY

Point to various numbers on the Number-Grid Poster as you ask children to add 10, subtract 20, and so on; for example, point to 17 and say: *Add 10.* Or, point to 49 and say: *Subtract 20.*

Encourage children to find the solutions using concrete models, such as base-10 blocks, and drawings, such as tally marks. For instance, children may draw 17 using tally marks and add 10 more tallies to find 17 + 10 = 27. Children may model 49 with 4 longs and 9 cubes and then subtract 2 longs to find 49 – 20 = 29.

After you have challenged children with a few problems, ask volunteers to explain their strategies for solving new problems and to write number models on the board to represent their strategies. Remember that each problem may be represented by more than one number model. For instance, children may subtract 30 from 80 by using either subtraction or addition strategies. Both $80 - 30 = 50$ and $30 + 50 = 80$ would be correct number models.

Links to the Future

Children continue using simple numerical patterns related to place value on the number grid. This is the first time children solve addition and subtraction problems by identifying a pattern in the digits. Finding rules for patterns and using them to solve addition and subtraction problems is a Grade 2 Goal.

When children are ready, ask them to add and subtract 10 and 20 mentally, without looking at the number grid, writing their answers on their slates. Encourage them to pose similar problems for others to solve.

Adjusting the Activity

Add and subtract 30s and 40s on the number grid. Also, pose addition and subtraction problems in which neither number is a multiple of 10 (for example, $13 + 26$) for children to solve on the number grid.

AUDITORY • KINESTHETIC • TACTILE • VISUAL

▶ Introducing the *Number-Grid Game*

PARTNER ACTIVITY

(*Math Masters,* p. 249; *My Reference Book,* pp. 142 and 143)

Ask children to turn to *My Reference Book,* pages 142 and 143, for the game rules. Use the transparency of the number grid (*Math Masters,* page 249) to explain the rules of the game. Players roll a die and use the Roll/Spaces table to move from 0 to 110 on the number grid.

Variations:

▷ A player lands on 110 *or past* to win.

▷ To practice subtracting 10s, start at 110 and move back to 0.

▷ Modify the Roll/Spaces table. For example, allow the same choice for 3 through 6 that the current table offers for 1 and 2.

▷ Play the game with 2 dice. For rolls of 7 to 12, move 7 to 12 spaces, respectively. This version provides practice with the addition facts and with adding 11 and 12.

Student Page

Games

Number-Grid Game

Materials ❑ 1 number grid
❑ 1 six-sided die
❑ 1 game marker for each player

Players 2 or more

Skill Counting on the number grid

Object of the game To land on 110 with an exact roll.

Roll	Spaces
⚀	1 or 10
⚁	2 or 20
⚂	3
⚃	4
⚄	5
⚅	6

Directions

1. Players put their markers at 0 on the number grid.
2. Take turns. When it is your turn:
   - Roll the die.
   - Use the table to see how many spaces to move your marker.
   - Move your marker that many spaces.
3. Continue playing. The winner is the first player to land on 110 with an exact roll.

My Reference Book, p. 142

Student Page

Games

Number Grid

−9	−8	−7	−6	−5	−4	−3	−2	−1	0
1	2	3	4	5	6	7	8	9	10
11	12	13	14	15	16	17	18	19	20
21	22	23	24	25	26	27	28	29	30
31	32	33	34	35	36	37	38	39	40
41	42	43	44	45	46	47	48	49	50
51	52	53	54	55	56	57	58	59	60
61	62	63	64	65	66	67	68	69	70
71	72	73	74	75	76	77	78	79	80
81	82	83	84	85	86	87	88	89	90
91	92	93	94	95	96	97	98	99	100
101	102	103	104	105	106	107	108	109	110

My Reference Book, p. 143

2 Ongoing Learning & Practice

▶ Identifying How Many Letters are in Your First Name

Children determine how many letters they have in their first names and write the number on stick-on notes. Draw a class tally chart on the Class Data Pad to show how many letters children have in their first names. Make a line plot of the results on the Class Data Pad using children's stick-on notes. Work as a class to determine the maximum and minimum values, the range, and the middle value of the data.

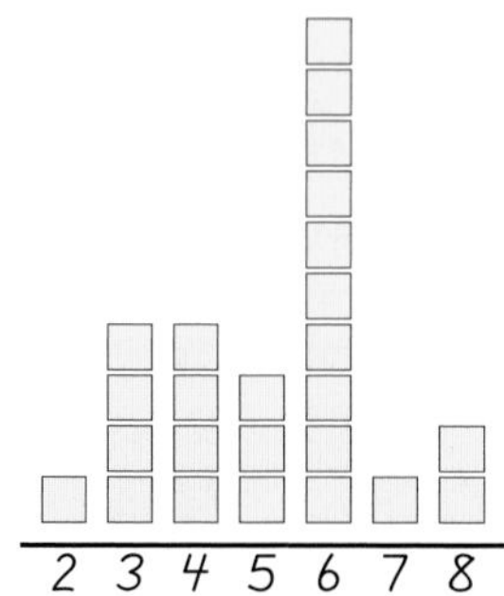

Encourage children to ask questions that can be answered using the graph. Ask questions such as the following to guide them:

- What questions can you ask that compare the data in one column with the data in another column?
- What other questions can you ask that can be answered using this graph?

Have children pose questions to their classmates, so that they have the opportunity to both ask and answer questions about the data.

Adjusting the Activity

Complete a similar routine determining the number of letters in middle or last names.

AUDITORY ♦ KINESTHETIC ♦ TACTILE ♦ VISUAL

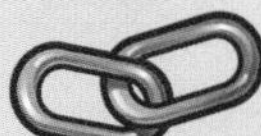

Links to the Future

In Grade 1, children have had multiple opportunities to explore, with teacher support, finding landmarks in various sets of data. Finding the maximum, minimum, mode, and median of a data set is a Grade 2 Goal.

Teaching Master

Name Date

LESSON 9•2 **Using Rules to Solve Problems**

"What's My Rule?"

Complete the tables.

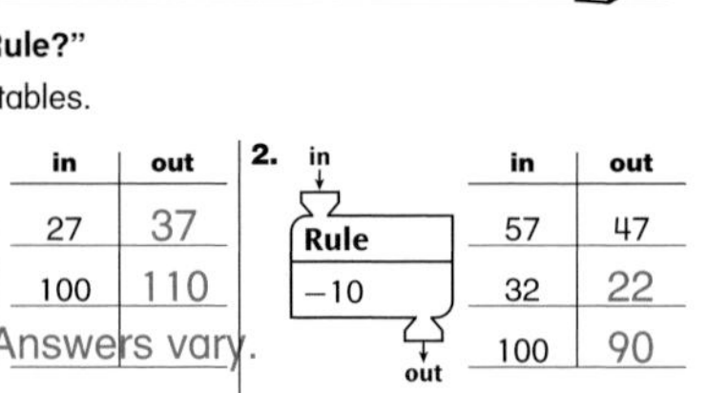

1. Rule +10

in	out
27	37
100	110
Answers vary.	

2. Rule −10

in	out
57	47
32	22
100	90

3. Rule +20

in	out
35	55
32	52
84	104
Answers vary.	

4. Rule −20

in	out
42	22
87	67
91	71
Answers vary.	

Frames-and-Arrows

Fill in the frames.

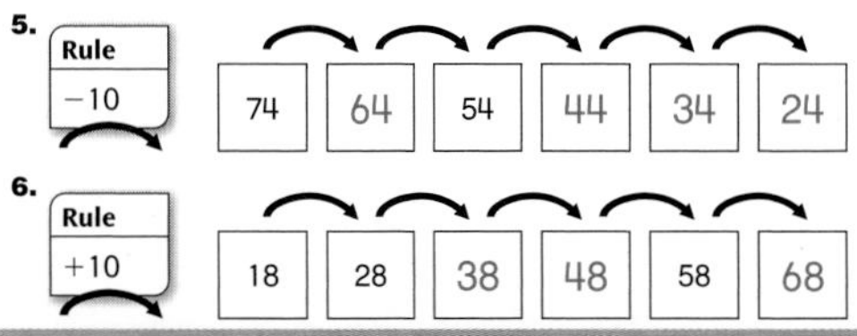

5. Rule −10: 74, 64, 54, 44, 34, 24

6. Rule +10: 18, 28, 38, 48, 58, 68

Math Masters, p. 254

▶ Practicing with "What's My Rule?" and Frames-and-Arrows

INDEPENDENT ACTIVITY

(*Math Masters,* p. 254)

Algebraic Thinking Use *Math Masters,* page 254 to provide practice solving "What's My Rule?" and Frames-and-Arrows problems.

▶ Math Boxes 9·2

INDEPENDENT ACTIVITY

(*Math Journal 2,* p. 179)

Mixed Practice Math Boxes in this lesson are paired with Math Boxes in Lesson 9-4. The skills in Problem 6 preview Unit 10 content.

Writing/Reasoning Have children draw, write, or verbalize an answer to the following question: *What is the pattern in the sums in Problem 2?* A reasonable answer should note that the ones digit is the same for all answers. Sample answer: I see the 7 in the 1s place.

▶ Home Link 9·2

(*Math Masters,* p. 255)

Home Connection Children solve addition and subtraction problems using a number grid.

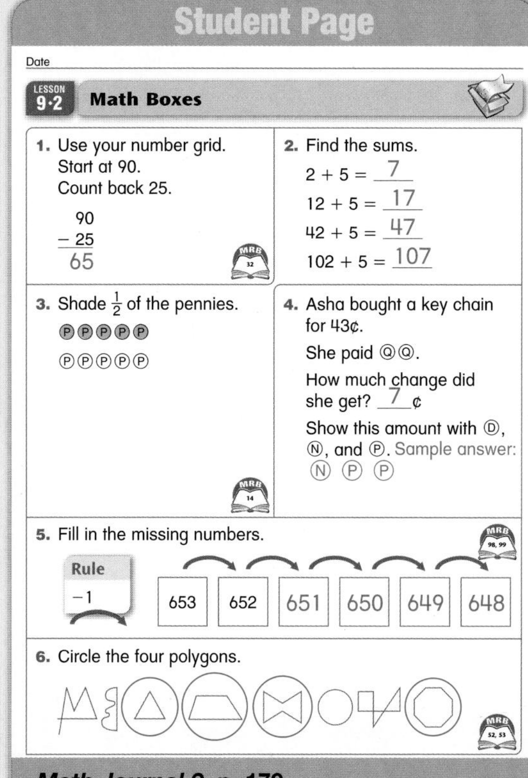

Student Page

Date

LESSON 9·2 **Math Boxes**

1. Use your number grid. Start at 90. Count back 25.
   90
   − 25
   65

2. Find the sums.
   2 + 5 = 7
   12 + 5 = 17
   42 + 5 = 47
   102 + 5 = 107

3. Shade $\frac{1}{2}$ of the pennies.
   Ⓟ Ⓟ Ⓟ Ⓟ Ⓟ
   Ⓟ Ⓟ Ⓟ Ⓟ Ⓟ

4. Asha bought a key chain for 43¢.
   She paid Ⓠ Ⓠ.
   How much change did she get? 7 ¢
   Show this amount with Ⓓ, Ⓝ, and Ⓟ. Sample answer: Ⓝ Ⓟ Ⓟ

5. Fill in the missing numbers.
   Rule: −1
   653, 652, 651, 650, 649, 648

6. Circle the four polygons.

Math Journal 2, p. 179

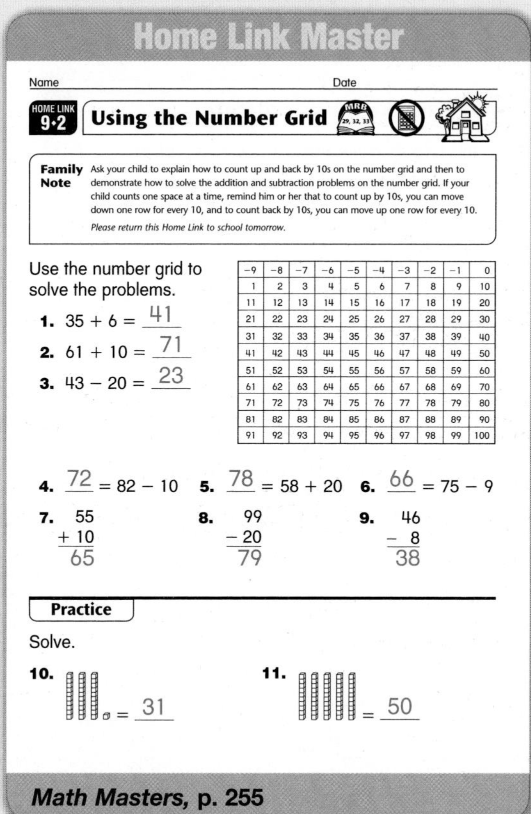

Home Link Master

Name Date

HOME LINK 9·2 **Using the Number Grid**

Family Note Ask your child to explain how to count up and back by 10s on the number grid and then to demonstrate how to solve the addition and subtraction problems on the number grid. If your child counts one space at a time, remind him or her that to count up by 10s, you can move down one row for every 10, and to count back by 10s, you can move up one row for every 10.
Please return this Home Link to school tomorrow.

Use the number grid to solve the problems.

1. 35 + 6 = 41
2. 61 + 10 = 71
3. 43 − 20 = 23

−9	−8	−7	−6	−5	−4	−3	−2	−1	0
1	2	3	4	5	6	7	8	9	10
11	12	13	14	15	16	17	18	19	20
21	22	23	24	25	26	27	28	29	30
31	32	33	34	35	36	37	38	39	40
41	42	43	44	45	46	47	48	49	50
51	52	53	54	55	56	57	58	59	60
61	62	63	64	65	66	67	68	69	70
71	72	73	74	75	76	77	78	79	80
81	82	83	84	85	86	87	88	89	90
91	92	93	94	95	96	97	98	99	100

4. 72 = 82 − 10
5. 78 = 58 + 20
6. 66 = 75 − 9
7. 55 + 10 = 65
8. 99 − 20 = 79
9. 46 − 8 = 38

Practice

Solve.

10. = 31
11. = 50

Math Masters, p. 255

Name Date

LESSON 9·2 **Adding and Subtracting 10s**

Build each number with base-10 blocks. Draw the blocks. Use | and •.

1. 24 — 34 — 54 — 64

2. 82 — 72 — 52 — 12

Try This

3. Describe a pattern you see on the page.
Sample answer: The numbers have the same number of cubes and different numbers of longs.

Math Masters, **p. 256**

Teaching Master

Name Date

LESSON 9·2 **Number-Grid Shortcuts**

1. Tabitha solved these problems on a number grid.
37 − 19 = 18
55 − 39 = 16
72 − 49 = 23

Tabitha said that she hopped rows to solve the problems. She said that she never moved back more than 1 space. Explain how you think she solved the problems.
Answers vary.

Explain how Tabitha's strategy can help you solve other problems on the number grid.
Answers vary.

Math Masters, **p. 257**

3 Differentiation Options

READINESS

SMALL-GROUP ACTIVITY

▶ Adding and Subtracting 10s

5–15 Min

(*Math Masters,* p. 256)

To explore digit patterns when counting forward and backward by multiples of ten, have children model numbers using base-10 blocks. Children complete the problems on *Math Masters,* page 256. When they have finished, ask them to describe to the group any patterns they see on the page. Sample answer: The numbers have the same number of cubes and different numbers of longs.

INDEPENDENT ACTIVITY

▶ Finding a Pattern for 9s

5–15 Min

(*Math Journal 2,* inside back cover and *Math Masters,* p. 257)

To further explore using number grid patterns to add and subtract numbers, have children solve a series of problems and develop a short-cut by using patterns on the grid. When children have finished *Math Masters,* page 257, have them share the strategies they came up with.

EXTRA PRACTICE

SMALL-GROUP ACTIVITY

▶ *Minute Math+*

5–15 Min

Use *Minute Math+,* page 42 to provide practice solving addition and subtraction problems with 10s.

9•3 Number-Grid Puzzles

Objective To reinforce counting, adding, and subtracting with 10s and 1s using number-grid patterns.

www.everydaymathonline.com

ePresentations | eToolkit | Algorithms Practice | EM Facts Workshop Game™ | Family Letters | Assessment Management | Common Core State Standards | Curriculum Focal Points | Interactive Teacher's Lesson Guide

1 Teaching the Lesson

Key Concepts and Skills

- Count forward and backward by 1s and 10s using a number grid. [Number and Numeration Goal 1]
- Identify the values of digits in a 2-digit number. [Number and Numeration Goal 3]
- Extend patterns on a number grid. [Patterns, Functions, and Algebra Goal 1]
- Solve number-grid puzzles. [Patterns, Functions, and Algebra Goal 1]

Key Activities

Children use patterns to fill in missing numbers on a number grid and then solve number-grid puzzles.

Key Vocabulary

number-grid puzzle

Materials

Math Journal 2, p. 180 and Activity Sheets 15 and 16
Home Link 9•2
Math Masters, pp. 258 and 259
base-10 blocks (flats, longs, cubes) ◆ slate ◆ Number-Grid Poster ◆ scissors

2 Ongoing Learning & Practice

Playing *Make My Design*

Math Journal 2, p. 137
per partnership: pattern blocks, 1 folder
Children practice naming and describing geometric figures and spatial relationships.

Ongoing Assessment: Recognizing Student Achievement

Use an Exit Slip (*Math Masters,* page 305).
[Geometry Goal 1]

Math Boxes 9•3

Math Journal 2, p. 181
Children practice and maintain skills through Math Box problems.

Home Link 9•3

Math Masters, p. 260
Children practice and maintain skills through Home Link activities.

3 Differentiation Options

READINESS

Playing Pin the Number on the Number Grid

Number-Grid Poster ◆ 3" by 3" stick-on notes
Children explore patterns on the number grid.

ENRICHMENT

Solving Number Codes

Math Masters, p. 261
Math Journal 2, inside back cover or Activity Sheet 15
Children solve number codes by using a number grid.

Advance Preparation

For Part 1, make one copy of *Math Masters,* page 258 for every 4 children. Cut the sheets apart, and place them near the Math Message. On the board, draw the grid column shown on this master. Make several copies of *Math Masters,* page 259. Cut out the grids and tape two of them together to make a 4 × 3 grid. Then cut out T- and L-shaped pieces from the grid. (*See examples.*) Follow this procedure to make several T- and L-shapes.

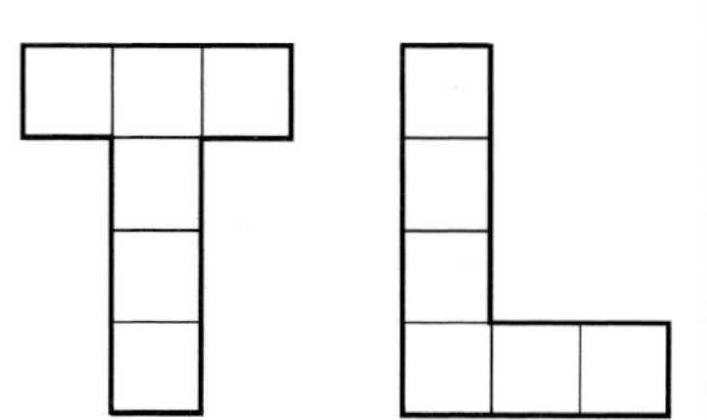

Getting Started

Mental Math and Reflexes

Display or draw base-10 blocks that represent 2- and 3-digit numbers. Children write the number on their slates.

●○○ 1 long, 8 cubes 18; 1 long, 13 cubes 23; 4 longs 40

●●○ 6 longs, 18 cubes 78; 7 longs, 20 cubes 90; 8 longs, 25 cubes 105

●●● 1 flat, 4 cubes 104; 1 flat, 4 longs, 12 cubes 152; 1 flat, 10 longs, 3 cubes 203

Math Message

Take a quarter-sheet of paper. Fill in the missing numbers.

Home Link 9·2 Follow-Up

Briefly go over the answers. Children share their strategies for solving the problems.

Teaching Master

Name Date

LESSON 9·3 **Number-Grid Pieces**

Name ______ This is part of a number grid. Fill in the missing numbers. 13, 23, 33, 43, 53	Name ______ This is part of a number grid. Fill in the missing numbers. 13, 23, 33, 43, 53
Name ______ This is part of a number grid. Fill in the missing numbers. 13, 23, 33, 43, 53	Name ______ This is part of a number grid. Fill in the missing numbers. 13, 23, 33, 43, 53

Math Masters, p. 258

1 Teaching the Lesson

▶ Math Message Follow-Up

WHOLE-CLASS ACTIVITY

Have children fill in the blank cells on the board and discuss how they used the number grid to solve the problem. Discuss the patterns in the problem:

- Which digit repeats in the 1s place? 3
- What is happening to the digits in the 10s place? Each time you move down one row, the digit in the 10s place is 1 more.
- Point to a digit in the 10s place. *What number does this digit represent?* The 2 in 23 represents 20; the 4 in 43 represents 40; and so on.

Tell children that they will use patterns on the number grid to solve **number-grid puzzles**.

▶ Filling in Pieces of the Number Grid

WHOLE-CLASS ACTIVITY

(*Math Journal 2,* Activity Sheets 15 and 16)

Ask children to close their eyes. Use a T-shaped piece to cover a portion of the Number-Grid Poster. (See illustration in margin.) Fill in one cell with the number that corresponds to the number under it on the grid.

Discuss how to fill in the remaining numbers on the T-piece. Write the missing numbers.

Repeat the process using the L-shaped piece.

Cover a portion of the grid with one of the remaining T- or L-shaped pieces, point to an empty cell, and ask children to write the number under it on their slates. Write or have one of the children write the rest of the missing numbers in the empty cells.

Repeat the process using another piece.

Adjusting the Activity

Begin by using only horizontal- or vertical-shaped pieces.

AUDITORY ◆ KINESTHETIC ◆ TACTILE ◆ VISUAL

Tell children to cut out the number-grid pieces from Activity Sheet 16. Have children work in pairs. While Partner A closes his or her eyes, Partner B places a number-grid piece on the number grid on Activity Sheet 16 so that it covers whole cells. Partner A fills in the covered numbers and then lifts the piece to check answers. Partners trade roles and repeat the process. They continue until all of the pieces have been used.

▶ Solving Number-Grid Puzzles

INDEPENDENT ACTIVITY

(*Math Journal 2,* p. 180 and Activity Sheet 15)

Children write the missing numbers on their number-grid puzzles. Have them check their work using the number grid on Activity Sheet 15.

Student Page

Date

LESSON 9·3 **Number-Grid Puzzles 1**

0	10	20	30	40		60	70	80	90	100	110
	9										
							68	78	88		
	7	17	27	37			67				
							66		86		
	5								85		
	4				44	54	64	74	84		104
	3		23						83		103
	2		22	32	42	52		72			102
			21				61			91	101

Math Journal 2, p. 180

Student Page

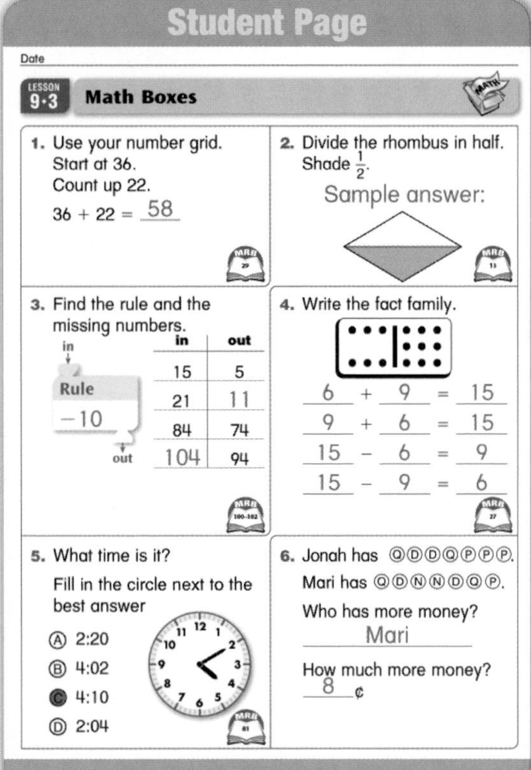
Date

LESSON 9·3 **Math Boxes**

1. Use your number grid. Start at 36. Count up 22.
36 + 22 = 58

2. Divide the rhombus in half. Shade $\frac{1}{2}$.
Sample answer:

3. Find the rule and the missing numbers.

Rule: −10

in	out
15	5
21	11
84	74
104	94

4. Write the fact family.
6 + 9 = 15
9 + 6 = 15
15 − 6 = 9
15 − 9 = 6

5. What time is it? Fill in the circle next to the best answer
Ⓐ 2:20
Ⓑ 4:02
● 4:10
Ⓓ 2:04

6. Jonah has ⓆⒹⒹⓆⓅⓅⓅ.
Mari has ⓆⒹⓃⓃⒹⓆⓅ.
Who has more money? Mari
How much more money? 8 ¢

Math Journal 2, p. 181

Home Link Master

Name Date

HOME LINK 9·3 **Number-Grid Puzzles**

Family Note Have your child show you how to complete the number-grid puzzles. Encourage him or her to explain patterns on the number grid that are helpful for solving the problems. For example, if you move up one row, the digit in the 10s place is 1 less.
Please return this Home Link to school tomorrow.

Show someone at home how to fill in the missing numbers.

1. 43, 53, 63, 73, 83

2. 23, 24, 25; 33; 43; 53; 63, 64; 73

3. 59; 69; 78, 79, 80; 88, 89, 90

Practice

4. Draw shapes that have exactly 4 sides and 4 corners. Write their names. Sample answers:
square rectangle rhombus trapezoid

Math Masters, p. 260

2 Ongoing Learning & Practice

Playing *Make My Design*

(*Math Journal 2,* p. 137)

Children practice naming and describing geometric figures and spatial relationships by playing *Make My Design.* For detailed instructions, see Lesson 7-1.

Ongoing Assessment: Recognizing Student Achievement

Use an **Exit Slip** (*Math Masters,* page 305) to assess children's ability to name 2-dimensional shapes. Have children list the shapes they used to create a design on the Exit Slip. Children are making adequate progress if they are able to name the shapes of the pattern blocks used. Some children may be better at spelling the names than others.

[Geometry Goal 1]

Math Boxes 9·3

(*Math Journal 2,* p. 181)

Mixed Practice Math Boxes in this lesson are paired with Math Boxes in Lesson 9-1. The skills in Problem 6 preview Unit 10 content.

Writing/Reasoning Have children draw, write, or verbalize an answer to the following question: *How do you know who has more money?* A reasonable answer should include a strategy for comparing two numbers, such as lining up coins or using a number line.

Home Link 9·3

(*Math Masters,* p. 260)

Home Connection Children show someone at home how to fill in the missing numbers on the number-grid puzzles.

3 Differentiation Options

READINESS

SMALL-GROUP ACTIVITY

5–15 Min

▶ Playing Pin the Number on the Number Grid

To explore using patterns in the number grid to find missing numbers, have children play Pin the Number on the Number Grid. First, have children look closely at the Number-Grid Poster and describe the patterns they see in the numbers. Ask: *Where are numbers with 5 in the ones place? With 5 in the tens place?* If no one mentions the following, be sure to include some version of each:

- The numbers get larger as you move down.
- The numbers get larger as you move to the right.
- The tens digit increases as you move down.
- The ones digit increases as you move to the right.
- The ones digit stays the same down a column.
- The tens digit stays the same across a row.

Next, blindfold one of the children. Tell the children a number between 1 and 100. The blindfolded child tries to place a sticky note on the poster as close to the selected number as possible. The child may ask for "hints" from other children. The hints have to be in terms of the patterns that were described; for example, "You have to add tens."

ENRICHMENT

PARTNER ACTIVITY

5–15 Min

▶ Solving Number Codes

(*Math Masters,* p. 261 and *Math Journal 2,* Activity Sheet 15 or inside back cover)

To apply their understanding of patterns on the number grid, have children solve arrow-path problems. Children use the key on *Math Masters,* page 261 to decipher number codes. The arrows direct their jumps on the number grid from a starting point to the final answer. Children fill in missing arrows and write their own codes for a partner to solve.

Teaching Master

Name Date

LESSON 9·3 **Solving Number Codes**

What number am I?

KEY
↑ = − 10
↓ = + 10
→ = + 1
← = − 1

1. 5 ↓ ↓ → → 27

2. 30 ↑ ← ← ← ← 16

3. 87 ↑ ↑ ↑ → → 59

Fill in the arrows.

4. 21 ↓ → → → 34

5. 65 ↑ ↑ ← ← ← ← 41

6. 104 ↑ ↑ ← ← ← ← 80

Write your own codes. Trade with a partner.
Answers vary.

7. ______

8. ______

Math Masters, p. 261

9•4 Adding and Subtracting 2-Digit Numbers

Objective To provide practice adding and subtracting 2-digit numbers.

Technology Resources www.everydaymathonline.com

ePresentations

eToolkit

Algorithms Practice

EM Facts Workshop Game™

Family Letters

Assessment Management

Common Core State Standards

Curriculum Focal Points

Interactive Teacher's Lesson Guide

1 Teaching the Lesson

Key Concepts and Skills

- Explain strategies used to solve problems involving the addition and subtraction of 2-digit by 2-digit numbers. [Operations and Computation Goal 2]
- Add and subtract 2-digit numbers using strategies based on place value and the relationship between addition and subtraction. [Operations and Computation Goal 2]
- Tell, write, and solve number stories. [Operations and Computation Goal 4]
- Write addition and subtraction number sentences using +, −, and =. [Patterns, Functions, and Algebra Goal 2]
- Use the properties of operations to add and subtract 2-digit numbers. [Patterns, Functions, and Algebra Goal 3]

Key Activities

Children use the data on their animal cards to make up and solve addition and subtraction number stories.

Ongoing Assessment: Informing Instruction See page 760.

Materials

Math Journal 2, p. 182
Home Link 9•3
slate ◆ animal cards from Unit 5 ◆ Number-Grid Poster ◆ base-10 blocks (optional)

2 Ongoing Learning & Practice

Practicing with Name-Collection Boxes

Math Masters, p. 262
Children use name-collection boxes to find equivalent names for numbers.

Math Boxes 9•4

Math Journal 2, p. 183
Children practice and maintain skills through Math Box problems.

Ongoing Assessment: Recognizing Student Achievement
Use Math Boxes, Problem 3.
[Number and Numeration Goal 4]

Home Link 9•4

Math Masters, p. 263
Children practice and maintain skills through Home Link activities.

3 Differentiation Options

READINESS

Practicing 2-Digit Addition and Subtraction

per partnership: 2 each of number cards 0–9 (from the Everything Math Deck, if available), base-10 blocks (longs and cubes), 1 penny, slate (optional)
Children use base-10 blocks to review adding and subtracting 2-digit numbers.

ENRICHMENT

Comparing the Sums of 2-Digit by 2-Digit Addition Problems

animal cards from Unit 5
Children solve two-digit addition problems and compare the sums.

ELL SUPPORT

Comparing the Weights of Objects

per group: bath scale, objects to weigh
Children weigh objects and order and compare weights.

Advance Preparation

You may want to make a transparency of Home Link 9•3 to use when you go over the answers.

***Teacher's Reference Manual,* Grades 1–3** p. 161

Getting Started

Mental Math and Reflexes

Have children answer the following rounding questions on their slates:

●○○ Is 17 closer to 10 or 20? 20 Is 24 closer to 20 or 30? 20

●●○ What multiple of 10 is closest to 33? 30 To 68? 70 To 86? 90

●●● Is 120 closer to 100 or 200? 100 Is 175 closer to 100 or 200? 200

Math Message

Take out your animal cards. Look at the side that shows the animal's length in inches. Which animal is the shortest? Which is the longest?

Home Link 9·3 Follow-Up

Briefly go over the answers. Ask children to describe how they used number-grid patterns to help them complete the puzzles.

1 Teaching the Lesson

▶ Math Message Follow-Up

Briefly go over the answers. The rabbit is the shortest animal on the cards; the porpoise is the longest. Discuss the meaning of the words *length* and *height*. Make sure children understand that *height* is used to refer to how tall someone or something is. *Length* is the size of something from one end to the other.

▶ Creating and Solving Silly Animal Stories

(*Math Journal 2,* p. 182)

Ask children to find the animal-card pictures of the rabbit and the raccoon. Then pose the following number story:

- Suppose the rabbit and the raccoon lie nose to nose. What will be their total length?

Have children share solution strategies. Some children may have added mentally and reasoned as follows: "Eleven is 1 more than 10. So I added 10 to 23; that's 33. Then I added 1 more; that's 34." Demonstrate this strategy on the Number-Grid Poster: Start at 23, add 10 by moving down one row to 33, then add 1 by moving one space to 34.

Summarize the number story by drawing a parts-and-total diagram and writing a number model.

Ask children to make up number stories about comparing or finding total lengths or weights of two animals on their cards. Suggest that they imagine two animals on the same weighing scale or one animal sitting on top of another. To support English language learners, discuss the meanings of the words *weight* and *scale.*

Student Page

Date

LESSON 9·4 **Silly Animal Stories**

Example:

Unit: inches

koala 24 in.
penguin 36 in.

How tall are the koala and penguin together?
24 + 36 = 60
60 inches

1. Silly Story

Unit

2. Silly Story

Unit

Math Journal 2, p. 182

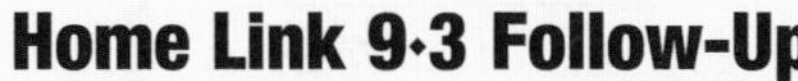

first-grade girl	43 in.	41 lb
7-year-old boy	50 in.	50 lb
cheetah	48 in.	120 lb
porpoise	72 in.	98 lb
penguin	36 in.	75 lb
beaver	30 in.	56 lb
fox	20 in.	14 lb
cat	12 in.	7 lb
raccoon	23 in.	23 lb
koala	24 in.	19 lb
eagle	35 in.	15 lb
rabbit	11 in.	6 lb

Animal card heights, lengths, and weights

Links to the Future

Children practice solving number stories that include 2-digit by 2-digit addition and subtraction. In first grade, children should be able to solve and explain strategies for solving 2-digit by 1-digit number stories; however, solving 2-digit by 2-digit addition and subtraction number stories is a Grade 2 Goal.

Teaching Master

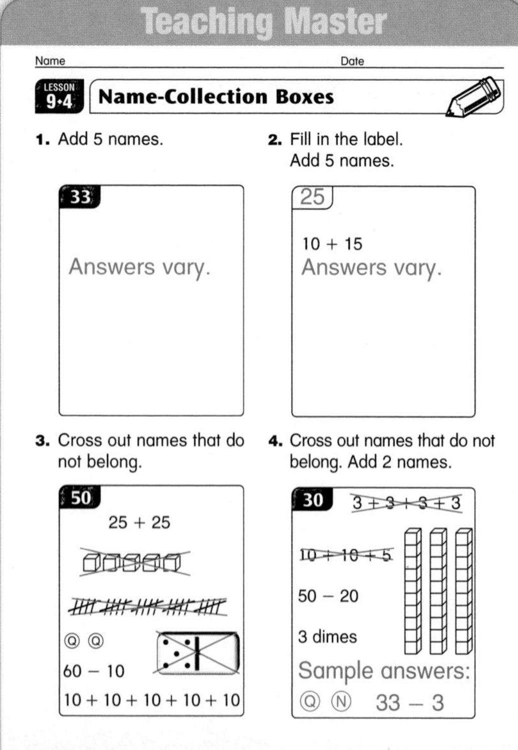

Name Date

LESSON 9•4 **Name-Collection Boxes**

1. Add 5 names.

33

Answers vary.

2. Fill in the label. Add 5 names.

25

10 + 15

Answers vary.

3. Cross out names that do not belong.

50

25 + 25

~~60 − 10~~

10 + 10 + 10 + 10 + 10

4. Cross out names that do not belong. Add 2 names.

30

~~3 + 3 + 3 + 3~~

~~10 + 10 + 5~~

50 − 20

3 dimes

Sample answers: 33 − 3

Math Masters, p. 262

Suggested number stories:

- If the koala stood on top of the penguin's head, how tall would they be together? 60 in.
- If the fox sat on top of the beaver, how much would they weigh together? 70 lb
- How much taller is the boy than the girl? 7 in.
- How much more does the cheetah weigh than the boy? 70 lb

Tell children to solve the number stories any way they can. Encourage children to use concrete models, such as base-10 blocks, and drawings to solve the problems. Have children share their solution strategies, and encourage them to try new strategies on subsequent number stories. For instance, you may wish to have children practice some common addition and subtraction strategies with the following number stories:

- **Counting on from the larger addend:** How much do the 15 lb eagle and the 7 lb cat weigh together? Start with the larger weight, 15 lb, and count up 7 lb to get 22 lb total.
- **Making ten:** If the 48 in. cheetah and the 23 in. raccoon sleep head-to-toe in a line, how long would they be together? Use base-10 blocks to represent the cheetah's length (4 longs, 8 cubes) and the raccoon's length (2 longs, 3 cubes). Add tens to tens and ones to ones to get 6 longs, 11 cubes. Trade 10 cubes for one long, composing a new ten and leaving 1 cube left over. The length is 7 tens, 1 one, or 71 inches total.
- **Counting up to subtract:** How much more does the 50 lb boy weigh than the 41 lb girl? Count up from 41 lb to 50 lb, a 9 lb difference.

When discussing solutions, display the appropriate unit box on the board. Ask children to suggest a number model for the problem. Keep in mind that more than one model may be appropriate. For example, when comparing the heights of the boy and the girl, the counting-up strategy can be represented by the addition number model $43 + 7 = 50$ or the subtraction number model $50 - 43 = 7$. Summarize with an appropriate situation diagram.

Adjusting the Activity

Have children model the number stories with base-10 blocks as they did in Lesson 5-5 with animal weight number stories.

AUDITORY • KINESTHETIC • TACTILE • VISUAL

Ongoing Assessment: Informing Instruction

Watch for children who have trouble deciding whether to add or subtract when solving a number story. Suggest that they act out the number story in order to better understand the situation. You may also want to help children select a situation diagram that fits the story.

After children have solved a few number stories as a class, divide the class into partnerships. Partners use their animal cards to make up and record two silly stories on journal page 182.

NOTE While children should learn to add and subtract on the number grid, they should also be encouraged to be flexible in their solution strategies. For example, there is no need for them to turn to the number grid, or any other aid, if they are able to find a correct answer mentally. There will also be times when a visual representation of a problem with pictures, doodles, counters, or base-10 blocks will result in a better understanding of its solution. Emphasizing the use of the number grid as a device for *checking* answers will, it is hoped, discourage children from relying solely on the number grid to *find* answers.

Select a few of the children's silly animal stories to act out with the class. Ask children to write the number model that matches the story.

2 Ongoing Learning & Practice

▶ Practicing with Name-Collection Boxes

(*Math Masters,* p. 262)

Use *Math Masters,* page 262 to provide practice with name-collection boxes.

▶ Math Boxes 9·4

(*Math Journal 2,* p. 183)

Mixed Practice Math Boxes in this lesson are paired with Math Boxes in Lesson 9-2. The skills in Problem 6 preview Unit 10 content.

Ongoing Assessment: Recognizing Student Achievement — **Math Boxes Problem 3**

Use **Math Boxes, Problem 3** to assess children's ability to find fractions of a set. Children are making adequate progress if they are able to shade $\frac{1}{4}$ of the dimes.

[Number and Numeration Goal 4]

▶ Home Link 9·4

(*Math Masters,* p. 263)

Home Connection Children solve 2-digit addition problems with the help of a number grid and base-10 block illustrations.

Student Page

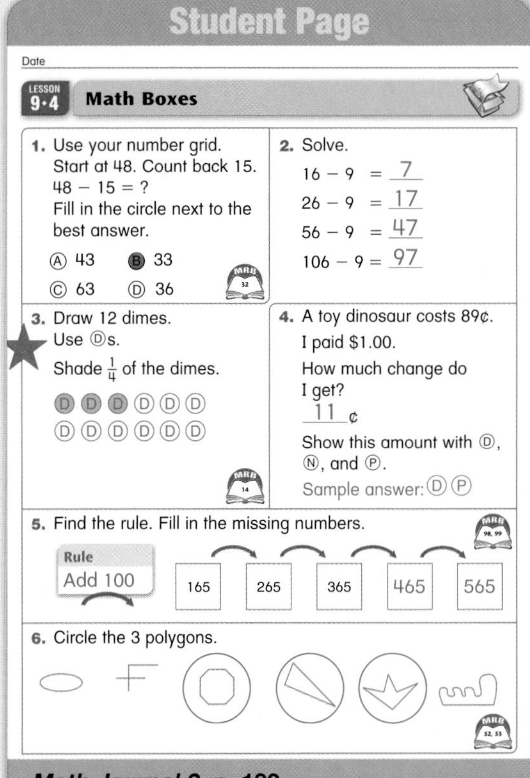

Date

LESSON 9·4 **Math Boxes**

1. Use your number grid. Start at 48. Count back 15. 48 − 15 = ? Fill in the circle next to the best answer.
   (A) 43 (B) 33 (C) 63 (D) 36

2. Solve.
   16 − 9 = 7
   26 − 9 = 17
   56 − 9 = 47
   106 − 9 = 97

3. Draw 12 dimes. Use Ⓓs. Shade $\frac{1}{4}$ of the dimes.
   Ⓓ Ⓓ Ⓓ Ⓓ Ⓓ Ⓓ
   Ⓓ Ⓓ Ⓓ Ⓓ Ⓓ Ⓓ

4. A toy dinosaur costs 89¢. I paid $1.00. How much change do I get? 11 ¢
   Show this amount with Ⓓ, Ⓝ, and Ⓟ.
   Sample answer: Ⓓ Ⓟ

5. Find the rule. Fill in the missing numbers.
   Rule: Add 100
   165, 265, 365, 465, 565

6. Circle the 3 polygons.

Math Journal 2, p. 183

Home Link Master

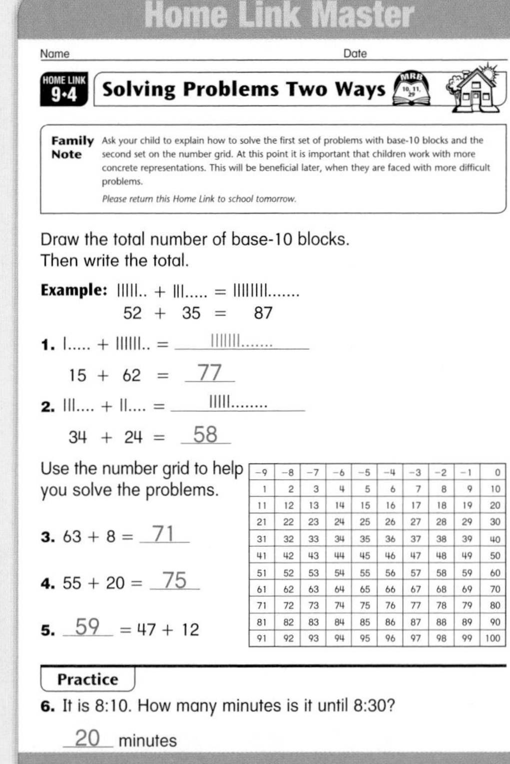

Name Date

HOME LINK 9·4 **Solving Problems Two Ways**

Family Note Ask your child to explain how to solve the first set of problems with base-10 blocks and the second set on the number grid. At this point it is important that children work with more concrete representations. This will be beneficial later, when they are faced with more difficult problems.

Please return this Home Link to school tomorrow.

Draw the total number of base-10 blocks. Then write the total.

Example: |||||.. + |||..... = ||||||||.......
52 + 35 = 87

1. |..... + ||||||.. = |||||||.......
   15 + 62 = 77

2. |||.... + ||.... = |||||........
   34 + 24 = 58

Use the number grid to help you solve the problems.

3. 63 + 8 = 71

4. 55 + 20 = 75

5. 59 = 47 + 12

−9	−8	−7	−6	−5	−4	−3	−2	−1	0
1	2	3	4	5	6	7	8	9	10
11	12	13	14	15	16	17	18	19	20
21	22	23	24	25	26	27	28	29	30
31	32	33	34	35	36	37	38	39	40
41	42	43	44	45	46	47	48	49	50
51	52	53	54	55	56	57	58	59	60
61	62	63	64	65	66	67	68	69	70
71	72	73	74	75	76	77	78	79	80
81	82	83	84	85	86	87	88	89	90
91	92	93	94	95	96	97	98	99	100

Practice

6. It is 8:10. How many minutes is it until 8:30? 20 minutes

Math Masters, p. 263

3 Differentiation Options

READINESS

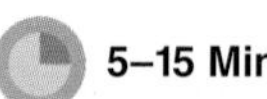

PARTNER ACTIVITY

5–15 Min

▶ Practicing 2-Digit Addition and Subtraction

To explore adding and subtracting 2-digit numbers using a concrete model, have partners use base-10 blocks. Each child turns over two number cards to create a 2-digit number and then represents that number with base-10 blocks. Next, partners flip a penny to determine whether to add or subtract—heads, they add; tails, they subtract. They work together to add or subtract the two 2-digit numbers. Children can record number models on their slates.

ENRICHMENT

PARTNER ACTIVITY

5–15 Min

▶ Comparing the Sums of 2-Digit by 2-Digit Addition Problems

To further explore 2-digit by 2-digit addition, children play a variation of *Addition Top-It* using the animal-length cards. Partners combine their decks of animal cards and place them in a stack on the table, length-side down. Each partner turns over 2 cards and finds the sum of the lengths. Partners compare their sums. The partner with the higher sum takes all 4 cards. The game is over when all of the cards from the stack have been played.

ELL SUPPORT

SMALL-GROUP ACTIVITY

5–15 Min

▶ Comparing the Weights of Objects

To provide language support for weight, provide children with opportunities to weigh a variety of objects using a bath scale. Label the names of the objects and then ask children to label the weights in pounds. Provide children with opportunities to hold the objects as they compare the weights. Ask them to list the weights in order from lightest to heaviest. Ask children to find an object that weighs about one pound.

Planning Ahead

For Lesson 9-5, you will need containers, a pourable substance such as unpopped popcorn, rice, or dried beans, 3 large cups, and 3 small cups. See the materials list for Part 1 in Lesson 9-5.

9•5 Exploring Capacity, Symmetry, and Heights

Explorations

Objectives To provide experiences comparing capacities of containers; creating a symmetrical design; and making a second height measurement.

Technology Resources www.everydaymathonline.com

ePresentations

eToolkit

Algorithms Practice

EM Facts Workshop Game™

Family Letters

Assessment Management

Common Core State Standards

Curriculum Focal Points

Interactive Teacher's Lesson Guide

1 Teaching the Lesson

Key Concepts and Skills

- Use standard measuring tools to measure length to the nearest inch. [Measurement and Reference Frames Goal 1]
- Use non-standard tools to estimate capacity. [Measurement and Reference Frames Goal 1]
- Draw plane shapes. [Geometry Goal 1]
- Complete line-symmetric designs. [Geometry Goal 2]

Key Activities

Exploration A: Children compare the capacities of three containers by measuring about how many cups of a pourable substance each container holds.

Exploration B: Children create the mirror image of a pattern-block design across a line of symmetry.

Exploration C: Children measure and record their heights in inches.

Ongoing Assessment: Recognizing Student Achievement Use Mental Math and Reflexes. [Number and Numeration Goal 3]

Ongoing Assessment: Informing Instruction See page 764.

Materials

Home Link 9•4
slate

Exploration A: Per workstation:
Math Masters, p. 264
3 containers of different sizes and shapes ◆ a pourable substance (such as dried beans) to fill containers ◆ 3 paper cups of one size and 3 of another size

Exploration B: Per workstation:
Math Masters, p. 265
pattern blocks ◆ Pattern-Block Template (optional)

Exploration C: Per workstation:
Math Journal 2, p. 184
height stick-on notes from Lesson 4•7 ◆ tape measure ◆ book

2 Ongoing Learning & Practice

Playing the *Number-Grid Game*
My Reference Book, pp. 142 and 143
per partnership: 1 number grid, 1 die, game markers

Math Boxes 9•5
Math Journal 2, p. 185

Home Link 9•5
Math Masters, p. 266

3 Differentiation Options

READINESS
Making Symmetrical Paintings
paint ◆ small brushes ◆ markers

ENRICHMENT
Measuring Capacity
per group: beans ◆ large bowl ◆ measuring cups (cup, pint)

EXTRA PRACTICE
Reviewing Symmetrical Shapes with Geoboards
per partnership: 1 geoboard, 2 rubber bands

ELL SUPPORT
Building a Math Word Bank
Differentiation Handbook, p. 126

Advance Preparation

For Exploration A, the same three containers (size and shape) should be used at each workstation.

Place one set of different-sized containers labeled *A, B,* and *C* near the Math Message. For Exploration C, tape a measuring tape to the doorframe or wall to facilitate measuring children's heights. You may wish to obtain the book ***LuLu's Lemonade*** by Barbara deRubertis (The Kane Press, 2000), as it relates to lesson content.

***Teacher's Reference Manual,* Grades 1–3** pp. 159–161

Getting Started

Mental Math and Reflexes

Write two or three digits on the board. On their slates, children write the largest numbers they can make with the digits. *Suggestions:*

●○○ 7, 2 72 4, 9 94 5, 8 85 1, 9 91

●●○ 1, 5, 2 521 3, 3, 2 332 0, 9, 1 910 2, 5, 9 952

●●● 9, 1, 2 921 4, 9, 9 994 9, 8, 1 981 5, 5, 9 955

Math Message

Pretend that these 3 containers are filled with popcorn. Which container would hold the most popcorn?

Home Link 9·4 Follow-Up

Ask children to compare adding base-10 blocks to counting on a number grid to solve problems. If no one suggests it, mention that adding one long is like moving down one row on the grid, and adding one cube is like moving one space to the right on the grid.

Ongoing Assessment: Recognizing Student Achievement

Mental Math and Reflexes 

Use **Mental Math and Reflexes** to assess children's ability to create numbers using given digits. Children are making adequate progress if they are able to write the largest numbers using two digits. Some children may be able to do the same with three digits.

[Number and Numeration Goal 3]

1 Teaching the Lesson

▶ Math Message Follow-Up

WHOLE-CLASS ACTIVITY

Make a tally chart of children's answers. Ask children to suggest strategies to determine which container would hold the most popcorn.

▶ Exploration A: Finding the Capacity of Containers

SMALL-GROUP ACTIVITY

(*Math Masters,* p. 264)

Children measure about how many small paper cups of unpopped popcorn (or another pourable substance) are needed to fill each container to the top. They repeat the procedure with a large cup.

Ongoing Assessment: Informing Instruction

Watch for children who do not fill their paper cups to the top. Remind them that they must do so in order to get an accurate measurement.

Teaching Master

Name Date

LESSON 9·5 **How Much a Container Holds**

1. Fill the small cup to the top. Pour the contents into a container. Repeat this until you have filled each container to the top. Answers vary.

   Container A holds about _____ small cups.

   Container B holds about _____ small cups.

   Container C holds about _____ small cups.

2. Now use the large cup to fill each container. Answers vary.

   Container A holds about _____ large cups.

   Container B holds about _____ large cups.

   Container C holds about _____ large cups.

3. Do the containers hold more small cups or more large cups?

   More small cups

4. Draw the containers in order from smallest to largest. Use the back of this page.

   Drawings vary.

Math Masters, p. 264

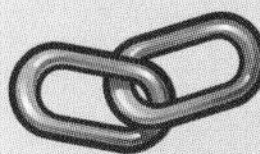

Links to the Future

The work with capacity in this lesson is an initial exposure to the topic. Children in *Everyday Mathematics* will continue to explore capacity in future grade levels.

▶ Exploration B: Using Symmetry

SMALL-GROUP ACTIVITY

(*Math Masters,* p. 265)

Children use pattern blocks to make the mirror image of a design across a line of symmetry. They draw the mirror image by tracing around the blocks or by using their Pattern-Block Templates. Then they color their designs.

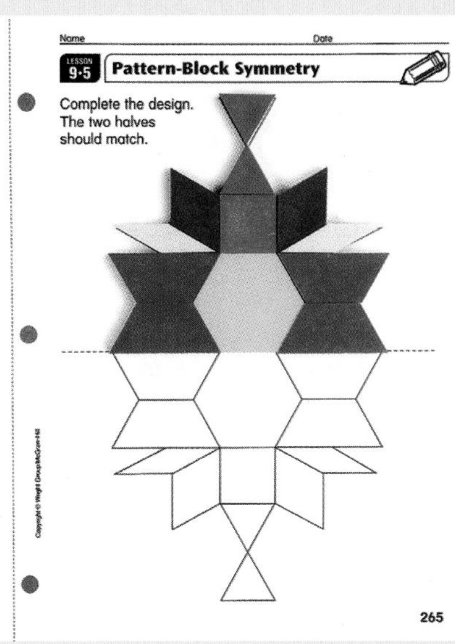
Name Date

LESSON 9·5 **Pattern-Block Symmetry**

Complete the design. The two halves should match.

265

Children use blocks to create a mirror image on *Math Masters,* page 265.

Adjusting the Activity

ELL

Have children create and draw their own symmetrical designs on sheets of paper. Encourage children to use at least three different pattern blocks in their designs.

AUDITORY ◆ KINESTHETIC ◆ TACTILE ◆ VISUAL

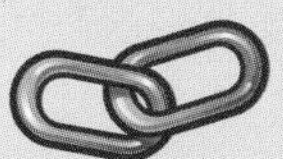

Links to the Future

In this lesson, children make the mirror image of an existing design across a line of symmetry. Creating and completing simple 2-dimensional symmetric designs is a Grade 2 Goal.

▶ Exploration C: Measuring and Recording Children's Heights

WHOLE-CLASS ACTIVITY

(*Math Journal 2,* p. 184)

To begin the activity, have children use the stick-on notes that you saved from Lesson 4-7 to fill in the data under "First Measurement" on journal page 184.

Then, follow the same procedure you used to measure children's heights in Lesson 4-7 to take a second measurement. Emphasize that children should stand straight, with their heads level, against the tape measure on the wall. Review how to use a book against the wall on top of the head. Remind them that the measurement is read at the bottom of the book. Have children record the date and their heights, in inches, under "Second Measurement." The final section, "Change in Height," will be completed in Lesson 10-1.

Social Studies Link Provide children with books about the heights of buildings from all over the world. Have children label the location of the buildings on a world map. Then have them make a bar graph about the heights of the buildings and use the graph to determine the typical height and middle value of the data.

Student Page

Date

LESSON 9·5 **My Height Record**

First Measurement

Date ____________

Height: about ________ inches   Answers vary.

A typical height for a first grader in my class was about ________ inches.

Second Measurement

Date ____________

Height: about ________ inches

A typical height for a first grader in my class is about ________ inches.

The middle height for my class is about ________ inches.

Change to Height

I grew about ________ inches.

The typical growth in my class was about ________ inches.

Math Journal 2, p. 184

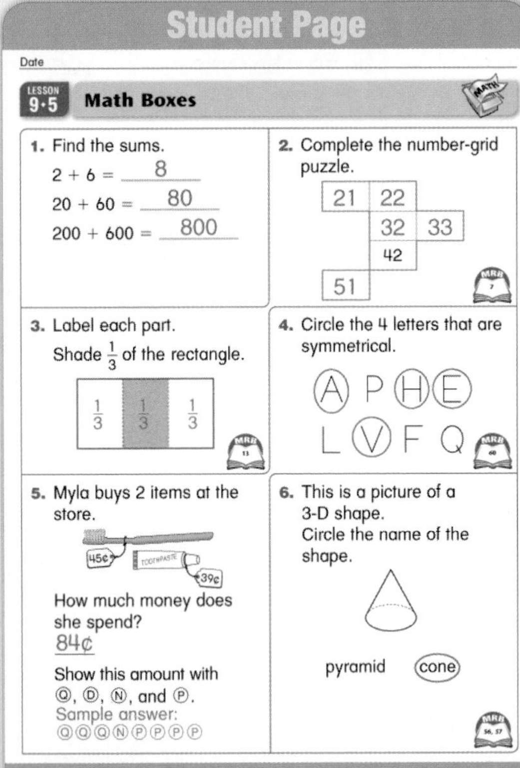
Student Page

Date

LESSON 9·5 **Math Boxes**

1. Find the sums.
2 + 6 = 8
20 + 60 = 80
200 + 600 = 800

2. Complete the number-grid puzzle.

21	22	
	32	33
	42	
51		

3. Label each part.
Shade $\frac{1}{3}$ of the rectangle.
$\frac{1}{3}$ $\frac{1}{3}$ $\frac{1}{3}$

4. Circle the 4 letters that are symmetrical.
A P H E
L V F Q

5. Myla buys 2 items at the store.
45¢ 39¢
How much money does she spend?
84¢
Show this amount with Ⓠ, Ⓓ, Ⓝ, and Ⓟ.
Sample answer:
ⓆⓆⓆⓃⓅⓅⓅⓅ

6. This is a picture of a 3-D shape.
Circle the name of the shape.
pyramid cone

Math Journal 2, p. 185

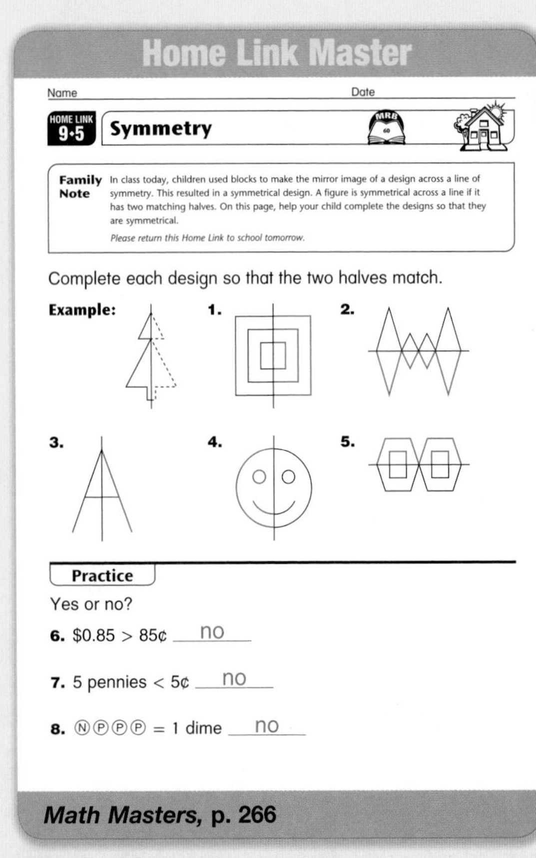
Home Link Master

Name Date

HOME LINK 9·5 **Symmetry**

Family Note In class today, children used blocks to make the mirror image of a design across a line of symmetry. This resulted in a symmetrical design. A figure is symmetrical across a line if it has two matching halves. On this page, help your child complete the designs so that they are symmetrical.

Please return this Home Link to school tomorrow.

Complete each design so that the two halves match.

Example: 1. 2.

3. 4. 5.

Practice

Yes or no?

6. \$0.85 > 85¢ no

7. 5 pennies < 5¢ no

8. ⓃⓅⓅⓅ = 1 dime no

Math Masters, p. 266

2 Ongoing Learning & Practice

▶ Playing the *Number-Grid Game*

(*My Reference Book,* pp. 142 and 143)

Children practice adding and subtracting on the number grid by playing the *Number-Grid Game.* For detailed instructions, see *My Reference Book*, pages 142 and 143.

▶ Math Boxes 9·5

(*Math Journal 2,* p. 185)

Mixed Practice Math Boxes in this lesson are paired with Math Boxes in Lesson 9-7. The skills in Problem 6 preview Unit 10 content.

Writing/Reasoning Have children draw, write, or verbalize an answer to the following question: *What is a fraction of a shape?* A reasonable answer should include a reference to equal parts. Sample answer: All of the pieces are the same size and shape.

▶ Home Link 9·5

(*Math Masters,* p. 266)

Home Connection Children draw mirror images of designs to continue the investigation of symmetry started in Exploration B.

3 Differentiation Options

READINESS

▶ Making Symmetrical Paintings

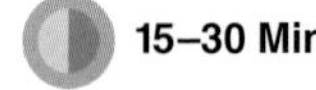

To explore the concept of symmetry, have children make symmetrical pictures with paint. Children fold their papers in half and then unfold them. They paint pictures on one half of the paper and then fold their papers over, pressing the painted half and the unpainted half together, while the paint is still wet. (Make sure children press evenly and firmly with both hands.)

After children unfold their papers, discuss what happened. Ask: *What does it mean when we say that things are symmetrical?* When the paint is dry, children can outline the designs they have created with markers—first on one side and then on the other.

ENRICHMENT

SMALL-GROUP ACTIVITY

▶ Measuring Capacity

5–15 Min

To further explore capacity, have children make estimates for how much a container holds. Place a cup and a pint container on a table. Label each container. Explain that cups and pints are units of measure that tell how much a container holds. Pour beans into a large bowl. First have children estimate about how many cups of beans are in one pint. Then have them check their estimates. Have children measure about how many cups and pints the bowl holds.

EXTRA PRACTICE

PARTNER ACTIVITY

▶ Reviewing Symmetrical Shapes with Geoboards

5–15 Min

To review symmetry, have children work in pairs to create symmetrical shapes on a geoboard. Both partners stretch their rubber bands around the middle column of pins on the same geoboard to create a line of symmetry. Partner A uses one of the rubber bands to create half a shape on one side of the line of symmetry. Partner B uses the other rubber band to complete the symmetrical shape. Partners switch roles and create a new symmetrical shape.

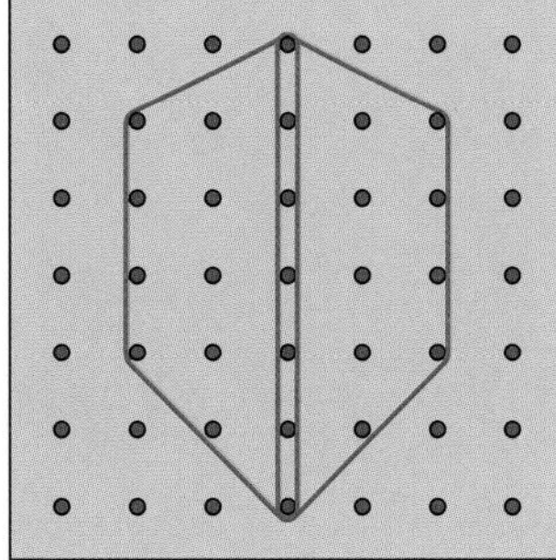

ELL SUPPORT

SMALL-GROUP ACTIVITY

▶ Building a Math Word Bank

5–15 Min

(*Differentiation Handbook,* p. 126)

To provide language support for capacity, have children use the Word Bank Template found on *Differentiation Handbook,* page 126. Ask children to write the terms *measurement* and *capacity,* draw pictures representing the terms, and write other words that describe them. See the *Differentiation Handbook* for more information.

9•6 Fractional Parts of the Whole

Objective To extend fraction concepts to fractions other than unit fractions.

Technology Resources www.everydaymathonline.com

ePresentations

eToolkit

Algorithms Practice

EM Facts Workshop Game™

Family Letters

Assessment Management

Common Core State Standards

Curriculum Focal Points

Interactive Teacher's Lesson Guide

1 Teaching the Lesson

Key Concepts and Skills

- Divide shapes into fractional parts.
  [Number and Numeration Goal 4]
- Model fractional parts of a region.
  [Number and Numeration Goal 4]
- Identify halves and fourths.
  [Number and Numeration Goal 4]
- Identify equivalent names for fractional parts of a region.
  [Number and Numeration Goal 4]

Key Activities

Children fold square pieces of paper in different ways to show that equal fractional parts of the same whole can be different shapes. They shade fractional parts of pattern-block shapes and divide circles into fractional parts.

Ongoing Assessment: Recognizing Student Achievement Use journal page 186.
[Number and Numeration Goal 4]

Ongoing Assessment: Informing Instruction See page 770.

Materials

Math Journal 2, p. 186
Home Link 9•5
Math Masters, pp. 267, 267A, and 267B
per partnership: pattern blocks (6 triangles, 3 rhombuses, and 2 trapezoids), Pattern-Block Template, additional pattern blocks (optional) ◆ slate ◆ scissors ◆ tool-kit coins or counters (optional)

2 Ongoing Learning & Practice

Finding the Range and Middle Value of a Data Set

animal cards from Unit 5
Children find the range and middle values of lengths or heights using data on their animal cards.

Practicing with the Number Grid

Math Masters, p. 268
Children practice counting by 2s and 4s and solving puzzles using number grids.

Math Boxes 9•6

Math Journal 2, p. 187
Children practice and maintain skills through Math Box problems.

Home Link 9•6

Math Masters, p. 269
Children practice and maintain skills through Home Link activities.

3 Differentiation Options

READINESS

Identifying Unit Fractions

Pattern-Block Template
Children identify unit fractions of 2-dimensional shapes.

ELL SUPPORT

Discussing Unit Fractions

Children compare and discuss similarities and differences of unit factions.

Advance Preparation

For Part 1, make one copy of *Math Masters,* page 267 per child. On pink paper, make one copy per child of *Math Masters,* pages 267A and 267B. Place all of the copies near the Math Message.

You may wish to obtain a copy of ***Fraction Action*** by Loreen Leedy (Holiday House, 1996), as it relates to lesson content.

***Teacher's Reference Manual,* Grades 1–3** pp. 60, 61

Getting Started

Mental Math and Reflexes

Tell number stories. Children may use coins or counters, or draw pictures to help them solve the problems. Children record answers on their slates.
Suggestions:

●○○ Pam shared 20 pennies equally with her sister. How many pennies did each girl get? 10 pennies

●●○ Luis divided his fruit bar into 4 equal pieces so that he could share it with 3 of his friends. What fraction of the fruit bar did each child get? $\frac{1}{4}$ of the fruit bar

●●● Anne planted daisies in the garden. When they bloomed, there were 8 flowers. Four of the flowers were white. What fraction of the flowers were white? $\frac{1}{2}$ or $\frac{4}{8}$ of the flowers

Math Message

Take a copy of Math Masters, *pages 267, 267A, and 267B. Cut out each of the squares and the two circles.*

Home Link 9·5 Follow-Up

Briefly review completed designs.

1 Teaching the Lesson

▶ Math Message Follow-Up

WHOLE-CLASS ACTIVITY

(*Math Masters,* pp. 267, 267A, and 267B)

Check that children have cut the shapes from *Math Masters,* pages 267, 267A, and 267B.

▶ Folding Squares to Make Fourths

WHOLE-CLASS ACTIVITY

Review the following terms used in discussing fractions: *half, fourths, fraction,* and *fractional part.* Write each term on the board with an example.

Children use the six squares they cut out for the following activities:

1. Fold two of the squares in half, each in a different way. Label each part with the fraction $\frac{1}{2}$.

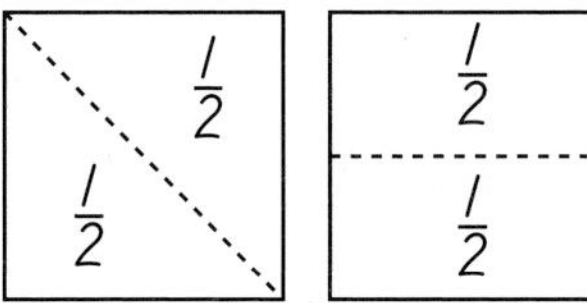

2. Fold three of the other squares into fourths, each in a different way. (Most children will probably be able to come up with at least two ways. Give them a little extra time to find out a third way.) Ask volunteers to display their work for the class.

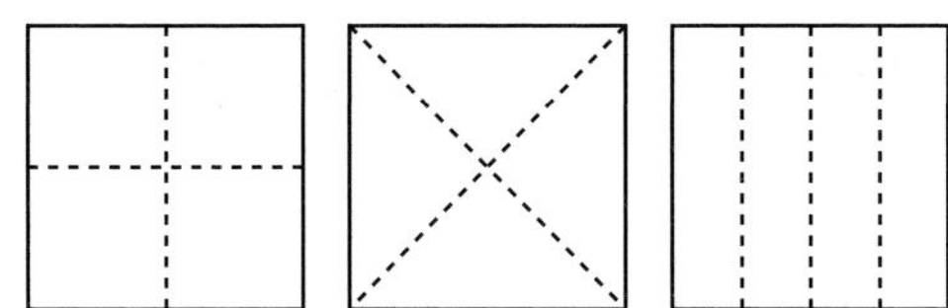

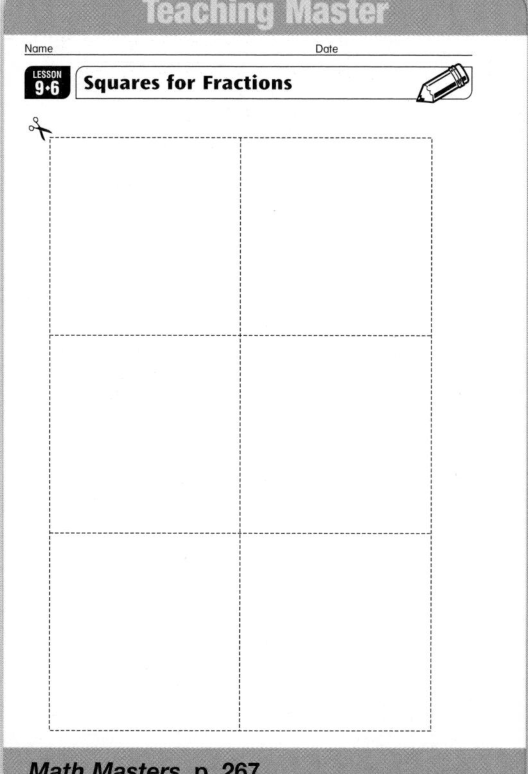

Math Masters, p. 267

- Pretend that the squares are granola bars that are divided into fourths in three different ways. If you wanted to eat one-fourth of a granola bar, would it matter which granola bar piece you chose? no Make sure children understand that even though the fractional parts of each square have different shapes, each part is the same amount, one-fourth of the square.

3. Take one of the fourths-squares and label each part with the fraction $\frac{1}{4}$.
4. Take another fourths-square and shade three of the parts.
   - *What fractional part of the square is shaded?* Three-fourths
   - *How do you write the fraction for the shaded part?* $\frac{3}{4}$

Discuss what the numbers 3 and 4 stand for in the fraction $\frac{3}{4}$: The 4 (the denominator) stands for the number of equal parts into which the square has been divided. The 3 (the numerator) stands for the number of shaded parts.

Ongoing Assessment: Informing Instruction

Watch for children who confuse the numerator and the denominator. Remind them that the bottom number in the fraction tells the number of equal parts into which the square has been divided and that the top number tells the number of shaded parts.

NOTE Children are not expected to learn the words *numerator* and *denominator* at this time.

5. Take the third fourths-square and shade two of its parts.
   - What fractional part of the square is shaded? Two-fourths or one-half
   - What is the fraction for the shaded part? $\frac{2}{4}$ or $\frac{1}{2}$

   Point out that two-fourths is another way of showing and saying *one-half*.

6. Fold the last unfolded square into eight equal parts and shade five of the parts.
   - What fractional part of the square is shaded? Five-eighths
   - How do you write the fraction for the shaded part? $\frac{5}{8}$

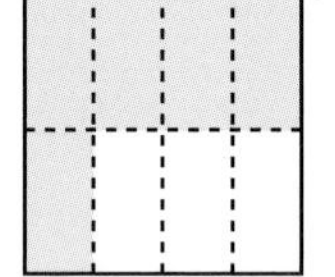
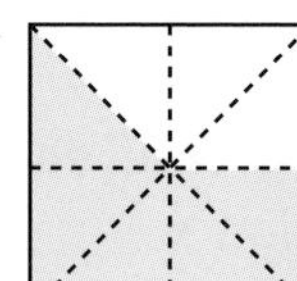
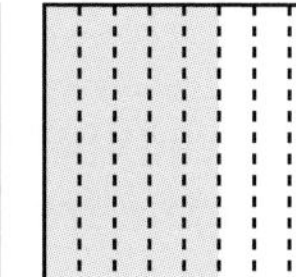

Music Link Introduce children to whole, half, and quarter notes. Allow children the opportunity to play the notes on a drum. Encourage children to compose a song using a pattern of notes.

▶ Making Fractions of a Circle

WHOLE-CLASS ACTIVITY

(*Math Masters,* pp. 267A and 267B)

Have children take out one circle cutout. Explain that the circle is meant to look like a round slice cut from a watermelon. Tell children that two friends will share this slice. Have children fold the circle into fair shares for two people. Discuss how, unlike with squares and rectangles, the shape of the halves is the same no matter how you fold the circle in half. Remind children that the shape is called a half circle.

Tell children that the whole slice is both of (or two of) the shares. Ask: *If you shared this watermelon slice with a friend, how much would each person get?* One-half of the slice Have children write $\frac{1}{2}$ in each share. Have children draw seeds in half of the slice.

Have children take out the second circle cutout. Explain that four friends will share this slice. Have children fold the paper into four shares. Discuss how the shape of the four quarters is the same no matter how the circle is folded. Remind children that this shape is called a quarter circle. Tell children that the whole slice is all of (or four of) the shares. Ask: *How much watermelon will each person get?* One-fourth of the slice Children write $\frac{1}{4}$ in each share. Remind children another way to say "fourths" is "quarters." Ask children to draw seeds in three-quarters of the slice.

Have children cut along the folded lines of both slices. Compare the sizes of the pieces of watermelon. Ask: *Which is smaller, one-half of the slice or one-fourth of the slice?* one-fourth Discuss what would happen to the size of the shares if more friends shared the slice. Ask: *As we make more shares, what will happen to the size of the pieces?* The pieces will get smaller.

Shading Fractional Parts of Shapes

PARTNER ACTIVITY

(*Math Journal 2,* p. 186)

Children use pattern blocks to divide shapes into equal parts. If necessary, do the first two problems together. Remind children that a fraction, such as $\frac{1}{2}$, means 1 out of 2 equal parts. Have children complete the rest of the page with a partner as you circulate and assist where needed.

NOTE This activity assumes that children have completed Exploration A in Lesson 6-7 and Exploration A in Lesson 8-9.

Adjusting the Activity

Ask questions such as: *Is there a pattern-block shape that fits inside the rhombus so that there are two equal parts?* yes; a triangle

AUDITORY • KINESTHETIC • TACTILE • VISUAL

Ongoing Assessment: Recognizing Student Achievement

Journal Page 186

Use **journal page 186** to assess children's ability to divide shapes into equal parts. Children are making adequate progress if they are able to divide all of the shapes into equal parts.

[Number and Numeration Goal 4]

Have partners share their completed journal page 186. Point out that children may have divided and shaded the shape differently but the fraction is still the same.

Student Page

Date

LESSON 9•6 **Pattern-Block Fractions**

Use pattern blocks to divide each shape into equal parts. Draw the parts using your Pattern-Block Template. Shade parts of the shapes.

1. Divide the rhombus into halves. Shade $\frac{1}{2}$ of the rhombus.

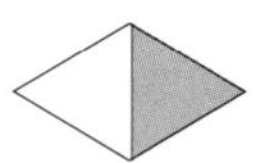

2. Divide the trapezoid into thirds. Shade $\frac{2}{3}$ of the trapezoid.

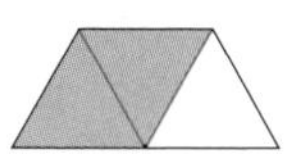

3. Divide the hexagon into halves. Shade $\frac{2}{2}$ of the hexagon.

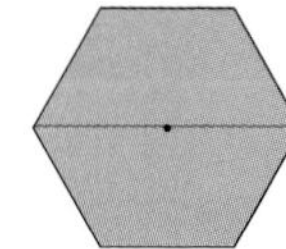

4. Divide the hexagon into thirds. Shade $\frac{2}{3}$ of the hexagon.

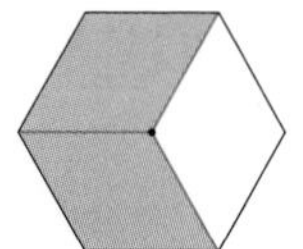

5. Divide the hexagon into sixths. Shade $\frac{4}{6}$ of the hexagon.

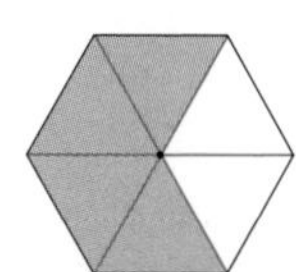

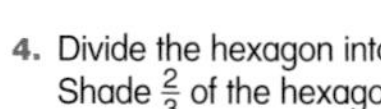

Math Journal 2, p. 186

largest length	smallest length
 porpoise 72 in.	 rabbit 11 in.

The range of a set of data is the difference between the largest and smallest number in the set. See data table on page 760.

range = largest – smallest

range = 72 – 11

range = 61 inches

NOTE Remember to use the Dice-Roll Activity on a regular basis to practice fact strategies. See Lesson 5-10 for detailed instructions. When your class is ready, you may wish to try some of the variations listed in Lesson 5-10.

Teaching Master

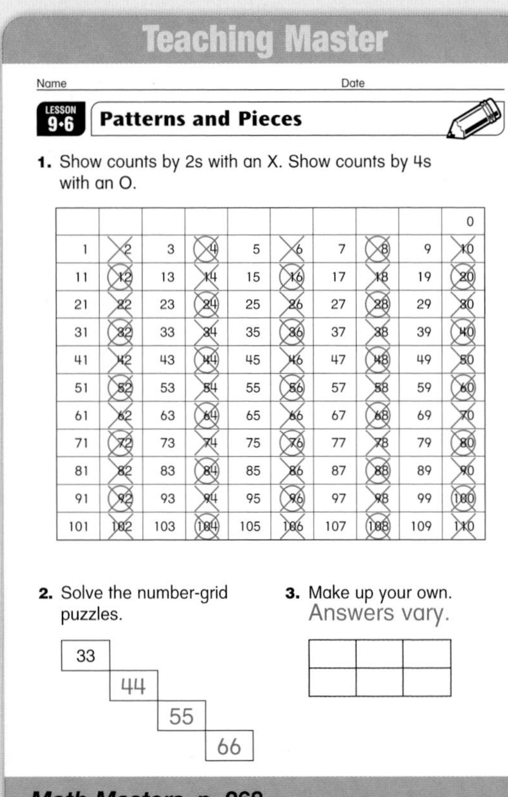

Name Date

LESSON 9·6 **Patterns and Pieces**

1. Show counts by 2s with an X. Show counts by 4s with an O.

									0
1	2	3	4	5	6	7	8	9	10
11	12	13	14	15	16	17	18	19	20
21	22	23	24	25	26	27	28	29	30
31	32	33	34	35	36	37	38	39	40
41	42	43	44	45	46	47	48	49	50
51	52	53	54	55	56	57	58	59	60
61	62	63	64	65	66	67	68	69	70
71	72	73	74	75	76	77	78	79	80
81	82	83	84	85	86	87	88	89	90
91	92	93	94	95	96	97	98	99	100
101	102	103	104	105	106	107	108	109	110

2. Solve the number-grid puzzles.

33
44
55
66

3. Make up your own. Answers vary.

Math Masters, **p. 268**

2 Ongoing Learning & Practice

▶ Finding the Range and Middle Value of a Data Set

WHOLE-CLASS ACTIVITY

Remind children of the meaning of the *range* of a set of data: It is the difference between the largest and smallest numbers in the set.

Ask children to arrange their animal cards in order according to the length/heights of the animals.

- Which animal has the longest length/height? The porpoise (72 in.)
- Which animal has the shortest length/height? The rabbit (11 in.)
- What is the range of the lengths/heights? 61 in.

Have children share how they found the range. Some possible strategies:

▷ "I found 72 on the number line and counted back 11 hops to 61."

▷ "I used my base-10 blocks and started with 7 longs and 2 cubes. I took 1 long and 1 cube away; then I had 6 longs and 1 cube left—that's 61."

▷ "I used my number grid. I started on number 72. I counted up one row to 62 and back 1 to 61 to take away 11 from 72."

Ask children to find the two animals whose lengths/heights are in the middle. What are those lengths/heights? 30 in. and 35 in.

Remind children that the middle number or numbers are one way of thinking of an "average" length/height for the set of animals.

Next, have children turn their cards over and arrange them in order according to the weight of the animals.

- What is the range of the weights? 114 lb
- What two weights are in the middle? 23 lb and 41 lb

▶ Practicing with the Number Grid

INDEPENDENT ACTIVITY

(*Math Masters,* p. 268)

Use *Math Masters,* page 268 to provide practice with the number grid.

Math Boxes 9·6

INDEPENDENT ACTIVITY

(*Math Journal 2,* p. 187)

Mixed Practice Math Boxes in this lesson are paired with Math Boxes in Lesson 9-8. The skills in Problem 6 preview Unit 10 content.

Home Link 9·6

INDEPENDENT ACTIVITY

(*Math Masters,* p. 269)

Home Connection Children match the shaded parts of circles with fractions. They shade fractional parts of circles.

3 Differentiation Options

READINESS

SMALL-GROUP DISCUSSION

Identifying Unit Fractions

5–15 Min

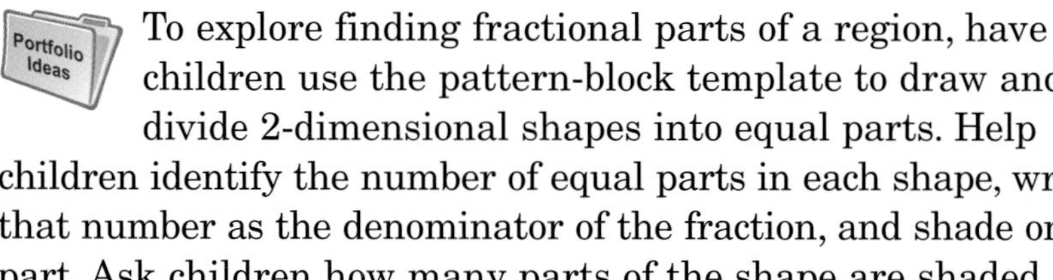

To explore finding fractional parts of a region, have children use the pattern-block template to draw and divide 2-dimensional shapes into equal parts. Help children identify the number of equal parts in each shape, write that number as the denominator of the fraction, and shade one part. Ask children how many parts of the shape are shaded. Write that number as the numerator of the fraction. Continue the activity until children can readily name unit fractions without teacher guidance. When children are comfortable naming the fractions, have them draw two shapes on a half sheet of paper and divide the shapes into equal parts. Have children write the fraction that tells about each part. For example, a circle divided into 4 equal parts would have each part labeled $\frac{1}{4}$.

ELL SUPPORT

SMALL-GROUP ACTIVITY

Discussing Unit Fractions

5–15 Min

To provide language support for fractions, have children draw pictures representing fractions with one in the numerator, such as $\frac{1}{2}$, $\frac{1}{3}$, and $\frac{1}{4}$. Ask children to compare the different fractions and discuss similarities and differences.

Student Page

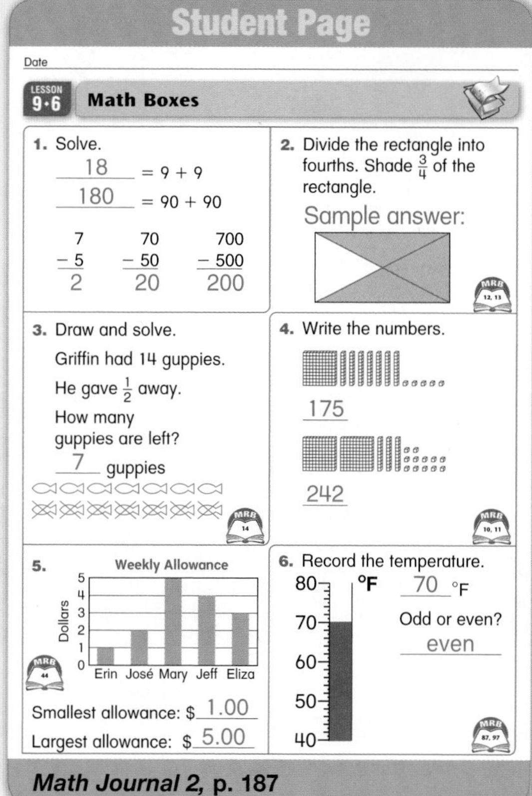

Date

LESSON 9·6 **Math Boxes**

1. Solve.
18 = 9 + 9
180 = 90 + 90
7 − 5 = 2; 70 − 50 = 20; 700 − 500 = 200

2. Divide the rectangle into fourths. Shade $\frac{3}{4}$ of the rectangle.
Sample answer:

3. Draw and solve.
Griffin had 14 guppies.
He gave $\frac{1}{2}$ away.
How many guppies are left?
7 guppies

4. Write the numbers.
175
242

5. Weekly Allowance
Smallest allowance: $ 1.00
Largest allowance: $ 5.00

6. Record the temperature.
70 °F
Odd or even?
even

Math Journal 2, p. 187

Home Link Master

Name Date

HOME LINK 9·6 **Fractional Parts**

Family Note In Unit 8, we worked with unit fractions, such as $\frac{1}{2}$, $\frac{1}{3}$, and $\frac{1}{4}$. Today, we started to explore fractions in which the number above the fraction bar is more than 1, such as $\frac{2}{3}$, $\frac{3}{4}$, and $\frac{5}{6}$. If your child is having trouble with some of the problems on this page, you might mention that $\frac{1}{2}$ means that 1 out of 2 parts is shaded, that $\frac{3}{6}$ means that 3 out of 6 parts are shaded, and so on. Or you might ask your child to explain the fractions to you in this way.

Please return this Home Link to school tomorrow.

Mark the fraction that tells what part of the circle is shaded.

1. $\frac{1}{2}$ $\frac{5}{6}$ ($\frac{1}{5}$) $\frac{5}{1}$
2. $\frac{2}{2}$ ($\frac{2}{3}$) $\frac{3}{4}$ $\frac{3}{1}$
3. $\frac{1}{6}$ $\frac{1}{5}$ $\frac{6}{5}$ ($\frac{5}{6}$)

Shade the circles. Sample answers:

4. Shade $\frac{4}{6}$.
5. Shade $\frac{3}{4}$.
6. Shade $\frac{5}{8}$.

Practice

7. Name or draw 4 squares you find in your home.
Answers vary.

Math Masters, p. 269

9•7 Comparing Fractions

Objectives To review fraction concepts; and to provide experiences using region models to compare fractions.

www.everydaymathonline.com

ePresentations

eToolkit

Algorithms Practice

EM Facts Workshop Game™

Family Letters

Assessment Management

Common Core State Standards

Curriculum Focal Points

Interactive Teacher's Lesson Guide

1 Teaching the Lesson

Key Concepts and Skills

- Compare fractional parts. [Number and Numeration Goal 4]
- Label fractional parts using fractional notation. [Number and Numeration Goal 4]
- Identify halves, thirds, fourths, sixths, and eighths. [Number and Numeration Goal 4]
- Identify and explain the meanings of *numerator* and *denominator*. [Number and Numeration Goal 4]

Key Activities

Children use fractional parts of paper strips to review fraction concepts and to compare pairs of fractions. They are introduced to the terms *numerator* and *denominator.*

Key Vocabulary

denominator ◆ numerator

Materials

Math Journal 2, p. 188
Home Link 9•6
Math Masters, p. 270
slate ◆ scissors ◆ paper clip or envelope

2 Ongoing Learning & Practice

Playing the *Difference Game*
My Reference Book, pp. 130 and 131
per partnership: 4 each of number cards 1–10 (from the Everything Math Deck, if available), tool-kit pennies
Children practice subtraction skills with coins.

Math Boxes 9•7
Math Journal 2, p. 189
Children practice and maintain skills through Math Box problems.

Ongoing Assessment: Recognizing Student Achievement
Use Math Boxes, Problem 2.
[Patterns, Functions, and Algebra Goal 1]

Home Link 9•7
Math Masters, p. 271
Children practice and maintain skills through Home Link activities.

3 Differentiation Options

READINESS

Matching Fractions
per partnership: 1 copy of *Math Masters,* p. 272
Children match fractions to shaded fractional parts.

ENRICHMENT

Comparing Fractions
Math Masters, p. 270
3" by 5" index cards
Children compare fractions to determine which one is smaller.

Advance Preparation

Make 1 copy of *Math Masters,* page 270 for each child and place the copies near the Math Message. For the optional Enrichment activity in Part 3, cut twelve 3" by 5" index cards in half to make 24 fraction cards. Using 2, 3, 4, 6, and 8 as denominators, write all of the corresponding unit and non-unit fractions on the cards.

***Teacher's Reference Manual,* Grades 1–3** pp. 61, 62, 69

Getting Started

Mental Math and Reflexes

Tell number stories. Have children record answers on their slates. *Suggestions:*

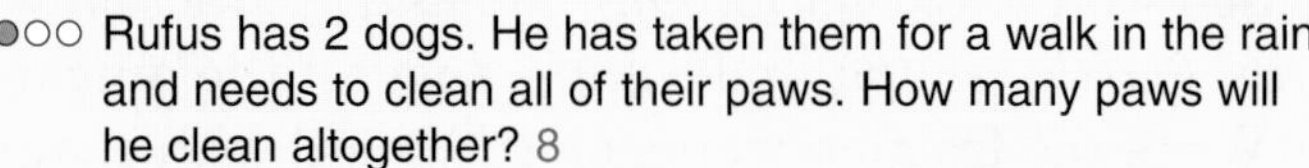

●○○ Rufus has 2 dogs. He has taken them for a walk in the rain and needs to clean all of their paws. How many paws will he clean altogether? 8

●●○ Marnie is folding her family's laundry. She has 10 socks to fold. How many pairs of socks are there altogether? 5

●●● Teresa baked bread for her family. She has 16 family members that would each like to eat a sandwich. How many slices of bread will they need altogether? 32

Math Message

Take one copy of Math Masters, *page 270. Write a fraction in each part of each fraction strip.*

Home Link 9·6 Follow-Up

Briefly go over the answers. Discuss which two circles have the same fraction of the whole shaded.

1 Teaching the Lesson

▶ Math Message Follow-Up

WHOLE-CLASS ACTIVITY

Check that children have labeled the equal parts of the fraction strips correctly.

NOTE Vocabulary words are listed to remind you to use them in discussions so that the children become familiar with the terminology. They are not meant to be memorized by children.

▶ Introducing the Terms *Numerator* and *Denominator*

WHOLE-CLASS ACTIVITY

ELL

(*Math Masters,* p. 270)

Remind children that the number on the bottom of a fraction tells the number of equal parts of something and that the number on the top tells the number of equal parts being talked about. For example, write the fraction $\frac{2}{3}$ on the board along with the meanings of the numerator and the denominator. (The 3 means that there are 3 equal parts of something; the 2 means that we are talking about 2 of the 3 parts.)

▷ The number on the bottom is called the **denominator** of the fraction. Write *denominator* on the board next to the 3 to support English language learners.

▷ The number on the top is called the **numerator** of the fraction. Write *numerator* on the board next to the 2.

Ask children to identify the numerator and denominator of the fraction $\frac{1}{6}$. Then have them use the strips on *Math Masters,* page 270 to explain the meanings of *denominator* and *numerator.* Repeat with the fraction $\frac{3}{4}$.

On their fraction strips, have children point to the fraction with the largest denominator ($\frac{1}{8}$) and the fraction with the smallest denominator ($\frac{1}{2}$). Compare the sizes of the $\frac{1}{8}$ and $\frac{1}{2}$ parts. Discuss what happened to the size of each part when the strip was divided into more shares.

Teaching Master

Name Date

LESSON 9·7 **Fraction Strips**

1-strip							
$\frac{1}{2}$	$\frac{1}{2}$						
$\frac{1}{4}$	$\frac{1}{4}$	$\frac{1}{4}$	$\frac{1}{4}$				
$\frac{1}{8}$	$\frac{1}{8}$	$\frac{1}{8}$	$\frac{1}{8}$	$\frac{1}{8}$	$\frac{1}{8}$	$\frac{1}{8}$	$\frac{1}{8}$
$\frac{1}{3}$	$\frac{1}{3}$	$\frac{1}{3}$					
$\frac{1}{6}$	$\frac{1}{6}$	$\frac{1}{6}$	$\frac{1}{6}$	$\frac{1}{6}$	$\frac{1}{6}$		

Math Masters, **p. 270**

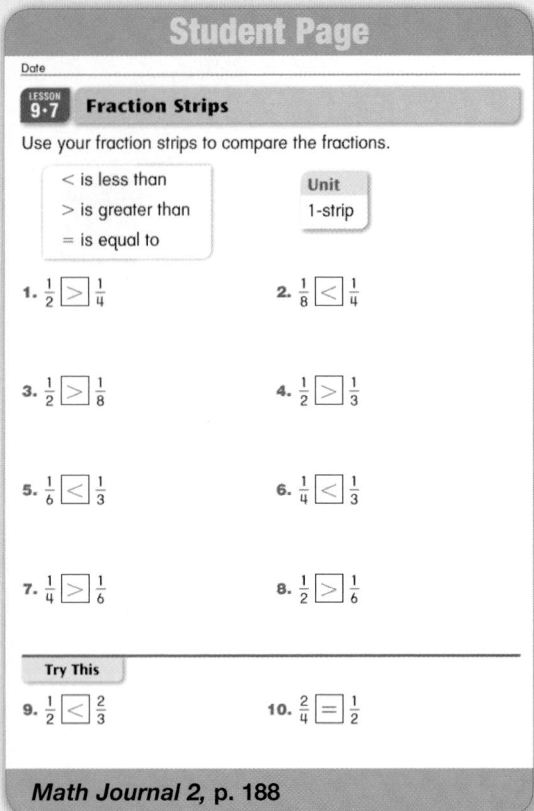
Student Page

Date

LESSON 9·7 **Fraction Strips**

Use your fraction strips to compare the fractions.

< is less than
> is greater than
= is equal to

Unit: 1-strip

1. $\frac{1}{2} > \frac{1}{4}$
2. $\frac{1}{8} < \frac{1}{4}$
3. $\frac{1}{2} > \frac{1}{8}$
4. $\frac{1}{2} > \frac{1}{3}$
5. $\frac{1}{6} < \frac{1}{3}$
6. $\frac{1}{4} < \frac{1}{3}$
7. $\frac{1}{4} > \frac{1}{6}$
8. $\frac{1}{2} > \frac{1}{6}$

Try This

9. $\frac{1}{2} < \frac{2}{3}$
10. $\frac{2}{4} = \frac{1}{2}$

Math Journal 2, p. 188

> **NOTE** Because the fraction strips will be used in Lesson 9-8, have children save them in their tool kits using an envelope or a paper clip.

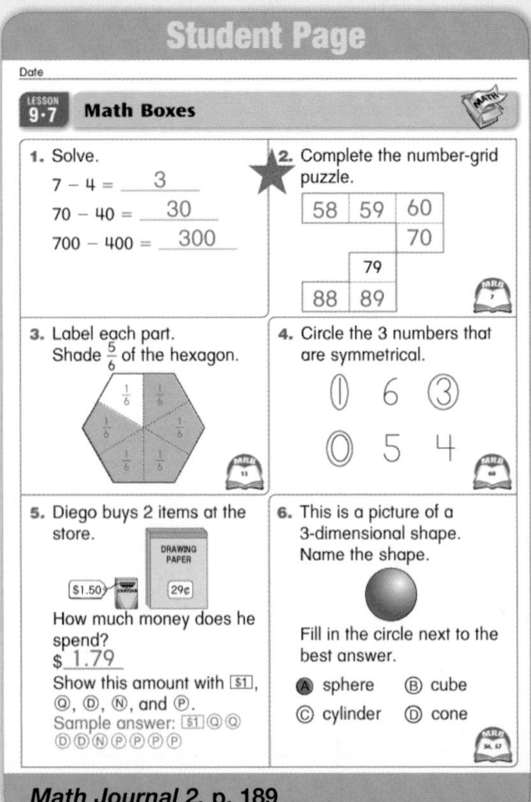
Student Page

Date

LESSON 9·7 **Math Boxes**

1. Solve.
$7 - 4 = $ 3
$70 - 40 = $ 30
$700 - 400 = $ 300

2. Complete the number-grid puzzle.

58	59	60
		70
	79	
88	89	

3. Label each part. Shade $\frac{5}{6}$ of the hexagon.

4. Circle the 3 numbers that are symmetrical.
0 6 3
0 5 4

5. Diego buys 2 items at the store.
$1.50 — DRAWING PAPER 29¢
How much money does he spend?
$ 1.79
Show this amount with [$1], Ⓠ, Ⓓ, Ⓝ, and Ⓟ.
Sample answer: [$1] Ⓠ Ⓠ Ⓓ Ⓓ Ⓝ Ⓟ Ⓟ Ⓟ Ⓟ

6. This is a picture of a 3-dimensional shape. Name the shape.
Fill in the circle next to the best answer.
Ⓐ sphere Ⓑ cube
Ⓒ cylinder Ⓓ cone

Math Journal 2, p. 189

▶ Discussing Fraction Concepts

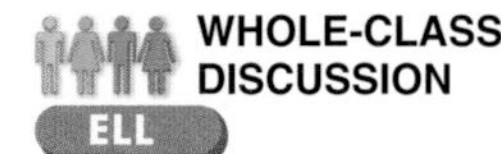

(*Math Masters,* p. 270)

Direct children's attention to *Math Masters,* page 270. Point out that each fraction strip is the same size as the 1-strip.

Discuss fraction words. Except for *half* and *halves,* fraction words such as *thirds, fourths, sixths,* and *eighths* suggest the number of equal parts. Write the fraction words on the board with examples to support English language learners.

- What is the fraction word for five (ten) equal parts of something? fifths; tenths
- Suppose the 1-strip were longer. Would $\frac{1}{2}$ of the longer strip be the same as $\frac{1}{2}$ of this strip? No, the actual size (and shape, or number from a set) of fractions always depends on the unit or whole amount being divided.

▶ Comparing Fractions

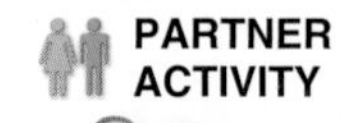

(*Math Journal 2,* p. 188; *Math Masters,* p. 270)

Have children cut out the fraction strips on *Math Masters,* page 270. The strips should *not* be cut apart into fraction pieces; they should *only* be cut along the dashed lines. Using the fraction strips, model how to compare the fractions in problem 1. Then children work with a partner to complete journal page 188.

When most of the children are finished, ask these questions:

- Which is larger, $\frac{1}{3}$ or $\frac{1}{4}$ of a 1-strip? $\frac{1}{3}$ of a 1-strip is larger.
- In Problems 1–8, how can you tell which is more, just by looking at the fractions and not using the fraction strips? If the numerator of both fractions is 1, then the fraction with the smaller denominator is more.

2 Ongoing Learning & Practice

▶ Playing the *Difference Game*

(*My Reference Book,* pp. 130 and 131)

Children practice subtraction skills with coins by playing the *Difference Game.* For detailed instructions, see Lesson 5-7.

▶ Math Boxes 9·7

(*Math Journal 2,* p. 189)

Mixed Practice Math Boxes in this lesson are paired with Math Boxes in Lesson 9-5. The skills in Problem 6 preview Unit 10 content.

Ongoing Assessment: Recognizing Student Achievement

Math Boxes Problem 2 

Use **Math Boxes, Problem 2** to assess children's ability to solve number-grid puzzles. Children are making adequate progress if they are able to complete the puzzle correctly.

[Patterns, Functions, and Algebra Goal 1]

▶ Home Link 9·7

INDEPENDENT ACTIVITY

(*Math Masters*, p. 271)

Home Connection Children compare pairs of fractions with the help of region models.

3 Differentiation Options

READINESS

PARTNER ACTIVITY

▶ Matching Fractions

5–15 Min

(*Math Masters*, p. 272)

To provide experience with identifying fractions, have children match fractions to circles divided into fractional parts. Begin by having children place all of the cards facedown so they are not touching. Partners take turns flipping over two cards to see if the fractions match. If the cards match, the child takes both cards. If the cards do not match, the child replaces both cards facedown to their original spots. Continue the activity until all of the cards have been matched.

ENRICHMENT

PARTNER ACTIVITY

▶ Comparing Fractions

5–15 Min

(*Math Masters*, p. 270)

To apply children's understanding of fractions, have children compare two fractions and identify which is smaller. Distribute one pile of fraction cards to each partnership. (See directions for preparing fraction cards in Advanced Preparation.) Children each flip over one card. Using the fraction strips (*Math Masters,* page 270) as a point of reference, children determine whose fraction is smaller. The partner with the smallest fraction wins. When they have gone through all of the cards, have children describe some of the comparison strategies they used. Encourage them to look for strategies they can use when comparing numerators and denominators. If children do not make this discovery themselves, point out that the shapes with fewer parts have smaller denominators but that each part is larger. Fractions of shapes with more parts have larger denominators but each part is smaller.

Home Link Master

Name Date

HOME LINK 9·7 Comparing Fractions

Family Note Today we divided unit strips into equal parts: halves, thirds, fourths, sixths, and eighths. Then we compared the sizes of the parts. Your child probably cannot tell which of two fractions is more by looking at the fractions, but he or she should be able to compare two fractions by looking at pictures of them. Encourage your child to label one part of each shape with a fraction before deciding which fraction is more or less.

Please return this Home Link to school tomorrow.

1. Which would you rather have, half of fruit bar A or half of fruit bar B? Explain your answer to someone at home.

   A; the half is larger.

2. Which is more, $\frac{1}{5}$ or $\frac{1}{3}$?

   $\frac{1}{3}$

3. Which is more, $\frac{1}{4}$ or $\frac{1}{6}$?

   $\frac{1}{4}$

Practice

4. Write the fact family.

   13, +,−, 6, 7

   6 + 7 = 13
   7 + 6 = 13
   13 − 6 = 7
   13 − 7 = 6

Math Masters, p. 271

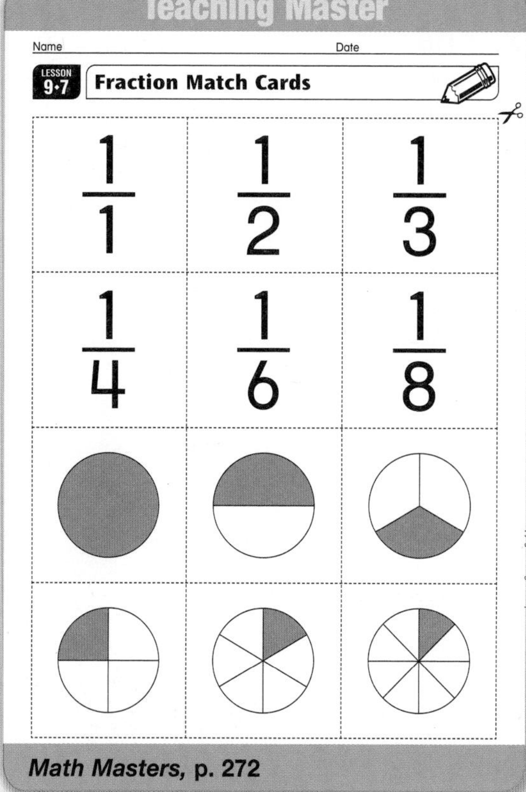
Teaching Master

Name Date

LESSON 9·7 Fraction Match Cards

$\frac{1}{1}$	$\frac{1}{2}$	$\frac{1}{3}$
$\frac{1}{4}$	$\frac{1}{6}$	$\frac{1}{8}$

Math Masters, p. 272

9•8 Many Names for Fractional Parts

Objective To introduce the idea that fractional parts of a whole have many names (equivalent fractions).

www.everydaymathonline.com

ePresentations

eToolkit

Algorithms Practice

EM Facts Workshop Game™

Family Letters

Assessment Management

Common Core State Standards

Curriculum Focal Points

Interactive Teacher's Lesson Guide

1 Teaching the Lesson

Key Concepts and Skills

- Use manipulatives to model equivalent fractions.
  [Number and Numeration Goal 4]
- Use = to describe the relationship between fractions.
  [Patterns, Functions, and Algebra Goal 2]

Key Activities

Children use pieces of fraction strips to explore renaming fractions.

Ongoing Assessment: Recognizing Student Achievement Use Mental Math and Reflexes.
[Operations and Computation Goal 3]

Ongoing Assessment: Informing Instruction See page 780.

Materials

Math Journal 2, pp. 190 and 191
Home Link 9•7
fraction strips from Lesson 9•7 ◆ scissors

2 Ongoing Learning & Practice

Playing *One-Dollar Exchange*
Math Masters, p. 224
My Reference Book, pp. 144 and 145
per partnership: 2 dice, 1 dollar, 20 dimes, 20 pennies
Children practice exchanging 10 pennies for 1 dime and 10 dimes for 1 dollar.

Math Boxes 9•8
Math Journal 2, p. 192
Children practice and maintain skills through Math Box problems.

Home Link 9•8
Math Masters, p. 273
Children practice and maintain skills through Home Link activities.

3 Differentiation Options

ENRICHMENT

Finding Fraction Combinations Equivalent to $\frac{1}{2}$ and to 1
Math Masters, pp. 270, 274, and 275
fraction pieces from Part 1
Children use fraction pieces to find fraction combinations that are equivalent to $\frac{1}{2}$ and to 1.

EXTRA PRACTICE

Using Name-Collection Boxes for Fractions
Math Masters, p. 325
Children practice finding equivalent names for fractions.

Advance Preparation

For the optional Extra Practice activity in Part 3, write a fraction in each of the first two name-collection boxes on *Math Masters,* page 325. Write the same two fractions in the last two name-collection boxes. Make enough copies for half of your class. Then cut the copies in half so each child has a half-sheet of paper.

Getting Started

Mental Math and Reflexes ★

Write two amounts of money on the board. Children show "thumbs-up" if they estimate the sum to be more than \$1, "thumbs-down" if they estimate that the sum is less than \$1, and a "fist" if they estimate that the sum is equal to \$1.

Suggestions:

●○○ 20¢ and 25¢; 100¢ and 10¢; 50¢ and 60¢

●●○ 80¢ and 50¢; 45¢ and 45¢; 5¢ and 90¢

●●● 33¢ and 66¢; 8¢ and 99¢; 75¢ and 35¢

Math Message

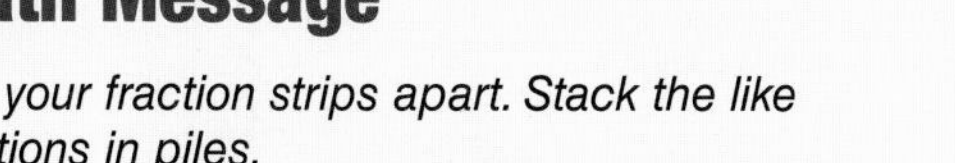

Cut your fraction strips apart. Stack the like fractions in piles.

Home Link 9·7 Follow-Up

Go over the answers. Review *numerator* and *denominator*: The denominator tells into how many equal parts the whole, or ONE, has been divided; the numerator tells how many parts are represented by the fraction. Ask children to explain why they chose fruit bar A or B.

Ongoing Assessment: Recognizing Student Achievement

Mental Math and Reflexes ★

Use **Mental Math and Reflexes** to assess children's ability to estimate sums. Children are making adequate progress if they are able to correctly estimate if sums in the first set are greater than, less than, or equal to \$1. Some children may be able to correctly estimate the sums in the second and third sets.

[Operations and Computation Goal 3]

1 Teaching the Lesson

▶ Math Message Follow-Up

WHOLE-CLASS ACTIVITY

Check that children have cut their fraction strips apart and sorted them.

▶ Naming Fractional Parts in Several Ways

WHOLE-CLASS ACTIVITY

Recall the use of name-collection boxes to collect many names for a number. Tell children that names can also be found for the same fractional part of a unit. Children will use their fraction pieces to find different names for fractional parts.

Ask children to take a $\frac{1}{2}$ fraction piece and to cover it with $\frac{1}{4}$ fraction pieces.

- How many $\frac{1}{4}$ pieces are needed to cover the $\frac{1}{2}$ piece? Two $\frac{1}{4}$ pieces, two-fourths, or two-quarters

Write on the board: $\frac{1}{2} = \frac{2}{4}$.

Links to the Future

In this lesson children find many names for fractional parts. Modeling equivalent names for $\frac{1}{2}$ is a Grade 2 Goal.

Student Page

Date

LESSON 9·8 **Many Names for Fractions**

1-strip

Use your fraction pieces to help you solve the following problems.

Example:

4 [$\frac{1}{8}$] = [$\frac{1}{2}$]

$\frac{4}{8} = \frac{1}{2}$

1. 2 [$\frac{1}{6}$] = [$\frac{1}{3}$]

$\frac{2}{6} = \frac{1}{3}$

2. 2 [$\frac{1}{8}$] = [$\frac{1}{4}$]

$\frac{2}{8} = \frac{1}{4}$

Math Journal 2, p. 190

Student Page

Date

LESSON 9·8 **Many Names for Fractions** *continued*

3. 4 [$\frac{1}{6}$] = [$\frac{1}{3}$][$\frac{1}{3}$]

$\frac{4}{6} = \frac{2}{3}$

4. 4 [$\frac{1}{8}$] = [$\frac{1}{4}$][$\frac{1}{4}$]

$\frac{4}{8} = \frac{2}{4}$

5. 6 [$\frac{1}{8}$] = [$\frac{1}{4}$][$\frac{1}{4}$][$\frac{1}{4}$]

$\frac{6}{8} = \frac{3}{4}$

Math Journal 2, p. 191

Next, have children take a $\frac{1}{3}$ fraction piece and cover it with $\frac{1}{6}$ fraction pieces.

- How many $\frac{1}{6}$ pieces are needed to cover the $\frac{1}{3}$ piece? Two $\frac{1}{6}$ pieces, or two-sixths

Write on the board: $\frac{1}{3} = \frac{2}{6}$.

Adjusting the Activity

ELL

Discuss with children what it means to have the same number in the numerator and denominator, such as $\frac{4}{4}$ or $\frac{6}{6}$. The fraction represents a whole. Encourage children to model this fractional representation of a whole using their fractional pieces.

AUDITORY ◆ KINESTHETIC ◆ TACTILE ◆ VISUAL

▶ Finding Names for Fractional Parts

(*Math Journal 2,* pp. 190 and 191)

Do the example on journal page 190 together. Have children cover the $\frac{1}{2}$ fraction piece with $\frac{1}{8}$ pieces. Point out that it takes four of the $\frac{1}{8}$ pieces to cover the larger piece.

4 [$\frac{1}{8}$] s = [$\frac{1}{8}$ | $\frac{1}{8}$ $\frac{1}{2}$ $\frac{1}{8}$ | $\frac{1}{8}$]

$\frac{4}{8} = \frac{1}{2}$

Children work independently to complete the pages as you circulate and assist where needed. Take time for children to share their answers and solution strategies.

Ongoing Assessment: Informing Instruction

Watch for children who use two different-sized fractional parts to make the total length of a strip. Remind them to use like fractional pieces to solve the problems.

2 Ongoing Learning & Practice

▶ Playing *One-Dollar Exchange*

PARTNER ACTIVITY

(*Math Masters,* p. 224; *My Reference Book*, pp. 144 and 145)

Children use their Place-Value Mat and one dollar, 20 dimes, and 20 pennies to play *One-Dollar Exchange*. For directions, see *My Reference Book*, pages 144 and 145.

▶ Math Boxes 9·8

INDEPENDENT ACTIVITY

(*Math Journal 2,* p. 192)

Mixed Practice Math Boxes in this lesson are paired with Math Boxes in Lesson 9-6. The skills in Problem 6 preview Unit 10 content.

Writing/Reasoning Have children draw, write, or verbalize an answer to the following question: *What is a fraction of a group of objects?* A reasonable answer should include reference to equal groups.

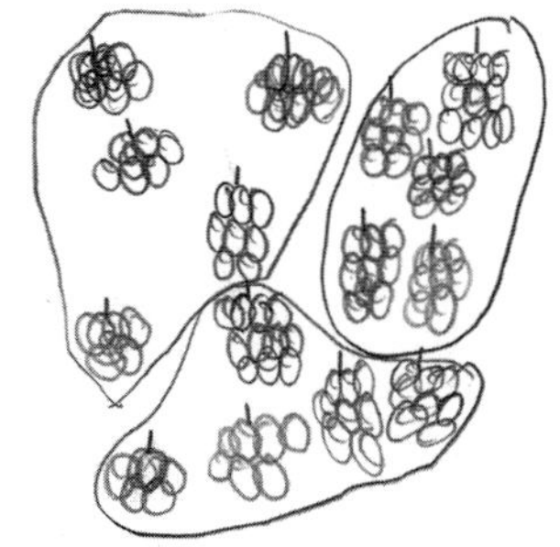

I made 3 Equal groups

One child's work in response to the Writing/Reasoning prompt

▶ Home Link 9·8

INDEPENDENT ACTIVITY

(*Math Masters,* p. 273)

Home Connection Children review fraction concepts and solve problems involving fractions.

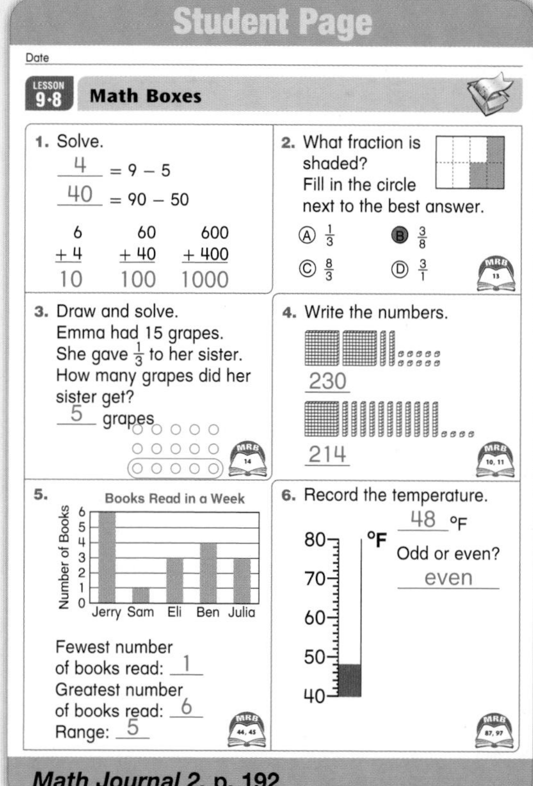

Student Page

Date

LESSON 9·8 **Math Boxes**

1. Solve.
4 = 9 − 5
40 = 90 − 50
6 + 4 = 10; 60 + 40 = 100; 600 + 400 = 1000

2. What fraction is shaded? Fill in the circle next to the best answer.
Ⓐ $\frac{1}{3}$ Ⓑ $\frac{3}{8}$ Ⓒ $\frac{8}{3}$ Ⓓ $\frac{3}{1}$

3. Draw and solve. Emma had 15 grapes. She gave $\frac{1}{3}$ to her sister. How many grapes did her sister get?
5 grapes

4. Write the numbers.
230
214

5. Books Read in a Week
Number of Books
Jerry Sam Eli Ben Julia
Fewest number of books read: 1
Greatest number of books read: 6
Range: 5

6. Record the temperature.
48 °F
Odd or even? even

Math Journal 2, p. 192

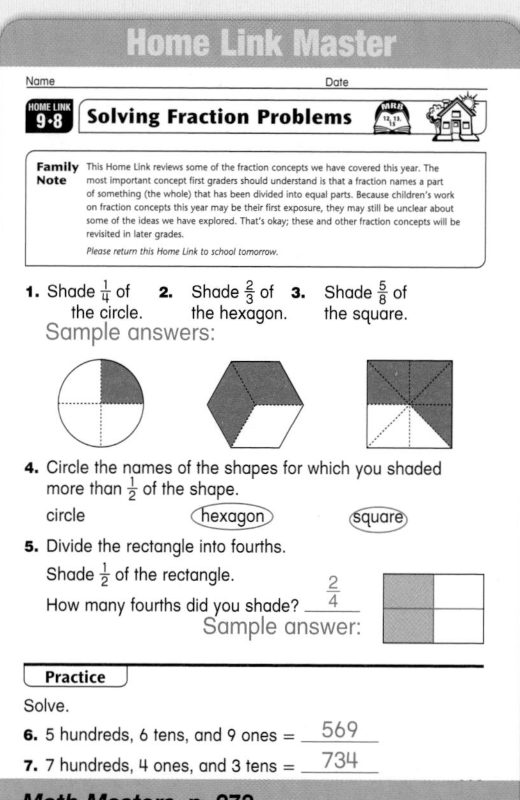

Home Link Master

Name Date

HOME LINK 9·8 **Solving Fraction Problems**

Family Note This Home Link reviews some of the fraction concepts we have covered this year. The most important concept first graders should understand is that a fraction names a part of something (the whole) that has been divided into equal parts. Because children's work on fraction concepts this year may be their first exposure, they may still be unclear about some of the ideas we have explored. That's okay; these and other fraction concepts will be revisited in later grades.

Please return this Home Link to school tomorrow.

1. Shade $\frac{1}{4}$ of the circle.
2. Shade $\frac{2}{3}$ of the hexagon.
3. Shade $\frac{5}{8}$ of the square.

Sample answers:

4. Circle the names of the shapes for which you shaded more than $\frac{1}{2}$ of the shape.
circle (hexagon) (square)

5. Divide the rectangle into fourths.
Shade $\frac{1}{2}$ of the rectangle.
How many fourths did you shade? $\frac{2}{4}$
Sample answer:

Practice

Solve.

6. 5 hundreds, 6 tens, and 9 ones = 569
7. 7 hundreds, 4 ones, and 3 tens = 734

Math Masters, p. 273

Teaching Master

Name Date

LESSON 9·8 **Finding Fraction Combinations**

Divide each 1-strip into fractional parts. Label the fractional parts.

1-strip
1-strip
1-strip
1-strip
1-strip

Math Masters, p. 274

Teaching Master

Name Date

LESSON 9·8 **Finding Fraction Combinations** *continued*

Divide each half of a 1-strip into fractional parts. Label the fractional parts.

Math Masters, p. 275

3 Differentiation Options

ENRICHMENT

INDEPENDENT ACTIVITY

▶ Finding Fraction Combinations Equivalent to $\frac{1}{2}$ and to 1

5–15 Min

(*Math Masters,* pp. 270, 274, and 275)

Portfolio Ideas

To further explore equivalent fractions, have children lay various combinations of fraction pieces on the 1-strips on *Math Masters*, page 274. Once they "fill" the 1-strip, have them draw lines on the 1-strip to show the fraction pieces they used and write their fraction names.

Encourage children to find 5 different ways to fill the 1-strip using fractional pieces. Then challenge them to complete *Math Masters,* page 275 in the same way. Ask children to share the ways the 1-strip and $\frac{1}{2}$-strip can be divided.

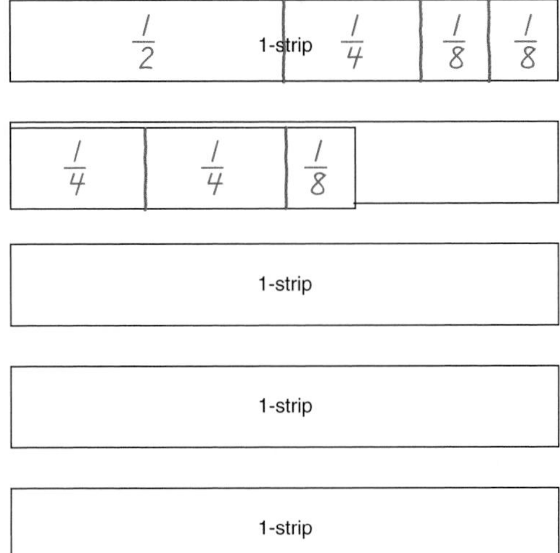

EXTRA PRACTICE

INDEPENDENT ACTIVITY

▶ Using Name-Collection Boxes for Fractions

5–15 Min

(*Math Masters,* p. 325)

Use *Math Masters,* page 325 to provide practice finding equivalent names for fractions.

9•9 Progress Check 9

Objective To assess children's progress on mathematical content through the end of Unit 9.

1 Looking Back: Cumulative Assessment

Input children's data from Progress Check 9 into the **Assessment Management Spreadsheets**.

Materials
- Home Link 9•8
- *Assessment Handbook,* pp. 118–125, 169–172, 199, and 232–235
- analog clock; slate; base-10 blocks (flats, longs, cubes)

CONTENT ASSESSED	LESSON(S)	ASSESSMENT ITEMS				
		SELF	ORAL/SLATE	WRITTEN PART A	WRITTEN PART B	OPEN RESPONSE
Read, write, and represent with base-10 blocks whole numbers through hundreds; identify place value of digits. [Number and Numeration Goal 3]	9•1, 9•2, 9•3, 9•5, 9•6, 9•8	6	3	6		✓
Use drawings to represent and explain simple fractions (halves, fourths) as equal parts of a collection. [Number and Numeration Goal 4]	9•1–9•8	2		2	8	
Compare sums. [Number and Numeration Goal 7]	9•1			1		
Know addition and subtraction facts. [Operations and Computation Goal 1]	9•1	4		1, 5	7	
Calculate and compare the values of combinations of coins. [Operations and Computation Goal 2]	9•1–9•5, 9•7, 9•8	5	4	3	8	
Show and tell time on an analog clock to the nearest half-hour or quarter-hour. [Measurement and Reference Frames Goal 4]	9•1, 9•3	1	1	4		
Extend numeric patterns and use them to solve problems; solve problems involving simple functions represented as function machines. [Patterns, Functions, and Algebra Goal 1]	9•1–9•4	3	2	5		✓
Use >, <, and = to compare numbers. [Patterns, Functions, and Algebra Goal 2]	9•4, 9•8			1		

2 Looking Ahead: Preparing for Unit 10

Math Boxes 9•9

Home Link 9•9: Unit 10 Family Letter

Materials
- *Math Journal 2,* p. 193
- *Math Masters,* pp. 276–279

Getting Started

Math Message • Self Assessment

Complete the Self Assessment (Assessment Handbook, *page 169*).

Home Link 9·8 Follow-Up

Briefly go over the answers.

1 Looking Back: Cumulative Assessment

▶ Math Message Follow-Up

INDEPENDENT ACTIVITY

(Self-Assessment, *Assessment Handbook*, p. 169)

The Self Assessment offers children the opportunity to reflect upon their progress.

▶ Oral and Slate Assessments

WHOLE-CLASS ACTIVITY

Problems 1 and 2 provide summative information and can be used for grading purposes. Problems 3 and 4 provide formative information that can be useful in planning future instruction.

Oral Assessment

1. Show a time on an analog clock. Children tell the time.
   - 1:00
   - 10:30
   - 12:45
   - 9:30
   - 5:45
   - 8:00
   - 6:15
   - 3:15
2. Draw function machines on the board. Put a question mark in the rule box. Children find the rule.

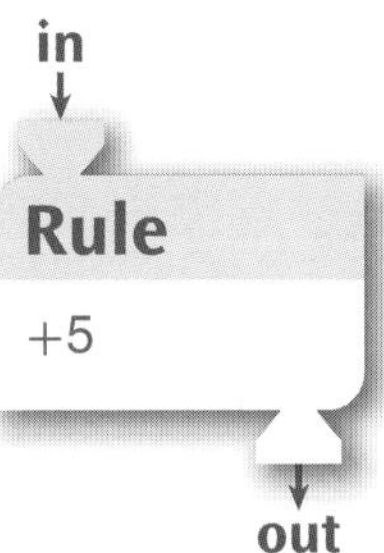

in	out
1	6
7	12
14	19

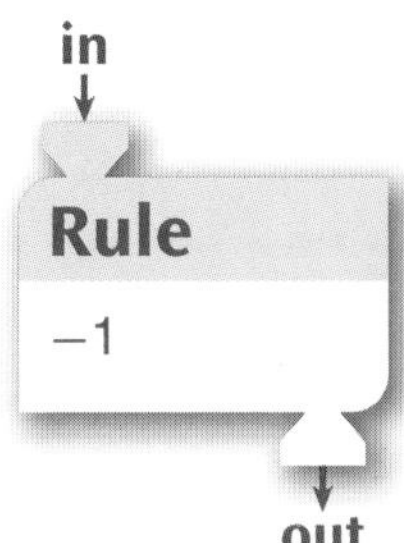

in	out
5	4
12	11
19	18

Assessment Master

Name Date

LESSON 9·9 **Self Assessment** Progress Check 9

Put a check in the box that tells how you do each skill.

Skills	I can do this by myself. I can explain how to do this.	I can do this by myself.	I can do this with help.
1. Draw hands on a clock face.			
2. Find fractions.			
3. Fill in rules and missing numbers on function machines.			
4. Know math facts.			
5. Count combinations of coins.			
6. Use base-10 blocks to count numbers.			

Assessment Handbook, p. 169

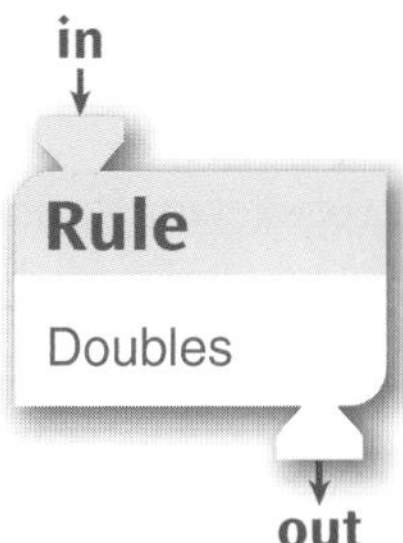

in	out
3	6
8	16
10	20

Slate Assessment

3. Show base-10 blocks. Children write the number represented by the blocks and the new number.
    - 1 long, 4 cubes; add one long 14; 24
    - 3 longs; remove one long 30; 20
    - 6 longs, 7 cubes; remove 2 longs 67; 47
    - 1 flat, 2 longs, and 9 cubes; add 3 longs and 1 cube 129; 160
4. Name amounts of money. Children show each amount by drawing on their slates using Ⓟ, Ⓝ, Ⓓ, Ⓠ, and [$1].
    - 35¢ Sample answer: Ⓠ Ⓓ
    - $0.51 Sample answer: Ⓠ Ⓠ Ⓟ
    - $1.00 Sample answer: [$1]
    - 16¢ Sample answer: Ⓓ Ⓝ Ⓟ
    - $0.79 Sample answer: Ⓠ Ⓠ Ⓠ Ⓟ Ⓟ Ⓟ Ⓟ
    - $1.25 Sample answer: [$1] Ⓠ

▶ Written Assessment

(*Assessment Handbook,* pp. 170 and 171)

Part A Recognizing Student Achievement

Problems 1–6 provide summative information and may be used for grading purposes.

Problem(s)	Description
1	Know easy addition and subtraction facts including +/–1, –0, and sums of 10.
1	Compare sums.
2	Use drawings to represent and explain simple fractions (fourths) as equal parts of a collection.
3	Know the value of a penny, nickel, dime, quarter and dollar bill; make exchanges between coins; calculate and compare the values of combinations of coins.

Assessment Master

Name Date

LESSON 9·9 **Written Assessment**

Part A

1. Write <, >, or =.
   1 + 9 = 8 + 2
   4 − 1 = 6 − 3
   7 − 0 > 2 + 1
2. 4 people share 12 cookies equally.
   How many cookies does each person get? 3 cookies
   How many cookies do 3 people get altogether? 9 cookies
3. Mia buys 2 flowers and 1 vase.

   How much money does Mia spend? 150 ¢ or $ 1.50
   Show this amount with Ⓠ, Ⓓ, Ⓝ, and Ⓟ. Sample answer: ⓆⓆⓆⓆⓆⓆ
4. Draw the hands.

   10:45

Assessment Handbook, p. 170

Assessment Master

Name Date

LESSON 9·9 **Written Assessment** *continued*

5. Find the rule and the missing numbers.

   Rule: +0 or −0

in	out
7	7
10	10
12	12
0	0

6. Write the numbers.

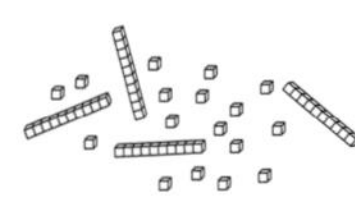

   57

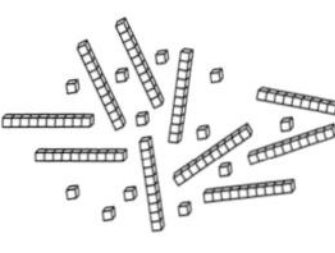

   112

Part B

7. Solve.
   12 − 6 = 6
   22 − 6 = 16
   112 − 6 = 106
   5 + 9 = 14
   50 + 90 = 140
   500 + 900 = 1400
8. Rene has ⒹⒹⒹⒹⒹⒹⒹⒹⒹⒹ.
   How much money does she have? 100 ¢
   Rene spent half of her money at the toy store.
   How much money does she have now? 50 ¢
   Show this amount with Ⓓs. ⒹⒹⒹⒹⒹ

Assessment Handbook, p. 171

Assessment Master

Name Date

LESSON 9·9 **Open Response** Progress Check 9

Number-Grid Patterns

1. Deena filled in the number-grid puzzle. Finish the puzzle and find her mistake. Cross out her mistake and write the correct number.

	36	37
		47
		57
		67
	76	
78		

78 should be 85.

2. Explain how you used patterns in the number grid to correct Deena's mistake.

Answers vary.

Assessment Handbook, p. 172

4	Show and tell time on an analog clock to the nearest quarter-hour.
5	Know addition and subtraction facts.
5	Solve problems involving simple functions represented as Function Machines.
6	Read, write, and represent whole numbers through hundreds with base-10 blocks.

Part B Informing Instruction

Problems 7 and 8 provide formative information that can be useful in planning future instruction.

Problem(s)	Description
7	Know addition and subtraction facts.
8	Use drawings to represent and explain simple fractions (halves) as equal parts of a region.
8	Know the value of a dime; calculate and compare the values of combinations of coins.

Use the checklists on pages 233 and 235 of the *Assessment Handbook* to record results. Then input the data into the **Assessment Management Spreadsheets** to keep an ongoing record of children's progress toward Grade-Level Goals.

▶ Open Response

(*Assessment Handbook*, p. 172)

Number-Grid Patterns

The open-response item requires children to apply skills and concepts from Unit 9 to solve a multistep problem. See the *Assessment Handbook*, pages 121–125 for rubrics and children's work samples for this problem.

Distribute Assessment Master, page 172. Read the problem aloud to children. Allow children to solve the problem and record their solutions on the page.

After children have had a chance to complete the page, invite individual children to explain their solution strategies. Encourage them to use words and drawings to explain their strategies as you list them on the board. Be sure to discuss both successful and unsuccessful strategies.

2 Looking Ahead: Preparing for Unit 10

▶ Math Boxes 9•9

INDEPENDENT ACTIVITY

(*Math Journal 2,* p. 193)

Mixed Practice This Math Boxes page previews Unit 10 content.

▶ Home Link 9•9: Unit 10 Family Letter

INDEPENDENT ACTIVITY

(*Math Masters,* pp. 276-279)

Home Connection The Unit 10 Family Letter provides families with information and activities related to Unit 10 topics.

Student Page

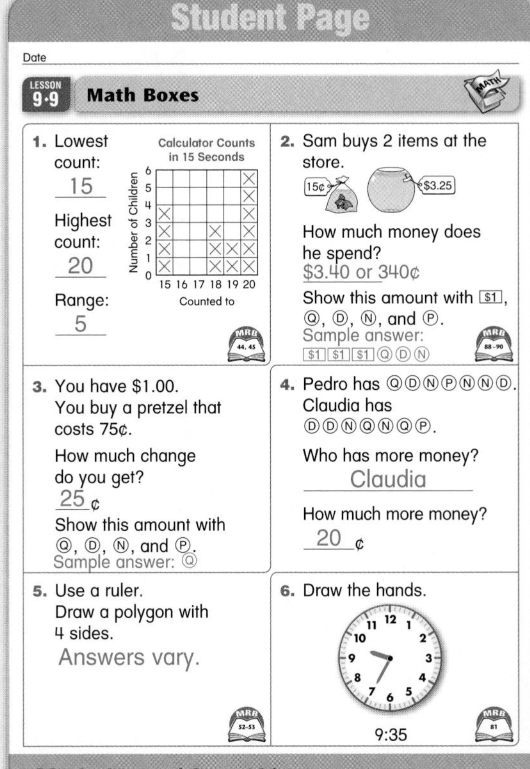

Date

LESSON 9•9 **Math Boxes**

1. Lowest count: 15
Highest count: 20
Range: 5
Calculator Counts in 15 Seconds

2. Sam buys 2 items at the store.
How much money does he spend? $3.40 or 340¢
Show this amount with $1, Ⓠ, Ⓓ, Ⓝ, and Ⓟ.
Sample answer: $1 $1 $1 Ⓠ Ⓓ Ⓝ

3. You have $1.00. You buy a pretzel that costs 75¢.
How much change do you get? 25 ¢
Show this amount with Ⓠ, Ⓓ, Ⓝ, and Ⓟ.
Sample answer: Ⓠ

4. Pedro has ⓆⒹⓃⓅⓃⓃⒹ. Claudia has ⒹⒹⓃⓆⓃⓆⓅ.
Who has more money? Claudia
How much more money? 20 ¢

5. Use a ruler. Draw a polygon with 4 sides.
Answers vary.

6. Draw the hands.
9:35

Math Journal 2, **p. 193**

Home Link Masters

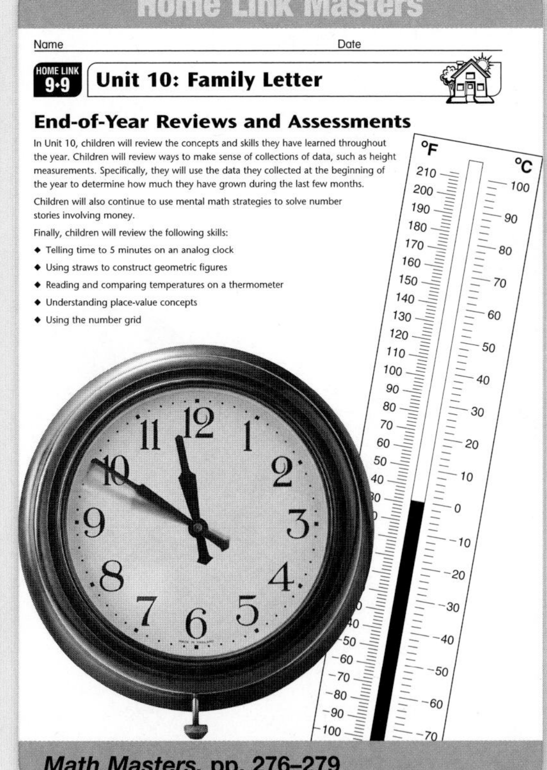

Name Date

HOME LINK 9•9 **Unit 10: Family Letter**

End-of-Year Reviews and Assessments

In Unit 10, children will review the concepts and skills they have learned throughout the year. Children will review ways to make sense of collections of data, such as height measurements. Specifically, they will use the data they collected at the beginning of the year to determine how much they have grown during the last few months.

Children will also continue to use mental math strategies to solve number stories involving money.

Finally, children will review the following skills:

- Telling time to 5 minutes on an analog clock
- Using straws to construct geometric figures
- Reading and comparing temperatures on a thermometer
- Understanding place-value concepts
- Using the number grid

Math Masters, **pp. 276–279**

Unit 10 Organizer

Year-End Review and Assessment

Overview

Unit 10 has three objectives:

- To analyze the children's height measurements made in Units 4 and 9. In the process, children review the standard procedures used to make sense of collections of data,
- To present you and the children with information about their progress on some of the concepts and skills presented in first grade. Therefore, most of the lessons contain reviews, reminders, and assessment activities, and
- To provide Summer Home Link activities for children and parents.

Linking to the Common Core State Standards

The content of Unit 10 addresses the Common Core State Standards for Mathematics in *Number and Operations in Base Ten.* The correlation of the Common Core State Standards to the *Everyday Mathematics* Grade 1 lessons begins on page CS1.

Contents

Learning In Perspective

	Lesson Objectives	Links to the Past	Links to the Future
10•1	To provide experiences with making a line plot and finding the typical values of a set of data.	In Units 1, 3, 4, and 6, children collect, organize, and analyze data to create line plots and bar graphs. The terms *range* and *middle value* are introduced. In Kindergarten, children collect and organize data to create class-constructed graphs.	In Grades 2–6, children collect, organize, and analyze data.
10•2	To review telling time on an analog clock and writing times in digital notation; to provide practice telling times in alternate ways; and to provide experiences with calculating elapsed times.	In Units 2–4 and 6, children review the hands on an analog clock and begin telling time to the nearest hour, half-hour, quarter-hour, and 5 minutes. Digital time is introduced. In Kindergarten, children begin telling time to the nearest hour and the minute hand is introduced.	In Grade 2, children tell time to the nearest half hour and 5 minutes. They tell and write time in digital notation. In Grade 3, children tell time to the nearest minute. Fractions of an hour and minutes before and after the hour are introduced. Children calculate elapsed years, days, hours, and minutes.
10•3	To review showing amounts of money with coins and to provide experiences with solving number stories involving addition of 2-digit numbers.	In Units 2–6, 8, and 9, children make exchanges between coins and find the values of coin combinations. Children tell and solve number stories and are introduced to addition and subtraction of 2-digit whole numbers using the number line and number grid.	In Grades 2 and 3, children practice counting money and making exchanges between coins. They solve number stories involving addition, subtraction, multiplication, division, and fractions, and use diagrams to solve some number stories.
10•4	To provide experiences with solving comparison number stories and calculating amounts of change from purchases.	In Units 1–6 and 8, children practice telling and solving number stories. They count up on the number line and number grid, with the calculator, and with diagrams. In Kindergarten, children begin telling and solving number stories and practice counting up.	In Grades 2 and 3, children solve number stories involving addition, subtraction, multiplication, division, and fractions. They use diagrams to solve some number stories and practice counting up to make change.
10•5	To review the names and some of the characteristics of polygons, as well as the names of basic 3-dimensional shapes.	In Units 4, 6, and 7, children explore plane shapes. They identify, describe, and model 3-dimensional figures. In Kindergarten, children identify and describe plane shapes. Children match common objects with rectangular prisms, cylinders, spheres, cubes, and cones.	In Grade 2, children identify, describe, and model plane shapes. Children identify, describe, and model 3-dimensional figures. In Grade 3, children identify, describe, model, and compare plane shapes. They describe figures and identify, model, and compare 3-dimensional figures.
10•6	To review reading temperatures in degrees Fahrenheit; and to provide experiences using information on a map to find temperature differences.	In Units 1, 2, and 4–9, children record the approximate daily temperature. They are introduced to how a thermometer works and read temperatures to the nearest 2 degrees. In Kindergarten, children work with temperatures as a part of daily routines.	Children in Grade 2 review the Fahrenheit and Celsius scales and solve problems involving temperature change, ranges in temperature, and temperature forecast.
10•7	To review place value through hundreds.	In Units 1, 4, 5, 8, and 9, children read, write, and model with manipulatives using whole numbers through hundreds. They identify places in such numbers and values of the digits in those places. In Kindergarten, children explore place value using manipulatives.	In Grade 2, children read, write, and model with manipulatives whole numbers up to 10,000. They identify places in such numbers and values of the digits in those places.

	Key Concepts and Skills	Grade 1 Goals*
10•1	Calculate the difference between two heights.	Operations and Computation Goal 2
	Solve a change-to-more problem.	Operations and Computation Goal 4
	Use a line plot and a table to organize data.	Data and Chance Goal 1
	Find the mode and median of a data set.	Data and Chance Goal 2
10•2	Count forward by 5s and then by 1s.	Number and Numeration Goal 1
	Tell and show time to the nearest 5 minutes and to the nearest minute on an analog clock.	Measurement and Reference Frames Goal 4
10•3	Count forward by 25s, 10s, and 5s.	Number and Numeration Goal 1
	Show amounts of money using combinations of quarters, dimes, and nickels.	Operations and Computation Goal 2
	Use a variety of strategies to add and subtract 2-digit numbers.	Operations and Computation Goal 2
	Tell, write, and solve number stories.	Operations and Computation Goal 4
	Write addition and subtraction number sentences, using $+$, $-$, and $=$.	Patterns, Functions, and Algebra Goal 2
10•4	Count forward by 25s, 10s, and 5s.	Number and Numeration Goal 1
	Compare quantities.	Number and Numeration Goal 7
	Add and subtract multiples of 10 using base-10 blocks.	Operations and Computation Goal 2
	Solve comparison number stories.	Operations and Computation Goal 4
	Identify money equivalencies.	Measurement and Reference Frames Goal 2
10•5	Name, model, and describe plane shapes using straws and twist-ties.	Geometry Goal 1
	Name, model, and describe solid figures.	Geometry Goal 1
	Identify and describe attributes of plane shapes and solid figures.	Geometry Goal 1
10•6	Estimate differences between pairs of 2-digit numbers.	Operations and Computation Goal 2
	Solve problems involving the addition or subtraction of 2-digit whole numbers.	Operations and Computation Goal 2
	Read temperatures and relate them to hot, warm, or cold events.	Measurement and Reference Frames Goal 3
10•7	Count forward by 10s or 100s from a 2- or 3-digit number.	Number and Numeration Goal 1
	Read, write, and model with base-10 blocks multidigit whole numbers through hundreds.	Number and Numeration Goal 3
	Express the value of digits in a multidigit number.	Number and Numeration Goal 3
	Create and solve number-grid puzzles.	Patterns, Functions, and Algebra Goal 1

*See the Appendix for a complete list of Grade 1 Goals.

A Balanced Curriculum

Ongoing Practice

Everyday Mathematics provides numerous opportunities for ongoing practice. These activities are embedded throughout the lessons:

Mental Math and Reflexes activities promote speed and accuracy in mental computation.

Math Boxes offer mixed practice and are paired across lessons as shown in the brackets below. This makes them useful as assessment tools.

Mixed practice	[10•1, 10•3], [10•2, 10•4, 10•6], [10•5, 10•7]
Mixed practice with multiple choice	10•3, 10•6, 10•7
Mixed practice with writing/reasoning opportunity	10•2, 10•3, 10•7

Home Links are daily homework assignments that review the content of the lesson and often contain ongoing facts practice.

Minute Math+ problems are offered for additional practice in Lessons 10•2, 10•4, and 10•7.

EM Facts Workshop Game provides online practice of basic facts and computation.

EXTRA PRACTICE **Extra Practice** activities are included in Lessons 10•2, 10•3, 10•4, and 10•6.

Practice through Games

Games are an essential component of practice in the *Everyday Mathematics* program. Games offer skills practice and promote strategic thinking. See the *Differentiation Handbook* for ways to adapt games to meet children's needs.

Lesson	Game	Skill Practiced
10•2	*Beat the Calculator*	Addition and subtraction facts and fact extensions [OC Goal 2]
10•3	*Coin-Dice*	Making coin exchanges [MRF Goal 2]
10•4	*$1, $10, $100 Exchange Game*	Exchanging $1, $10, and $100 bills [MRF Goal 2]
10•4	*Dime-Nickel-Penny Grab*	Calculating and comparing the values of combinations of coins [OC Goal 2]
10•5	*Time Match*	Matching digital and analog clocks [MRF Goal 4]

[NN] Number and Numeration [OC] Operations and Computation [DC] Data and Chance
[MRF] Measurement and Reference Frames [GEO] Geometry [PFA] Patterns, Functions, and Algebra

Problem Solving 

Good problem solvers use a variety of strategies, including the following:

- Draw a picture.
- Act out the problem.
- Make a table, chart, or list.
- Look for a pattern.
- Try a simpler version of the problem.
- Make a guess and try it out.

The table below lists some of the opportunities in this unit for children to practice these strategies.

Lessons that teach *through* problem solving, not just *about* problem solving

Lesson	Activity
10•1	Find the typical height of children in class.
10•2	Calculate elapsed time.
10•3	Determine how much money is needed to purchase two or more items.
10•5	Construct polygons.
10•6	Find the difference between high and low temperatures.
10•7	Make and solve number-grid puzzles.

See Chapter 18: Problem Solving in the *Teacher's Reference Manual* for more information.

The Language of Mathematics

Everyday Mathematics provides lesson-specific suggestions to help all children acquire, process, and express mathematical ideas. Throughout Unit 10, there are lesson-specific language development notes that address the needs of English language learners, indicated by ELL.

ELL SUPPORT Activities to support English language learners are in Part 3 of Lessons 10•4, 10•5, and 10•6.

The *English Learners Handbook* and the *Differentiation Handbook* have suggestions for promoting language development and acquisition of mathematics vocabulary. See Unit 10 in each handbook.

Literacy Connection

Lesson 10•2 *It's About Time, Max!,* by Kitty Richards, Kane Press, 2000

Lesson 10•6 *Welcome to the Green House,* by Jane Yolen, Putnam Publishing Group, 1997

Welcome to the Ice House, by Jane Yolen, Putnam Publishing Group, 1998

Arctic Tundra (One Small Square Series), by Donald Silver, McGraw-Hill, 1997

Cactus Desert (One Small Square Series), by Donald Silver, McGraw-Hill, 1997

Tropical Rain Forest (One Small Square Series), by Donald Silver, McGraw-Hill, 1997

For more literacy connections, see the *Home Connection Handbook,* Grades 1–3.

Cross-Curricular Links 

Literature – Lesson 10•2
Science – Lesson 10•6
Language Arts – Lesson 10•4
Social Studies – Lesson 10•6

Balanced Assessment

Daily Assessments

- **Recognizing Student Achievement** – A daily assessment that is included in every lesson to evaluate children's progress toward the Grade 1 Grade-Level Goals.
- **Informing Instruction** – Notes that appear throughout the unit to help anticipate children's common errors and suggest appropriate problem-solving strategies.

Lesson	Recognizing Student Achievement	Informing Instruction
10•1	Find data landmarks. [DC Goal 2]	
10•2	Know the movement of the minute hand. [MRF Goal 4]	Set the hour hand of a clock.
10•3	Compare numbers using <, >, and =. [NN Goal 7]	
10•4	Find differences in amounts of money. [OC Goal 2]	Make change.
10•5	Estimate sums. [OC Goal 3]	
10•6	Compare temperatures. [MRF Goal 3]	Identify warmer and cooler temperatures on a thermometer.
10•7	Solve number-grid puzzles. [PFA Goal 1]	Differentiate between hundreds, tens, and ones places.

[NN] Number and Numeration
[MRF] Measurement and Reference Frames
[OC] Operations and Computation
[GEO] Geometry
[DC] Data and Chance
[PFA] Patterns, Functions, and Algebra

Portfolio Opportunities

The following lessons provide opportunities to gather samples of children's mathematical writings, drawings, and creations to add balance to the assessment process: Lessons 10•2, 10•3, 10•4, 10•7, and 10•8.

See pages 16 and 17 in the *Assessment Handbook* for more information about portfolios and how to use them.

Unit Assessment

Progress Check 10 – A cumulative assessment of concepts and skills taught in Unit 10 and in previous units, providing information for evaluating children's progress and planning for future instruction. These assessments include oral/slate, written, and open-response activities, as shown below in the sample Progress Check lesson opener.

2•10 Progress Check 2

Objective To assess children's progress on mathematical content through the end of Unit 2.

1 Looking Back: Cumulative Assessment

Input children's data from Progress Check 2 into the **Assessment Management Spreadsheets.**

Materials
- Home Link 2•9
- *Assessment Handbook,* pp. 60–67, 152–156, 203, and 232–235
- slate

Content Assessed	Lesson(s)	Assessment Items: Self	Oral/Slate	Written: Part A	Written: Part B	Open Response
Identify the digits in numbers and express their values. [Number and Numeration Goal 1]	2•1, 2•3, 2•5, 2•7–2•9			10		
Find equivalent names for whole numbers. [Number and Numeration Goal 4]	2•5, 2•7–2•9			5		
Use basic facts to compute extended facts. [Operations and Computation Goal 1]	2•1–2•9	1	1–4	1–4	11, 12	
Use paper-and-pencil algorithms to solve problems involving the addition and subtraction of whole numbers. [Operations and Computation Goal 2]	2•1–2•9	4, 5, 6		6, 7	13, 14	✓
Use strategies to make estimates. [Operations and Computation Goal 5]	2•7, 2•8				13, 14	
Apply parts-and-total and comparison situations. [Operations and Computation Goal 6]	2•4–2•9	3		6, 7		
Tell and show time on an analog clock. [Measurement and Reference Frames Goal 4]	2•1, 2•3, 2•6, 2•8			8, 9		✓
Find and use rules to solve problems. [Patterns, Functions, and Algebra Goal 1]	2•1–2•9	2		3, 4	11, 12	

2 Looking Ahead: Preparing for Unit 3

Math Boxes 2•10

Home Link 2•10: Unit 3 Family Letter

Materials
- *Math Journal 1,* p. 54
- *Math Masters,* pp. 60–63

152 Unit 2 Progress Check 2

Core Assessment Resources

Assessment Handbook

- **Unit 10 Assessment Overview,** pages 126–133
- **Unit 10 Assessment Masters,** pages 173–176
- **Unit 10 Individual Profiles of Progress,** pages 236, 237, and 248
- **Unit 10 Class Checklists,** pages 238, 239, and 249
- **End-of-Year Assessment,** pages 191–196
- **Quarterly Checklist: Quarter 4,** pages 246 and 247
- **Math Logs,** pages 254–256
- **Exit Slip,** page 251
- **Other Student Assessment Forms,** pages 252, 253, 257, and 258

Assessment Management Spreadsheets

The Assessment Management Spreadsheets consist of the Digital Class Checklists and Individual Profile of Progress Checklists. Use them to monitor, record, and report children's progress.

Addressing All Needs

Differentiated Instruction

Adjusting the Activity – suggests adaptations that target advanced learners, English language learners, or learners who need additional instructional support.

ELL SUPPORT / **ELL** – provides lesson-specific suggestions to help English language learners understand and process the mathematical content.

READINESS – accesses children's prior knowledge or previews content that prepares children to engage in the lesson's Part 1 activities.

EXTRA PRACTICE – provides additional opportunities to apply the mathematical content of the lesson.

ENRICHMENT – enables children to apply or further explore the mathematical content of the lesson.

Lesson	Adjusting the Activity	ELL Support/ ELL	Readiness	Extra Practice	Enrichment
10•1	•	•	•		•
10•2	•	•	•	•	•
10•3	•		•	•	
10•4	•	•	•	•	•
10•5		•	•		•
10•6	•	•	•	•	•
10•7	•		•		•

Additional Resources

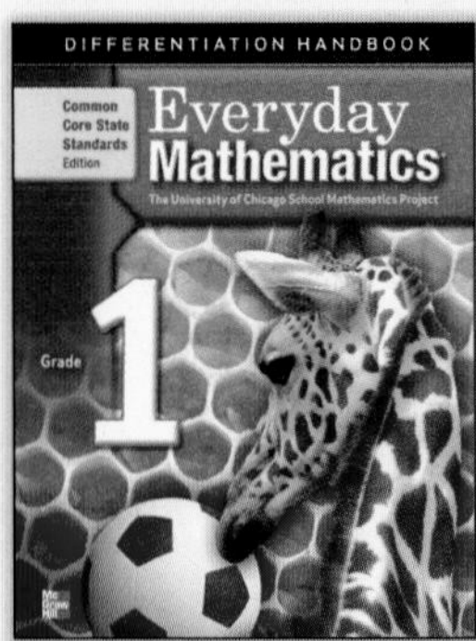

Differentiation Handbook
Provides ideas and strategies for differentiating instruction.
Pages 113–118

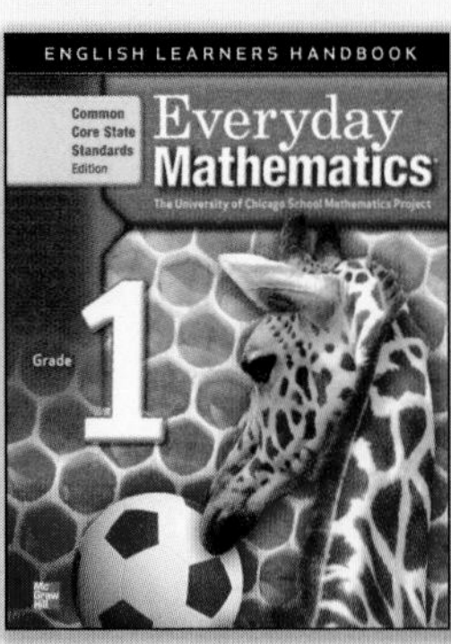

English Learners Handbook
Contains lesson-specific comprehension strategies.
Pages 102–108

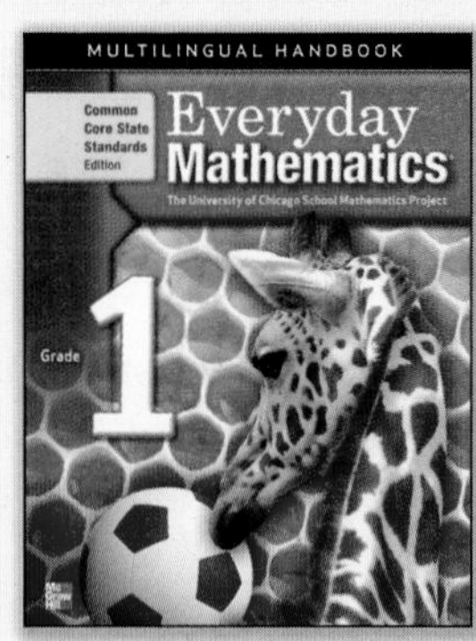

Multilingual Handbook
Previews concepts and vocabulary. It is written in six languages.
Pages 203–216

Planning Tips

Multiage Classroom

Companion Lessons from Grades K and 2 can help you meet instructional needs of a multiage classroom. The full Scope and Sequence can be found in the Appendix.

Grade K	1•13	6•4, 6•13, 8•2, 8•3	6•8, 8•8	6•8, 8•8	4•10, 6•3	Routine 7	5•15, 7•10
Grade 1	**10•1**	**10•2**	**10•3**	**10•4**	**10•5**	**10•6**	**10•7**
Grade 2	3•5, 7•7, 9•2	1•3, 3•3, 12•2	3•2, 3•7, 4•6	6•2, 10•1, 11•2	5•1–5•9, 8•2	1•12, 4•4	1•8, 10•8

Pacing for Success

Pacing depends on a number of factors, such as children's individual needs and how long your school has been using *Everyday Mathematics*. At the beginning of Unit 10, you may want to use tools available at www.everydaymathonline.com to help you set your pace.

Home Support

Unit 10 Family Letter (English/Spanish) provides families with an overview, Do-Anytime Activities, Building Skills through Games, a list of vocabulary, and answers to the daily homework (Home Links). Family Letters in English, Spanish, and seven other languages are also available online.

Home Links are the daily homework assignments. They consist of active projects and ongoing review problems.

Home Support Resources

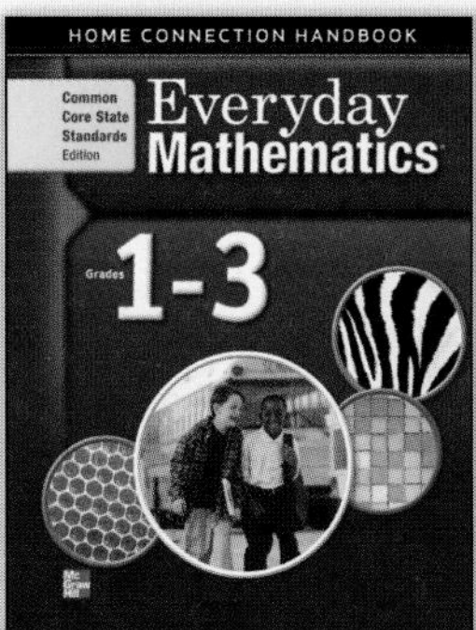

Home Connection Handbook
Offers ideas and reproducible masters for communicating with families. See Table of Contents for unit information.

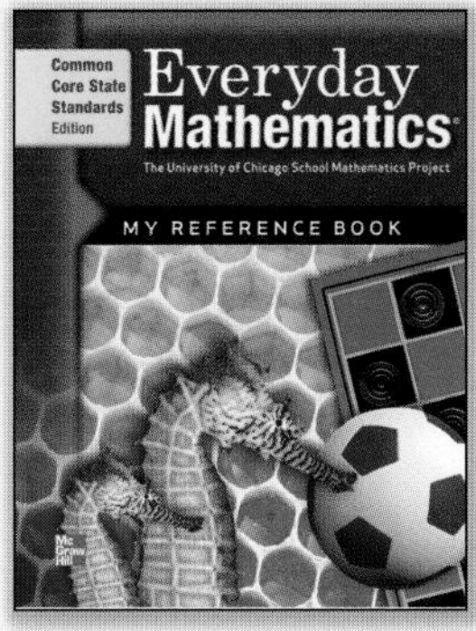

My Reference Book
Provides a resource for children and parents.
Pages 124, 125, 128, 129, 152, 153

Technology Resources

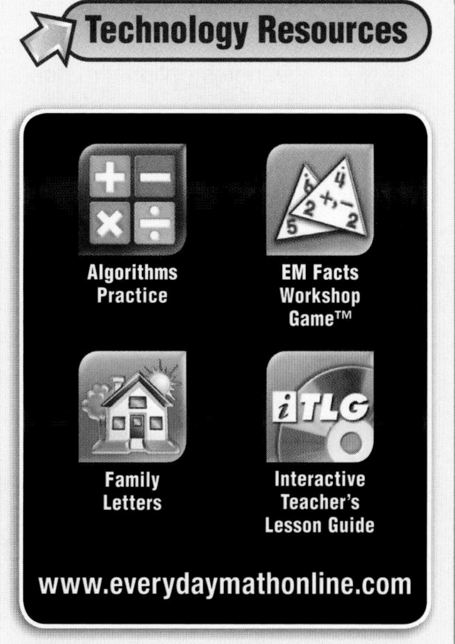

Unit 10 Organizer

Materials

Technology Resources www.everydaymathonline.com

ePresentations

eToolkit

Algorithms Practice

EM Facts Workshop Game™

Family Letters

Assessment Management

Common Core State Standards

Curriculum Focal Points

Interactive Teacher's Lesson Guide

Lesson	Masters	Manipulative Kit	Other Items
10•1	Home Link Master, p. 281 Teaching Masters, pp. 280 and 282	slate	demonstration clock; stick-on notes; Class Data Pad; Animal Cards; calculator
10•2	Home Link Master, p. 283 Teaching Master, p. 284 Teaching Aid Master, p. 305	slate; tool-kit clock	demonstration clock; labeled stick-on notes; *It's About Time, Max!;* calculator
10•3	Transparency of *Math Masters,* p. 285* Home Link Master, p. 287 Teaching Master, p. 286	base-10 blocks; tool-kit coins; per partnership: 2 dice	stick-on notes; Class Data Pad; calculator
10•4	Transparency of *Math Masters,* p. 285* Home Link Master, p. 288 Teaching Aid Masters, pp. 331–334 Game Master, p. 342 *Differentiation Handbook,* p. 126	base-10 blocks*; slate; tool-kit coins and bills; per partnership: 2 dice	overhead base-10 blocks*; magazine or newspaper ads
10•5	Teaching Masters, pp. 212A, 212B, 288A, and 288B Home Link Master, p. 289 Game Masters pp. 354, 355, and 359		models of regular polyhedrons; 10 long straws, 10 short straws, and 20 twist-ties per child; scissors; tape; stickers; markers; glue; craft supplies
10•6	Transparency of *Math Masters,* p. 290* Home Link Master, p. 291 Teaching Master, p. 292 *Differentiation Handbook,* p. 126	slate	Class Thermometer Poster; per partnership: 2 pennies; calculator*
10•7	Teaching Aid Masters, pp. 319* and 335 Home Link Master, p. 293 Teaching Master, p. 110	slate; per group: number cards 1–9; base-10 blocks (flats, longs, and cubes)	straws (10 singles, 10 bundles of 10); ten each of play money $1, $10, and $100 bills; number scroll; materials for math games
10•8	Assessment Masters, pp. 173–176 and 191–196 Home Link Masters, pp. 294–297 Teaching Masters, pp. 110 and 335	slate; tool-kit coins	calculator

*Denotes optional materials

Mathematical Background

The discussion below highlights the major content ideas presented in Unit 10 and helps establish instructional priorities.

Considerations of Year-End Data

(Lesson 10◆1)

Children should have completed their second height measurement in Unit 9. In this lesson, they calculate how much they have grown during the last few months. While doing this, there will be opportunities to discuss variation and change, as well as to review and reinforce some of the important basic procedures that help people make sense of data.

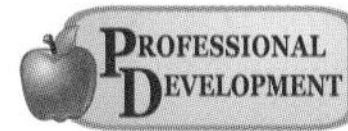

To further explore data analysis, see Section 12.2.4 of the *Teacher's Reference Manual.*

Review and Assessment

The authors believe that children must be exposed to concepts and skills many times and in many ways, often only briefly, before they finally attain secure mastery and command of those concepts and skills. Most children need reminders of what they have already been exposed to with each new exposure, even for concepts and skills previously learned. Also, most teachers find that children learn at different rates; only rarely are children all at the same level at the same time for any given skill or concept. Therefore, assessment at the end of the year, especially the first-grade year, should in most cases focus on progress rather than on mastery. You will probably find, however, that many children do indeed have substantial mastery in some areas. At the same time, you may find that in other areas, nearly all children have a long way to go.

Children's progress needs to be monitored at frequent intervals and especially at the end of a school year. This end-of-year monitoring gives both you and the second grade teachers a sense of each child's progress and the general level at which the second-grade groups might expect to start after suitable reminders and reviews. Pre-summer assessment also gives each child an awareness of what he or she has accomplished over the course of the school year.

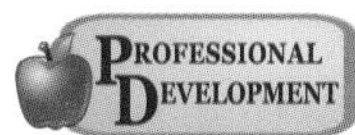

To read more about assessment, refer to Chapter 7 of the *Teacher's Reference Manual.*

Summer Home Links

Summer Home Links are suggested in a Family Letter. You may want to augment the letter with your own notes to fit your situation and to express your sense of what children might enjoy and profit from as summer mathematics activities.

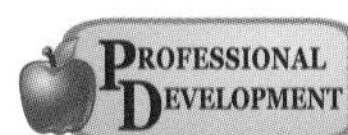

For more information about Summer Home Links, see Section 8.1 in the *Teacher's Reference Manual.*

10·1 Data Day: End-of-Year Heights

Objective To provide experience making a line plot and finding the typical values of a set of data.

www.everydaymathonline.com

ePresentations

eToolkit

Algorithms Practice

EM Facts Workshop Game™

Family Letters

Assessment Management

Common Core State Standards

Curriculum Focal Points

Interactive Teacher's Lesson Guide

1 Teaching the Lesson

Key Concepts and Skills

- Calculate the difference between two heights.
  [Operations and Computation Goal 2]
- Solve a change-to-more problem.
  [Operations and Computation Goal 4]
- Use a line plot and a table to organize data.
  [Data and Chance Goal 1]
- Find the mode and median of a data set.
  [Data and Chance Goal 2]

Key Activities

Children make a line plot of the class's second height measurements and use it to find the height of a typical child in the class. Then they find the middle value of the set of heights. They figure out how many inches they have grown and determine the most common growth.

Materials

Math Journal 2, p. 184
demonstration clock ◆ Class Data Pad ◆ slate ◆ stick-on notes

2 Ongoing Learning & Practice

Solving Problems with Fractions
Math Masters, p. 280
Children practice working with fractions.

Math Boxes 10·1
Math Journal 2, p. 194
Children practice and maintain skills through Math Box problems.

Ongoing Assessment: Recognizing Student Achievement
Use Math Boxes, Problem 1.
[Data and Chance Goal 2]

Home Link 10·1
Math Masters, p. 281
Children practice and maintain skills through Home Link activities.

3 Differentiation Options

READINESS

Telling and Solving Animal Growth Number Stories
Animal Cards (*Math Journal 1,* Activity Sheets 7 and 8) ◆ slate
Children use animal-length cards to tell and solve number stories about growth.

ENRICHMENT

Counting on Calculators
Math Masters, p. 282
calculator
Children work in small groups to collect data about calculator counts.

Advance Preparation

Place a pad of stick-on notes near the Math Message. For Part 1, draw a horizontal number line on the Class Data Pad. Number the line from 38 to 56 (or use numbers that are appropriate for your class) and label it "Inches Tall."

***Teacher's Reference Manual,* Grades 1–3** pp. 118, 119

Getting Started

Mental Math and Reflexes

Show a time on the demonstration clock. Children record the time in digital notation on their slates.

●○○ 7:00; 3:30; 6:30; 12:00

●●○ 8:15; 4:15; 4:45; 2:45

●●● 10:10; 11:40; 7:50; 3:25

Math Message

Look up the second measurement of your height on journal page 184. Write your second height measurement on a stick-on note.

1 Teaching the Lesson

Interactive whiteboard-ready ePresentations are available at www.everydaymathonline.com to help you teach the lesson.

▶ Math Message Follow-Up

WHOLE-CLASS ACTIVITY

(*Math Journal 2,* p. 184)

Check that children have copied their second height measurements correctly onto their stick-on notes. Explain that they will use the stick-on notes to make a line plot of their end-of-the-year heights.

▶ Finding the Typical Height of Children in the Class

WHOLE-CLASS ACTIVITY

ELL

(*Math Journal 2,* p. 184)

Have children put their stick-on notes above the number line on the Class Data Pad to form a line plot. Ask: *What does the number of stick-on notes in a column tell you?* It tells how many children have the corresponding height on the number line.

Discuss how children arrived at a typical height for children in the class at the time they made their first height measurements. (See Lesson 4-7, Exploration A.) Use the same procedure to find the typical second height measurement; that is, count the number of stick-on notes for each height. Then ask: *Which height has the largest number of stick-on notes?* Explain that this is one way to find a typical height of a child in the class at the time the measurements were made. To support English language learners, label the typical height.

Children record this typical height on page 184 in their journals.

NOTE The value that occurs most often in a set of data is called the *mode.* It is not necessary for children to learn this word at this time.

Student Page

Date ______

LESSON 9·5 **My Height Record**

First Measurement

Date ______

Height: about ______ inches

A typical height for a first grader in my class was about ______ inches.

Second Measurement

Date ______

Height: about ______ inches

A typical height for a first grader in my class is about ______ inches.

The middle height for my class is about ______ inches.

Change to Height

I grew about ______ inches.

The typical growth in my class was about ______ inches.

Math Journal 2, p. 184

NOTE You may want to show children how their line plot would look if it were created using graphing software.

▶ Finding the Middle Value of the Height Data

WHOLE-CLASS ACTIVITY

(*Math Journal 2,* p. 184)

Remind the class that another way to find a typical height is to find the middle value of all of the heights. Review the method taught in Lesson 6-12 for finding the middle value by moving stick-on notes below a line plot. Then explain that the following procedure is similar to what children did in Lesson 6-12. (This procedure will transition children so that they will be able to find the middle value of a data set independently.)

- ▷ Mark an X on the last stick-on note at each end of the line plot. (If there are several stick-on notes forming a column at one end of the line plot, mark the top one.)

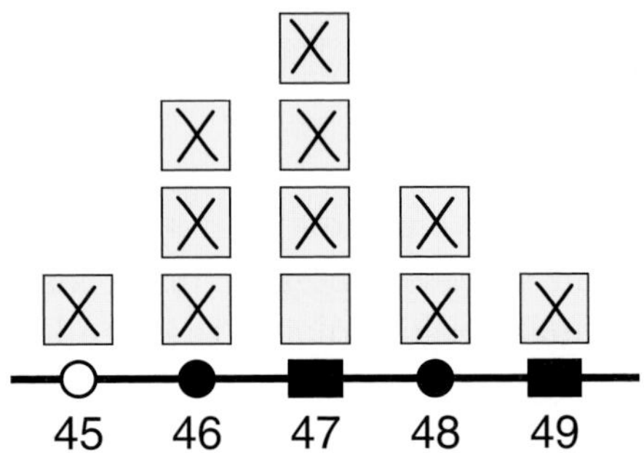

- ▷ Repeat this procedure over and over.
- ▷ Eventually, there will be only one or two notes left unmarked. If one note remains unmarked, the number on that note is the middle value. If two notes remain, the numbers on those notes are the middle values. You can use the number halfway between the two middle values as the typical height. Label the middle value.

Have children record this middle value in their journals.

NOTE Another name for the middle value is the *median.* It is not necessary for children to learn this word at this time.

Adjusting the Activity

Have each child take a stick-on note and line up in order. Children can find the middle value by sitting down in pairs—the highest and lowest sitting down each time—until only one or two children remain. If there is one child left, that is the middle value. If there are two children left, the middle value is the number halfway between the two numbers.

AUDITORY • KINESTHETIC • TACTILE • VISUAL

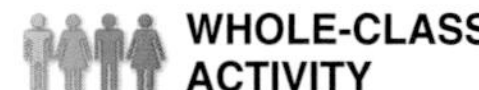

Finding Out How Much Children Grew

WHOLE-CLASS ACTIVITY

(*Math Journal 2,* p. 184)

Ask children to calculate about how many inches they grew between their first and second measurements and to record the number in their journals. Then, by a show of hands, determine how many children grew about 1 inch, about 2 inches, and so on. Record the results in a table on the Class Data Pad. Ask: *What is the typical growth of the children in the class?*

Explain that people are different and that children grow at different rates and times. Have children use the data they collected to make a prediction about the typical growth of first graders in their school or community.

2 Ongoing Learning & Practice

Solving Problems with Fractions

INDEPENDENT ACTIVITY

(*Math Masters,* p. 280)

Use *Math Masters*, page 280 to provide practice for solving problems with fractions.

Math Boxes 10•1

INDEPENDENT ACTIVITY

(*Math Journal 2,* p. 194)

Mixed Practice Math Boxes in this lesson are paired with Math Boxes in Lesson 10-3.

Ongoing Assessment: Recognizing Student Achievement

Math Boxes Problem 1

Use **Math Boxes, Problem 1** to assess children's ability to find data landmarks. Children are making adequate progress if they are able to find the highest temperature and the lowest temperature. Some children may also be able to find the range.

[Data and Chance Goal 2]

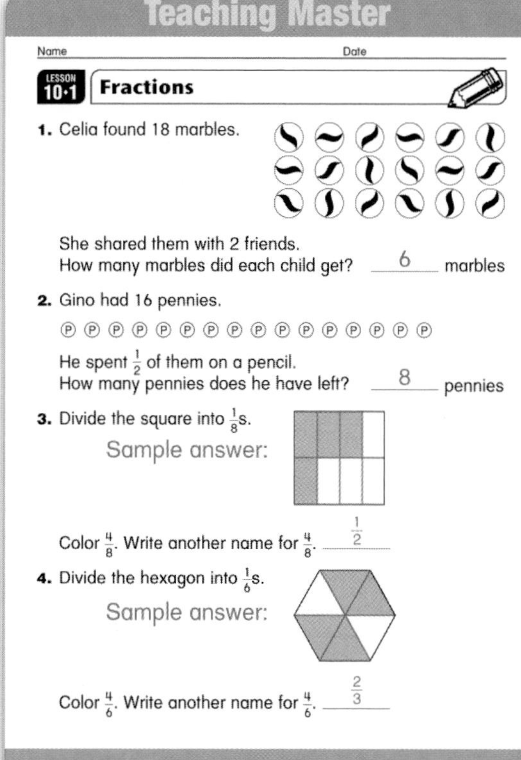

Teaching Master

Name Date

LESSON 10•1 **Fractions**

1. Celia found 18 marbles.

She shared them with 2 friends.
How many marbles did each child get? 6 marbles

2. Gino had 16 pennies.

He spent $\frac{1}{2}$ of them on a pencil.
How many pennies does he have left? 8 pennies

3. Divide the square into $\frac{1}{8}$s.
Sample answer:

Color $\frac{4}{8}$. Write another name for $\frac{4}{8}$. $\frac{1}{2}$

4. Divide the hexagon into $\frac{1}{6}$s.
Sample answer:

Color $\frac{4}{6}$. Write another name for $\frac{4}{6}$. $\frac{2}{3}$

Math Masters, **p. 280**

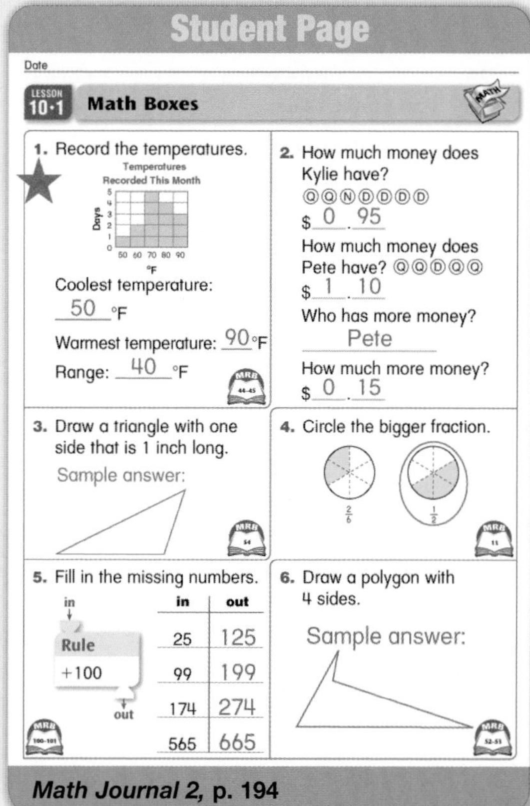

Student Page

Date

LESSON 10•1 **Math Boxes**

1. Record the temperatures.

Coolest temperature: 50 °F
Warmest temperature: 90 °F
Range: 40 °F

2. How much money does Kylie have?
$ 0 . 95
How much money does Pete have?
$ 1 . 10
Who has more money? Pete
How much more money? $ 0 . 15

3. Draw a triangle with one side that is 1 inch long.
Sample answer:

4. Circle the bigger fraction.
$\frac{2}{6}$ $\frac{1}{2}$

5. Fill in the missing numbers.

Rule +100

in	out
25	125
99	199
174	274
565	665

6. Draw a polygon with 4 sides.
Sample answer:

Math Journal 2, **p. 194**

Home Link Master

Name ______ Date ______

HOME LINK 10•1 **Graphing Birth Months** 

Family Note Today your child figured out about how many inches he or she has grown in the last few months. We collected height information for the whole class and graphed it. We also found the typical height and the typical growth of the children in the class.

Help your child graph the months in which friends and family members were born. For each person, your child should color one box above the birth month.

Please return this Home Link to school tomorrow.

Birth Months of Friends and Family Members

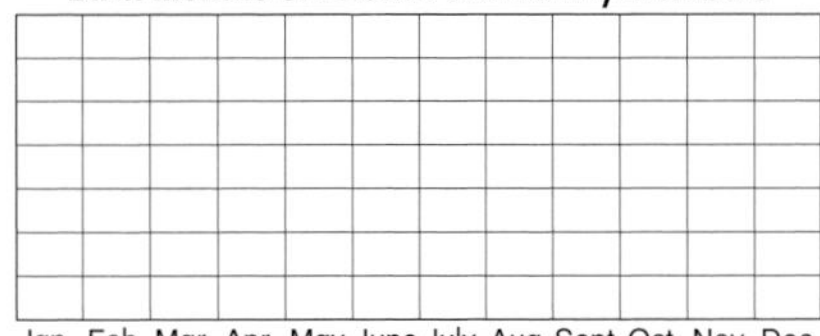

1. Which month had more births than any other month? Answers vary.
2. How many births were in that month? ______
3. Which month had the fewest births? ______
4. How many births were in that month? ______

Practice

Write <, >, or =.

5. 40 > 36
6. 123 = 100 + 23
7. ⓠⓠⓠ > ⓠⓓⓝⓝ

***Math Masters,* p. 281**

▶ Home Link 10•1

(*Math Masters,* p. 281)

Home Connection Children collect data about the month in which friends and family members were born and then graph the data.

3 Differentiation Options

READINESS

SMALL-GROUP ACTIVITY

▶ Telling and Solving Animal Growth Number Stories

5–15 Min

To provide experience calculating differences, have children tell and solve number stories, using animal-length cards from Unit 5. First, model how to tell an animal growth number story. Then have children draw and solve the number story on a slate. Children can then take turns telling animal growth number stories to the group. *For example:*

- The raccoon is 23 inches long. It grows 3 inches. How long is the raccoon now? 26 inches
- The beaver was 30 inches long. Now it is 34 inches long. How many inches did the beaver grow? 4 inches

ENRICHMENT

▶ Counting on Calculators

5–15 Min

(*Math Masters,* p. 282)

To further explore data collections, have children perform a counting experiment on their calculators. Children make predictions on how high they can count in different ways in 15 seconds. Have children alternate as the group's timer. Begin by explaining what 15 seconds looks like on a clock. When children have finished the experiment, list all of their counts by 1s on the board. Find the middle value. Then list all of their counts by 2s. Find the middle value. Discuss their predictions for the different counts and the results for the whole group. Have them describe for which count their prediction was closer and why this might be the case.

Teaching Master

Name ______ Date ______

 **Calculator Counts** 

Use your calculator to do the following counts. Answers vary.

1. Predict how high you can count by 1s in 15 seconds: ______

   Program your calculator to count by 1s.
   When the timer says go, begin counting.
   When the timer says stop, stop counting.

   How high did you count? ______

   Was your prediction too high, too low, or just right? ______

2. Predict how high you can count by 2s in 15 seconds: ______

   Tell how you made your prediction.

   ______

   Program your calculator to count by 2s.
   When the timer says go, begin counting.
   When the timer says stop, stop counting.

   How high did you count? ______

   Was your prediction too high, too low, or just right? ______

3. Tell a friend what you think would happen if you counted by 3s or 4s on your calculator.

***Math Masters,* p. 282**

10•2 Review: Telling Time

Objectives To review telling time on an analog clock and writing times in digital notation; to provide practice telling times in alternate ways; and to provide experiences with calculating elapsed times.

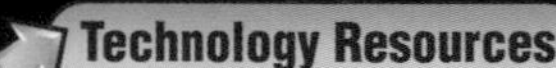

www.everydaymathonline.com

ePresentations

eToolkit

Algorithms Practice

EM Facts Workshop Game™

Family Letters

Assessment Management

Common Core State Standards

Curriculum Focal Points

Interactive Teacher's Lesson Guide

1 Teaching the Lesson

Key Concepts and Skills

- Count forward by 5s and then by 1s. [Number and Numeration Goal 1]
- Tell and show time to the nearest 5 minutes and to the nearest minute on an analog clock. [Measurement and Reference Frames Goal 4]

Key Activities

Children review and practice using hand movements on an analog clock to tell time to 5 minutes. They review and practice recording time in digital notation. They set their clocks to a time on the quarter-hour and figure out how many minutes will elapse until a later time.

Ongoing Assessment: Recognizing Student Achievement Use the Math Message. [Measurement and Reference Frames Goal 4]

Ongoing Assessment: Informing Instruction See page 807.

Materials

Math Journal 2, p. 195
Home Link 10•1
slate ◆ demonstration clock ◆ tool-kit clock

2 Ongoing Learning & Practice

Playing *Beat the Calculator* with Facts and Fact Extensions
per partnership: calculator
Children practice addition and subtraction facts and fact extensions.

Math Boxes 10•2
Math Journal 2, p. 196
Children practice and maintain skills through Math Box problems.

Home Link 10•2
Math Masters, p. 283
Children practice and maintain skills through Home Link activities.

Minute Math+
Minute Math®+, pp. 78, 83, and 111
Children practice with number stories.

3 Differentiation Options

READINESS

Telling Time on an Analog Clock
labeled stick-on notes ◆ demonstration clock
Children match the times shown on digital and analog clocks.

ENRICHMENT

Calculating Elapsed Time
Math Masters, p. 284
tool-kit clocks
Children use tool-kit clocks to solve elapsed time problems.

EXTRA PRACTICE

Reading About Time
Math Masters, p. 305
Children read *It's About Time, Max!* to practice telling time.

Advance Preparation

For the optional Readiness activity in Part 3, label stick-on notes with times throughout the school day, such as 9:15, 10:00, 12:30, and 1:45. For the optional Extra Practice activity in Part 3, obtain a copy of ***It's About Time, Max!*** by Kitty Richards (Kane Press, 2000).

***Teacher's Reference Manual,* Grades 1–3** pp. 162, 196–198

Getting Started

Mental Math and Reflexes

Ask children the following rounding questions. Have them write the answers on their slates.

●○○ Is 49 closer to 40 or 50? 50 Is 64 closer to 60 or 70? 60 Is 87 closer to 80 or 90? 90

●●○ Is 98 closer to 90 or 100? 100 Is 125 closer to 100 or 200? 100 Is 195 closer to 100 or 200? 200

●●● Is 189 closer to 180 or 190? 190 Is 230 closer to 200 or 300? 200 Is 275 closer to 200 or 300? 300

Math Message ★

How many minutes does it take for the minute hand to move around the clock? 60 minutes *How many minutes does it take for the minute hand to move from the 2 to the 3?* 5 minutes

Home Link 10·1 Follow-Up

Children share the results of their surveys. Discuss the number of people they interviewed, which months have the most and fewest birth dates, and so on.

1 Teaching the Lesson

▶ Math Message Follow-Up

Check responses and review as needed.

Ongoing Assessment: Recognizing Student Achievement

Math Message ★

Use the **Math Message** to assess children's knowledge of the movement of the minute hand. Children are making adequate progress if they are able to answer both questions correctly.

[Measurement and Reference Frames Goal 4]

▶ Reviewing Telling Time to Five Minutes

Show a time on a demonstration clock and have children tell the time.

Adjusting the Activity

Have children tell and demonstrate with their arms where each hand points before saying the time.

AUDITORY ◆ KINESTHETIC ◆ TACTILE ◆ VISUAL

Next, name a time and have children show it on their tool-kit clocks. Repeat as needed.

Then pose a few problems that involve elapsed time; for example, show five o'clock on your demonstration clock. Then ask: *About how many minutes is it until quarter-past 5?* Limit the problems to times on the quarter-hour.

▶ Reviewing Digital Notation for Recording Time

1. On your demonstration clock, show a time on the hour such as ten o'clock. Ask children what this would look like on a digital clock. 10:00 Review what the numbers before and after the colon mean: The number before the colon stands for the hour, and the number after the colon stands for minutes after the hour.
2. Show a time on the demonstration clock. Children write the time in digital notation on their slates. Start with times on the quarter-hour and proceed to times in 5-minute intervals.
3. Reverse the procedure. Write a time on the board in digital notation and have children show it on their tool-kit clocks.

Ongoing Assessment: Informing Instruction

Watch for children who need help setting the hour hand of the clock. You may ask them to name the hour, then set the hour hand there, with the minute hand pointing straight up. Then have them count off the minutes past the hour while moving the minute hand and adjusting the hour hand accordingly.

4. Elicit alternate ways of naming the time. For example, what does 3:45 mean? 45 minutes after 3; 15 minutes before 4; quarter-to 4 Repeat with 5-minute interval times suggested by both you and the children. Write each of the names on the board to support English language learners.

▶ Practicing with Time

PARTNER ACTIVITY

(*Math Journal 2,* p. 195)

In Problem 1, one partner sets a time on the tool-kit clock while the other partner records that time on the analog clock face and in digital notation under the clock face. Partners take turns setting the clock and recording times.

In Problem 2, children take turns writing a time in digital notation and drawing hands on the clock to show that time.

Children complete Problem 3 independently.

Student Page

Date

LESSON 10·2 **Clock-Face Record**

1. Ask a partner to show times on a tool-kit clock. Draw the hands on the clock. Write the times to match. Answers vary.

   ___:___ ___:___ ___:___

2. Write a time for each clock face. Draw the hands to match. Answers vary.

   ___:___ ___:___ ___:___

3. Set your tool-kit clock to 3:00. How many minutes until 3:25? 25 minutes

   Set your tool-kit clock to 1:30. How many minutes until 1:55? 25 minutes

   Set your tool-kit clock to 10:45. How many minutes until 11:20? 35 minutes

Math Journal 2, p. 195

Telling Time to Minutes

Using your demonstration clock and children's tool-kit clocks, review the minute marks between the numbers. Ask: *How many minutes are in an hour?* 60 minutes

Show a time on the demonstration clock at a one-minute interval. Help children tell the time by counting by 5s around their tool-kit clocks until they reach the number just before your setting. Then have them count on by 1s for the additional minutes. To support English language learners, discuss the different pronunciations of five past the hour. For example, 3:05 is read, "three-oh-five," in which the number zero may be interpreted as the letter *O*. Emphasize other ways to read 3:05, such as "five past three."

Links to the Future

Although this lesson includes times to the nearest five minutes and the nearest minute, do not expect children to master these skills at this time. Throughout first grade, the focus has been on telling time on analog and digital clocks to the half-hour and quarter-hour. Telling time to the nearest 5 minutes is a Grade 2 Goal.

2 Ongoing Learning & Practice

Playing *Beat the Calculator* with Facts and Fact Extensions

Partners take turns being the "Calculator" and the "Brain" while you are the "Caller." Call out a basic addition or subtraction fact and have children respond. Then for each fact, call out a fact extension; for example, using the subtraction fact 13 – 6, you can use 23 – 6 or 130 – 60 as a fact extension.

Children tally wins for Brain and Calculator after each fact or extension, regardless of who takes on each role. At the end of the activity, if the Calculator has more wins, children probably need more mental practice. If the Brain wins, congratulations!

Links to the Future

The variation of *Beat the Calculator* in this lesson encourages children to use basic facts to solve fact extensions quickly. Using basic facts to compute extended facts is a Grade 3 Goal.

Math Boxes 10·2

(*Math Journal 2,* p. 196)

Mixed Practice Math Boxes in this lesson are linked to Math Boxes in Lessons 10-4 and 10-6.

Writing/Reasoning Have children draw, write, or verbalize an answer to the following question: *How do you solve a number-grid puzzle?* A reasonable answer should include a reference to patterns on the number grid. Sample answer: You can use a number grid by looking at the tens and going backward so you can figure it out.

Home Link 10·2

(*Math Masters,* p. 283)

Home Connection Children use an analog clock or watch to practice telling time. They change the hands on the clock or watch to practice reading various times.

Minute Math+

SMALL-GROUP ACTIVITY

Use *Minute Math+,* pages 73, 83, and 111 to provide practice with time and number stories.

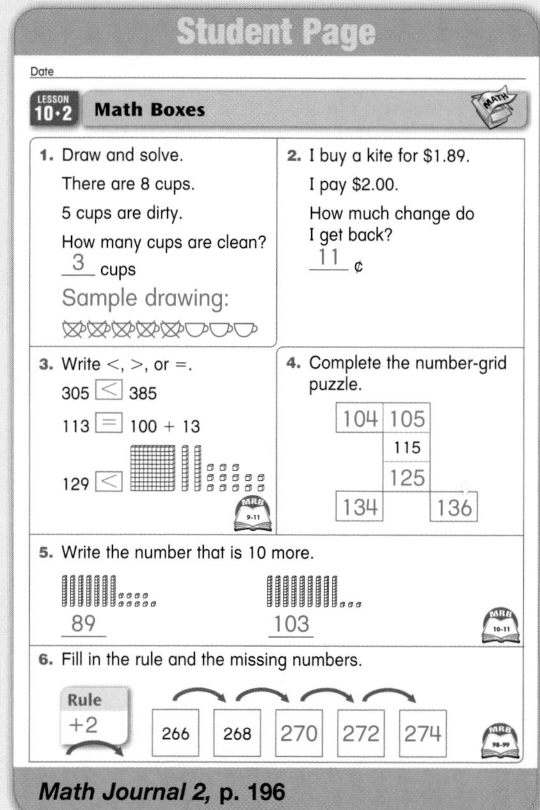

Student Page

Date

LESSON 10·2 **Math Boxes**

1. Draw and solve.
There are 8 cups.
5 cups are dirty.
How many cups are clean?
3 cups
Sample drawing:

2. I buy a kite for $1.89.
I pay $2.00.
How much change do I get back?
11 ¢

3. Write <, >, or =.
305 < 385
113 = 100 + 13
129 <

4. Complete the number-grid puzzle.
104, 105, 115, 125, 134, 136

5. Write the number that is 10 more.
89 103

6. Fill in the rule and the missing numbers.
Rule +2
266, 268, 270, 272, 274

Math Journal 2, p. 196

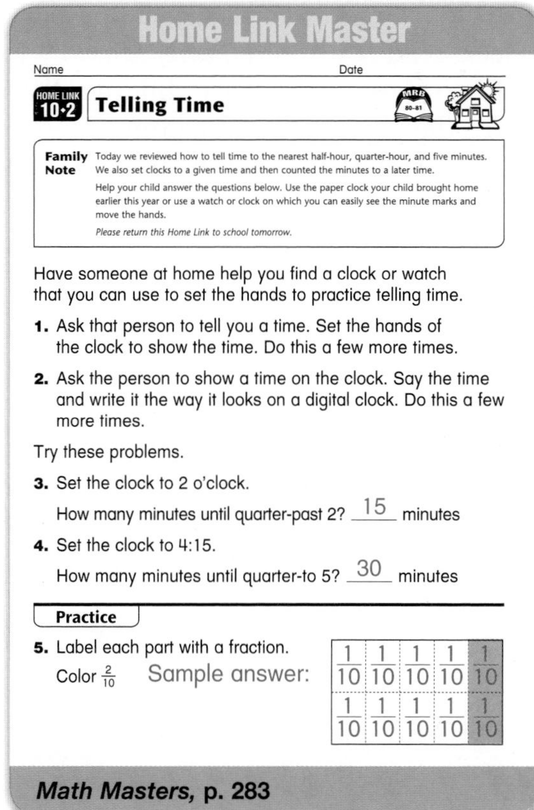

Home Link Master

Name Date

HOME LINK 10·2 **Telling Time**

Family Note Today we reviewed how to tell time to the nearest half-hour, quarter-hour, and five minutes. We also set clocks to a given time and then counted the minutes to a later time.
Help your child answer the questions below. Use the paper clock your child brought home earlier this year or use a watch or clock on which you can easily see the minute marks and move the hands.
Please return this Home Link to school tomorrow.

Have someone at home help you find a clock or watch that you can use to set the hands to practice telling time.

1. Ask that person to tell you a time. Set the hands of the clock to show the time. Do this a few more times.
2. Ask the person to show a time on the clock. Say the time and write it the way it looks on a digital clock. Do this a few more times.

Try these problems.

3. Set the clock to 2 o'clock.
How many minutes until quarter-past 2? 15 minutes
4. Set the clock to 4:15.
How many minutes until quarter-to 5? 30 minutes

Practice

5. Label each part with a fraction.
Color $\frac{2}{10}$ Sample answer:

$\frac{1}{10}$	$\frac{1}{10}$	$\frac{1}{10}$	$\frac{1}{10}$	$\frac{1}{10}$
$\frac{1}{10}$	$\frac{1}{10}$	$\frac{1}{10}$	$\frac{1}{10}$	$\frac{1}{10}$

Math Masters, p. 283

Teaching Master

Name ______________________ Date ______________

Elapsed Time

Use your tool-kit clock. Write the answers.

1. It is 11:15. Lunch is in a half-hour. What time is lunch? 11:45
2. It is 7:10. The bus will pick you up in 20 minutes. What time will the bus come? 7:30
3. It is 10:15. Your math class begins at 11:00. How many minutes until math class begins? 45 minutes
4. Your bedtime is at 9:00. It is 8:10. How many minutes until bedtime? 50 minutes

Try This

5. You go to bed at 9:00 P.M. You get up at 7:15 A.M. How long do you sleep? 10 hours and 15 minutes
6. Write and solve your own elapsed time problem. Answers vary.

Math Masters, p. 284

3 Differentiation Options

READINESS

WHOLE-CLASS ACTIVITY

▶ Telling Time on an Analog Clock

5–15 Min

To provide experience telling time, have children post stick-on notes labeled with various digital times as they appear on the classroom (or other designated) analog clock. Distribute at least one labeled stick-on note to each child. Children post their notes in a predetermined area and say the time aloud when the time on the note appears on the clock.

ENRICHMENT

INDEPENDENT ACTIVITY

▶ Calculating Elapsed Time

5–15 Min

(*Math Masters,* p. 284)

To apply their understanding of time concepts, children use their tool-kit clocks to determine elapsed time. Have children discuss how to solve the problems on *Math Masters*, page 284 before they actually determine the elapsed time. After children have completed the page, have them share their answers.

EXTRA PRACTICE

SMALL-GROUP ACTIVITY

▶ Reading About Time

5–15 Min

(*Math Masters,* p. 305)

Literature Link To provide practice telling time on an analog clock, read ***It's About Time, Max!*** by Kitty Richards. (The Kane Press, 2000) Have children choose something they do during the day. On an Exit Slip (*Math Masters*, page 305), have them draw the activity and tell the time they do it.

10•3 Mental Arithmetic: Using a Vending Machine Poster

Objectives To review showing amounts of money with coins and to provide experiences with solving number stories involving addition of 2-digit numbers.

Technology Resources www.everydaymathonline.com

ePresentations

eToolkit

Algorithms Practice

EM Facts Workshop Game™

Family Letters

Assessment Management

Common Core State Standards

Curriculum Focal Points

Interactive Teacher's Lesson Guide

1 Teaching the Lesson

Key Concepts and Skills

- Count forward by 25s, 10s, and 5s. [Number and Numeration Goal 1]
- Show amounts of money using combinations of quarters, dimes, and nickels. [Operations and Computation Goal 2]
- Use a variety of strategies to add and subtract 2-digit numbers. [Operations and Computation Goal 2]
- Tell, write, and solve number stories. [Operations and Computation Goal 4]
- Write addition and subtraction number sentences, using +, −, and =. [Patterns, Functions, and Algebra Goal 2]

Key Activities

Children show which coins they would use to purchase a single item from a vending machine. They show how much money they would need to purchase two or more items. They do a Buyer and Vendor activity.

Ongoing Assessment: Recognizing Student Achievement
Use Mental Math and Reflexes.
[Number and Numeration Goal 7]

Materials

Math Journal 2, pp. 197 and 198
Home Link 10•2
transparency of *Math Masters,* p. 285 (optional) ◆ tool-kit coins (at least 5 nickels, 10 dimes, and 2 quarters per child) ◆ base-10 blocks

2 Ongoing Learning & Practice

Graphing and Analyzing Data
Class Data Pad ◆ stick-on notes
Children count the number of pencils in their desks. They use the collected data to create a bar graph and to determine data landmarks.

Practicing with Fact Families
Math Masters, p. 286
Children use fact triangles to practice with fact family extensions.

Math Boxes 10•3
Math Journal 2, p. 199
Children practice and maintain skills through Math Box problems.

Home Link 10•3
Math Masters, p. 287
Children practice and maintain skills through Home Link activities.

3 Differentiation Options

READINESS

Counting Coins
per group: tool-kit coins, calculator
Children practice counting mixed collections of coins.

EXTRA PRACTICE

Playing *Coin-Dice*
per partnership: tool-kit coins, 2 dice
Children practice making coin exchanges.

Advance Preparation

***Teacher's Reference Manual,* Grades 1–3** pp. 120–126

Getting Started

Mental Math and Reflexes 

Dictate a pair of numbers. Have children write them on their slates with a space between the numbers. Then have children write <, >, or = in the space to compare them.

●○○ 23, 32 < ; 45, 67 < ; 93, 89 >
●●○ 77, 97 < ; 103, 31 > ; 111, 111 =
●●● 390, 309 > ; 199, 229 < ; 575, 475 >

Math Message

A bag of sunflower seeds costs $0.60. Draw coin symbols to show one way to pay for them. Use Ⓠ, Ⓓ, *and* Ⓝ.

Home Link 10·2 Follow-Up

Briefly go over the answers.

Ongoing Assessment: Recognizing Student Achievement

Mental Math and Reflexes 

Use **Mental Math and Reflexes** to assess children's ability to compare numbers. Children are making adequate progress if they are able to compare the numbers in the first two sets of problems. Some children may be able to compare the numbers in the third set.

[Number and Numeration Goal 7]

1 Teaching the Lesson

▶ Math Message Follow-Up

WHOLE-CLASS DISCUSSION

Children share different ways to make 60 cents.

▶ Using Coin Combinations to Make Purchases

WHOLE-CLASS ACTIVITY

(*Math Journal 2,* p. 197; *Math Masters,* p. 285)

Ask children if they have ever bought food from a vending machine and, if so, how they knew how much each item cost. After children share their responses, display the overhead transparency of the Vending Machine Poster (*Math Masters,* page 285). Have children turn to the poster on journal page 197 to show how they would find the price of an item in the vending machine.

Suggest or have children select an item to buy from the vending machine. Children use tool-kit coins to show the exact coins they would use to pay for the item. Repeat the activity as needed.

Adjusting the Activity

Before beginning the activity, discuss all of the items on the Vending Machine Poster.

AUDITORY ◆ KINESTHETIC ◆ TACTILE ◆ VISUAL

Student Page

Date

LESSON 10·3 **Vending Machine Poster**

Snacks

CRACKERS, PEANUTS, PRETZELS, JELLY BEANS, JELLY BEANS, COOKIES

30¢ 55¢ 65¢ 45¢ 50¢

CORN CHIPS, GRANOLA, SUNFLOWER SEEDS, MINTS, MINTS, GUM

75¢ 40¢ 60¢ 35¢ 25¢

5¢ 10¢ 25¢

$1.00

A B C D E F G H I J

Push Open for Your Selection.

Change Coin Return

Math Journal 2, p. 197

Adding 2-Digit Vending Machine Prices

(*Math Journal 2,* p. 197)

Using the items and prices shown on the poster, model stories that involve two or more items. For example, *I want to buy a granola bar and a bag of sunflower seeds. How much money do I need?* Then ask children to create their own number stories.

For each number story, children share and discuss their strategies. Encourage the use of mental arithmetic, coins, the number line, the number grid, or base-10 blocks to work out solutions. For at least one number story, have children model the prices using base-10 blocks. For instance, children may model the prices of the pretzels (65¢; or 6 longs, 5 cubes) and the gum (25¢; or 2 longs, 5 cubes). Remind children to add tens to tens and ones to ones, composing a new 10 from the ones if necessary. Write number models and draw situation diagrams for selected problems.

If children exhibit success with the addition problems, consider posing some 2-digit subtraction problems. For instance, ask children how much more the sunflower seeds cost than the granola bars. Remind children that they can count up (from 40¢ to 60¢) to subtract.

NOTE Change the number of items and the prices as appropriate to keep interest high and the activity challenging.

Doing a Buyer and Vendor Activity

(*Math Journal 2,* pp. 197 and 198)

Partners combine their tool-kit nickels, dimes, and quarters. If children are missing coins, supply additional coins from the class money supply.

Partners take turns being the "buyer" and the "vending machine." The buyer gives the vending machine the exact amount in coins to purchase an item. The vending machine determines if the coins equal the correct amount. Each buyer records his or her purchases in Problems 1–4 on journal page 198.

Student Page

Date

LESSON 10·3 **Buying from the Vending Machine**

Pretend to buy items from the vending machine. Draw pictures or write the names of items you buy. Show the coins you use to pay for the items. Use Ⓝ, Ⓓ, and Ⓠ. Write the total cost.

1. 2.

Answers vary for Exercises 1–4.

3. 4.

Show the cost of these items. Use Ⓝ, Ⓓ, and Ⓠ. Write the total cost. Sample answers:

5. PRETZELS, JELLY BEANS
ⓆⓆⒹⓃ ⒹⒹⒹⒹⓃ
Total cost: $ 1.10

6. GRANOLA, MINTS
ⓆⒹⓃ ⓆⒹ
Total cost: $ 0.75

Math Journal 2, p. 198

Teaching Master

Name _______________ Date _______________

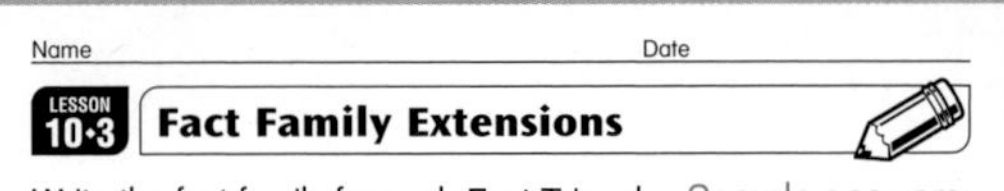

LESSON 10·3 **Fact Family Extensions**

Write the fact family for each Fact Triangle. Sample answers:

1.

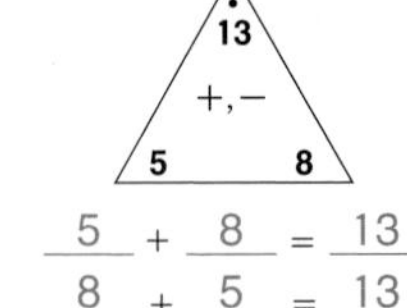

5 + 8 = 13
8 + 5 = 13
13 − 5 = 8
13 − 8 = 5

2.

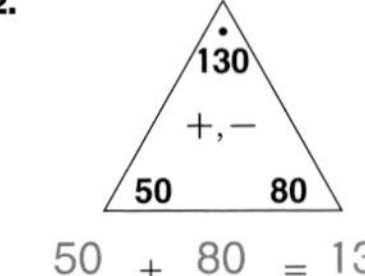

50 + 80 = 130
80 + 50 = 130
130 − 50 = 80
130 − 80 = 50

3.

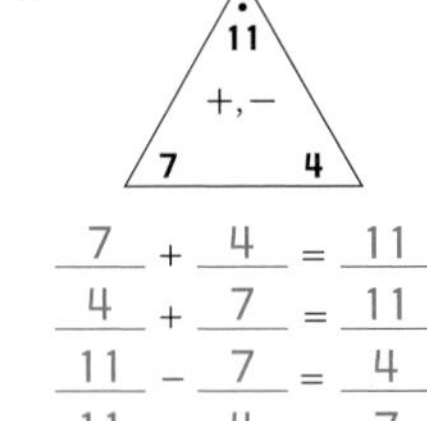

7 + 4 = 11
4 + 7 = 11
11 − 7 = 4
11 − 4 = 7

4.

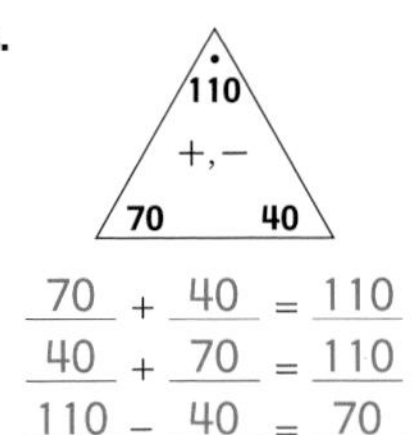

70 + 40 = 110
40 + 70 = 110
110 − 40 = 70
110 − 70 = 40

Math Masters, p. 286

Student Page

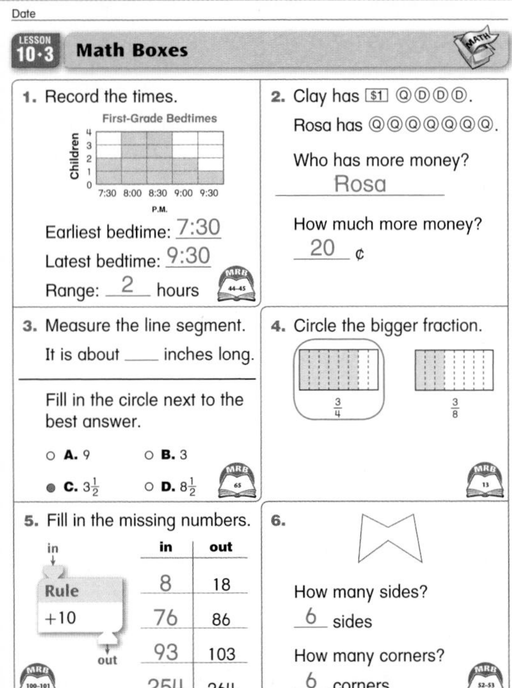

Date _______________

LESSON 10·3 **Math Boxes**

1. Record the times.

First-Grade Bedtimes

Earliest bedtime: 7:30
Latest bedtime: 9:30
Range: 2 hours

2. Clay has $1 Ⓠ Ⓓ Ⓓ Ⓓ.
Rosa has Ⓠ Ⓠ Ⓠ Ⓠ Ⓠ Ⓠ.
Who has more money? Rosa
How much more money? 20 ¢

3. Measure the line segment.
It is about ___ inches long.
Fill in the circle next to the best answer.
○ A. 9 ○ B. 3
● C. $3\frac{1}{2}$ ○ D. $8\frac{1}{2}$

4. Circle the bigger fraction.
$\frac{3}{4}$ $\frac{3}{8}$

5. Fill in the missing numbers.

Rule: +10

in	out
8	18
76	86
93	103
254	264

6. How many sides? 6 sides
How many corners? 6 corners

Math Journal 2, p. 199

2 Ongoing Learning & Practice

▶ Graphing and Analyzing Data

WHOLE-CLASS ACTIVITY

Ask children to record on stick-on notes how many pencils they have in their desks. Explain that they will use the information to make a bar graph showing the number of pencils in each child's desk. Children have seen and worked through many data routines this year. In this lesson, it is their turn to show you what they know. Scribe on the Class Data Pad as the class works together to create a bar graph. Guide children in determining what label should be on each axis and how to title the graph. Once the bar graph is complete, have children work with a partner or small group to determine the minimum, maximum, and middle values, as well as the range.

▶ Practicing with Fact Families

INDEPENDENT ACTIVITY

FACTS PRACTICE

(*Math Masters,* p. 286)

Use *Math Masters,* page 286 to provide practice with fact family extensions.

▶ Math Boxes 10·3

INDEPENDENT ACTIVITY

(*Math Journal 2,* p. 199)

Mixed Practice Math Boxes in this lesson are paired with Math Boxes in Lesson 10-1.

Writing/Reasoning Have children draw, write, or verbalize an answer to the following question: *How do you add 10 to a number?* A reasonable answer should explain an addition strategy such as using base-10 blocks, the number grid, or counting on.

▶ Home Link 10·3

INDEPENDENT ACTIVITY

(*Math Masters,* p. 287)

Home Connection Children use pictures to solve number stories.

3 Differentiation Options

READINESS

SMALL-GROUP ACTIVITY

▶ Counting Coins

5–15 Min

To provide experience counting combinations of coins, have children count collections of quarters, dimes, and nickels and then find the total of all of the coins. Children take a small, random handful of tool-kit coins. They separate the coins into groups of quarters, dimes, and nickels and then find and record on a half-sheet of paper a total for each group of coins. Children then find the total of *all* of the coins and record on the half-sheet of paper a number sentence for the grand total. Encourage children to use calculator counts to check their totals.

EXTRA PRACTICE

PARTNER ACTIVITY

▶ Playing *Coin-Dice*

5–15 Min

Children practice making coin exchanges by playing *Coin-Dice*. Add quarters if appropriate for children. For detailed instructions, see Lesson 3-12.

Planning Ahead

For the optional Enrichment activity in Part 3 of Lesson 10-4, you will need a collection of advertisements from magazines, catalogs, and newspapers showing prices that are appropriate for children's computational skills.

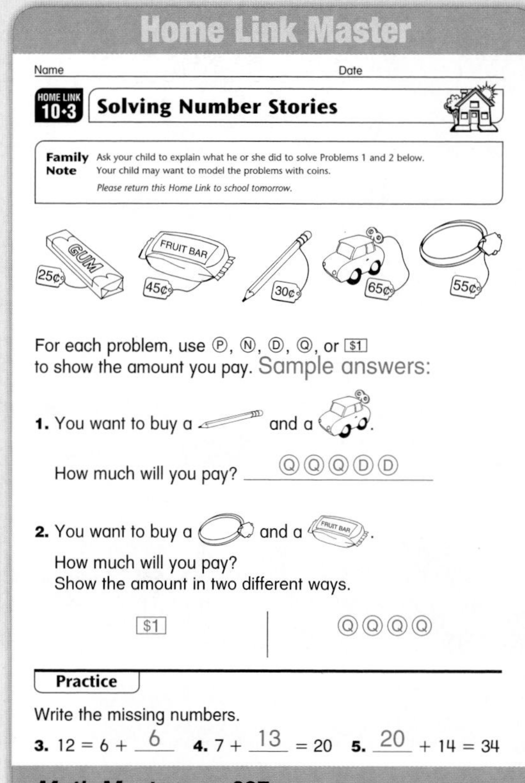

Home Link Master

Name Date

HOME LINK 10·3 **Solving Number Stories**

Family Note Ask your child to explain what he or she did to solve Problems 1 and 2 below. Your child may want to model the problems with coins.

Please return this Home Link to school tomorrow.

For each problem, use Ⓟ, Ⓝ, Ⓓ, Ⓠ, or $1 to show the amount you pay. Sample answers:

1. You want to buy a pencil and a car.

How much will you pay? Ⓠ Ⓠ Ⓠ Ⓓ Ⓓ

2. You want to buy a ring and a fruit bar.

How much will you pay?
Show the amount in two different ways.

$1	Ⓠ Ⓠ Ⓠ Ⓠ

Practice

Write the missing numbers.

3. 12 = 6 + 6 **4.** 7 + 13 = 20 **5.** 20 + 14 = 34

Math Masters, p. 287

10•4 Mental Arithmetic (Continued)

Objective To provide experience solving comparison number stories and calculating amounts of change from purchases.

Technology Resources www.everydaymathonline.com

ePresentations

eToolkit

Algorithms Practice

EM Facts Workshop Game™

Family Letters

Assessment Management

Common Core State Standards

Curriculum Focal Points

Interactive Teacher's Lesson Guide

1 Teaching the Lesson

Key Concepts and Skills

- Count forward by 25s, 10s, and 5s.
  [Number and Numeration Goal 1]
- Compare quantities.
  [Number and Numeration Goal 7]
- Add and subtract multiples of 10 using base-10 blocks.
  [Operations and Computation Goal 2]
- Solve comparison number stories.
  [Operations and Computation Goal 4]
- Identify money equivalencies.
  [Measurement and Reference Frames Goal 2]

Key Activities

Children use the Vending Machine Poster to make up and solve comparison number stories that pose questions such as "How much more (or less)?" and "How much change?" They do a variation of the Buyer and Vendor activity in which the buyer does not pay with exact change.

Ongoing Assessment: Informing Instruction See page 818.

Materials

Math Journal 2, p. 197
Home Link 10•3
transparency of *Math Masters,* p. 285 (optional) ◆ slate ◆ tool-kit coins and dollar bills ◆ overhead base-10 blocks (optional) ◆ base-10 blocks (optional)

2 Ongoing Learning & Practice

Playing *$1, $10, $100 Exchange Game*
Math Masters, pp. 331–334
per partnership: 2 dice ◆ scissors
Children practice exchanging ten $1 bills for one $10 bill, and ten $10 bills for one $100 bill.

Math Boxes 10•4
Math Journal 2, p. 200
Children practice and maintain skills through Math Box problems.

Ongoing Assessment: Recognizing Student Achievement
Use Math Boxes, Problem 2.
[Operations and Computation Goal 2]

Home Link 10•4
Math Masters, p. 288
Children practice and maintain skills through Home Link activities.

Minute Math+
Minute Math®+, pp. 81, 93, and 99
Children practice with number stories.

3 Differentiation Options

READINESS
Comparing Pennies
per partnership: tool-kit coins
Children compare quantities of pennies.

ENRICHMENT
Creating and Solving Number Stories
magazine or newspaper ads
Children create and solve number stories based on ads from magazines and newspapers.

EXTRA PRACTICE
Playing *Dime-Nickel-Penny Grab*
Math Masters, p. 342
tool-kit coins
Children practice making money exchanges.

ELL SUPPORT
Building a Math Word Bank
Differentiation Handbook, p. 126
Children add the terms *change* and *making change* to their Math Word Banks.

Advance Preparation

For the optional Enrichment activity in Part 3, collect advertisements from magazines, catalogs, and newspapers showing prices that are appropriate for children's number stories.

Getting Started

Mental Math and Reflexes

Show or draw a set of longs and cubes on the overhead or board. Children write the number represented by the base-10 blocks on their slates. Then change the number by multiples of 10. Encourage children to use base-10 blocks from their kits; they may add and subtract longs to find the new number and write it on their slates. Remind children to add tens to tens and ones to ones, only composing a new ten when needed. Continue with additional problems. Ask: *How can we find the new number without counting the base-10 blocks?* Sample answer: Increase or decrease the digit in the tens place by the number of longs that were added or removed.

Math Message

Look at the vending machine on journal page 197. Draw two of your favorite snacks. Then draw the coins you need to buy the snacks. Use Ⓠ, Ⓓ, and Ⓝ.

Home Link 10·3 Follow-Up

Briefly review the answers to the problems. Have children show coins on the overhead or draw coins on the board to show their solutions.

1 Teaching the Lesson

▶ Math Message Follow-Up

WHOLE-CLASS DISCUSSION

Review several purchases. Then discuss the amounts of money needed to purchase two or more items from the vending machine.

▶ Comparing Prices

WHOLE-CLASS DISCUSSION

(*Math Journal 2,* p. 197; *Math Masters,* p. 285)

Use a transparency of *Math Masters,* page 285 or journal page 197 to refer to the vending machine. Model number stories that compare the prices of items in the vending machine. For example: *How much less do the crackers cost than the corn chips?* 45¢ *Will two boxes of mints cost more or less than one bag of corn chips?* less *How much less?* 5¢

Children then pose and solve similar comparison number stories. Encourage them to solve the problems mentally. They share solution strategies, using coins to model the solutions.

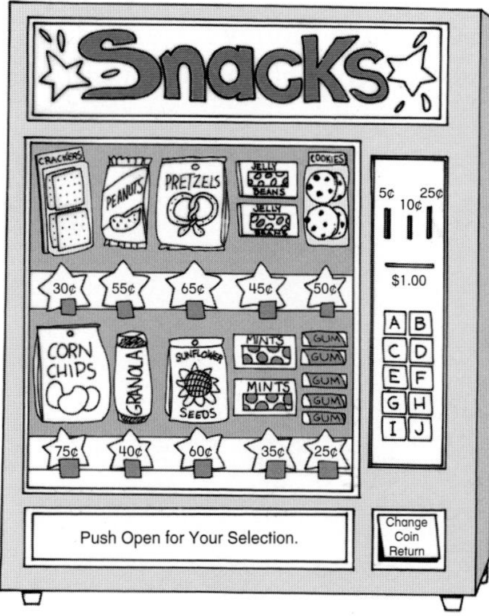

Vending Machine Poster from *Math Journal 2,* page 197 and *Math Masters,* page 285

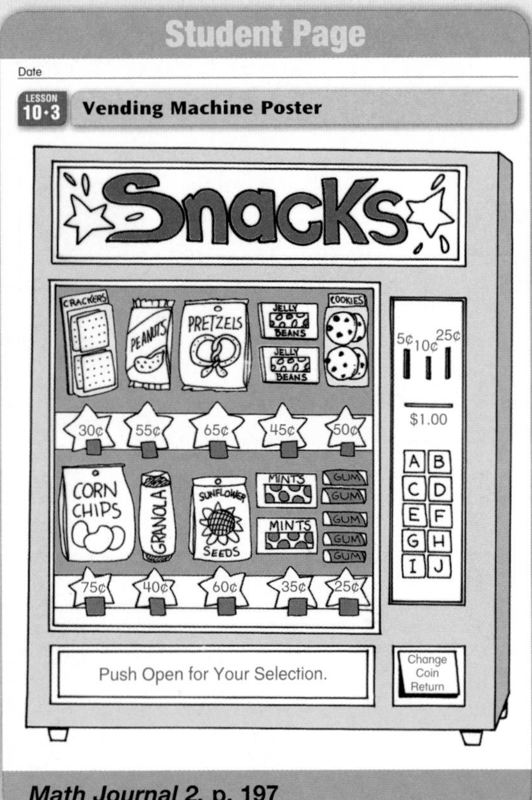

Math Journal 2, p. 197

Making Change

WHOLE-CLASS ACTIVITY

(*Math Journal 2,* p. 197)

Ask children what happens when you do not put the exact amount of money into a vending machine. Explain that today during math class they will explore making change while doing a variation of the Buyer and Vendor activity.

Pretend that the exact coins are not available to purchase an item from the vending machine. Model number stories that ask: "How much change will you get?" For example: *Tim has 2 quarters. He wants to buy a granola bar. Does he have enough money?* yes *How much change will he get back?* 10¢ *Which coins might he get back?* 1 dime or 2 nickels

Have children pose and solve similar number stories and share solution strategies. Encourage them to act out transactions, using tool-kit coins.

Ongoing Assessment: Informing Instruction

Watch for children who make change by counting up by 1s instead of by 5s and 10s. Remind them that the vending machine uses only quarters, dimes, and nickels.

Adjusting the Activity

Have children use a $1 bill to pay for an item; this requires them to make change for $1. Or, have them count up by 25s (quarters), as well as by 10s and by 5s.

AUDITORY ◆ KINESTHETIC ◆ TACTILE ◆ VISUAL

Making Change

PARTNER ACTIVITY

(*Math Journal 2,* p. 197)

Using money from their tool kits, partners take turns being the buyer and the vending machine. The buyer may put in either the correct amount or too much money for an item. The vending machine determines whether change should to be returned and, if so, how much.

2 Ongoing Learning & Practice

▶ Playing *$1, $10, $100 Exchange Game*

PARTNER ACTIVITY

15–30 Min

(*Math Masters,* pp. 331–334)

Explain that the *$1, $10, $100 Exchange Game* is similar to the *One-Dollar Exchange Game* that children learned in Unit 8. In this version of the game, children exchange ten $1 bills for one $10 bill, and ten $10 bills for one $100 bill.

Players use play money, two dice, and a Place-Value Mat (*Math Masters,* page 333). Ask children to cut out the play money from copies of *Math Masters,* pages 331, 332, and 334. Have players pool their money to begin the game. The bank starts with one $100 bill, twenty $10 bills, and twenty $1 bills. The first player to make an exchange for $100 is the winner.

NOTE Some children may ask about the penny and dime "names" for $1, $10, and $100 on the Place-Value Mat, and cents names on the play money bills. Children are not expected to learn and remember these equivalents, except that 100 pennies and 10 dimes both are equal to one dollar.

One Hundred Dollars $100 10,000 pennies 1,000 dimes	Ten Dollars $10 1,000 pennies 100 dimes	One Dollar $1 100 pennies 10 dimes

Place-Value Mat for $1, $10, $100 from *Math Masters,* page 333

▶ Math Boxes 10•4

INDEPENDENT ACTIVITY

(*Math Journal 2,* p. 200)

Mixed Practice Math Boxes in this lesson are linked to Math Boxes in Lessons 10-2 and 10-6.

Ongoing Assessment: Recognizing Student Achievement

Math Boxes Problem 2

Use **Math Boxes, Problem 2** to assess children's ability to find differences between amounts of money. Children are making adequate progress if they are able to determine the difference between two amounts of money.

[Operations and Computation Goal 2]

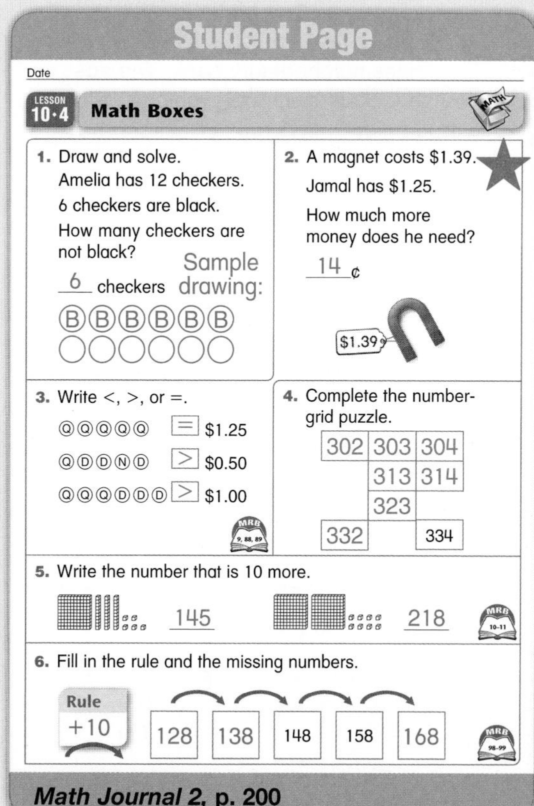

Student Page

Date

LESSON 10•4 **Math Boxes**

1. Draw and solve.
Amelia has 12 checkers.
6 checkers are black.
How many checkers are not black?
6 checkers
Sample drawing:
Ⓑ Ⓑ Ⓑ Ⓑ Ⓑ Ⓑ
○ ○ ○ ○ ○ ○

2. A magnet costs $1.39.
Jamal has $1.25.
How much more money does he need?
14 ¢
$1.39

3. Write <, >, or =.
ⓆⓆⓆⓆⓆ = $1.25
ⓆⒹⒹⓃⒹ > $0.50
ⓆⓆⓆⒹⒹⒹ > $1.00

4. Complete the number-grid puzzle.
302 303 304
313 314
323
332 334

5. Write the number that is 10 more.
145
218

6. Fill in the rule and the missing numbers.
Rule +10
128 138 148 158 168

Math Journal 2, p. 200

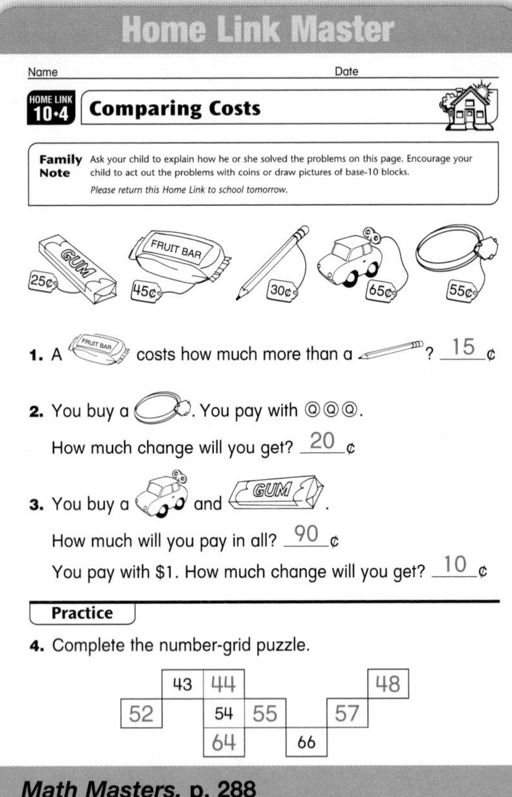
Home Link Master

Name Date

HOME LINK 10·4 **Comparing Costs**

Family Note Ask your child to explain how he or she solved the problems on this page. Encourage your child to act out the problems with coins or draw pictures of base-10 blocks.

Please return this Home Link to school tomorrow.

GUM 25¢ FRUIT BAR 45¢ 30¢ 65¢ 55¢

1. A [fruit bar] costs how much more than a [pencil]? 15 ¢

2. You buy a [yo-yo]. You pay with Ⓠ Ⓠ Ⓠ.
   How much change will you get? 20 ¢

3. You buy a [car] and [GUM].
   How much will you pay in all? 90 ¢
   You pay with $1. How much change will you get? 10 ¢

Practice

4. Complete the number-grid puzzle.

		43	44			48
52		54	55		57	
		64		66		

Math Masters, p. 288

Language Arts Link Consider adding these number stories to your class number-story book. The ads should be included with the problems, or children can draw pictures to illustrate their stories.

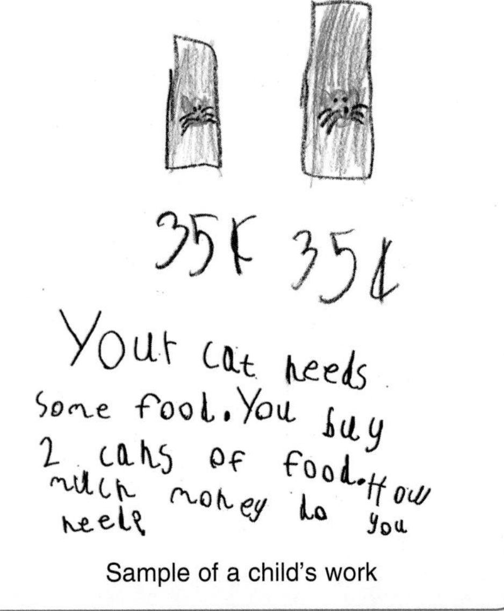

Sample of a child's work

▶ Home Link 10·4

INDEPENDENT ACTIVITY

(*Math Masters,* p. 288)

Home Connection Children solve number stories involving comparisons and making change. They are encouraged to act out the problems with coins or by drawing pictures of base-10 blocks.

▶ *Minute Math+*

SMALL-GROUP ACTIVITY

Use *Minute Math+,* pages 81, 93, and 99 to provide practice with number stories.

3 Differentiation Options

READINESS

PARTNER ACTIVITY

▶ Comparing Pennies

5–15 Min

To explore comparing money amounts using a concrete model, have children grab handfuls of pennies and compare their totals by lining up the pennies. Children each grab a small handful of pennies. They predict who has more and line up their pennies next to each other to do a one-to-one comparison. On a half-sheet of paper, have children draw a picture to record what they did. They might draw circles to represent the pennies and label their individual amounts as well as the difference. Encourage children to write a number sentence to represent the difference between their penny totals.

ENRICHMENT

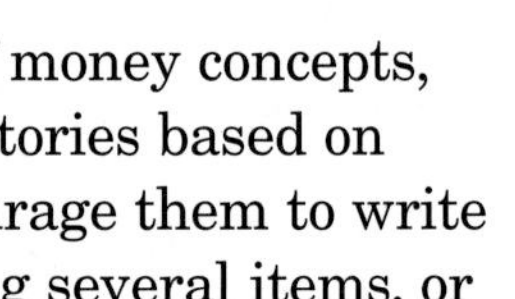

INDEPENDENT ACTIVITY

▶ Creating and Solving Number Stories

30+ Min

Portfolio Ideas

To apply children's understanding of money concepts, have them write and solve number stories based on magazine and newspaper ads. Encourage them to write comparison stories, stories that involve buying several items, or stories that require making change. Children can use coins to act out solutions.

EXTRA PRACTICE

PARTNER ACTIVITY

▶ Playing *Dime-Nickel-Penny Grab*

5–15 Min

(*Math Masters,* p. 342)

Children practice making money exchanges by playing *Dime-Nickel-Penny Grab.* For detailed instructions, see Lesson 3-13.

ELL SUPPORT

SMALL-GROUP ACTIVITY

▶ Building a Math Word Bank

5–15 Min

(*Differentiation Handbook,* p. 126)

To provide language support for money, have children use the Word Bank Template found on *Differentiation Handbook,* page 126. Ask children to write the terms *change* and *making change*, draw pictures representing the terms, and write other words that describe them. See the *Differentiation Handbook* for more information.

Game Master

Name Date

***Dime-Nickel-Penny Grab* Record Sheet**

1. Draw your coins in the chart using Ⓓ, Ⓝ, and Ⓟ.
2. Record your total.
3. Record your partner's total.
4. Circle the greater number of cents in each round.

	Dimes Ⓓ	Nickels Ⓝ	Pennies Ⓟ	My Total	My Partner's Total
Round 1					
Round 2					
Round 3					
Round 4					
Round 5					
Round 6					
Round 7					

Math Masters, p. 342

10•5 Year-End Geometry Review

Objective To review the names and some of the characteristics of polygons, as well as the names of basic 3-dimensional shapes.

www.everydaymathonline.com

ePresentations

eToolkit

Algorithms Practice

EM Facts Workshop Game™

Family Letters

Assessment Management

Common Core State Standards

Curriculum Focal Points

Interactive Teacher's Lesson Guide

1 Teaching the Lesson

Key Concepts and Skills

- Name, model, and describe plane shapes using straws and twist-ties. [Geometry Goal 1]
- Name, model, and describe solid figures. [Geometry Goal 1]
- Identify and describe attributes of plane shapes and solid figures. [Geometry Goal 1]

Key Activities

Children review characteristics of polygons and defining and non-defining attributes of shapes. They construct polygons out of straws and twist-ties. Children identify and model 3-dimensional shapes.

Ongoing Assessment: Recognizing Student Achievement Use Mental Math and Reflexes. [Operations and Computation Goal 3]

Materials

Math Journal 2, pp. 201–203
Math Masters, pp. 212A, 212B, 288A, and 288B
Home Link 10•4
per child: 10 long straws, 10 short straws, and 20 twist-ties ◆ scissors ◆ tape ◆ stickers ◆ markers ◆ glue ◆ craft supplies

2 Ongoing Learning & Practice

Playing *Time Match*
Math Masters, pp. 354, 355, and 359
My Reference Book, pp. 152 and 153
Children practice telling time on digital and analog clocks.

Math Boxes 10•5
Math Journal 2, p. 204
Children practice and maintain skills through Math Box problems.

Home Link 10•5
Math Masters, p. 289
Children practice and maintain skills through Home Link activities.

3 Differentiation Options

READINESS

Reviewing Polygons and 3-Dimensional Shapes
Children play *I Spy* to review characteristics of 2- and 3-dimensional shapes.

ENRICHMENT

Constructing Regular Polyhedrons
Math Journal 2, p. 203
models of regular polyhedrons ◆ straws ◆ twist-ties
Children construct regular polyhedrons out of straws and twist-ties.

ELL SUPPORT

Comparing 2- and 3-Dimensional Shapes
Children compare and contrast 2- and 3-dimensional shapes.

Advance Preparation

For Part 1, display some 2- and 3-dimensional items from the Shapes Museum. Place straws and twist-ties in containers near the Math Message. Using heavy construction paper or another firm paper (the firmer, the better), copy one set of *Math Masters,* pages 212A, 212B, 288A, and 288B for each partnership. Gather stickers, markers, glue, and other craft supplies, so that children may decorate their solids. You may wish to locate the book ***Color Zoo*** by Lois Ehlert (J.B. Lippincott, 1989) as it relates to lesson content.

***Teacher's Reference Manual,* Grades 1–3** p. 153

Getting Started

Mental Math and Reflexes ★

Write two amounts of money on the board. Children show "thumbs-up" if they estimate that the sum is more than $1, "thumbs-down" if they estimate that the sum is less than $1, and a "fist" if they estimate that the sum is equal to $1. *Suggestions:*

●○○ 10¢ and 50¢; 25¢ and 75¢; 90¢ and 35¢

●●○ 45¢ and 45¢; 70¢ and 30¢; 5¢ and 80¢

●●● 31¢ and 65¢; 47¢ and 47¢; 89¢ and 29¢

Math Message

Take 10 long straws, 10 short straws, and 20 twist-ties. Find some triangles and other polygons in the room.

Home Link 10•4 Follow-Up

Have volunteers share their strategies for solving the problems. Expect a variety of solution strategies.

Ongoing Assessment: Recognizing Student Achievement

Mental Math and Reflexes ★

Use **Mental Math and Reflexes** to assess children's ability to estimate sums. Children are making adequate progress if they are able to correctly estimate whether sums in the first set are greater than, less than, or equal to $1. Some children may be able to correctly estimate the sums in the second and third sets.

[Operations and Computation Goal 3]

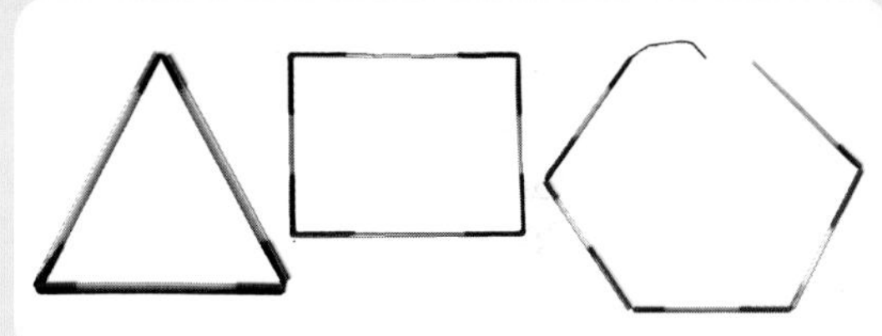

Examples of constructions from straws and twist-ties

1 Teaching the Lesson

▶ Math Message Follow-Up

WHOLE-CLASS DISCUSSION

Children identify triangles and other polygons they found. Review the key characteristics of polygons that are given in the following activity.

▶ Constructing Polygons out of Straws and Twist-Ties

PARTNER ACTIVITY

PROBLEM SOLVING

(*Math Journal 2,* pp. 201 and 202)

Direct children's attention to journal page 201. Review the characteristics of polygons:

▷ Polygons are made up of straight sides.

▷ The corner of a polygon is where two sides meet.

▷ Sides meet only at their ends.

▷ The sides are connnected—there aren't any gaps.

Bring out the chart paper with Defining and Non-Defining Attributes of Triangles and Squares from Lesson 7-4. Have children look at the Triangles section of journal page 201. Triangles are polygons so they must have all the attributes of polygons. Ask children if any of the attributes of polygons are

Student Page

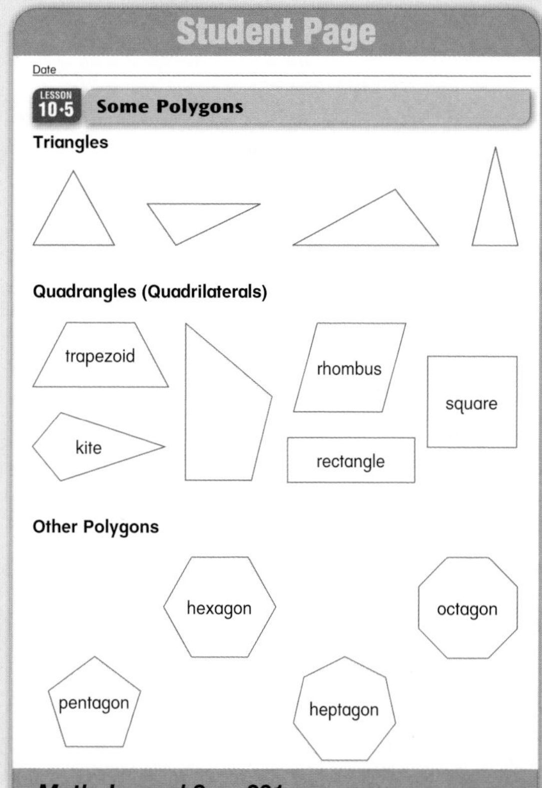

Math Journal 2, p. 201

Student Page

Date

LESSON 10·5 **Reviewing Polygons**

Use straws and twist-ties to make the following polygons. Draw the polygons. Record the number of corners and sides for each polygon. Sample drawings are given for Exercises 1–3.

1. Make a square.
   Number of sides 4
   Number of corners 4
2. Make a triangle.
   Number of sides 3
   Number of corners 3
3. Make a hexagon.
   Number of sides 6
   Number of corners 6
4. Make a polygon of your choice. Answers vary.
   Write its name. ______
   Number of sides ______
   Number of corners ______
5. Make another polygon of your choice. Answers vary.
   Write its name. ______
   Number of sides ______
   Number of corners ______

Math Journal 2, p. 202

Student Page

Date

LESSON 10·5 **Reviewing 3-Dimensional Shapes**

Word Bank		
sphere	rectangular prism	pyramid
cube	cone	cylinder

Write the name of each 3-dimensional shape.

1. cone
2. cube
3. rectangular prism
4. sphere
5. pyramid
6. cylinder

Five Regular Polyhedrons

The faces that make each shape are identical.

tetrahedron 4 faces | cube 6 faces | octahedron 8 faces | dodecahedron 12 faces | icosahedron 20 faces

Math Journal 2, p. 203

missing from their list of triangle attributes and put those on the chart. Next, direct their attention to the Quadrangles section of journal page 201 and the Defining Attributes of Squares list on the chart paper. Ask:

- Is the kite a square? Why or why not? Sample answer: No. Its sides aren't the same lengths and the corners look different.
- Is the rectangle on this page a square? Sample answer: No. Even though the corners all look the same, there is one set of long sides and one set of short sides so the sides aren't all the same length.
- How is the hexagon on this page like triangles and squares? How is it different? Sample answer: Triangles have 3 sides, squares have 4 sides each, and the hexagon has 6 sides, but they are all polygons with the traits of polygons.

Explain that even though the hexagon on their journal page has corners that all look the same and sides that are the same length, the defining attribute of a hexagon is that it is a polygon with 6 sides. The sides and corners do not have to be the same.

Working with a partner, children construct polygons and answer questions on journal page 202. Each partnership should construct a square, a triangle, a hexagon, and 2 or more other polygons. Remind children that when they construct the hexagon, it does not have to look exactly like the hexagon on journal page 201. While children work on their polygons, you may wish to ask them to construct a quadrangle that is NOT a square for one of their choice polygons and indicate which defining attributes it is missing.

▶ Reviewing the Names of 3-Dimensional Shapes

INDEPENDENT ACTIVITY

(*Math Journal 2,* p. 203)

Children write the names of six 3-dimensional shapes.

Review the names after children have completed journal page 203. Discuss the characteristics of each shape: flat versus curved surfaces, number of faces, and number of corners. Then discuss the polyhedrons at the bottom of the page. Explain that all of the faces on each shape are the same. Ask questions such as: *What shape makes up the octahedron?* triangles This portion of the page will be used for the optional Enrichment activity in Part 3.

▶ Constructing Solids

SMALL-GROUP ACTIVITY

(*Math Masters,* pp. 212A, 212B, 288A, 288B)

Tell children that they will be working in pairs to make cubes, rectangular prisms, cylinders, and cones. They will then work in small groups using these shapes to create larger figures. Begin by demonstrating how to cut and fold each template to construct the solids (see directions on pages 647 and 651 for constructing the cylinder and the cone, respectively). Provide each partnership with scissors, tape, and templates for each solid from *Math Masters,* pages 212A, 212B, 288A, and 288B.

After children have made the solids, have them work in small groups to combine their solids into new, composite figures. For instance, children may tape their solids together to make a figure that looks like a castle. Small groups may divide the work by having pairs of children work together to make a composite figure and then combining the pairs' composite figures into a new shape. Provide children with stickers, markers, glue, and craft supplies (such as felt and buttons) to decorate their figures, and model for children how to decorate the hollow figures gently. Add completed figures to the Shapes Museum.

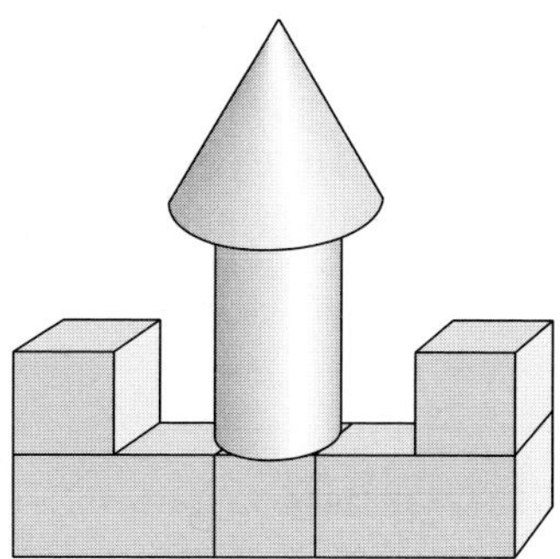

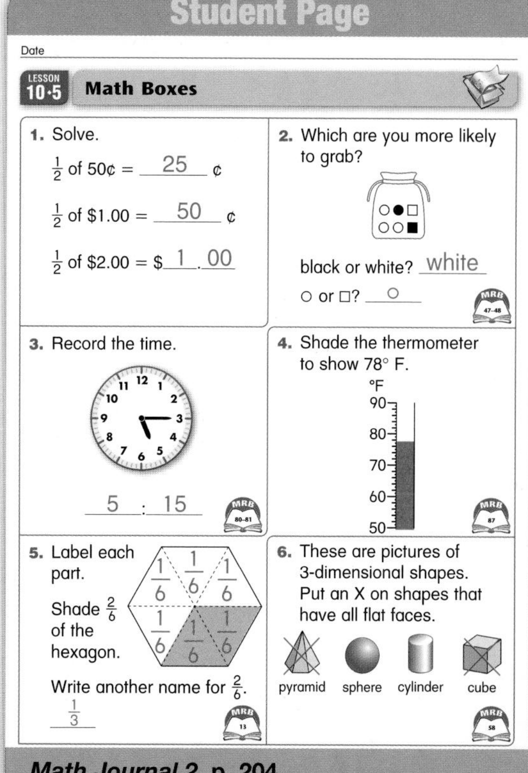

Student Page

Date

LESSON 10•5 **Math Boxes**

1. Solve.
$\frac{1}{2}$ of 50¢ = 25 ¢
$\frac{1}{2}$ of \$1.00 = 50 ¢
$\frac{1}{2}$ of \$2.00 = \$1.00

2. Which are you more likely to grab?
black or white? white
○ or □? ○

3. Record the time.
5 : 15

4. Shade the thermometer to show 78° F.

5. Label each part.
Shade $\frac{2}{6}$ of the hexagon.
Write another name for $\frac{2}{6}$. $\frac{1}{3}$

6. These are pictures of 3-dimensional shapes. Put an X on shapes that have all flat faces.
pyramid sphere cylinder cube

Math Journal 2, p. 204

NOTE Decorating the hollow figures may be difficult for some children. Have them use firm paper to construct the solids and decorate them with stickers and craft materials that may be gently glued onto the figures.

2 Ongoing Learning & Practice

▶ Playing *Time Match*

PARTNER ACTIVITY

(*Math Masters,* pp. 354, 355, and 359; *My Reference Book,* pp. 152 and 153)

Children play *Time Match* to practice telling time using digital and analog clocks. For detailed instructions, see Lesson 4-4.

▶ Math Boxes 10•5

INDEPENDENT ACTIVITY

(*Math Journal 2,* p. 204)

Mixed Practice Math Boxes in this lesson are paired with Math Boxes in Lesson 10-7.

▶ Home Link 10•5

INDEPENDENT ACTIVITY

(*Math Masters,* p. 289)

Home Connection Children identify polygons with names from a Word List and solve polygon riddles.

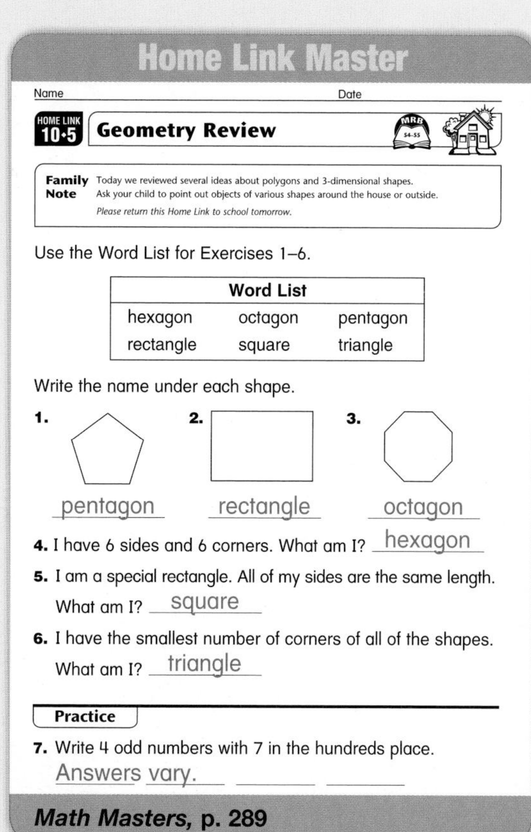

Home Link Master

Name Date

HOME LINK 10•5 **Geometry Review**

Family Note Today we reviewed several ideas about polygons and 3-dimensional shapes. Ask your child to point out objects of various shapes around the house or outside.
Please return this Home Link to school tomorrow.

Use the Word List for Exercises 1–6.

Word List		
hexagon	octagon	pentagon
rectangle	square	triangle

Write the name under each shape.

1. pentagon
2. rectangle
3. octagon

4. I have 6 sides and 6 corners. What am I? hexagon
5. I am a special rectangle. All of my sides are the same length. What am I? square
6. I have the smallest number of corners of all of the shapes. What am I? triangle

Practice

7. Write 4 odd numbers with 7 in the hundreds place.
Answers vary.

Math Masters, p. 289

3 Differentiation Options

READINESS

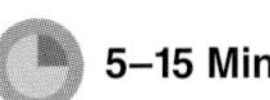

▶ Reviewing Polygons and 3-Dimensional Shapes

To provide experience with attributes of 2- and 3-dimensional shapes, have children play the game *I Spy*. Begin by generating and recording a list of vocabulary words used to describe shapes. Include words such as *sides, corners, faces, points, edges, length,* and *size.* Also, generate and record a list of different 2- and 3-dimensional shapes that children know. Have children give each other clues about shapes they "spy" in the room. For example, one child says, "I spy with my little eye a shape with 4 sides the same length." Children in the group guess which shape the child "spies."

ENRICHMENT

INDEPENDENT ACTIVITY

15–30 Min

▶ Constructing Regular Polyhedrons

(*Math Journal 2,* p. 203)

To further explore the properties of 3-dimensional figures using a concrete model, have children build polyhedrons with straws and connectors. Display labeled models of polyhedrons and have children look at the five regular polyhedrons shown on journal page 203. Tell children that polyhedrons are 3-dimensional shapes that have all flat faces. Prisms and pyramids are examples of polyhedrons. *Regular polyhedrons* are special because all of the faces are the same. There are only five kinds of regular polyhedrons.

Invite each child to build his or her own regular polyhedron out of straws and twist-ties. Children should be able to build a tetrahedron or cube, but don't be surprised if someone tries to build an octahedron.

ELL SUPPORT

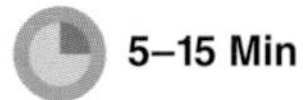

▶ Comparing 2- and 3-Dimensional Shapes

To provide language support for shapes, ask children to create lists of 2- and 3-dimensional shapes, using words and pictures. Have them explain how 2- and 3-dimensional shapes are alike and how they differ.

Planning Ahead

For Lesson 10-6, you may want to find a recent national weather map from a newspaper, a large classroom map of the United States, and a local forecast from a current newspaper.

10•6 Review: Thermometers and Temperature

Objectives To review reading temperatures in degrees Fahrenheit; and to provide experience using information on a map to find temperature differences.

Technology Resources www.everydaymathonline.com

ePresentations

eToolkit

Algorithms Practice

EM Facts Workshop Game™

Family Letters

Assessment Management

Common Core State Standards

Curriculum Focal Points

Interactive Teacher's Lesson Guide

1 Teaching the Lesson

Key Concepts and Skills

- Estimate differences between pairs of 2-digit numbers.
  [Operations and Computation Goal 2]
- Solve problems involving the addition or subtraction of 2-digit whole numbers.
  [Operations and Computation Goal 2]
- Read temperatures and relate them to hot, warm, or cold events.
  [Measurement and Reference Frames Goal 3]

Key Activities

Children review thermometers and temperature. They are introduced to a weather map and use the information on the map to find differences between high and low temperatures for selected cities.

Ongoing Assessment: Recognizing Student Achievement Use the Math Message.
[Measurement and Reference Frames Goal 3]

Ongoing Assessment: Informing Instruction See page 830.

Materials

Math Journal 2, pp. 205 and 206
Home Link 10•5
transparency of *Math Masters,* p. 290 (optional) ◆ Class Thermometer Poster (°F/°C) ◆ slate ◆ calculator (optional)

2 Ongoing Learning & Practice

Math Boxes 10•6
Math Journal 2, p. 207
Children practice and maintain skills through Math Box problems.

Home Link 10•6
Math Masters, p. 291
Children practice and maintain skills through Home Link activities.

3 Differentiation Options

READINESS

Finding the Difference Using a Number Grid
Math Journal 2, inside back cover
pennies
Children find the differences between numbers using a number grid.

ENRICHMENT

Comparing Temperature Scales
Class Thermometer Poster
Children are introduced to the Celsius scale.

EXTRA PRACTICE

Practicing with Temperature
Math Masters, p. 292
Children practice skills related to temperature.

ELL SUPPORT

Building a Math Word Bank
Differentiation Handbook, p. 126
Children add the terms *thermometer* and *weather* to their Math Word Banks.

Advance Preparation

You may wish to obtain the following books that relate to lesson content: ***Welcome to the Green House*** by Jane Yolen (Putnam Publishing Group, 1997); ***Welcome to the Ice House*** by Jane Yolen (Putnam Publishing Group, 1998); ***Cactus Desert, Arctic Tundra,*** and ***Tropical Rain Forest*** (from the One Small Square Series) by Donald Silver (McGraw-Hill, 1997).

***Teacher's Reference Manual,* Grades 1–3** pp. 170, 171, 190

Getting Started

Mental Math and Reflexes

Write the number that is:

●○○ 10 more than 33 43 ; 10 less than 29 19 ; 10 more than 56 66

●●○ 20 more than 41 61 ; 20 more than 80 100 ; 20 less than 92 72

●●● 100 more than 68 168 ; 100 less than 349 249 ; 50 more than 155 205

Math Message 

Which is cooler: 10°F or 40°F?

Which is warmer: 5°F or 35°F?

Home Link 10·5 Follow-Up

Briefly go over the answers.

1 Teaching the Lesson

▶ Math Message Follow-Up

WHOLE-CLASS ACTIVITY

Ask volunteers to point to the first two temperatures being compared, 10°F and 40°F, on the Class Thermometer Poster (°F/°C). Ask children to explain how they knew which temperature was cooler. Sample answer: The red liquid does not go up as high when it is 10°F as when it is 40°F. So 10°F is cooler than 40°F. Repeat the same procedure for determining which temperature is warmer, 5°F or 35°F.

Science Link When bears are active, their normal body temperature is about 100°F. When bears hibernate during the winter (sometimes for seven months), their body temperatures drop about 12 degrees, even when the temperature outside is far below 0. Ask: *What is a bear's body temperature when it hibernates during the winter?* About 88°F

Ongoing Assessment: Recognizing Student Achievement

Math Message 

Use **Math Message** to assess children's ability to compare temperatures. Children are making adequate progress if they are able to use a thermometer to tell which temperature is warmer or cooler. Some children will be able to do this without the use of a thermometer.

[Measurement and Reference Frames Goal 3]

▶ Reviewing Temperature and Thermometers

WHOLE-CLASS DISCUSSION

Use the Class Thermometer Poster (°F/°C) to review or point out the following:

- ▷ Temperature tells about how hot or cold something is.
- ▷ Temperature is measured with thermometers; in the United States, it is usually in units of Fahrenheit degrees (°F).
- ▷ The numbers on a thermometer are in tens. (Review how to read the marks on a thermometer.)

Discuss the temperatures of various things or those associated with certain events. Label the Class Thermometer Poster (°F/°C) with the temperatures. *For example:*

▷ water freezes: 32°F

▷ room temperature: about 70°F

▷ body temperature: 98.6°F

▷ very hot summer day: in the 90s

▷ water boils: 212°F (at sea level)

▶ Introducing Weather Maps

WHOLE-CLASS ACTIVITY

(*Math Journal 2,* p. 205; *Math Masters,* p. 290)

Social Studies Link Use the transparency of the U.S. Weather Map (*Math Masters,* page 290) as children follow along on the weather map on journal page 205. Discuss questions children may have about the map, cities, or temperatures. Ask children to find their state, both on the classroom map and on the journal map.

Explain that the two numbers next to each city represent the warmest and coldest temperatures for a certain day. As a group, find the cities with the warmest and coldest temperatures. Record these on the board.

If available, record on the board the warmest temperature and coldest temperature for your area. Use the classroom daily thermometer reading to record today's outdoor temperature.

Student Page

Date

LESSON 10·6 **U.S. Weather Map**

U.S. Weather Map: Spring High/Low Temperatures (°F)

Burlington 54/28
New York City 58/42
Buffalo 50/36
Miami 80/68
Atlanta 72/50
Memphis 70/54
Chicago 56/40
Minneapolis 54/36
Dallas 76/56
Denver 60/34
Phoenix 84/52
Seattle 58/44
Los Angeles 70/50
San Francisco 62/50

Math Journal 2, p. 205

NOTE For practice in finding differences between high and low temperatures using the Celsius scale, go to www.everydaymathonline.com.

▶ Finding Differences Between High and Low Temperatures

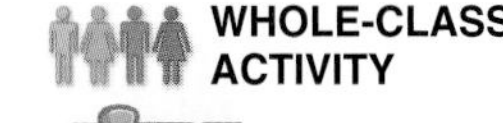

PROBLEM SOLVING

(*Math Journal 2,* pp. 205 and 206)

NOTE: You may wish to use a recent national weather map from a newspaper, a large classroom map of the United States, and a local forecast from a current newspaper to enhance the discussion of high-low temperature readings.

Children pose questions about the high-low temperature differences for cities on the map or from the local forecast; for example, "How much warmer is Denver's high temperature of 60°F than its low temperature of 34°F?" Suggest that children estimate temperature differences, perhaps in 10-degree intervals, before finding exact temperature differences.

Children share their solution strategies as you record them on the board. Encourage them to write number models for the solutions. The following are possible number models for the Denver example:

$34 + 26 = 60$

$60 - 34 = 26$

Unit
°F

Student Page

Date

LESSON 10·6 **Temperature Chart**

1.

City	Warmest Temperature	Coldest Temperature	Difference
Answers vary.	___ °F	___ °F	___ °F
	___ °F	___ °F	___ °F
	___ °F	___ °F	___ °F

2. Of your 3 cities, Answers vary.

_______ has the warmest temperature at ___ °F.

_______ has the coldest temperature at ___ °F.

The difference between these two temperatures is ___ °F.

3. On the map,

Phoenix has the warmest temperature at 84 °F.

Burlington has the coldest temperature at 28 °F.

The difference between these two temperatures is 56 °F.

Math Journal 2, p. 206

Student Page

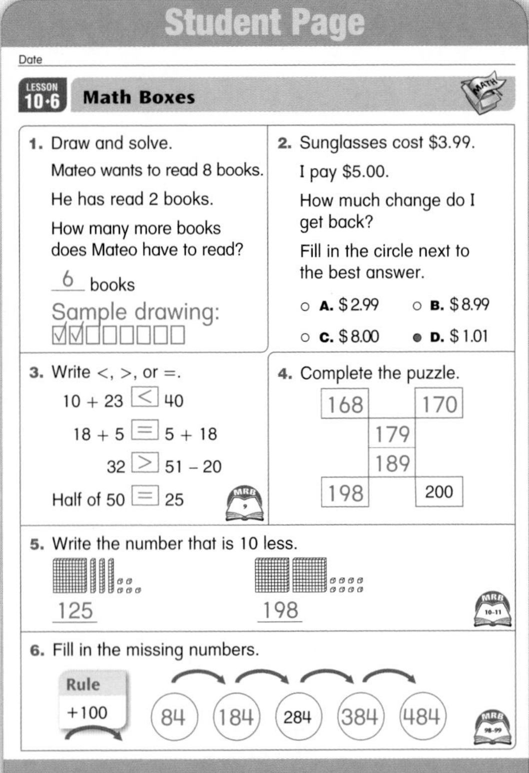
Date

LESSON 10·6 **Math Boxes**

1. Draw and solve.
   Mateo wants to read 8 books.
   He has read 2 books.
   How many more books does Mateo have to read?
   6 books
   Sample drawing:

2. Sunglasses cost $3.99.
   I pay $5.00.
   How much change do I get back?
   Fill in the circle next to the best answer.
   ○ A. $2.99 ○ B. $8.99
   ○ C. $8.00 ● D. $1.01

3. Write <, >, or =.
   10 + 23 < 40
   18 + 5 = 5 + 18
   32 > 51 − 20
   Half of 50 = 25

4. Complete the puzzle.
   168, 170, 179, 189, 198, 200

5. Write the number that is 10 less.
   125 198

6. Fill in the missing numbers.
   Rule +100
   84, 184, 284, 384, 484

Math Journal 2, p. 207

Guide children in recording high temperatures, low temperatures, and temperature differences for three cities in Problem 1 on journal page 206. Then, working with partners or in small groups, children record the same information for one more city and then complete Problems 2 and 3.

NOTE You may want to choose all three cities as a class so that everyone lists the same cities. This will make it easier to check children's answers.

Ongoing Assessment: Informing Instruction

Watch for children who confuse warmer and cooler temperatures. Remind them that warmer temperatures have higher numbers than cooler temperatures and that the red liquid in a thermometer goes up higher when the temperature is warmer.

Adjusting the Activity

Have children use a calculator to find the difference between 2-digit high and low temperatures.

AUDITORY ◆ KINESTHETIC ◆ TACTILE ◆ VISUAL

2 Ongoing Learning & Practice

▶ Math Boxes 10·6

INDEPENDENT ACTIVITY

(*Math Journal 2,* p. 207)

Mixed Practice Math Boxes in this lesson are linked to Math Boxes in Lesson 10-2 and 10-4.

▶ Home Link 10·6

INDEPENDENT ACTIVITY

(*Math Masters,* p. 291)

Home Connection Children compare pairs of temperature readings.

Home Link Master

Name Date

HOME LINK 10·6 **Comparing Temperatures**

Family Note The focus of this Home Link is on finding how much warmer or colder one temperature is than another. Ask your child to explain how he or she solved each problem. One strategy might be to count on the thermometer or on a number grid. Your child might be able to solve some of the problems mentally.

Please return this Home Link to school tomorrow.

1. Which temperature is 10° warmer than 38°F? 48 °F
2. Which temperature is 20° warmer than 52°F? 72 °F
3. Which temperature is 40° colder than 86°F? 46 °F
4. Which temperature is 20° colder than 78°F? 58 °F
5. Which temperature is 30° warmer than 50°F? 80 °F
6. Which temperature is 20° colder than 44°F? 24 °F

°F; Body Temperature 100; 90; 80; Room Temperature 70; 60; 50; 40; Water Freezes 30; 20

Practice

7. Rule −5
   110, 105, 100, 95, 90

Math Masters, p. 291

3 Differentiation Options

READINESS

▶ Finding the Difference Using a Number Grid

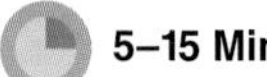

(*Math Journal 2,* inside back cover)

To explore finding differences using the number grid, have children cover two different 2-digit numbers with pennies and find the difference between the two covered numbers. They may count up or back to find the difference. Have them describe their strategies for finding the difference between two numbers. Encourage children to use the pattern of going up or down rows, counting forward or backward by 10s, to make their strategies more efficient.

ENRICHMENT

▶ Comparing Temperature Scales

To further explore temperature, have children compare the Celsius scale to the Fahrenheit scale on a thermometer. Direct children's attention to the Celsius (°C) scale of the Class Thermometer Poster (°F/°C). Tell them that most of the world uses the Celsius scale. Set the poster to show that water freezes at 32°F, which is the same temperature as 0°C. Have children take turns setting the poster to a certain temperature, while another child states the temperature in both degrees Celsius and degrees Fahrenheit.

EXTRA PRACTICE

▶ Practicing with Temperature

(*Math Masters,* p. 292)

Use *Math Masters,* page 292 to provide practice with temperature.

ELL SUPPORT

▶ Building a Math Word Bank

(*Differentiation Handbook,* p. 126)

To provide language support for temperature, have children use the Word Bank Template found on *Differentiation Handbook,* page 126. Ask children to write the terms *thermometer* and *weather,* draw pictures representing the terms, and write other words that describe them. See the *Differentiation Handbook* for more information.

Teaching Master

Name Date

LESSON 10·6 **Temperature Review**

Which temperature is

1. 10° warmer than 32°F? 42 °F
2. 10° colder than 34°F? 24 °F
3. 20° warmer than 42°F? 62 °F
4. 20° warmer than 18°F? 38 °F
5. 30° colder than 76°F? 46 °F
6. When Randy woke up, it was 68°F. When he went to bed, it was 76°F. How many degrees warmer was it when Randy went to bed? 8 °F

Try This

7. Water freezes at what temperature? 32 °F

Average room temperature is 70 °F.

How many degrees colder is the temperature when water freezes than the average room temperature? 38 °F

°F 120 110 100 90 80 70 60 50 40 30 20 10 0 −10 −20 −30 −40

Body Temperature → 100; Room Temperature → 70; Water Freezes → 32

Math Masters, p. 292

10•7 Review: Place Value, Scrolls, and Number Grids

Objective To review place value through hundreds.

Technology Resources www.everydaymathonline.com

ePresentations

eToolkit

Algorithms Practice

EM Facts Workshop Game™

Family Letters

Assessment Management

Common Core State Standards

Curriculum Focal Points

Interactive Teacher's Lesson Guide

1 Teaching the Lesson

Key Concepts and Skills

- Count forward by 10s or 100s from a 2- or 3-digit number. [Number and Numeration Goal 1]
- Read, write, and model with base-10 blocks multidigit whole numbers through hundreds. [Number and Numeration Goal 3]
- Express the value of digits in a multidigit number. [Number and Numeration Goal 3]
- Create and solve number-grid puzzles. [Patterns, Functions, and Algebra Goal 1]

Key Activities

Children do a variety of activities that review place-value concepts through hundreds. They make up number-grid puzzles, using numbers in the hundreds and possibly thousands.

Ongoing Assessment: Informing Instruction See page 834.

Ongoing Assessment: Recognizing Student Achievement Use *Math Masters,* page 335. [Patterns, Functions, and Algebra Goal 1]

Materials

Home Link 10•6
Math Masters, p. 319 (optional); p. 335
ten each of play money $1, $10, and $100 bills ◆ straws (10 singles, 10 bundles of 10) ◆ base-10 blocks (10 cubes, 10 longs, 10 flats) ◆ slate

2 Ongoing Learning & Practice

Playing Favorite Math Games
per group: materials for math games
Children play math games.

Completing *Math Journal 2*
Math Journal 2
Children help one another complete journal pages they missed.

Assessing Children's Progress with Scrolls
Math Masters, p. 110
number scroll
Children continue to work on number scrolls.

Math Boxes 10•7
Math Journal 2, p. 208
Children practice and maintain skills through Math Box problems.

Home Link 10•7
Math Masters, p. 293
Children practice and maintain skills through Home Link activities.

Minute Math+
Minute Math®+, p. 96
Children practice with fractions.

3 Differentiation Options

READINESS

Missing Digits
per group: number cards 1–9 (from the Everything Math Deck, if available), base-10 blocks (flats, longs, and cubes)
Children explore place value using a concrete model.

ENRICHMENT

Writing Numbers in Expanded Notation
per partnership: base-10 blocks (flats, longs, and cubes) ◆ slate
Children make and write number models for 3-digit numbers using expanded notation.

Getting Started

Mental Math and Reflexes

Children use any strategy they choose to solve number stories involving fractions. *Suggestions:*

●○○ Ramón divided his granola bar into 4 pieces so that he could share it equally with 3 of his friends. What fraction of the granola bar did each person receive? $\frac{1}{4}$ of the granola bar

●●○ Mei got 8 birthday balloons. Two balloons were red. What fraction of the balloons was red? $\frac{1}{4}$ or $\frac{2}{8}$ of the balloons

●●● Peter had 10 dimes. He lost $\frac{1}{5}$ of them. How many dimes did he lose? 2 dimes How much money is that? 20¢

Continue as time permits.

Math Message

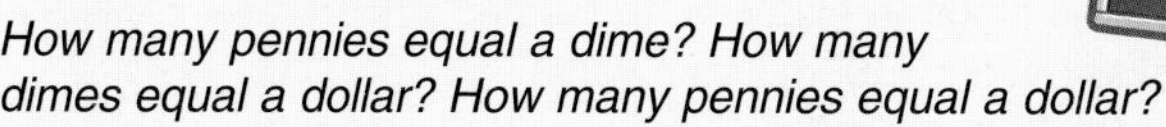

How many pennies equal a dime? How many dimes equal a dollar? How many pennies equal a dollar?

Home Link 10·6 Follow-Up

Briefly go over the answers.

1 Teaching the Lesson

▶ Math Message Follow-Up

WHOLE-CLASS ACTIVITY

Discuss the answers to the questions. Then explain that pennies, dimes, and dollars are one example of exchanges in our base-10 number system. Use straws; base-10 blocks; and \$1, \$10, and \$100 bills to review and reinforce these exchanges and their reversibility.

Discuss what 10 flats are worth and what ten \$100 bills are worth.

▶ Reviewing Place Value in 2-, 3-, and 4-Digit Numbers

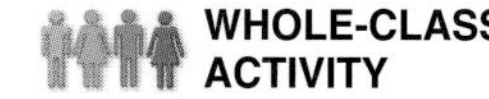

WHOLE-CLASS ACTIVITY

Choose activities that cover concepts and skills you want to review and assess or use your own place-value exercises.

Suggestions:

1. Write multidigit numbers on the board, such as 389. Children read them by stating the place value of each digit; for example, "3 is in the hundreds place; 8 is in the tens place; 9 is in the ones place."

2. Children write multidigit numbers on their slates (or on paper) to your specifications. For example: *Write a 3-digit number with a 9 in the tens place. Write a number with a 5 in the hundreds place.*

3. Write two or three separate digits on the board. Children write on their slates (or on paper) the largest possible number and the smallest possible number using those digits. For example, for 2, 8, and 5, the answers would be 852 and 258.

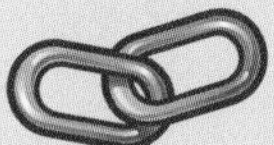

Links to the Future

In this lesson, children review place value in 2-, 3-, and 4-digit numbers. At this time, children should not be expected to master place value beyond 1,000. Place value through 10,000 is a Grade 2 Goal.

4. Write the largest and smallest single-digit numbers. 9 and 0 Write the largest and smallest 2-digit numbers. 99 and 10 Repeat for the 3-digit numbers and 4-digit numbers, if appropriate. 999 and 100; 9,999 and 1,000
5. Review counting by 10s from any 2- or 3-digit number. For example, count up orally by 10s beginning with 156: 156, 166, 176, 186, and so on. Children can write some of the counts on their slates. Extend this by having children count by hundreds; for example, 186, 286, 386, ...
6. Display a collection of base-10 blocks on the overhead. Ask children to write the number. At first, display sets that do not require regrouping. Then try some sets that must be regrouped.
7. Write a number on the board or overhead and have children show base-10 blocks for your number. Ask if they can find another way to show the number, perhaps by trading a flat for 10 longs.

Ongoing Assessment: Informing Instruction

Watch for children who confuse the hundreds, tens, and ones places when writing and making numbers. Encourage these children to use a Place-Value Mat (*Math Masters,* page 319) to organize numbers in relation to their place value.

Adjusting the Activity

Have children make a 3-digit number (such as 213) using base-10 blocks. Children stand at the front of the room. From left to right: 2 each hold one flat, 1 holds one long, and 3 each hold one cube. Count from the flats to the cubes: 100, 200, 210, 211, 212, 213. Each time you count a new base-10 block, instruct children to hold their base-10 blocks above their heads.

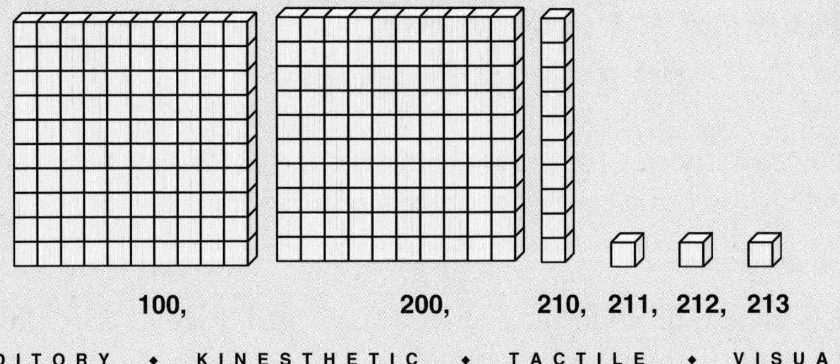

AUDITORY ◆ KINESTHETIC ◆ TACTILE ◆ VISUAL

Extending Number-Grid Puzzles to Hundreds

(*Math Masters,* p. 335)

Pass out one copy of *Math Masters,* page 335 to each child. Children fold the master into four equal parts. Each part can be used for a separate number-grid puzzle. Lines can be drawn between the four parts, or they can be cut apart.

Children draw a line around some of the grid cells in one part of the sheet to indicate a puzzle piece and then write a 2- or 3-digit number in one of the cells. Encourage each partner to create at least one puzzle using 3-digit numbers. Partners solve the puzzle by filling in all of the numbers in the piece.

Remind children that duplicates of the scroll sheets can be used over the summer to make number-grid puzzles. Encourage children to make a booklet of the puzzles.

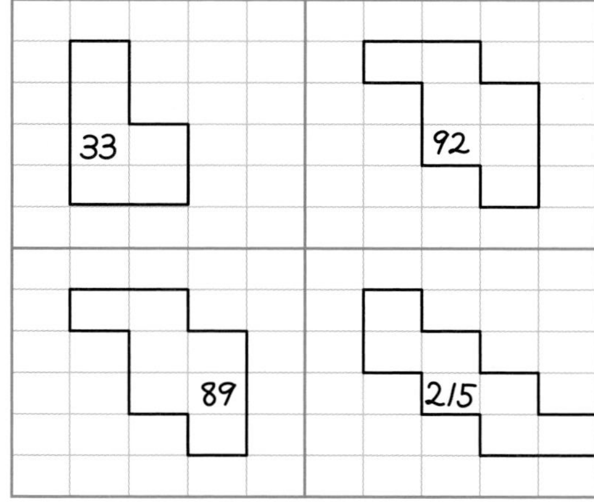

Examples of number-grid puzzles

Ongoing Assessment: Recognizing Student Achievement

Math Masters Page 335

Use ***Math Masters,* page 335** to assess children's ability to solve number-grid puzzles. Children are making adequate progress if they are able to solve 2-digit number-grid puzzles. Some children may be successful with 3-digit number-grid puzzles.

[Patterns, Functions and Algebra Goal 1]

Teaching Aid Master

Name Date

Blank Number Grid

Math Masters, p. 335

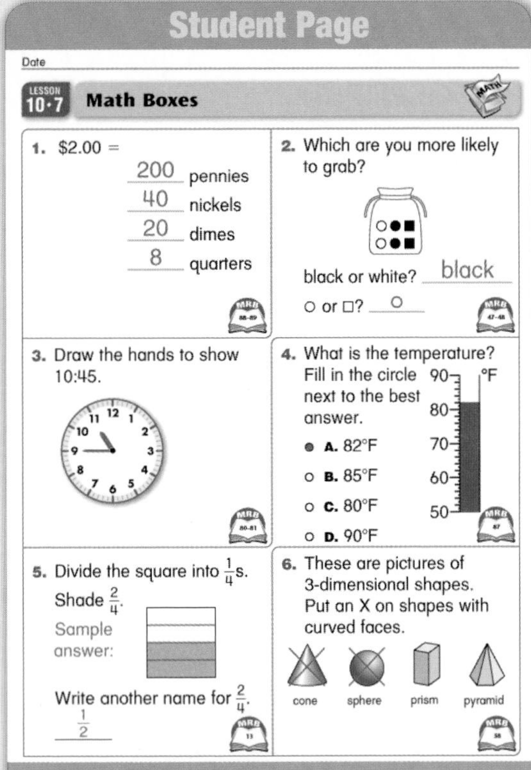
Student Page

Date

LESSON 10·7 Math Boxes

1. $2.00 =
200 pennies
40 nickels
20 dimes
8 quarters

2. Which are you more likely to grab?
black or white? black
○ or □? ○

3. Draw the hands to show 10:45.

4. What is the temperature? Fill in the circle next to the best answer.
● A. 82°F
○ B. 85°F
○ C. 80°F
○ D. 90°F

5. Divide the square into $\frac{1}{4}$s. Shade $\frac{2}{4}$.
Sample answer:
Write another name for $\frac{2}{4}$. $\frac{1}{2}$

6. These are pictures of 3-dimensional shapes. Put an X on shapes with curved faces.
cone sphere prism pyramid

Math Journal 2, p. 208

901				905					910
	912			915				919	
		923		925			928		
			934	935		937			
				945	946				
951	952	953	954	955	956	957	958	959	960
			964	965		967			
		973		975			978		
	982			985				989	
991				995					1000

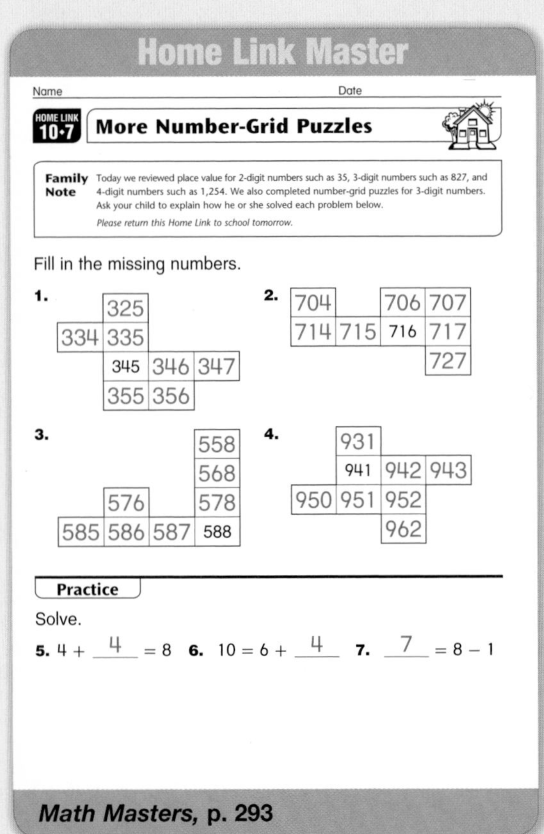
Home Link Master

Name Date

HOME LINK 10·7 More Number-Grid Puzzles

Family Note: Today we reviewed place value for 2-digit numbers such as 35, 3-digit numbers such as 827, and 4-digit numbers such as 1,254. We also completed number-grid puzzles for 3-digit numbers. Ask your child to explain how he or she solved each problem below.
Please return this Home Link to school tomorrow.

Fill in the missing numbers.

1. 325; 334, 335; 345, 346, 347; 355, 356

2. 704, 706, 707; 714, 715, 716, 717; 727

3. 558; 568; 576, 578; 585, 586, 587, 588

4. 931; 941, 942, 943; 950, 951, 952; 962

Practice

Solve.

5. 4 + 4 = 8 6. 10 = 6 + 4 7. 7 = 8 − 1

Math Masters, p. 293

2 Ongoing Learning & Practice

▶ Playing Favorite Math Games

SMALL-GROUP ACTIVITY

Children choose math games they have enjoyed playing. Or, you may want to assign games on the basis of children's needs.

▶ Completing *Math Journal 2*

PARTNER ACTIVITY

Children help one another complete missed journal pages.

▶ Assessing Children's Progress with Scrolls

INDEPENDENT ACTIVITY

(*Math Masters,* p. 110)

Assess how far individual children have progressed with their scrolls. Many children may want to add pages to their scrolls. You might suggest that children make patterns of filled-in blanks on some pages rather than filling in every blank (see margin). Children can share some of the patterns and designs they created on their scroll sheets.

▶ Math Boxes 10·7

INDEPENDENT ACTIVITY

(*Math Journal 2,* p. 208)

Mixed Practice Math Boxes in this lesson are paired with Math Boxes in Lesson 10-5.

Writing/Reasoning Have children draw, write, or verbalize an answer to the following question: *How do you read a clock?* A reasonable answer should include a reference to the minute and hour hands. Sample answer: I know the long hand is the minutes. You count by 5s. The short hand is the hour. You count by 1s.

▶ Home Link 10·7

INDEPENDENT ACTIVITY

(*Math Masters,* p. 293)

Home Connection Children complete 3-digit number-grid puzzles.

▶ *Minute Math+*

SMALL-GROUP ACTIVITY

Use *Minute Math+*, page 96 to provide practice with fractions.

3 Differentiation Options

READINESS

SMALL-GROUP ACTIVITY

5–15 Min

▶ Missing Digits

To explore place value using a concrete model, have children complete a "Missing-Digits" activity with base-10 blocks. Review the value of flats, longs, and cubes before beginning the activity.

Directions:

1. One child draws 3 number cards and makes a 3-digit number.
2. Each child records the number on a half-sheet of paper and builds the number with the fewest possible base-10 blocks.
3. Children now take turns. The first child thinks of a number that involves changing one of the digits in the number.
4. All children use base-10 blocks to model the change and then record a number sentence and the new number.
5. Repeat Steps 3 and 4 until all children have had a turn to change the number.

Example:

The first child draws 2, 3, and 7 and makes the number 327.

All children use 3 flats, 2 longs, and 7 cubes to build 327. They record 327 on their half-sheets of paper.

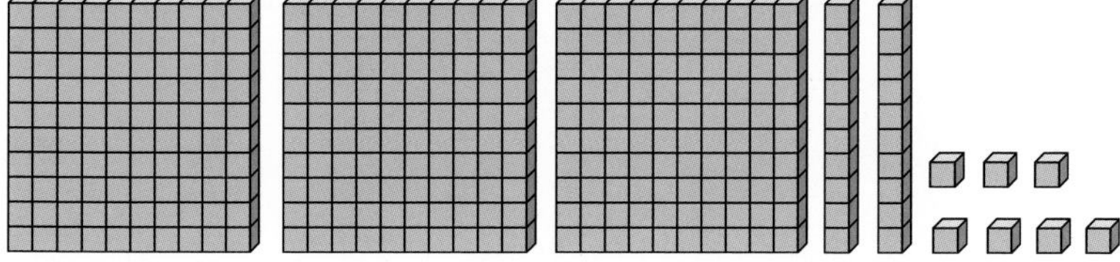

First child says, "I am thinking of a number that is 40 more than 327." All children take 4 more longs and add it to their numbers.

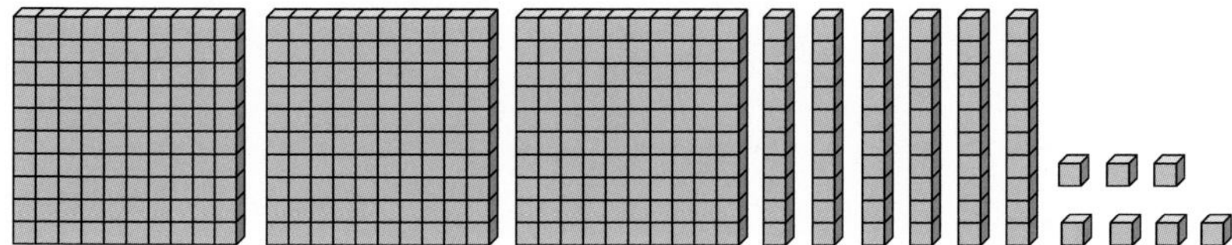

They record $327 + 40 = 367$ on their half-sheets of paper.

ENRICHMENT

▶ Writing Numbers in Expanded Notation

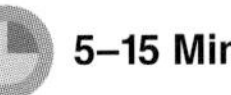

To apply children's understanding of place value, have them write numbers in expanded notation. Have one child write a 3-digit number on a slate. Have the other child represent this 3-digit number with the fewest number of base-10 blocks. Then have partners work together to write an appropriate number model for the flats, longs, and cubes. *For example:*

▷ A child uses 3 flats, 2 longs, and 1 cube to represent the number 321.

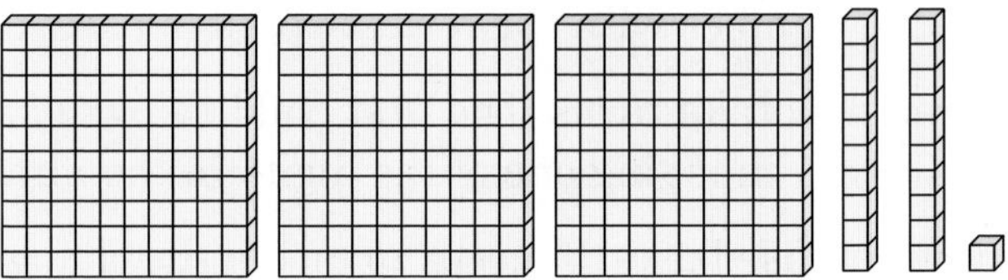

▷ On the other slate, partners write the following number model in expanded notation to represent the values of the base-10 blocks.

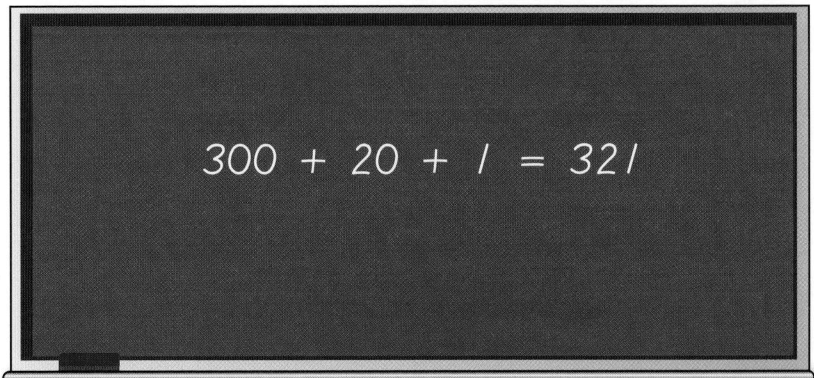

10•8 Progress Check 10

Objective To assess children's progress on mathematical content through the end of Unit 10.

1 Looking Back: Cumulative Assessment

The **End-of-Year Assessment** in the *Assessment Handbook* is a written assessment that you may use to assess children's proficiency with Grade-Level Goals.

Input children's data from Progress Check 10 and the End-of-Year Assessment into the **Assessment Management Spreadsheets**.

Materials

- Home Link 10•7
- *Assessment Handbook,* pp. 126–133, 173–176, 186, and 236–239
- slate; tool-kit coins; calculator

CONTENT ASSESSED	LESSON(S)	ASSESSMENT ITEMS				
		SELF	ORAL/SLATE	WRITTEN		OPEN RESPONSE
				PART A	PART B	
Name numbers; work with place value. [Number and Numeration Goal 3]	10•2, 10•4, 10•6, 10•7		3	5–7		
Compare and order whole numbers up to 1,000. [Number and Numeration Goal 7]	10•2–10•4, 10•6, 10•7	5		3		
Demonstrate proficiency with addition and subtraction facts. [Operations and Computation Goal 1]	10•2	3	2	4		
Solve addition and subtraction problems; calculate/compare the values of coins. [Operations and Computation Goal 2]	10•1–10•6	4, 6	1, 3	2, 5, 6		✓
Solve number stories. [Operations and Computation Goal 4]	10•1, 10•3, 10•4	6	4			
Use graphs to answer simple questions. [Data and Chance Goal 2]	10•1, 10•3				8, 9	
Make exchanges between coins. [Measurement and Reference Frames Goal 2]	10•3, 10•4, 10•7	4				
Solve number-grid puzzles. [Patterns, Functions, and Algebra Goal 1]	10•7	1		1		
Write, solve, and explain number sentences. [Patterns, Functions, and Algebra Goal 2]	10•3, 10•4, 10•6, 10•7	2		3, 5, 6		✓

2 Looking Ahead: Preparing for Grade 2

Math Boxes 10•8

Home Link 10•8: End-of-Year Family Letter

Materials

- *Math Journal 2,* p. 209
- *Math Journal 1,* Activity Sheets 4 and 5
- *Math Masters,* pp. 110, 294–297, 324, and 335
- *Assessment Handbook,* pp. 134, 135, 191–196, and 198

Getting Started

Math Message • Self Assessment

Complete the Self Assessment (Assessment Handbook, *page 173*).

Home Link 10·7 Follow-Up

Briefly go over the answers.

1 Looking Back: Cumulative Assessment

▶ Math Message Follow-Up

INDEPENDENT ACTIVITY

(Self Assessment, *Assessment Handbook,* p. 173)

The Self Assessment offers children the opportunity to reflect upon their progress.

▶ Oral and Slate Assessments

WHOLE-CLASS ACTIVITY

Problems 2 and 3 provide summative information and can be used for grading purposes. Problems 1 and 4 provide formative information.

Oral Assessment

1. Have children solve the following riddles using their tool-kit coins:
   - I have 13¢.
     I have 5 coins.
     I have more pennies than nickels.
     What coins do I have? 2 nickels and 3 pennies
   - I have 46¢.
     I have 5 coins.
     I have more nickels than any other coin.
     What coins do I have? 1 quarter, 1 dime, 2 nickels, 1 penny
2. Play the game *Beat the Calculator* with addition and subtraction facts.

Slate Assessment

3. Have children write on their slates the number that is 10 more or 10 less. Then have them circle the digit in the specified place.
   - Write the number that is 10 more than 15. Circle the tens place. (2)5
   - Write the number that is 10 less than 39. Circle the tens digit. (2)9
   - Write the number that is 10 less than 76. Circle the ones digit. 6(6)

Assessment Master

Name Date

LESSON 10·8 **Self Assessment** Progress Check 10

Put a check in the box that tells how you do each skill.

Skill	I can do this by myself. I can explain how to do this.	I can do this by myself.	I can do this with help.
1. Solve number-grid puzzles.			
2. Use +, −, and = to write number models.			
3. Solve addition and subtraction facts.			
4. Make change.			
5. Compare numbers larger than 100.			
6. Solve 2-digit by 1-digit number stories.			

Assessment Handbook, p. 173

- Write the number that is 10 more than 101. Circle the hundreds digit. 111
- Write the number that is 10 more than 293. Circle the tens digit. 303
- Write the number that is 10 less than 565. Circle the tens digit. 555

4. Tell the following number stories. Children record a number model and the answers on their slates. Encourage children to use manipulatives, drawings, doodles, and other strategies to solve the problems.
   - Maddie had 14 stickers on her folder. Amelia had 23 stickers on her folder. How many stickers did Maddie and Amelia have in all? 37 stickers
   - Andrew has 36 markers. Six of Andrew's markers are blue. Malcolm gives him 22 more markers. How many markers does Andrew have now? 58 markers

Written Assessment

(*Assessment Handbook,* pp. 174 and 175)

Part A Recognizing Student Achievement

Problems 1–7 provide summative information and may be used for grading purposes.

Problem(s)	**Description**
1	Solve number-grid puzzles.
2	Know and compare the value of pennies, nickels, dimes, and quarters.
3	Compare whole numbers up to 1,000 using >, <, and =.
4	Demonstrate proficiency with addition and subtraction facts.
5, 6	Write number sentences using the symbols +, –, and =.
7	Identify places in such numbers and the values of the digits in those places.

Part B Informing Instruction

Problems 8 and 9 provide formative information that can be useful in planning future instruction.

Problem(s)	**Description**
8	Find the maximum and minimum of a data set.
9	Use graphs to answer simple questions and draw conclusions.

Assessment Master

Name Date

LESSON 10•8 **Written Assessment** Progress Check 10

Part A

1. Complete the number-grid puzzles.

186	187	188
196	197	198
206	207	208

101	102	103
111	112	113
121	122	123

2. I buy an apple for 15¢. I pay 25¢. How much change do I get? 10 ¢

   I buy gum for $0.72. I pay $1.00. How much change do I get? $ 0 . 28

3. Write <, >, or =.

   154 < 372 — 727 > 272
   94 < 149 — 233 < 322
   406 = 406 — 510 > 501

4. Fill in the missing number.

   8 + 8 = 16 — 14 – 9 = 5
   5 + 7 = 12 — 13 – 6 = 7
   9 + 3 = 12 — 17 – 9 = 8

Assessment Handbook, p. 174

Assessment Master

Name Date

LESSON 10•8 Written Assessment *continued*

5. Write the number. 38
   Write the number that is 10 less. 28
   Write the number model to show 10 less base-10 blocks. 38 – 10 = 28

6. Write the number. 52
   Write the number that is 10 more. 62
   Write the number model to show 10 more base-10 blocks. 52 + 10 = 62

7. Circle the hundreds place: 222 371 101 599 428 630
   Circle the tens place: 390 45 200 810 167 333

Part B

8. Dinner Times

   Children: 0 1 2 3 4 5; 4:00 5:00 6:00 7:00 P.M.

   Earliest Dinner Time: 4:00 P.M.
   Latest Dinner Time: 7:00 P.M.
   Range: 3 hours

9. Use the graph to answer the question.
   What is the typical dinner time? 5:00 P.M.

Assessment Handbook, p. 175

Assessment Master

Name Date

LESSON 10•8 **Open Response** Progress Check 10

Counting Books

Roel has 3 more books than Carol. Together they have 9 books.

See the *Assessment Handbook* for rubrics and children's work samples.

1. Find the number of books each one has. Show your work.

2. Explain how you found your answer.

Assessment Handbook, p. 176

Use the checklists on pages 237 and 239 of the *Assessment Handbook* to record results. Then input the data into the **Assessment Management Spreadsheets** to keep an ongoing record of children's progress toward Grade-Level Goals.

Student Page

Date

LESSON 10•8 **Math Boxes**

1. What time is it?

6 : 40

2. Write the amount.

ⓆⓃⒹⓅⓅⒹ

52 ¢

3. What day is it today?

Answers vary.

What day will it be tomorrow?

Answers vary.

4. Complete the number-grid puzzle.

	125	
134	135	136
144	145	146

5. Count by 2s.

36, 38, 40,
42, 44, 46,
48, 50, 52,
54, 56, 58

6. What is the temperature?

62 °F

Math Journal 2, p. 209

▶ Open Response

INDEPENDENT ACTIVITY

(*Assessment Handbook,* p. 176)

Counting Books

The open-response item requires children to apply skills and concepts from Unit 10 to solve a multistep problem. See *Assessment Handbook,* pages 129–133 for rubrics and children's work samples for this problem.

Distribute *Assessment Handbook,* page 176. Read the problem aloud to children. Allow children to solve the problem and record their solutions on the page.

After children have had a chance to complete the multistep problem, invite individual children to explain their solution strategies. Encourage them to use words and drawings to explain their strategies as you list them on the board. Be sure to discuss both successful and unsuccessful strategies.

2 Building Background for Grade 2

▶ Math Boxes 10•8

INDEPENDENT ACTIVITY

(*Math Journal 2,* p. 209)

Mixed Practice This Math Boxes page previews Grade 2.

▶ Home Link 10•8: End-of-Year Family Letter

(*Math Masters,* pp. 110, 294–297, 324, and 335; *Math Journal 1,* Activity Sheets 4 and 5)

Home Connection Give each child one copy of the Family Letter and one copy of each of the following: *Math Masters,* pages 110, 294–297, 324 and 335; *Math Journal 1,* Activity Sheets 4 and 5. The End-of-Year Family Letter thanks family members for their participation in *First Grade Everyday Mathematics*, suggests home-based activities for the summer, and provides a preview of *Second Grade Everyday Mathematics*. Children can use the other pages for other summer mathematics activities. These include a set of dominoes, a copy of the Addition/Subtraction Facts Table, a number grid, and a blank scroll page. Children's families can make copies of the scroll page if children want additional sheets for their scrolls. Encourage children to show you their scrolls in the fall.

▶ End-of-Year Assessment

(*Assessment Handbook,* pp. 191–196)

The End-of-Year Assessment (*Assessment Handbook,* pages 191–196) provides an additional assessment opportunity that you may use as part of your balanced assessment plan. This assessment covers many of the important concepts and skills presented in *First Grade Everyday Mathematics.* It should be used along with ongoing and periodic assessments. Please see pages 134 and 135 in the *Assessment Handbook* for further information.

Home Link Masters

Name ______________________ Date ______________

HOME LINK 10•8 **Family Letter**

End-of-Year Family Letter

Congratulations! By completing *First Grade Everyday Mathematics* your child has accomplished a great deal. Thank you for all of your support!

This Family Letter is provided for you to use as a resource throughout your child's school vacation. It includes a list of Do-Anytime Activities, game directions, an Addition/Subtraction Facts Table, and a sneak preview of what your child will be learning in *Second Grade Everyday Mathematics.*

Enjoy your summer!

Do-Anytime Activities

To help your child review many of the things he or she has learned in first grade, we suggest the following activities for you and your child to do together over the summer. These activities build on the skills your child learned this year and help prepare him or her for *Second Grade Everyday Mathematics.*

Telling Time and Using Money

- Practice telling time by using a variety of clocks—billboard clocks, wristwatches, clocks with hands, and digital clocks—in a variety of situations.
- Set alarm clocks and timers on objects such as ovens, microwave ovens, and DVD players.
- Record the time spent doing various activities.
- Use real money in a variety of situations: allowance, savings, purchases (including getting change back), and using vending machines.

Weather Watch

- Invite your child to share your interest in weather predictions and temperature reports from the radio, the television, and local and national newspapers.
- Observe temperatures shown on business signs, aquarium thermometers, and so on.
- Read and set temperatures on heating and cooling thermostats and oven dials.

Math Masters, pp. 294–297

Appendices

Contents

Project 1

Geometric Gift Wrap and Greeting Cards

Objective To provide opportunities to use geometric shapes to create designs for gift wrap and greeting cards.

Technology Resources www.everydaymathonline.com

eToolkit

Algorithms Practice

EM Facts Workshop Game™

Family Letters

Assessment Management

Common Core State Standards

Curriculum Focal Points

Interactive Teacher's Lesson Guide

1 Doing the Project

Recommended Use During or after Unit 3

Key Concepts and Skills

- Use plane shapes to make designs.
  [Geometry Goal 1]
- Make line-symmetric designs.
  [Geometry Goal 2]
- Make repeating patterns.
  [Patterns, Functions, and Algebra Goal 1]

Key Activities

Children use pattern-block shapes to create designs. Then they print their designs to create wrapping paper or greeting cards.

Materials

- pattern blocks
- paper towels or pieces of sponge
- small paper plates
- tempera paint
- Pattern-Block Template
- plain paper for gift wrap such as newsprint is fine
- paper for greeting cards
- *A Cloak for the Dreamer* by Aileen Friedman

2 Extending the Project

Children create patterns using tangrams and letters of the alphabet; they write what they learned about geometric shapes; they discuss places where shapes are found; and they learn how to make shapes with their bodies.

Children practice skills through Home Link activities.

Materials

- sets of tangrams
- *Kente Colors*
- *The Spider Weaver: A Legend of Kente Cloth*
- *Babar's Yoga for Elephants*

Advance Preparation

For Doing the Project in Part 1, you may want to obtain ***A Cloak for the Dreamer*** by Aileen Friedman (Scholastic Inc., 1995).

You may want to obtain the following books for the optional Extension Suggestions in Part 2:

▷ ***Kente Colors*** by Debbi Chocolate (Walker and Company, 1997)

▷ ***The Spider Weaver: A Legend of Kente Cloth*** by Margaret Musgrove (Blue Sky Press, 2001)

▷ ***Babar's Yoga for Elephants*** by Laurent de Brunhoff (Harry N. Adams, Inc., 2006)

1 Doing the Project

▶ Using Pattern-Block Shapes to Create Wrapping Paper or Greeting Cards

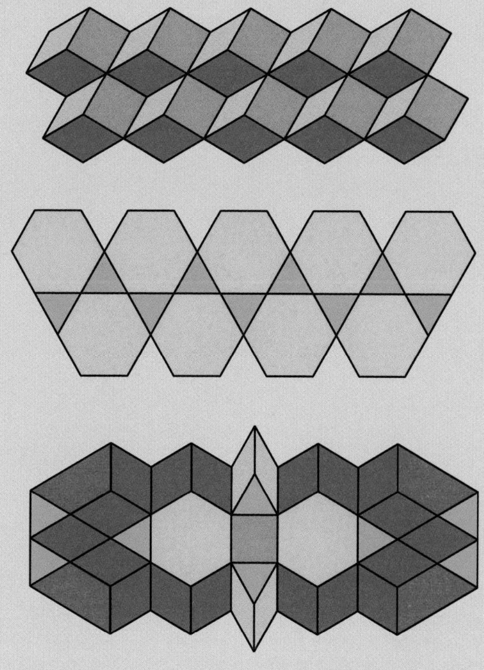

Working in small groups, have children use pattern-block shapes to create designs for wrapping paper or greeting cards. Encourage them to include patterns in their designs. *For example:*

▷ patterns in which two or three different shapes and colors repeat

▷ patterns in which the sizes of the shapes vary

▷ patterns that are symmetrical

Point out that new shapes can be made by combining pattern-block shapes; for example, three rhombuses form a regular hexagon (equal sides and equal angles). A regular hexagon will *tessellate*—that is, the whole paper can be covered by hexagons without gaps or overlaps.

Literature Link Read ***A Cloak for the Dreamer*** by Aileen Friedman (Scholastic Inc., 1995). Discuss designs that do or do not tessellate.

▶ Printing with Pattern-Block Shapes

NOTE Encourage children to demonstrate or explain how they used pattern blocks to create their designs using words such as *slide, flip,* or *turn.* Have them use positional words such as *above, below,* and *to the right of.*

When children complete their designs, explain one of the two suggestions for printing the designs to make wrapping paper or greeting cards:

Stenciling with the Pattern-Block Template

Show children how to use small pieces of sponge or crumpled paper towels as daubers. As they use the Pattern-Block Template as a stencil, they should hold it against the paper, and fill in an open area with paint. Tell children that this technique works best when the daubers are fairly dry.

Printing with Pattern Blocks

Children can make small "stamp pads" from folded paper towels saturated with tempera paint. They need to keep these in plastic trays. Have them dip one side of a pattern block into the paint, and then press the pattern block onto the paper.

Alternatively, they may spread finger paint on plates or other waterproof surfaces, and use them as stamp pads to put paint on the blocks.

After children have made a variety of gift wrappings and greeting cards, bring them together to describe their designs. Help them name the shapes they used. If appropriate, count various shapes.

2 Extending the Project

Extension Suggestions

- Have children use sets of tangrams and create repeating designs.
- Suggest that children make repeating designs with letters of the alphabet.
- Ask each child to write what they learned about geometric shapes. Display the children's writings next to their geometric designs.

Literature Link To further explore geometric patterns you may want to read: ***Kente Colors*** by Debbi Chocolate (Walker and Company, 1997) or ***The Spider Weaver: A Legend of Kente Cloth*** by Margaret Musgrove (Blue Sky Press, 2001).

Physical Education Link Read ***Babar's Yoga for Elephants*** by Laurent de Brunhoff (Harry N. Abrams, Inc., 2006). Use the book's step-by-step instructions for basic yoga techniques and positions. Ask children to do the downward-facing dog, plough, and triangle poses. Discuss how these poses are all shape-related.

Social Studies Link Tell children that Frank Lloyd Wright, an architect famous for his use of shapes in the buildings he designed, believed that geometric shapes could be found "hidden" within everyday objects that people have made. Ask children to try to find "hidden" geometric shapes in their designs.

Home Link Suggestion

Many of the textile arts, such as cross-stitch, needlepoint, and quilting, use basic geometric shapes to create designs and pictures of objects. Ask children to bring in fabrics that have shapes in their patterns; for example, handmade quilts, rugs, pillows, baby blankets, tablecloths, or clothing.

Project

2 Amaryllis Plant

Objectives To provide opportunities to observe plant growth over time; and to provide opportunities to collect and graph data.

Technology Resources www.everydaymathonline.com

eToolkit

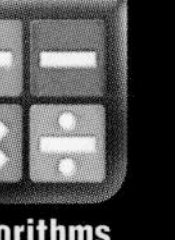
Algorithms Practice

EM Facts Workshop Game™

Family Letters

Assessment Management

Common Core State Standards

Curriculum Focal Points

Interactive Teacher's Lesson Guide

1 Doing the Project

Recommended Use During or after Unit 4

Key Concepts and Skills

- Measure height with standard measuring tools.
  [Measurement and Reference Frames Goal 1]
- Collect and organize data in a bar graph.
  [Data and Chance Goal 1]

Key Activities

Children plant an amaryllis bulb and observe and chart the growth of an amaryllis plant to maturity.

Key Vocabulary

bulb

Materials

- Class Data Pad
- 2–3 amaryllis bulbs
- container of lukewarm water
- 2–3 plant pots with a diameter slightly larger than the diameter of the bulb and with a small drainage hole
- 2–3 saucers
- potting soil
- tape measure
- magnifying lens
- strips of construction paper

2 Extending the Project

Children create a poster that identifies the needs of living things; they learn to take care of plants; they photograph plants; they draw pictures and make a timeline or journal about the growth of an amaryllis plant; they measure and record how much the plant is watered; they discuss the parts of a plant; and they compare different plants using a Venn diagram.

Children practice skills through Home Link activities.

Materials

- poster board
- camera
- photographs of amaryllis plants
- measuring tools for water
- materials for growing additional plants of any variety
- *The Empty Pot*
- *From Seed to Plant*
- *How Plants Grow*

Advance Preparation

Amaryllis bulbs are usually sold at nurseries until April. An amaryllis grows quickly. As much as 24 inches of stem growth can be observed over a period of 6 to 8 weeks. It is strongly recommended that you plant more than one bulb, as there is a possibility that one bulb may not grow. Do not discard a bulb that fails to grow; keep it for children to observe as it decomposes. *Warning:* An amaryllis bulb is poisonous if eaten.

You may want to obtain the following books for the optional Extension Suggestions in Part 2:

▷ ***The Empty Pot*** by Demi (Henry Holt and Company Inc., 1996)

▷ ***From Seed to Plant*** by Gail Gibbons (Holiday House, 1993)

▷ ***How Plants Grow*** by Angela Royston (Heineman Library, 2001)

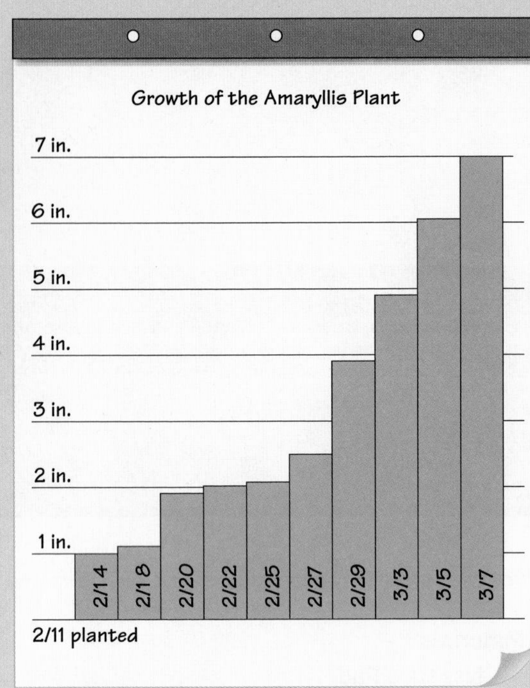

NOTE Measure 1 inch increments from the baseline of the graph to make sure the strips are accurately represented on the graph.

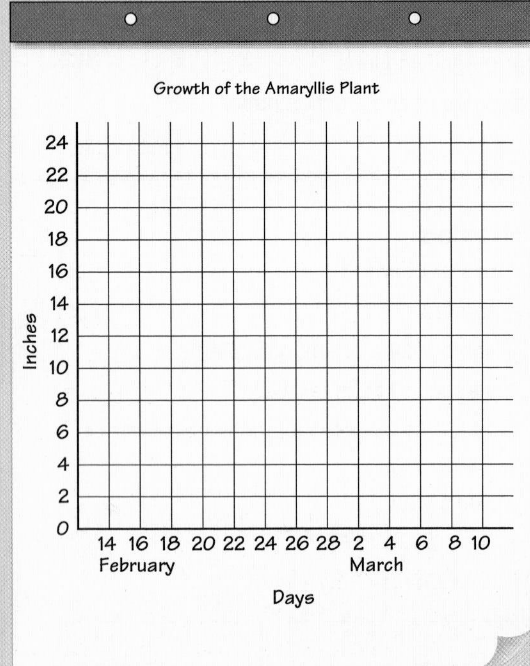

NOTE You may wish to measure and record the growth of the amaryllis using both centimeters and inches.

1 Doing the Project

Planting the Amaryllis Bulb

Explain to children that a **bulb** is a type of seed that is planted underground and is often larger than most seeds. Bulbs will grow into mature plants when properly nurtured.

Soak the bulbs and roots in a container of lukewarm water for several hours before planting. Encourage children to observe and draw a picture of the bulbs before they are planted.

Plant the bulbs so that $\frac{1}{3}$ of the bulbs rise above the potting soil. Be careful not to damage the roots.

Put the pots on saucers for drainage. Place the plants in as much light as possible because direct sunlight and warm temperatures will stimulate growth. Water bulbs sparingly until green shoots begin to appear. Then add more water as needed.

Graphing the Growth of the Amaryllis Plant

Have children measure the plant's height at regular intervals—daily, if you wish.

When the plant is measured, be sure the measurements are taken from the same spot at the bottom of the plant.

The following graphing methods work well:

- Have children cut strips of construction paper equal in length to the height of the plant. Date these strips and mount them from a baseline on the Class Data Pad.
- Have children find the amount of growth between two different points in time; for example, on February 14th the plant was 1 inch tall and on February 22nd the plant was 2 inches tall. The plant grew 1 inch.
- Draw a grid like the one in the margin on the Class Data Pad. Allow for 24 inches of growth over 6 to 8 weeks. Have children mark heights above the corresponding dates on the graph. It doesn't matter if measurements are skipped for some dates, but measurements should not be recorded on incorrect dates.

Have children make estimates of future growth; for example, ask them what they think the height will be on a particular date. Follow up by comparing their estimates with the actual measurement for that day.

Mark on the graph when buds and blossoms appear. Allow time for children to closely examine the large flowers using a magnifying lens.

2 Extending the Project

Extension Suggestions

- Discuss responsibility and respect for living things and the environment. List ways that children can respect the environment so that living things can grow. Have children create posters that identify the needs of living things (food, water, oxygen, and light) and how they can help to fulfill those needs.

Literature Link Children can learn how to take care of a plant while listening to ***The Empty Pot*** by Demi (Henry Holt and Company Inc., 1996).

- Photograph the amaryllis from time to time; date and display the photos with the graph. Search online for professional photographs of the amaryllis plant. Children may enjoy trying to mimic the professional perspectives they see in the images.
- Have children make a timeline or journal about the plant's growth. They might include pictures, poems, or stories about the plant as well as measurements and descriptions.
- Have children use measuring tools to measure and record the amount of water that the amaryllis receives.
- Discuss the parts of a plant and their functions. (*See margin.*)
- Grow additional plants. Keep records of their growth and changes. Compare different plants to one another using a Venn diagram.

Science Link Children may enjoy reading the following books in order to help them learn more about the parts of a plant and photosynthesis: ***From Seed to Plant*** by Gail Gibbons (Holiday House Inc., 1993); and ***How Plants Grow*** by Angela Royston (Heinemann Library, 2001).

Language Arts Link Tell children that the name *amaryllis* comes from Greek mythology. *Amaryllis* means "splendid beauty."

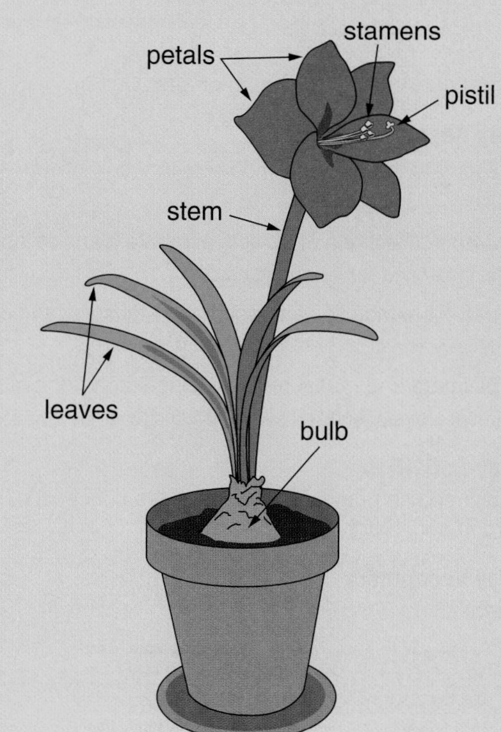

Home Link Suggestion

Have children draw three pictures—one of an amaryllis bulb, one of a young amaryllis plant, and one of a mature amaryllis plant. Encourage them to share the pictures with their family and challenge their family members to put the pictures in order from youngest to most mature.

Project 3

Pumpkin Math

Objectives To provide opportunities to estimate weight and girth; compare objects; and count a large collection of objects.

Technology Resources www.everydaymathonline.com

eToolkit

Algorithms Practice

EM Facts Workshop Game™

Family Letters

Assessment Management

Common Core State Standards

Curriculum Focal Points

Interactive Teacher's Lesson Guide

1 Doing the Project

Recommended Use During or after Unit 5

Key Concepts and Skills

- Estimate the number of objects in a collection.
  [Number and Numeration Goal 2]
- Count collections of objects accurately and reliably.
  [Number and Numeration Goal 2]
- Use a balance scale to estimate, measure, and compare weight.
  [Measurement and Reference Frames Goal 1]
- Estimate and measure girth using standard measuring tools.
  [Measurement and Reference Frames Goal 1]

Key Activities

Children use pumpkins to explore the concepts of girth and weight. In addition, they group and count pumpkin seeds.

Key Vocabulary

girth

Materials

- three pumpkins
- stick-on notes
- bath scale
- ruler
- string
- note cards
- clear tape
- scissors
- knife
- colander
- newspaper
- small paper cups

2 Extending the Project

Children make pumpkin pies and describe parts of the pies using fractions; they make pumpkins with geometric faces; they read literature selections about pumpkins; and they explore the nutritional value of pumpkins.

Children practice skills through Home Link activities.

Materials

- ingredients and supplies for making and serving pumpkin pie
- construction paper
- Pattern-Block Template
- *Full House: An Invitation to Fractions*
- *Pumpkin Pumpkin*
- *Pumpkin Jack*
- *Pumpkin Circle: The Story of a Garden*
- *Pumpkins*

Advance Preparation

You will need three pumpkins of various sizes. Use stick-on notes to label the pumpkins *A, B,* and *C*. Pumpkin A should be small enough for a child to comfortably hold in his or her hand.

For the optional activities in Part 2, obtain the following books: ***Full House: An Invitation to Fractions*** by Dayle Ann Dodds (Candlewick Press, 2009); ***Pumpkin Pumpkin*** by Jeanne Titherington (Greenwillow Books, 1990); ***Pumpkin Jack*** by Will Hubbell (Albert Whitman, 2003); ***Pumpkin Circle: The Story of a Garden*** by George Levenson (Tricycle Press, 2004); ***Pumpkins*** by Jacqueline Farmer (Charlesbridge Publishing, Inc., 2004).

1 Doing the Project

Comparing Weights and Weighing Pumpkins

Label two columns on the board *Lighter than Pumpkin A* and *Heavier than Pumpkin A*. Ask children to suggest classroom items that belong in each column. Record their suggestions. After the list is complete, "check" children's comparisons by allowing them to act as pan balances. Have a child hold Pumpkin A in one hand and one of the objects from the chart in the other hand. Encourage the child to raise and lower the "hand pans" to show which object is heavier or lighter. Encourage children to state weight comparisons using language such as, "My book bag is heavier than Pumpkin A but my stapler is lighter than Pumpkin A."

After children act as pan balances, discuss weight. Explain that in the United States weight is measured in pounds (lb). Place Pumpkin A on the bath scale and record its weight. Ask children to estimate the weights of the objects in the comparison chart based on the weight of Pumpkin A.

Conclude the activity by weighing each of the three pumpkins and recording the weights. Allow a volunteer to put the pumpkins in order from lightest to heaviest.

Estimating and Measuring the Girth of Pumpkins

Divide the children into three groups; each group will work with a different pumpkin.

Explain to children that **girth** is the distance around the widest part of an object. Ask each group to cut a length of string to represent its estimate for the girth of its pumpkin. Have each group measure its string using an inch ruler and record its girth estimate, in inches, on a note card. Each group attaches its string to a note card with clear tape.

Wrap a string around each pumpkin and cut it to show the actual girth. Allow three volunteers to measure the three strings and record the actual girths on note cards. Tape the strings and note cards on the board and label them *Actual Girth of Pumpkin X*. Encourage each group to compare its estimate to the actual girth of its pumpkin.

▶ Relating Weight and Girth

Ask:

- Which pumpkin has the largest girth? Does this pumpkin weigh the most?
- Which pumpkin has the smallest girth? Does the smallest pumpkin weigh the least?

Put the pumpkins in order from lightest to heaviest. Draw them approximately to scale. Put the pumpkins in order from smallest to largest girth. Draw them approximately to scale. Is the order the same or different? Encourage children to reference the drawings when making this comparison.

▶ Counting Pumpkin Seeds

Remove the pulp of each pumpkin. Wash the seeds from each pumpkin in a separate colander. Spread the seeds on separate newspapers to dry overnight. Ask children to estimate the total number of seeds in each pumpkin. Encourage them to explain their estimates; for example, "I think there are 200 seeds in this pumpkin because I counted 100 seeds in my pumpkin, and my pumpkin is smaller than this one."

When the seeds are dry, divide the class into three groups. Give each group all of the seeds from one of the pumpkins. Children check the reasonableness of their estimates by counting the seeds. Ask each group to count its seeds by placing each group of 10 seeds in a separate small cup. Then, as a whole class, use the cups to count the seeds in each pumpkin by 10s. When you get to 100, make one tally mark on the board. Continue in this manner until all of the seeds for a pumpkin have been counted. Count the tallies to determine the total number of seeds in a pumpkin. Repeat this activity for the other two pumpkins.

Ask:

- Does the largest pumpkin have the greatest number of seeds?
- Does the smallest pumpkin have the fewest number of seeds?
- Were your estimates close to the actual number of seeds in each pumpkin?

2 Extending the Project

Extension Suggestions

▷ Make pumpkin pies. Write the recipe on the board and discuss it with the class before making the pies. Measure and mix the ingredients while pointing out the various fractions used on measuring utensils.

Literature Link Read ***Full House: An Invitation to Fractions*** by Dayle Ann Dodds (Candlewick Press, 2009) before you divide the pumpkin pies into equal parts. Then divide the pies, name fractional parts, and encourage children to describe the pies using sentences like the following: "I am eating $\frac{1}{10}$ of the pumpkin pie. Together, Jamal and I ate $\frac{2}{10}$ of the pie."

Art Link Children cut pumpkins out of construction paper. Then they use their Pattern-Block Templates to draw or cut out eyes, noses, and mouths to make geometric faces on the pumpkins.

Literature Link Children may explore books about pumpkins, such as ***Pumpkin Pumpkin*** by Jeanne Titherington (Greenwillow Books, 1990); ***Pumpkin Jack*** by Will Hubbell (Albert Whitman, 2003); and ***Pumpkin Circle: The Story of a Garden*** by George Levenson (Tricycle Press, 2004).

Social Studies Link Find out how the tradition of pumpkin pie was begun by the colonists. Read ***Pumpkins*** by Jacqueline Farmer (Charlesbridge Publishing, Inc., 2004) to learn about additional interesting pumpkin facts.

Health Link Explore the nutritional value of pumpkins.

Home Link Suggestion

Start a classroom seed collection, beginning with pumpkin seeds. Have children bring seeds from home, such as apple seeds, corn kernels, sunflower seeds, acorns, and so on. The seeds can be compared, labeled, and made into seed mosaics.

Project

All About Time

Objective To provide children with opportunities to explore time.

Technology Resources www.everydaymathonline.com

Family Letters

1 Doing the Project

Recommended Use During or after Unit 6

Key Concepts and Skills

- Count by 1s.
  [Number and Numeration Goal 1]
- Mark the passage of time in seconds.
  [Measurement and Reference Frames Goal 4]
- Make calendars to identify days, weeks, months, and dates.
  [Measurement and Reference Frames Goal 4]

Key Activities

Children explore various timepieces and use the second hand for timing tasks. Children discuss the layout of a calendar and make a personal calendar to show the passage of twelve months.

Materials

- *Math Masters,* p. 300; p. 301 (at least 12 copies per child)
- Class Data Pad
- class calendar
- stapler
- various timepieces, preferably with second hands
- green and red dots
- working analog clock with a second hand

2 Extending the Project

Children measure time using nonstandard units; they tally their weekly activities; they time five different activities and order the activities from the least amount of time an activity takes to the greatest amount of time; they count to 15 using different methods; they discuss the passage of time in relation to topics such as the seasons and tides; and they read fiction and non-fiction books about time, months, and seasons.

Children practice skills through Home Link activities.

Materials

- stopwatches
- children's personal calendars
- *Sunshine Makes the Seasons*
- *Dear Rebecca, Winter Is Here*
- *Chimp Math: Learning About Time from a Baby Chimpanzee*
- *Telling Time: How to Tell Time on Digital and Analog Clocks!*

Advance Preparation

You will need a calendar for the current or upcoming year to provide accurate information about the first day of each month.

You may want to obtain the following books for the optional Extension Suggestions in Part 2:

▷ ***Sunshine Makes the Seasons*** by Franklyn M. Branley (HarperCollins Children's Books, 2005)

▷ ***Dear Rebecca, Winter Is Here*** by Jean Craighead George (HarperCollins Children's Books, 1995)

▷ ***Chimp Math: Learning About Time from a Baby Chimpanzee*** by Ann Whitehead Nagda and Cindy Bickel (Henry Holt and Company Inc., 2002)

▷ ***Telling Time: How to Tell Time on Digital and Analog Clocks!*** by Jules Older (Charlesbridge Publishing, 2000)

1 Doing the Project

▶ Timing in Seconds

Show children a variety of timepieces—preferably with second hands—such as a watch, an analog clock, a pocket watch, and so on. Discuss the following concepts:

- ▷ It takes 60 seconds for the second hand to move around the clock face once.
- ▷ There are 60 seconds in a minute.
- ▷ A second is shorter than a minute.
- ▷ The second hand moves faster than the minute hand.

Practice reading seconds by watching a clock and calling out 5-second intervals up to 60 seconds. Note that the 5-second intervals fall on the hour numbers displayed on the clock. It may be helpful to label the analog clock with the second counts for children to use as a reference.

Tell children that they will participate in various activities that will be timed in seconds. Explain that they will calculate the time in seconds using the second hand on an analog clock. When the second hand points straight up, they should give the "start" command. Instruct them to count the seconds, using the 5-second interval marks. For example, when the second hand points to the 1, say "5," when it points to the 2, say "10," and so on. Instruct children to say, "stop," when the correct number of seconds have passed. You may want to mark the start and stop points on the clock with green and red dots. Practice as a whole group until children are comfortable with the procedure.

▶ Timing Activity

(*Math Masters,* p. 300)

Divide children into partnerships. Have one child be the timer and the second child count and record his or her results on *Math Masters,* page 300. Children switch roles and repeat the activity.

Encourage children to compare the collected data.

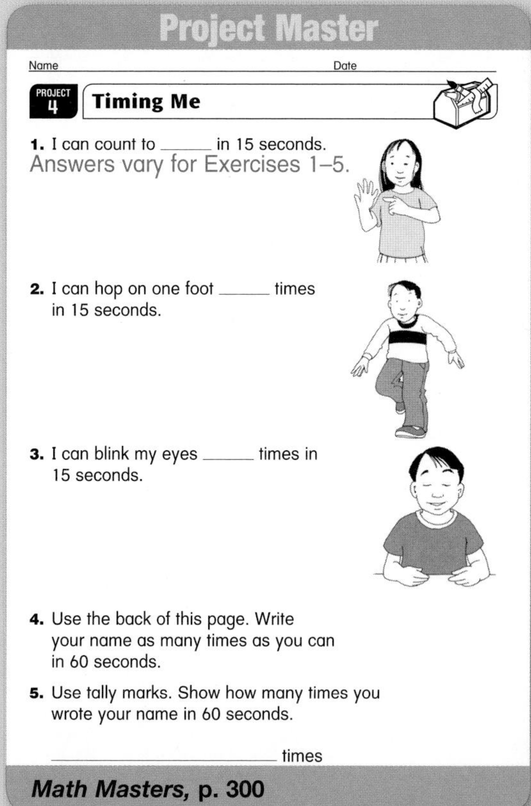
Project Master

Name Date

PROJECT 4 **Timing Me**

1. I can count to ______ in 15 seconds.
Answers vary for Exercises 1–5.

2. I can hop on one foot ______ times in 15 seconds.

3. I can blink my eyes ______ times in 15 seconds.

4. Use the back of this page. Write your name as many times as you can in 60 seconds.

5. Use tally marks. Show how many times you wrote your name in 60 seconds.

______ times

Math Masters, p. 300

Project Master

Name Date

PROJECT 4 **Calendar**

Sun.	Mon.	Tues.	Wed.	Thurs.	Fri.	Sat.

***Math Masters,* p. 301**

What are the months of the year?	On what day of the week does the month begin?	How many days are in the month?
January	Monday	31 days
February	Thursday	28 days
March	Thursday	31 days
April	Sunday	30 days
May	Tuesday	31 days
June	Friday	30 days
July	Sunday	31 days
August	Wednesday	31 days
September	Saturday	30 days
October	Monday	31 days
November	Thursday	30 days
December	Saturday	31 days

This sample chart is for the year 2007.

Making Personal Calendars

(*Math Masters,* p. 301)

Discuss with children that in addition to seconds, minutes, and hours, time can be counted in days, months, and years. Help children determine how many minutes are in an hour, how many hours are in a day, how many days are in a week, and how many months are in a year. Identify the days, weeks, and months on a class calendar and recite the days and months in order.

Ask children how they think people might keep track of important events that occur during the year. Invite each child to make a personal calendar. Discuss how their personal calendars will be different from the classroom calendar; for example, size, information recorded on it, and so on. Make a chart on the Class Data Pad to help children know on which day each month begins and how many days are in each month.

Give each child 12 copies of *Math Masters*, page 301. This page provides a grid for dates and space for an illustration. Have children put their calendar pages in chronological order and staple them together.

NOTE Children may want to make additional calendars for the school staff, such as the nurse and principal.

2 Extending the Project

Extension Suggestions

- Children may enjoy measuring time with nonstandard units; for example, ask: *In the amount of time it takes me to walk from one side of the room to the other, how many times can you do a jumping jack?*
- Have children tally on their personal calendars how many times they do various activities in a day, a week, or a month. *For example:*
  - brush their teeth
  - go to the park
  - read a book
- Provide stopwatches for children to use as they time themselves doing five different activities. Then have children put the activities in order from the least amount of time an activity takes to the greatest amount of time.

▷ Time children counting to 15 in several different ways such as: 1, 2, 3 ...; 1,001, 1,002, 1,003 ...; 1 Mississippi, 2 Mississippi, 3 Mississippi ...; 1, clap, clap, 2, clap, clap, 3, clap, clap ... . After trying a variety of different methods, discuss which way appears to be their most accurate method for estimating seconds. Challenge children to count using this method while you time them for 30 seconds. Compare children's counts to the actual elapsed time.

Science Link Discuss measuring the passage of time in relation to the seasons, tides, sunrise/sunset, and so on. ***Sunshine Makes the Seasons*** by Franklyn M. Branley (HarperCollins Children's Books, 2005) is a simple book that will help children understand the causes of seasonal changes.

Literature Link You might want to read aloud or allow children to explore these fiction and non-fiction books about time, months, and seasons: ***Dear Rebecca, Winter Is Here*** by Jean Craighead George (HarperCollins Children's Books, 1995); ***Chimp Math: Learning About Time from a Baby Chimpanzee*** by Ann Whitehead Nagda and Cindy Bickel (Henry Holt and Company Inc., 2002); and ***Telling Time: How to Tell Time on Digital and Analog Clocks!*** by Jules Older (Charlesbridge Publishing, 2000).

Home Link Suggestion

Have children bring their personal calendars home and ask family members to help them add upcoming family events to their calendars.

Project

5 Apple Math

Objective To provide opportunities to classify, count, compare, and measure.

Technology Resources www.everydaymathonline.com

eToolkit

Algorithms Practice

EM Facts Workshop Game™

Family Letters

Assessment Management

Common Core State Standards

Curriculum Focal Points

Interactive Teacher's Lesson Guide

1 Doing the Project

Recommended Use During or after Unit 7

Key Concepts and Skills

- Count collections of objects accurately and reliably. [Number and Numeration Goal 2]
- Tell and solve comparison number stories. [Operations and Computation Goal 4]
- Collect and organize data in a real graph and a bar graph. [Data and Chance Goal 1]
- Measure girth using standard measuring tools. [Measurement and Reference Frames Goal 1]
- Use a pan balance to measure and compare weights. [Measurement and Reference Frames Goal 1]

Key Activities

Children sort apples, gather quantitative data by counting apple seeds, and create a real graph on the floor. They also tell number comparison stories, measure the girth of apples with string, and weigh apples using a pan balance.

Materials

- *Math Masters,* p. 329
- apples (2 per partnership)
- construction paper
- scissors
- glue or transparent tape
- pan balance
- string
- ruler
- 1 plastic spoon per child
- stick-on notes
- masking tape

2 Extending the Project

Children make applesauce or baked apples; they research the life cycle of an apple tree; they take a field trip to an apple orchard or a local produce market; they find nutritional information for apple products; and they create family trees.

Children practice skills through Home Link activities.

Materials

- ingredients and items needed to make applesauce or baked apples
- *A Tree Is a Plant*
- *Tree*
- *Me and My Family Tree*

Advance Preparation

Gather apples of as many different varieties, colors, shapes, and sizes as possible. Use masking tape to make a large grid on the floor that will be used for the real graph in Part 1.

You may want to obtain the following books for the optional Extension Suggestions in Part 2:

▷ ***A Tree Is a Plant*** by Clyde Robert Bulla (HarperCollins Publisher, 2001)

▷ ***Tree*** by David Burnie (Dorling Kindersley, 2004)

▷ ***Me and My Family Tree*** by Joan Sweeney (Random House Children's Books, 2000)

1 Doing the Project

Classifying, Counting, and Comparing Apples

(*Math Masters,* p. 329)

Have children sort apples in different ways; for example, by color, shape, variety, or size. Compare their results by asking questions such as: *Are there more red apples or green apples? Are there fewer small apples or large apples? Of which variety do we have the most or fewest?*

Explain to children that they will use the results of their apple comparisons to make a graph.

Decide as a class if you will graph the apples according to color, size, shape, or variety. Have children use stick-on notes to label the axes. Children take turns placing apples on the graph. When all of the apples have been accurately placed, have each child use *Math Masters,* page 329 to make a bar graph that represents the data.

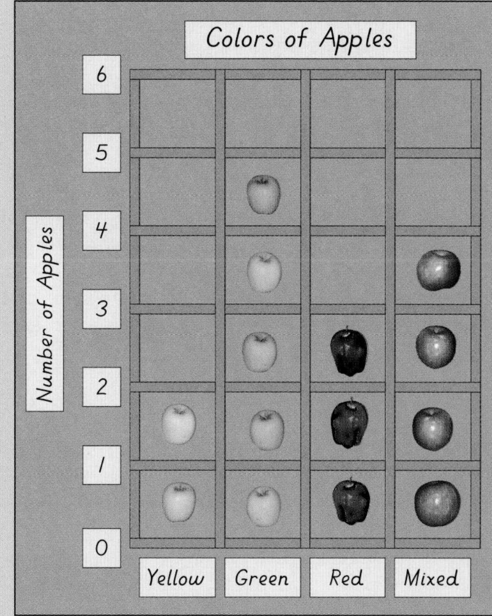

Making Apple Trees

Have children make apple trees from green and brown construction paper. Then they cut out a number of apples and fasten them onto their trees. Last, they number their apples 1, 2, and so on.

Ask partners to compare the number of apples on each other's trees and act out a comparison number story for their classmates. For example: *Al has 4 apples. Francesca has 3 apples. Who has fewer apples?* Francesca *How many fewer?* 1

Children use their apple trees to tell comparison stories.

Counting Apple Seeds

Give each partnership two halves of an apple. Have children use a plastic spoon to remove the seeds. When all of the seeds have been collected, one partner tapes or glues the seeds onto a quarter-sheet of paper and the other partner writes the total number of seeds. Have the class order the papers from the least to the greatest number of seeds.

▶ Measuring the Girth of an Apple

Remind children that girth is the distance around the widest part of an object. Ask children to measure the girth of an apple by wrapping a string around it. They should touch both ends of the string together without overlapping.

Have partners line up their strings alongside a ruler and record the measurements in inches on a quarter-sheet of paper. Remind children to label their measurements.

To arrange the apples in order from smallest girth to largest girth, ask for the child that thinks his or her apple has the smallest girth to share that measurement. Ask if anyone has an apple with a larger girth until all of the apples have been placed in order.

▶ Weighing Apples

Show children a pan balance. Remind them that it can be used for comparing the weights of objects. Direct their attention to the triangle on the pan balance that points to a line. Explain that the triangle only points to the line when the scale is balanced or has the same amount of weight on both sides. Put an apple on one side of the pan balance and point out how the triangle moves away from the line.

NOTE After items are "weighed," ask children to line them up in order by weight from lightest to heaviest.

A pan balance

Find two apples that are very close in weight. Cut one of the apples into fractional pieces. Ask which fractions the pieces represent—one-half, one-quarter, and so on. Put all of the pieces on one side of the scale and place the whole apple on the other side. Compare the weights of the apples. Ask: *Do the apple pieces and the whole apple balance the scale?* yes

Compare the weights of other items to apples such as boxes of crayons, pencils, or a drinking cup.

2 Extending the Project

▶ Extension Suggestions

- ▷ Make applesauce or baked apples.
- ▷ Research the life cycle of an apple tree.
- ▷ Take a field trip to an apple orchard and learn about the kinds of apples grown there and how much they cost. Explain to children that one large basket of apples is sometimes referred to as a bushel.
- ▷ Have children tell about a visit to a local produce market. *What varieties of apples do they sell? How much do they cost?*

Literature Link To further explore the life cycle of a tree, have children read ***A Tree Is a Plant*** by Clyde Robert Bulla (HarperCollins Publisher, 2001) or ***Tree*** by David Burnie (Dorling Kindersley, 2004).

Health Link Have children find nutritional information for apples and apple products.

Social Studies Link Read the book ***Me and My Family Tree*** by Joan Sweeney (Random House Children's Books, 2000). Have children draw their own family trees and label them with names of family members.

▶ Home Link Suggestion

Have children ask their families to help them look for different scales used to weigh objects. Some examples may include a bath scale, a food scale at the grocery store, or a postal scale at the post office. Have children draw pictures of the scales they find.

Project 6

Celebrate the Hundredth Day

Objective To provide opportunities to explore the number 100.

Technology Resources www.everydaymathonline.com

eTookit | Algorithms Practice | EM Facts Workshop Game™ | Family Letters | Assessment Management | Common Core State Standards | Curriculum Focal Points | Interactive Teacher's Lesson Guide

1 Doing the Project

Recommended Use On or around the hundredth day of school

Key Concepts and Skills

- Estimate the number of objects in a collection.
  [Number and Numeration Goal 2]
- Count collections of objects accurately and reliably.
  [Number and Numeration Goal 2]
- Use manipulatives to model equal parts of a collection.
  [Number and Numeration Goal 4]
- Calculate the values of combinations of coins.
  [Operations and Computation Goal 2]

Key Activities

Children celebrate the hundredth day of school by participating in a variety of activities involving the number 100.

Materials

Depending on your choice of activities:

- Class Thermometer Poster (°F)
- collections of small items
- transparent containers
- 100 toothpicks
- large piece of paper
- 100 pattern blocks
- 12-inch ruler
- masking tape
- classroom books
- pan balance
- 100-piece jigsaw puzzle
- tool-kit coins
- clock or watch with a second hand
- calculator
- base-10 blocks

2 Extending the Project

Children fill a name-collection box for 100; they solve number stories related to 100; they find how many centimeters are in a meter; they read literature selections related to 100; and they find out what world events happened 100 years ago and draw pictures to show their predictions for 100 years from now.

Children practice skills through Home Link activities.

Materials

- 100 base-10 cubes
- meter stick
- 12-month calendar
- *One Hundred Hungry Ants*
- *100th Day Worries*

Advance Preparation

Ask each child to collect and bring to school 100 small items. The items should be arranged in a display that is easy to count. For example, a child can glue 100 paper clips to cardboard in 10 rows of 10, or string 100 beads on 5 strings of 20. These collections will be displayed in a Hundreds Museum.

Look through the suggested activities on pages 449–450 and obtain materials for those activities you choose to do.

For the optional activities in Part 2, obtain the following books: ***One Hundred Hungry Ants*** by Elinor J. Pinczes (Houghton Mifflin Co., 1993); ***100th Day Worries*** by Margery Cuyler (Simon and Schuster Children's Publishing, 2005).

1 Doing the Project

Sharing the Hundreds Collections

Have children show and describe their collections of 100 items.

Make a class Hundreds Museum with the collections. Use some of the collections for the Suggested Celebration Activities that follow.

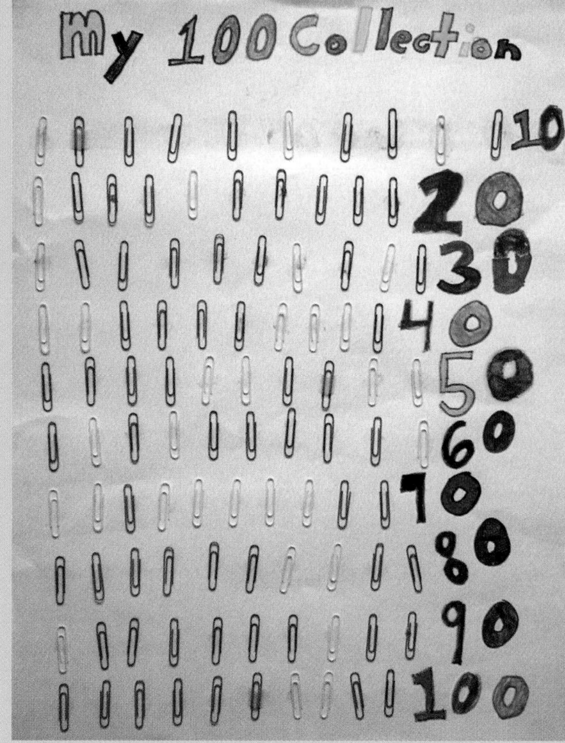

Suggested Celebration Activities

Following are suggestions for ways of celebrating the 100th day of first grade. Some teachers may choose to devote the whole day to doing 100th day activities; others may spend only part of the day. Choose those activities you wish, and add your own.

1. Fill transparent containers with more or less than 100 small items, such as pretzels, buttons, or erasers. Have children estimate the number of items in each container and record their estimates on the board. Reveal the exact numbers and count aloud with the children to double-check the quantities.
2. Give 100 toothpicks to small groups of 2–5 children. Ask them to estimate how many toothpicks each child would get if the toothpicks were shared equally. Children check their estimates by sharing the toothpicks and then gluing the toothpicks on a large sheet of paper in equal groups.
3. For each partnership or small group, have available 100 pattern blocks. Let children make patterns, mosaics, or designs.
4. Have children make 100 tally marks on the board.
5. With children's help, use 12-inch rulers to measure 100 feet in the hallway. Use masking tape to mark off the distance.

6. During a recreation time, have a 100-foot race.
7. Ask children to estimate where they would end up if they took 100 heel-to-toe steps from the start. Then have them actually take the steps and compare the distance to 100 standard feet.
8. Invite children to locate page 100 in several books.
9. Ask children to use the pan balance to weigh and compare collections of 100 small items from the Hundreds Museum.
10. Provide 100-piece jigsaw puzzles for children to work on during free time.
11. Ask children to find different ways to make $1.00 (100 cents) using their tool-kit coins. Have them record their coin combinations using Ⓠ, Ⓓ, Ⓝ, and Ⓟ.
12. Have children say when they think 100 seconds has passed while you time them. Then have them estimate how many times they can say the alphabet in 100 seconds, and then try it. Ask children how many hours are in 100 minutes. About $1\frac{1}{2}$ hours
13. Have children use their calculators. Tell them to press [ON/C] 0 [+] 10, then [=] 100 times, and report the result. 1,000
14. Ask children to list 100 words on a piece of paper.
15. Provide children with base-10 blocks and challenge them to build structures that total 100 or a multiple of 100.
16. Have children set the Classroom Thermometer Poster (°F) to 100°F. Ask children to describe what they might do or wear on a 100°F day.

Language Arts Link Invite children who speak languages other than English to teach the class how to say 100 in their languages. Use the chart below for other suggestions.

Language	100	Pronunciation
Chinese	*yibai*	(ee-by)
French	*cent*	(sahN)
German	*hundert*	(HUN-dert)
Italian	*cento*	(CHEHN-toh)
Japanese	*hyaku*	(hyah-koo)
Korean	*baek*	(bake)
Portuguese	*cem*	(say)
Russian	*sto*	(stoh)
Spanish	*cien*	(see-EHN)
Turkish	*yüz*	(yewz)

2 Extending the Project

Extension Suggestions

- Make a large name-collection box for 100 on the board. Have children fill in names for 100 throughout the day. Encourage children to make names using addition, subtraction, coins, base-10 blocks, tallies, and number stories. Challenge them to think of 100 different names!
- Tell number stories related to 100. For example: *How many people would it take to have a total of 100 fingers?* 10 people *How many people would it take to have a total of 100 eyes?* 50 people *How many cars would it take to have a total of 100 wheels?* 25 cars
- Line up 100 base-10 cubes along a meterstick. Remind children that each cube measures 1 centimeter. Ask: *How many centimeters are in 1 meter?* 100 centimeters

Literature Link Read the following books related to the number 100 and the hundredth day of school: ***One Hundred Hungry Ants*** by Elinor J. Pinczes (Houghton Mifflin Co., 1993) and ***100th Day Worries*** by Margery Cuyler (Simon and Schuster Children's Publishing, 2005).

Social Studies Link Find out what major world events happened 100 years ago. Share facts about everyday life during that time. Ask children to make predictions about life 100 years from now. Children can write and illustrate their predictions.

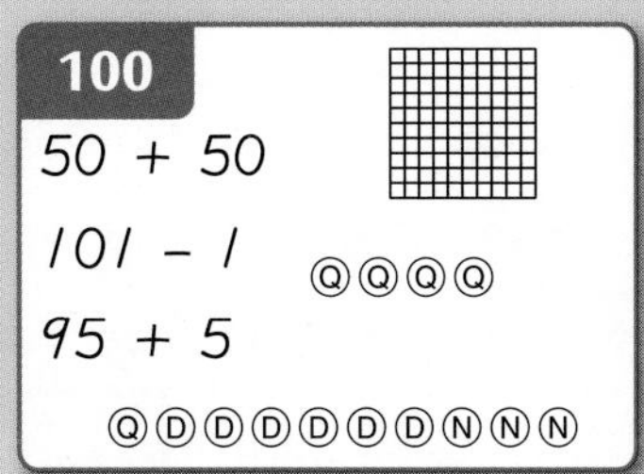

Home Link Suggestion

Have children count 100 days from today on a calendar at home. Have them discuss with a family member what they might be doing 100 days from now and draw a picture. *What month will it be? What season of the year? Will they be celebrating a family occasion at that time?*

Project

7 Weather and Probability

Objective To introduce the basic language of probability to describe events.

Technology Resources www.everydaymathonline.com

eToolkit

Algorithms Practice

EM Facts Workshop Game™

Family Letters

Assessment Management

Common Core State Standards

Curriculum Focal Points

Interactive Teacher's Lesson Guide

1 Doing the Project

Recommended Use During or after Unit 7

Key Concepts and Skills

- Compare quantities.
  [Number and Numeration Goal 7]
- Describe events using basic probability terms.
  [Data and Chance Goal 3]

Key Activities

Children discuss probability, use weather data to make predictions, and discuss the likelihood of events. They make a class book of weather events that are likely or unlikely during different seasons.

Key Vocabulary

likely ◆ unlikely

Materials

- ◆ Class Data Pad
- ◆ Class Weather Chart
- ◆ *Cloudy With a Chance of Meatballs* (optional)

2 Extending the Project

Children use the Class Weather Chart to create a bar graph; they write and perform a TV news weather report; they learn about the job of a meteorologist; they learn what causes the seasons to change; and they identify different ways to describe probability terms.

Children practice skills through Home Link activities.

Materials

- ◆ Class Weather Chart
- ◆ videotaping equipment (optional)
- ◆ *What Will the Weather Be?*
- ◆ *The Reasons for Seasons*

Advance Preparation

You will need data about the weather in your area for the current month. This information can come from your Class Weather Chart or the Internet.

For Doing the Project in Part 1, you may want to obtain ***Cloudy With a Chance of Meatballs*** by Judith Barrett (Simon and Schuster Children's Publishing, 1982).

You may want to obtain the following books for the optional Extension Suggestions in Part 2:

▷ ***What Will the Weather Be?*** by Lynda Dewitt (HarperCollins Publishers, 1993)

▷ ***The Reasons for Seasons*** by Gail Gibbons (Holiday House, 1996)

1 Doing the Project

▶ Discussing Weather Forecasts

Begin a discussion about probability by asking children about weather forecasts. Ask:

- How did you decide whether or not to wear a coat (or bring an umbrella) to school today?
- What does a weather forecast tell you?
- What words do weather reporters use to talk about the weather?
- What information does a weather reporter use to make his or her predictions?

As children share their ideas, make a list on the Class Data Pad of probability words such as ***likely, unlikely***, *chance*, *impossible*, *possible,* and *certain.*

NOTE Of all of the strands of mathematics, probability is one of the most useful in daily life. The vocabulary of qualitative probability—likely, unlikely, impossible, certain, and so on—should be introduced early as the basis for mathematical probability in *Everyday Mathematics* and beyond. Through repeated use, children will gradually make these terms part of their vocabularies.

▶ Predicting Weather Events

Share local weather data with the class for the current month. Discuss trends in the weather. Ask:

- Have there been more sunny days or rainy (snowy) days this month?
- What kind of weather did we have on the greatest number of days? On the fewest number of days?
- Based on the weather we have had in the past few days, what do you predict the weather will be tomorrow?

List children's predictions in a column on the Class Data Pad under the heading *Likely*. Then make a new column titled *Unlikely*. Ask children to think of weather events that are unlikely to occur on the following day. Encourage children to be imaginative. Unlikely events could include raining cats and dogs or a 100°F day in the winter.

NOTE You may wish to review temperature using both the Fahrenheit and Celsius scales on page 87 of the *My Reference Book.*

Literature Link Read ***Cloudy With a Chance of Meatballs*** by Judith Barrett (Simon and Schuster Children's Publishing, 1982). In the fictional town of Chewandswallow, the weather comes in the form of food. Use this funny story to talk about weather events that are unlikely or even impossible!

▶ Making a Class Book of Weather

Ask children to name the different seasons. Fall, winter, spring, and summer Tell children that weather varies by season, changing the likelihood of weather events such as rain, snow, or fog.

Ask the class to suggest a few likely weather events—occasions of different types of weather—for each season. Then share ideas about seasonal, weather-related activities such as ice skating, raking leaves, or swimming at the beach.

Have children make a class book of weather events and weather-related activities that are likely or unlikely during different seasons. Children choose a season and record it on a page. Then they write a statement about likely weather for that season and illustrate it. They repeat the activity with a statement about unlikely weather for that season. Remind children that each statement must include the word *likely* or *unlikely*.

NOTE Adapt the discussion of seasons to fit your climate. It may be more appropriate to talk about dry and rainy seasons or other weather events such as hurricanes or tornadoes.

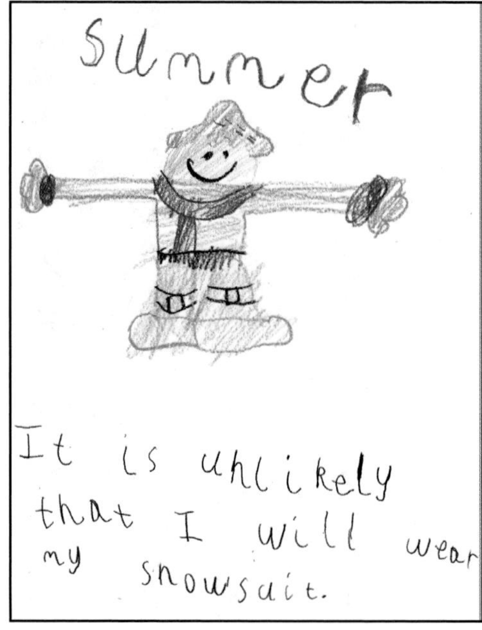

Children write and illustrate statements that describe likely and unlikely seasonal events.

2 Extending the Project

▶ Extension Suggestions

- ▷ Ask children if weather forecasts are always accurate. Discuss the fact that weather forecasts are predictions. Explain the difference between *likely* and *certain* events.
- ▷ Use the data from the Class Weather Chart to create a weather bar graph.
- ▷ Have small groups of children write and perform a TV news weather report. You may wish to videotape the performances.

Science Link Children can learn more about the job and tools of a meteorologist by reading ***What Will the Weather Be?*** by Lynda DeWitt (HarperCollins Publishers, 1993).

Science Link Help children understand what causes the seasons to change by reading ***The Reasons for Seasons*** by Gail Gibbons (Holiday House, 1996).

Language Arts Link Ask children to think of different ways of saying *likely*, *unlikely*, *certain*, and *impossible*. Encourage children to use informal, everyday language. For example, a child might say, "no way," "never," and "definitely not" for *impossible;* or "for sure," "guaranteed," and "definitely" for *certain*.

▶ Home Link Suggestion

Have children watch a weather forecast on TV or listen to one on the radio. Ask children to list any probability words that they hear and bring the list to school. Children can compare weather forecasts and discuss their accuracy.

Project

8 A Flea Market

Objective To provide opportunities to practice buying-and-selling situations using coins.

Technology Resources www.everydaymathonline.com

eToolkit

Algorithms Practice

EM Facts Workshop Game™

Family Letters

Assessment Management

Common Core State Standards

Curriculum Focal Points

Interactive Teacher's Lesson Guide

1 Doing the Project

Recommended Use During or after Unit 8

Key Concepts and Skills

- Calculate and compare values of combinations of coins.
  [Operations and Computation Goal 2]
- Use a calculator to solve subtraction problems.
  [Operations and Computation Goal 2]

Key Activities

Children create and work in a classroom flea market. Children practice paying for items and making change for the customers using coins and calculators. They practice adding and subtracting 1- and 2-digit prices.

Materials

- toys, books, puzzles, and other items from home and classroom
- 3" by 5" index cards
- tool-kit coins
- stick-on notes or masking tape
- calculator

2 Extending the Project

Children conduct a flea-market sale using half-off coupons; they make a tally chart to determine how to use the proceeds from the flea market; they discuss the types of markets found in their community; and they read literature selections related to stores and selling items.

Children practice skills through Home Link activities.

Materials

- handmade half-off coupons
- proceeds from class flea market
- *Grandma Went to Market: A Round-the-World Counting Rhyme*
- *Mama and Papa Have a Store*
- *Market!*

Advance Preparation

Send a letter home describing the project. Explain that items from home will not be returned to their child once they have been sold to a classmate during the flea market. Give families an option of sending 2 or 3 items or cutting pictures of items out of catalogs and gluing them to index cards. Decide on an amount of money for each child to use. Children can bring money from home or take that amount from their tool kits. Label items with prices using stick-on notes or masking tape.

You may want to obtain the following books for the optional Extension Suggestions in Part 2:

▷ ***Grandma Went to Market: A Round-the-World Counting Rhyme*** by Stella Blackstone (Houghton Mifflin Co., 1996)

▷ ***Mama and Papa Have a Store*** by Amelia Lau Carling (Dial, 1998)

▷ ***Market!*** by Ted Lewin (HarperCollins Publisher, 1996)

1 Doing the Project

Discussing the Flea Market

Explain that a flea market provides an opportunity for people to sell items they no longer want, or to exchange them for someone else's items that they might want. Tell children to talk with an adult at home about items they might bring to school for the flea market. These could include unwanted toys, books, puzzles, stuffed animals, and so on.

Set a date for the flea market. Decide whether the market will be open several consecutive days or for several chosen days in a given time period. Children should bring items to school several days before.

Pricing the Items

Set a range in which all items will be priced; 5 to 50 cents works well. Be sure children understand the idea of the price range. Children can price the items they bring to class.

Talk about money and change. Ask:

- If I have a nickel and a dime, how much money do I have? 15¢
- Suppose I bought your toy car for 5 cents and gave you a dime. How much change should you give me back? 5¢
- I have 35 cents. Can I buy a book for 10 cents and a pen for 30 cents? No, the book and pen together cost 40¢.

Flea market items

Give an example of bartering by sharing the following conversation:

Josephine: *I want to barter for your purse, Shawna. Can I give you my two dolls and 15¢?*

Shawna: *No, I will not accept your barter Josephine. I want your two dolls and 20¢ since my purse is priced at 50¢.*

Holding the Flea Market

Establish a space in the classroom to store and display the items for the flea market before it opens. Decide on the time of day that the market will be open. Have children help plan and organize "shopping times" for other classes to participate in the flea market.

▶ Making Change

Have children take turns being the cashier. You may want to write the following steps for making change with a calculator on the board. Be sure children understand that the amount the customer pays is entered into the calculator first.

1. Clear the calculator.
2. Enter the amount the customer gives you.
3. Press [−].
4. Enter the cost of the item being purchased.
5. Press [=].
6. This number is the amount of change you owe the customer.

▶ Using a Shopkeeper's Journal

Explain to children that long before cash registers and computers, shopkeepers kept records of sales by writing them down. Have children staple pieces of blank paper together to create a shopkeeper's journal. Tell them that they will record their transactions, or number stories, while working as the cashier. Encourage them to use any strategy they wish.

▶ Reviewing the Results

Have each "shift" use their shopkeeper's journals to report how much money they have made.

Children can use calculators to find the grand total. Compare the total amount received with the total amount of money at the start of the project. Ask whether all of the money was spent.

Have children talk about their experiences. For example: *Did cheaper items sell faster? Were some items overpriced?*

2 Extending the Project

Extension Suggestions

- Have children make half-off discount coupons for the flea market. Use them to conduct a half-off sale at the end of the project. You may also consider reducing items for a "quick sale" during the last few minutes or days of the sale.
- Discuss how the proceeds from the flea market should be spent. You may consider donating the proceeds to a local charity or buying something for the classroom. Have children vote for their preferences and then tally and record their votes in a chart. If children decide to buy something for the classroom, bring in school supply catalogs so that children can determine whether they have enough money to buy the items they want.

NOTE If children used their tool-kit coins, have them divide the coins so that each child puts the correct coins back into his or her kit.

Language Arts Link You may want to read the following books aloud: ***Grandma Went to Market: A Round-the-World Counting Rhyme*** by Stella Blackstone (Houghton Mifflin Co. 1996); and ***Mama and Papa Have a Store*** by Amelia Lau Carling (Dial, 1998).

Social Studies Link Read ***Market!*** by Ted Lewin (HarperCollins Publisher, 1996). Discuss the different types of markets that can be found in your community.

Home Link Suggestion

Ask families to accompany their children to a local market and give children a number of coins to spend.

Project

9 Ad Wizard

Objective To practice strategies for adding and subtracting with 2-digit numbers.

Technology Resources www.everydaymathonline.com

eToolkit

Algorithms Practice

EM Facts Workshop Game™

Family Letters

Assessment Management

Common Core State Standards

Curriculum Focal Points

Interactive Teacher's Lesson Guide

1 Doing the Project

Recommended Use During or after Unit 5

Key Concepts and Skills

- Add 2-digit numbers to 1-digit numbers and multiples of 10.
  [Operations and Computation Goal 2]
- Subtract multiples of 10.
  [Operations and Computation Goal 2]
- Use number grids, base-10 blocks, and other strategies to add and subtract.
  [Operations and Computation Goal 2]
- Write or draw to represent addition and subtraction strategies.
  [Operations and Computation Goal 2]

Key Activities

Children make advertisements to practice adding and subtracting 2-digit numbers, including multiples of 10. They review strategies for addition and subtraction. They illustrate their strategies with words and drawings.

Materials

- *Math Masters,* pp. 302–302F
- print ads children bring from home
- base-10 blocks
- number grid
- counters
- scissors
- glue sticks
- markers and craft supplies
- posterboard

***See* Advance Preparation**

2 Extending the Project

Children make advertisements with their own items and prices; they reexamine prices in print ads they bring to class; and they read about tricks of advertising.

Materials

- *Math Masters,* p. 302G
- *The Berenstain Bears and the Trouble with Commercials* by Jan Berenstain

Advance Preparation

Ask children to bring advertisements from print materials like newspapers and magazines. You may wish to send a letter home describing the project and this request. Make one copy per child of *Math Masters,* pages 302, 302A, 302B, 302D, and 302F; make three copies per child of *Math Masters,* pages 302C and 302E.

1 Doing the Project

Learning about Ads

Discuss with children what advertisements or ads are. Ask children to describe ads they have read in newspapers or magazines, viewed on television, seen on billboards or the Internet, or heard on the radio. As children share, keep a running list of features that make ads memorable; for example, the ads have products children want, bargains or sales, eye-catching graphics, or funny or clever slogans.

Display some of the print ads children brought from home. As a class, examine these ads to make another list of features that are common to the ads. This list may include the names of the stores, lists or pictures of one or more items that the stores sell, the prices of the items, or slogans.

Tell children that today they will be making ads for items sold in their own imaginary pet stores. Remind children that good ads include features from both lists. Post the lists, along with some of the print ads children brought from home, so that children can refer to them.

Language Arts Link Discuss the difference in meaning and spelling between *ad,* as in advertisement, and *add,* as in to perform addition.

Determining the Right Price

(*Math Masters,* pp. 302 and 302A)

Tell children that they are going to determine prices for items and show how they determined prices as a class before they plan their own ads. Tell them that they may use base-10 blocks, number grids, counters, tally marks, or other strategies in determining prices.

Ask children to determine the combined price of the hamster and hamster wheel on *Math Masters,* page 302. Have several children explain their strategies for determining the total price. Help children write or draw to illustrate their strategies on page 302. For instance, children may need assistance with drawing tally marks, counters, or base-10 shorthand. Help children write number models on the page to correspond with the strategies they illustrate.

During the discussion, be sure to emphasize the following strategies:

▷ **Counting on from the larger addend**

Strategy: Start with the larger price, 16, and count up 8.

Number model: 16 + 8 = 24

Math Masters, p. 302

Math Masters, p. 302A

Project Master

Name Date

PROJECT 9 Pet Store Items 1

Price: $75	Price: $9
Price: $24	Price: $8
Price: $53	Price: $7

Math Masters, p. 302B

Project Master

Name Date

PROJECT 9 Ad Template for Two Items

________________'s Pet Store

Paste picture here.	Paste picture here.

Write or draw to show how you found the total price.

Number Model: ________________

Total Price: $________

Math Masters, p. 302C

▷ **Making ten**

Strategy: Use base-10 blocks to represent 16 (1 long, 6 cubes) and 8 (8 cubes). Add the blocks together, adding tens to tens and ones to ones: 8 cubes + 1 long, 6 cubes = 1 long, 14 cubes. Trade 10 cubes for 1 long, composing a 10 and leaving 4 cubes left over: 2 longs, 4 cubes = 2 tens, 4 ones = 24.

Number model: $16 + 8 = 10 + 6 + 8 = 10 + 14 =$
$10 + 10 + 4 = 20 + 4 = 24$

Provide children with *Math Masters,* page 302A. Ask children to determine the price of the fish tank if it is on sale for \$20 off. Have several children explain their strategies for determining the price. Help them illustrate their strategies and write appropriate number models.

During the discussion, be sure to emphasize the following strategies:

▷ **Using the number grid**

Strategy: Find 50 on the number grid. To subtract 20, stay in the same column, and move up two rows to 30.

Number model: $50 - 20 = 30$

▷ **Counting up to subtract**

Strategy: Use a number grid. Start at 20 and move down rows to reach 50. Count by tens as you move down 3 rows. The difference is 30.

Number model: $20 + 30 = 50$ or $50 - 20 = 30$

▶ Making Ads

INDEPENDENT ACTIVITY

(*Math Masters,* pp. 302B–302E)

Tell children that they will start by making advertisements for which they add the prices of two items. They will then make ads for which they subtract to find the sale price of an item.

Provide children with scissors, glue sticks, and copies of *Math Masters*, pages 302B and 302C. Have children cut out the pictures of the dog and the leash on page 302B. Show children how to glue the items onto the template on page 302C to make their ads. Remind children that they are adding the prices of the two items, and review how to fill out the rest of the page as they did on *Math Masters*, page 302.

After children have made ads for the first row of items, have them independently complete two more ads. For each ad, children should match a pet with a pet accessory. Circulate and assist children until they each have made three ads.

Next, provide children with copies of *Math Masters*, pages 302D and 302E. Emphasize to children that they are now subtracting to determine the sale price of an item. Review how to fill out the rest of the template on page 302E as they did on *Math Masters*, page 302A.

As with the previous ads, you may wish to complete one ad with the whole class before having children make their own ads. To make their ads, children should match each pet or pet accessory with a sale price. Circulate and assist children until they each have made two more ads.

Provide each child with a piece of posterboard, markers, and other craft materials as needed. Have children display their six ads on the posterboard and decorate the posters. Encourage children to refer to the lists they made at the beginning of class about common and memorable features of ads to generate ideas for decorating their posters. Children may wish to add slogans, drawings, and color to their posters.

▶ Checking the Ads

PARTNER ACTIVITY

(*Math Masters,* p. 302F)

When children are finished, display their store posters. Have pairs of children place their ads side-by-side so that they may examine them. Ask the partnerships to look closely at others' ads to make sure the prices are correct. Have the partnerships work through any questionable prices together.

After children have examined the ads, discuss the following questions:

- Did you and your partner get the correct prices for all of the items?
- If not, which prices did you change?
- What strategies did you use to determine the correct prices?
- What made the ads on your partner's store poster memorable?

Finally, have children practice explaining how they solve 2-digit addition and subtraction problems by completing *Math Masters,* page 302F.

Display the store posters for several days after the project, so that children get a chance to look at more of them.

2 Extending the Project

▶ Extension Suggestions

▷ Have children imagine their own pet store items, draw pictures of their imagined items, and write prices for the items using *Math Masters,* page 302G. You may wish to have children determine the total prices for these items and make new ads.

▷ Have children reexamine the print ads they brought to class. Ask them to consider whether the prices on the ads are correct.

Language Arts Link Children can learn more about advertisements and being cautious consumers by reading ***The Berenstain Bears and the Trouble with Commercials*** by Jan Berenstain (HarperCollins, 2007).

Project Master

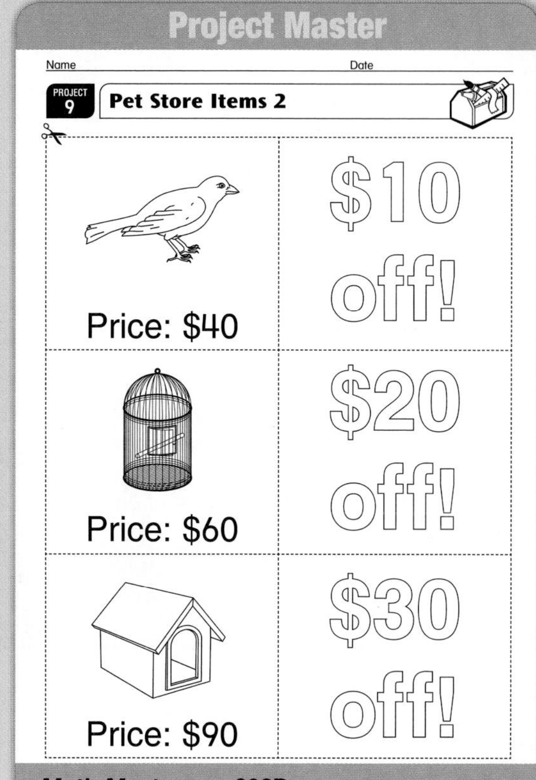
Name Date

PROJECT 9 **Pet Store Items 2**

Price: $40	$10 off!
Price: $60	$20 off!
Price: $90	$30 off!

Math Masters, p. 302D

Project Master

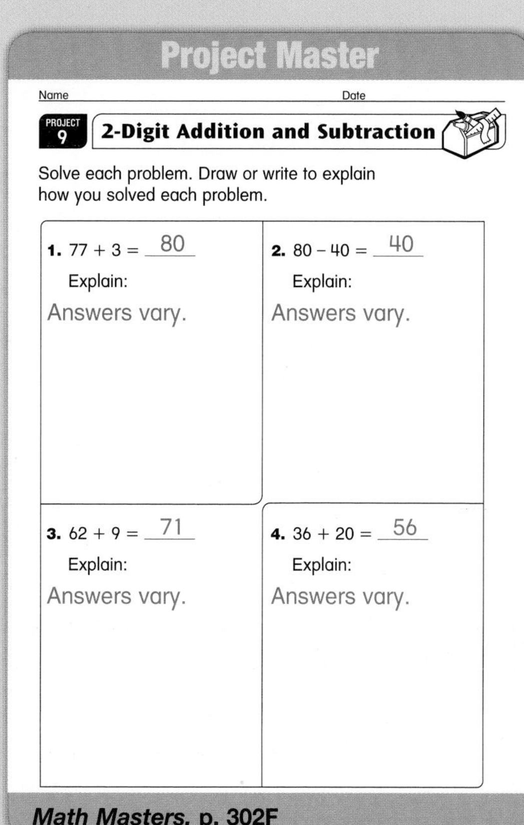
Name Date

PROJECT 9 **2-Digit Addition and Subtraction**

Solve each problem. Draw or write to explain how you solved each problem.

1. 77 + 3 = 80
Explain:
Answers vary.

2. 80 − 40 = 40
Explain:
Answers vary.

3. 62 + 9 = 71
Explain:
Answers vary.

4. 36 + 20 = 56
Explain:
Answers vary.

Math Masters, p. 302F

Project

10 Shape City

Objective To construct composite figures from plane shapes and solid figures.

Technology Resources www.everydaymathonline.com

eToolkit

Algorithms Practice

EM Facts Workshop Game™

Family Letters

Assessment Management

Common Core State Standards

Curriculum Focal Points

Interactive Teacher's Lesson Guide

1 Doing the Project

Recommended Use During or after Unit 7

Key Concepts and Skills

- Compose plane shapes. [Geometry Goal 1]
- Compose solid figures. [Geometry Goal 1]
- Construct composite shapes from plane shapes and solid figures. [Geometry Goal 1]

Key Activities

Children review plane shapes, solid figures, and composite shapes. They learn about cities, including the buildings, people, animals, and objects one might find in a city. They construct models of city buildings from solid figures. They construct models of people, animals, and objects from plane shapes. They use their constructions to create a class model of a city.

Materials

- *Math Masters,* pp. 212A, 212B, 288A, 288B, 302H, 302I, 302J, and 302K
- pattern blocks
- circle blocks (from *Math Masters,* page 205A)
- solid figures collected in the Shapes Museum
- scissors
- scotch and masking tape
- glue sticks and glue
- Pattern-Block Templates
- white construction paper (5 sheets per small group)
- markers
- chart paper (optional)

***See* Advance Preparation**

2 Extending the Project

Children find plane shapes and solid figures in pictures from magazines; they combine and trace pattern blocks to make composite shapes; they make familiar shapes from other shapes; and they read about cities.

Materials

- old magazines
- pattern blocks
- *Busy, Busy Town* by Richard Scarry

Advance Preparation

Before beginning the project, clear a space (approximately 4 feet by 4 feet) in the classroom or in the hallway outside of your classroom for children to construct their city model. You may wish to use masking tape to mark this space on the floor and to mark roads within the city. On firm colored paper (the firmer, the better), copy two sets of *Math Masters,* pages 212A, 212B, 288A, and 288B for each small group. Consider cutting out some of the templates on these pages in advance. On firm white paper, copy two sets of *Math Masters,* pages 302H, 302I, and 302J for each small group. Make one copy of *Math Masters,* page 302K and cut out the building tags from this page before the lesson.

Collect (or have children collect) old magazines for the project extensions.

1 Doing the Project

Exploring Composite Shapes

WHOLE-CLASS ACTIVITY

Tell children that they are going to be learning more about shapes. Ask children to name plane shapes they know. Make a list of plane shapes on the board or on chart paper. Be sure the list includes the following plane shapes: square, rectangle, triangle, trapezoid, hexagon, rhombus, parallelogram, circle, half-circle, and quarter-circle.

Ask children to name the solid figures they know. Make a separate list of these shapes on the board or on chart paper. Be sure the list includes the following solid figures: cube, rectangular prism, cylinder, cone, pyramid, and sphere.

Remind children that they can combine the shapes they know to make new shapes. Provide children with pattern blocks, circle blocks (introduced in Lesson 7-4), and solid figures from the Shapes Museum. Encourage them to try combining shapes to form several different composite shapes.

Circulate and monitor children as they make new shapes. Children should combine plane shapes with plane shapes and solid figures with solid figures. When children have made composite shapes they like, ask them to combine multiple composite shapes to make a new one.

NOTE Children do not need to tape or fasten their shapes together. At this point, they are simply exploring different ways to combine shapes. Later in the project, they will connect their shapes together.

After children have explored composite shapes, ask several children to share interesting shapes they constructed. As each child shares, pose the following questions to the rest of class:

- Does the new shape remind you of other shapes?
- Which shapes make up the new shape?
- Can you make the same shape?

Tell children that when they see an unfamiliar shape, they can often break it down into simpler shapes that they know.

▶ Learning about Cities

Explain that children are going to use the shapes they know to build a model of a city. Many people, including people who design buildings, make models of their constructions before they actually build them. Tell children they may have done something similar when they played with blocks. In this project, children are going to combine simple plane shapes and solid figures to design and model the things they would find in a city.

Discuss what cities are and what children may find in and around cities. Make separate lists of buildings children have seen in cities and of the people, animals, and objects they have seen in cities. You may wish to ask children the following questions:

- What is the name of the city, village, or town where you live (or nearest to where you live)? What other cities have you been to? What other cities have you heard of?
- What are some places or buildings you might visit in a city? Sample answers: House, school, store, hospital, park, library
- Who are some people you might see at a hospital? Sample answers: Patients, doctors, nurses At a school? Sample answers: Other children, teachers, maintenance staff At a store? Sample answers: Shoppers, cashiers At other places?
- What animals or other objects might you see in a city when you are outside? Sample answers: Dogs, cats, cars, stop lights, benches, signs

Tell children that today they will use what they know about cities and shapes to make models of buildings, people, animals, and things.

NOTE In this project, the term "city" is used generically, to represent any town, village, or settlement, not just an urban or metropolitan area. You may use whichever term (village, town, or city) your class would best understand. Children should discuss and model generic buildings and people such as hospitals and doctors, not specific ones, such as the Empire State Building.

▶ Modeling Buildings with Solid Figures

(*Math Masters,* pp. 212A, 212B, 288A, and 288B)

Review the list children made of buildings in a city. Have each small group select its own building to model with solid figures. Some possible buildings include school, bank, library, store, police station, or hospital.

Distribute two sets of *Math Masters,* pages 212A, 212B, 288A, and 288B to each small group. Tell children that they may use these pages to make solid figures, which they will combine to make models of their buildings. If necessary, demonstrate how to cut out, fold, and tape each template into a solid (see Lessons 7-5, 7-6, and 10-5 for more on these templates). Provide children with scissors and tape, and have them work together in their groups to construct the solid figures. Each small group should construct two of each solid figure: cube, cone, rectangular prism, and cylinder.

NOTE Some children may have difficulty cutting out the templates. You may wish to pair children with strong fine-motor skills with those who have difficulty with fine-motor tasks, or you may wish to cut a few of each template before the project begins.

After children have composed their solid figures, have them work in their small groups to combine the solid figures into a model of their building. They may fasten the solid figures together using tape or glue. Remind them that the models do not have to look exactly like the buildings they represent and that they do not have to use all of their solid figures to make their composite figures. What is important is that they combine solid figures in some way to make a composite figure that resembles a building.

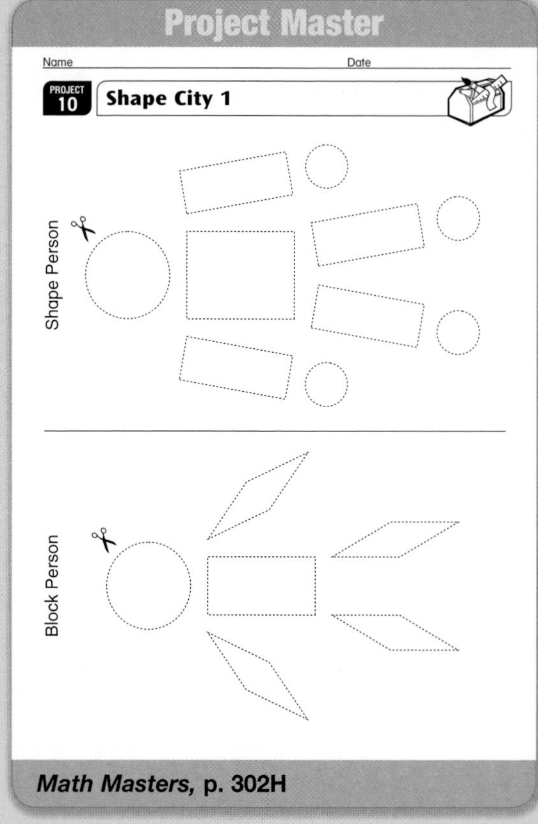

Math Masters, p. 302H

Modeling People, Animals, and Objects with Plane Shapes

SMALL-GROUP ACTIVITY

(*Math Masters,* pp. 302H, 302I, and 302J)

Review the list of people, animals, and objects children see around a city. Tell children that they will use plane shapes to model people, animals, or objects they would see at the building they constructed. For instance, if children modeled a school with their solid figures, they could now model people with plane shapes and then color or decorate them to look like teachers and students.

Children should have their pattern blocks, circle blocks, and Pattern-Block Templates ready to compose shapes and composite shapes. Provide each small group with five sheets of white construction paper and two sets of *Math Masters,* pages 302H, 302I, and 302J. Explain that these masters give children some ideas for how to model various people, animals, and objects with plane shapes.

NOTE You may wish to discuss each item on the masters with children. The masters distinguish Block Figures, or those that can be made with pattern blocks and circle blocks, from Shape Figures, or those that can be made with other shapes not found on the Pattern-Block Template. Some of the items are modeled more realistically than others, and the items are not to scale, so that they are easier for children to construct.

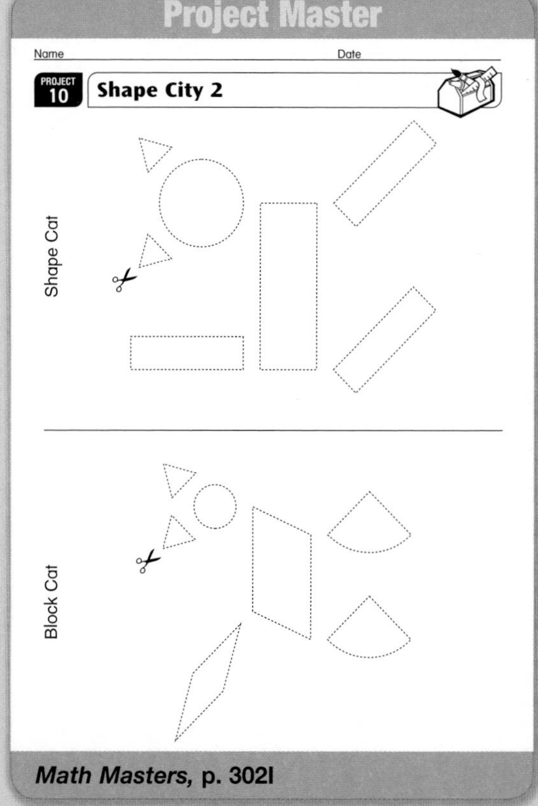

Math Masters, p. 302I

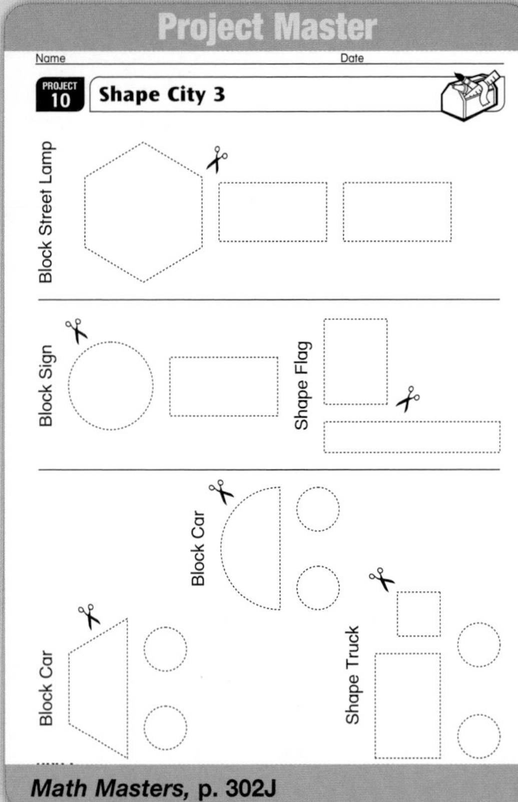

Math Masters, p. 302J

NOTE The three options presented here are ordered in terms of increasing difficulty. Depending on the skill level of your class, you may wish to introduce only Option 1 or only Options 1 and 2. You may then challenge some children to use Option 3.

NOTE Some children may try to make a stop sign with the hexagon. You may wish to remind them that stop signs are actually octagons.

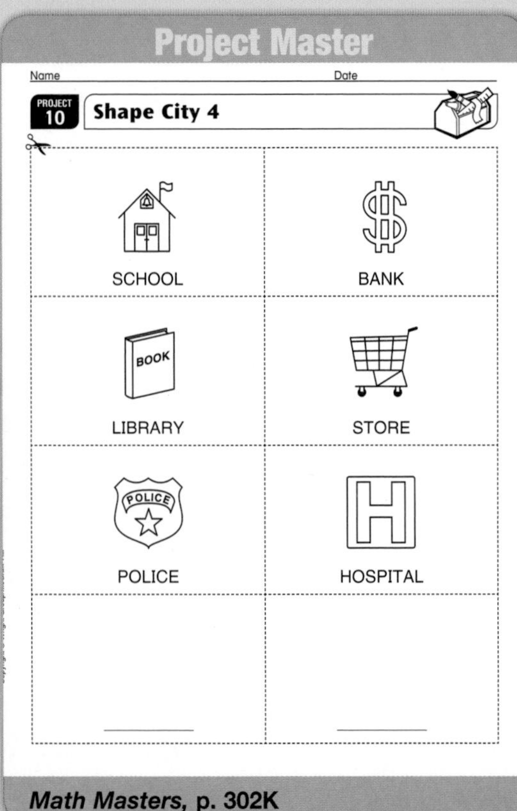

Math Masters, p. 302K

Discuss and model at least one of the three options children may use to construct their composite figures. Demonstrate the options by using the Block Person on *Math Masters,* page 302H as an example.

Option 1: Use the masters. Demonstrate this option for children by cutting out the component shapes for the Block Person from *Math Masters,* page 302H. Fold a piece of the white construction paper in half, and use a glue stick to affix the shapes, in the form of a person, to one half of the folded construction paper. Set the construction paper upright, so that the figure will stand up.

Option 2: Use pattern blocks and circle blocks. Demonstrate this option for children on the overhead by arranging pattern blocks and circle blocks so that they make the person. Trace the outline of the figure on the overhead. Tell children that they will trace the composite figure onto one half of their folded construction paper so that the figure will stand up.

Option 3: Use the Pattern-Block Template. Demonstrate this option for children on the overhead by using the Pattern-Block Template to draw each component shape for the person. Tell children that they will trace the shapes, in the form of a person, onto one half of their folded construction paper so that the figure will stand up.

After each small group has composed four or five figures, provide children with markers to color and decorate their figures. Remind them to decorate the figures based on the building where they will be placed. For instance, if they modeled a police station, they may wish to decorate one of the people they modeled in blue or black to resemble a police officer.

▶ Building the City

WHOLE-CLASS ACTIVITY

(*Math Masters,* p. 302K)

Provide each small group with the appropriate building tag from *Math Masters,* page 302K. (Use the blank tags to label buildings children create for which tags are not included.) Children color or decorate the tags using markers. Before the lesson, you should have cleared a space to house the model city. (To organize the city, you may wish to make roads within the city using masking tape or gray construction paper.) When children are finished decorating their tags, have each small group bring the tag, the building model, and the models of people, animals, and objects to this space.

Have each small group place its models in the city space. Each small group presents its models to the class by explaining what the building is and what the people, animals and objects are.

When each small group has placed its models in the city area, remind children that they used very simple shapes to make new shapes. Those new shapes allowed them to model a whole city. If they wish, they can continue making models with blocks and other toys.

Celebrate the city with children by leaving it intact for a few days after the project and allowing children to play with it. Take a photograph to remember the city before you deconstruct it.

2 Extending the Project

▶ Extension Suggestions

- ▷ Offer children old magazines. Have children examine pictures in the magazines and circle any familiar plane shapes and solid figures they see.
- ▷ Provide pairs of children with scratch paper and pattern blocks. Have each partnership sit back to back or hide their work with folders so that children cannot see what their partners are doing. Tell children to combine several pattern blocks and trace the outline of the new shape on the paper. Then have partners switch papers. Children then place pattern blocks in their partner's figure to determine the component shapes their partners used to make the composite shapes.
- ▷ Provide each member of a partnership with the same set of four or five pattern blocks. For instance, each child may take two triangles, a square, and a fat rhombus. Have each partnership sit back to back or hide their work with folders so that children cannot see what their partners are doing. Tell children to combine the pattern blocks into a new shape. When they are finished, partners reveal their composite shape to see if they made the same shape.
- ▷ Provide children with pattern blocks and solid figures from the Shapes Museum. Challenge children to make shapes they know from the pattern blocks and solid figures. For instance, you may wish to tell children to do the following:
  - Make a hexagon from triangles or rhombuses.
  - Make a rectangular prism from cubes.
  - Make a trapezoid from triangles.

Language Arts Link To further explore the people, places, and things in cities, you may wish to read ***Busy, Busy Town*** by Richard Scarry (Golden Books, 2000).

First Grade Key Vocabulary

For a more comprehensive glossary that includes additional entries and illustrations, please refer to the *Teacher's Reference Manual.*

NOTE: In a definition, terms in italics are defined elsewhere in this glossary.

A

addend Any one of a set of numbers that are added. For example, in 5 + 3 + 1, the addends are 5, 3, and 1.

addition fact Two 1-digit numbers and their *sum,* such as 9 + 7 = 16.

A.M. The abbreviation for *ante meridiem,* meaning "before the middle of the day" in Latin. From midnight to noon.

analog clock (1) A clock that shows the time by the positions of the hour and minute hands.
(2) Any device that shows time passing in a continuous manner, such as a sundial. Compare to *digital clock.*

area The amount of *surface* inside a 2-*dimensional figure.* The figure might be a *triangle* or *rectangle* in a plane, the curved *surface* of a *cylinder,* or a state or country on the Earth's surface. Commonly, area is measured in square *units* such as square miles, square *inches,* or square *centimeters.*

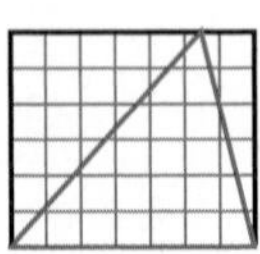

A triangle with area 21 square units

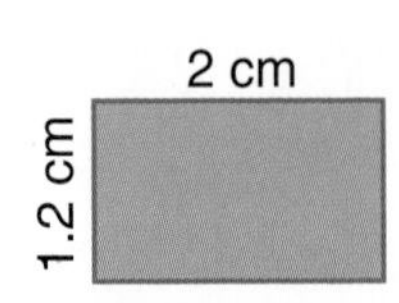

A rectangle with area 1.2 cm × 2 cm = 2.4 cm²

The area of the United States is about 3,800,000 square miles.

arithmetic facts The *addition facts* (whole-number *addends* 9 or less); their inverse subtraction facts; multiplication facts (whole-number factors 9 or less); and their inverse division facts, except there is no division by zero. There are

100 addition facts:	0 + 0 = 0 through 9 + 9 = 18
100 subtraction facts:	0 − 0 = 0 through 18 − 9 = 9
100 multiplication facts:	0 × 0 = 0 through 9 × 9 = 81
90 division facts:	0 / 1 = 0 through 81 / 9 = 9

See *fact power.*

arm span A *unit* of length equal to 6 *feet,* or 2 *yards.* It is used mainly by people who work with boats and ships to measure depths underwater and lengths of cables.

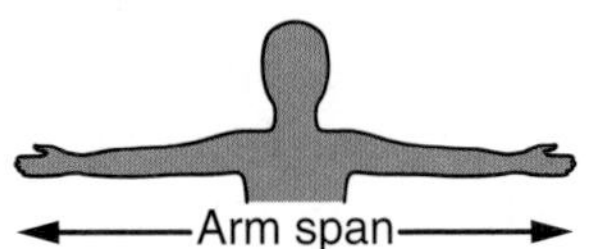

arrow rule In *Everyday Mathematics,* an operation that determines the number that goes into the next *frame* in a *Frames-and-Arrows* diagram. There may be more than one arrow rule per diagram.

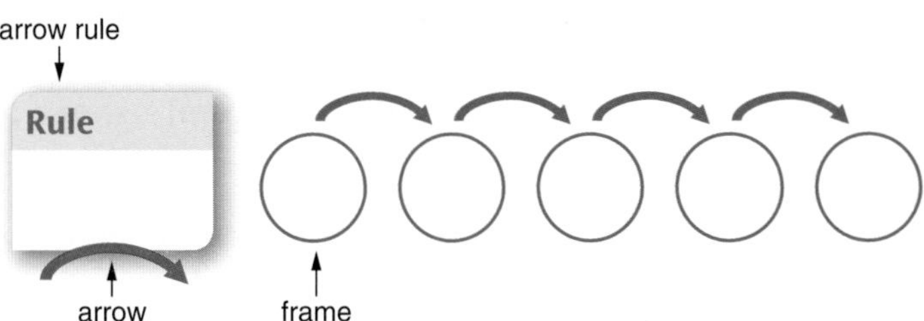

attribute A feature of an object or common feature of a *set* of objects. Examples of attributes include size, shape, color, and number of sides.

average A typical value for a set of numbers. In everyday life, average usually refers to the *mean* of the *set,* found by adding all the numbers and dividing the *sum* by the number of numbers. In statistics, several different averages, or *landmarks,* are defined, including *mean, median,* and *mode.*

B

bar graph A graph with horizontal or vertical bars that represent *data.*

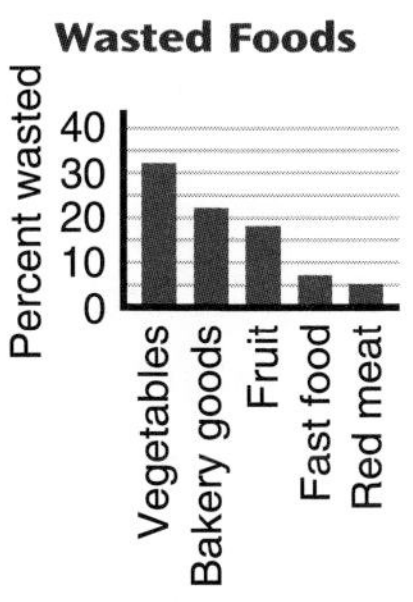

Source: The Garbage Product

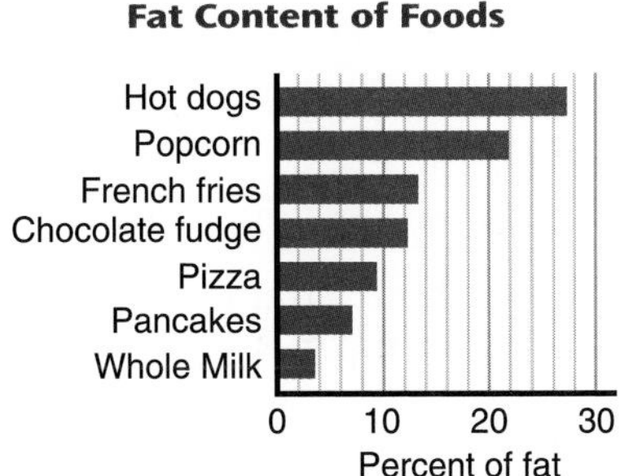

Source: The New York Public Library Desk Reference

base 10 Our system for writing numbers that uses only the 10 symbols 0, 1, 2, 3, 4, 5, 6, 7, 8, and 9, called *digits.* You can write any number using one or more of these 10 digits, and each digit has a value that depends on its place in the number (its *place value*). In the base-10 system, each place has a value 10 times that of the place to its right, and 1 tenth the value of the place to its left.

base-10 blocks A *set* of blocks to represent ones, tens, hundreds, and thousands in the *base-10 place-value* system. In *Everyday Mathematics,* the unit block, or *cube,* has 1-cm edges; the ten block, or *long,* is 10 unit blocks in length; the hundred block, or *flat,* is 10 longs in width; and the thousand block, or big cube, is 10 flats high. See *cube, long,* and *flat* for photos of the blocks. See *base-10 shorthand.*

base-10 shorthand In *Everyday Mathematics,* a written notation for *base-10 blocks.*

Name	Base-10 block	Base-10 shorthand
cube		
long		
flat		
big cube		

C

calendar (1) A *reference frame* to keep track of the passage of time. Many different calendars exist, including the Gregorian calendar currently used by most of the Western world, the Hebrew calendar and the Islamic calendar. (2) A practical model of the reference frame, such as the large, reusable Class Calendar in *First* through *Third Grade Everyday Mathematics.* (3) A schedule or listing of events.

August 2007

Sunday	Monday	Tuesday	Wednesday	Thursday	Friday	Saturday
			1 Dr.'s appt. 3:00	2	3	4
5	6	7	8	9	10	11
12	13 Mom's b-day	14	15	16	17	18
19	20	21	22	23	24	25
26	27	28	29	30	31	

capacity (1) The amount of space occupied by a *3-dimensional figure.* Same as volume. (2) Less formally, the amount a container can hold. Capacity is often measured in *units* such as quarts, gallons, cups, or liters.

Celsius A temperature scale on which pure water at sea level freezes at 0° and boils at 100°. The Celsius scale is used in the *metric system.* A less common name for this scale is centigrade, because there are 100 units between the freezing and boiling points of water. Compare to *Fahrenheit.*

cent A penny; $\frac{1}{100}$ of a dollar. From the Latin word *centesimus,* which means "a hundredth part."

centimeter (cm) A metric *unit* of length equivalent to 10 millimeters, $\frac{1}{10}$ of a decimeter, and $\frac{1}{100}$ of a *meter.*

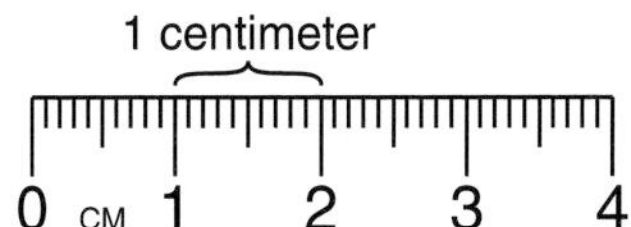

pictograph A graph constructed with pictures or symbols.

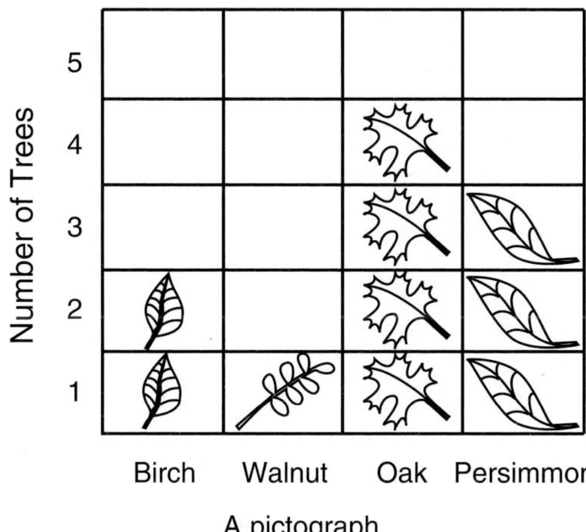

A pictograph

place value A system that gives a *digit* a value according to its position, or place, in a number. In our standard, *base-10* (decimal) system for writing numbers, each place has a value 10 times that of the place to its right and 1 tenth the value of the place to its left.

thousands	hundreds	tens	ones	.	tenths	hunderedths

A place-value chart

plane figure A *2-dimensional figure* that is entirely contained in a single plane. For example, *triangles, squares, pentagons, circles,* and parabolas are plane figures; *lines,* rays, *cones, cubes,* and *prisms* are not.

P.M. The abbreviation for *post meridiem,* meaning "after the middle of the day" in Latin. From noon to midnight.

point In *Everyday Mathematics,* an exact location in space. Points are usually labeled with capital letters. In formal Euclidean geometry, a point is an undefined geometric term.

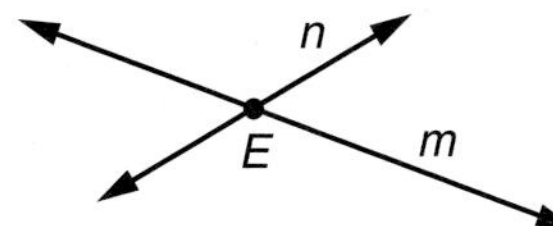

Lines *m* and *n* intersect at point *E*.

polygon A *2-dimensional figure* formed by three or more *line segments* (*sides*) that meet only at their endpoints (*vertices*) to make a closed path. The *sides* may not cross one another.

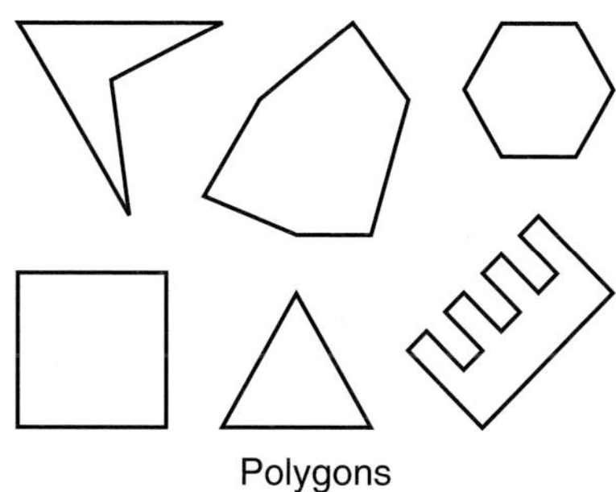
Polygons

polyhedron A *3-dimensional figure* formed by *polygons* with their interiors (*faces*) and having no holes. Plural is polyhedrons or polyhedra.

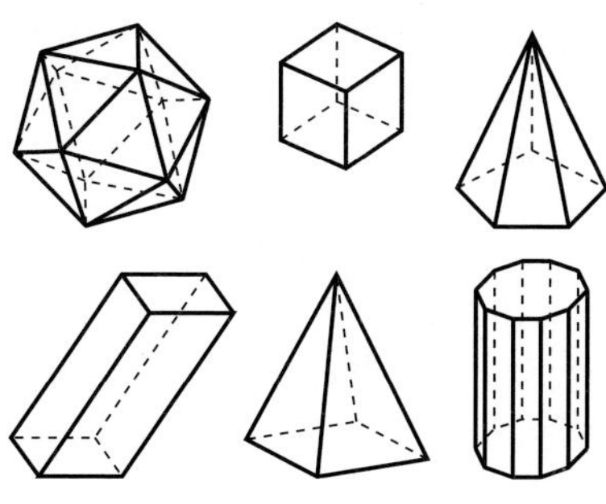
Polyhedrons

positive numbers Numbers greater than 0; the opposites of the *negative numbers.* Positive numbers are plotted to the right of 0 on a horizontal *number line* or above 0 on a vertical number line.

poster In *Everyday Mathematics,* a page displaying a collection of illustrated numerical *data.* A poster may be used as a source of data for developing *number stories.*

pound (lb) A *U.S. customary* unit of *weight* equal to 16 ounces and defined as 0.45359237 kilograms.

prism A *polyhedron* with two parallel and congruent polygonal regions for bases and lateral *faces* formed by all of the *line segments* with endpoints on corresponding edges of the bases. The lateral faces are all *parallelograms.* Lateral faces intersect at lateral edges. In a right prism, the lateral faces are rectangular. Prisms get their names from the shape of their bases.

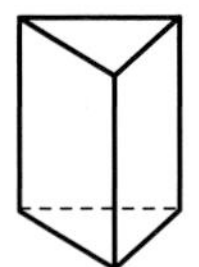
A triangular prism

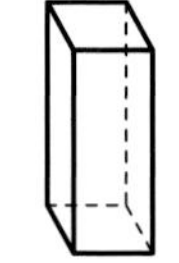
A rectangular prism

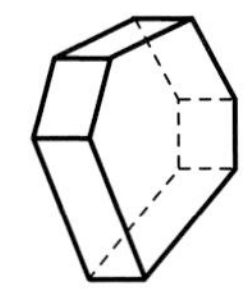
A hexagonal prism

probability A number from 0 through 1 giving the likelihood of an event happening. The closer a probability is to 1, the more likely the event is to happen. The closer a probability is to 0, the less likely the event is to happen. For example, the probability that a *fair* coin will show heads is $\frac{1}{2}$.

program a calculator To instruct a calculator to repeat a calculation using its memory instead of having the user enter a key sequence over and over. In *Everyday Mathematics,* children program their calculators to *skip count* using the machines' built-in constant operation feature.

Project In *Everyday Mathematics,* a thematic activity to be completed in one or more days by small groups or by a whole class. Projects often involve collecting and analyzing *data* and are usually cross-curricular in nature.

property (1) A generalized statement about a mathematical relationship such as the Distributive Property of Multiplication over Addition. (2) Same as *attribute.*

$$\frac{12 \text{ miles}}{1 \text{ hour}} = \frac{n \text{ miles}}{3 \text{ hours}}$$

pyramid A *polyhedron* made up of any polygonal region for a base, a *point* (apex) not in the plane of the base, and all of the *line segments* with one endpoint at the apex and the other on an *edge* of the base. All *faces* except the base are triangular. Pyramids get their name from the shape of their base.

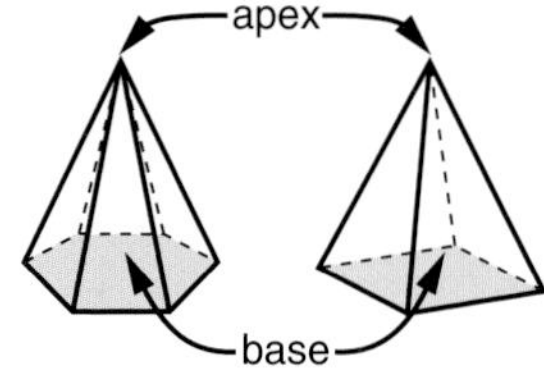

quadrangle Same as *quadrilateral.*

quadrilateral A 4-sided *polygon.* See *square, rectangle, parallelogram, rhombus, kite,* and *trapezoid.*

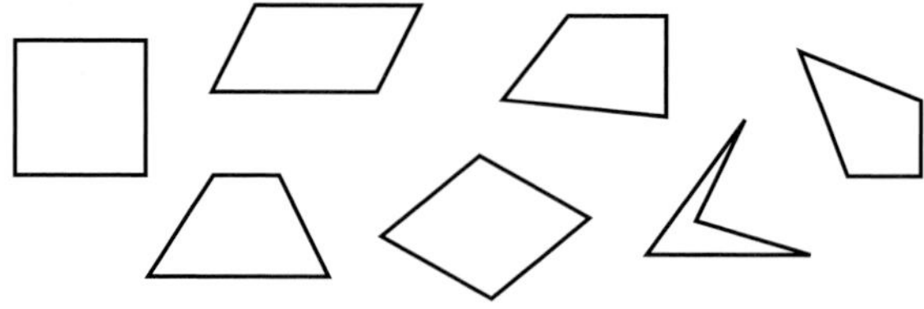
Quadrilaterals

range The *difference* between the *maximum* and the *minimum* in a *set* of *data.* Used as a measure of the spread of the data.

rational counting Counting using one-to-one matching. For example, counting a number of chairs, people, or crackers.

rational numbers Numbers that can be written in the form $\frac{a}{b}$, where a and nonzero b are integers. The decimal form of a rational number either terminates or repeats. For example, $\frac{2}{3}$, $-\frac{2}{3}$, 0.5, 20.5, and 0.333 . . . are rational numbers.

rectangle A *parallelogram* with all right angles.

rectangular prism A *prism* with rectangular bases. The four *faces* that are not bases are either *rectangles* or *parallelograms.* For example, a shoe box models a rectangular prism in which all sides are rectangles.

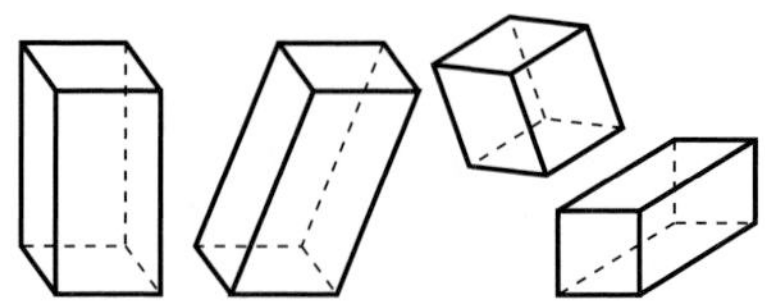
Rectangular prisms

rectangular pyramid A *pyramid* with a rectangular base.

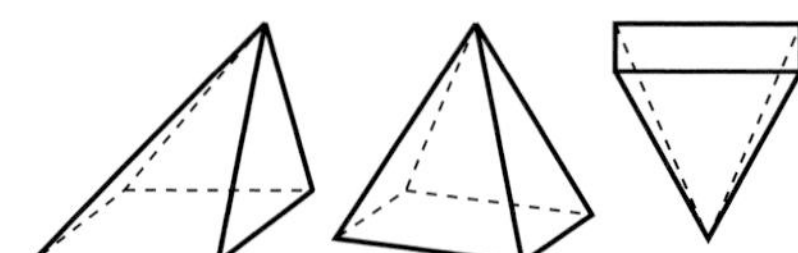
Rectangular pyramids

reference frame A system for locating numbers within a given context, usually with reference to an origin or zero point. For example, *number lines,* clocks, *calendars, temperature* scales, and maps are reference frames.

regular polygon A *polygon* in which all *sides* are the same length and all angles have the same measure.

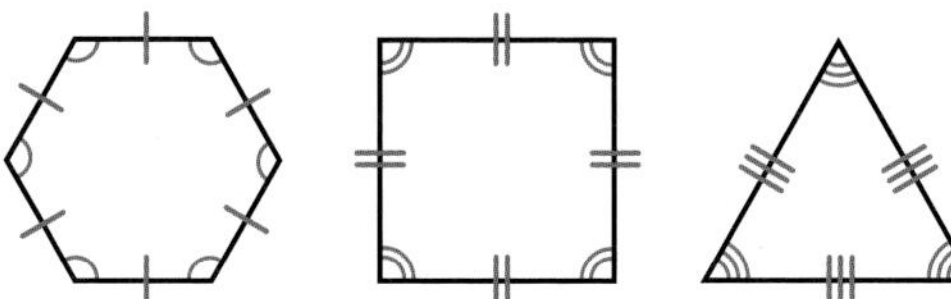

Regular polygons

regular polyhedron A *polyhedron* whose *faces* are all *congruent* regular *polygons* and in which the same number of faces meet at each *vertex.* The five regular polyhedrons, known as the Platonic solids, are shown below.

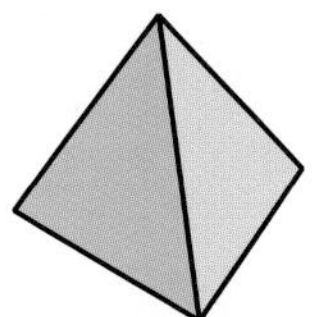

Tetrahedron (4 equilateral triangles)

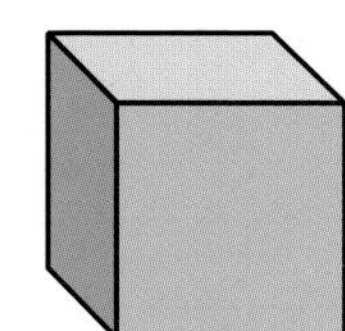

Cube (6 squares)

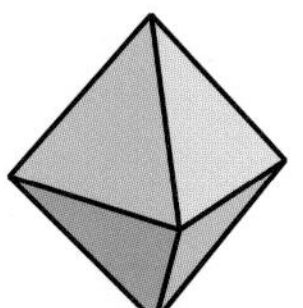

Octahedron (8 equilateral triangles)

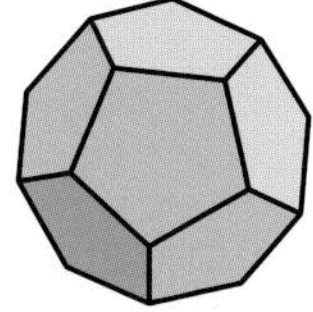

Dodecahedron (12 regular pentagons)

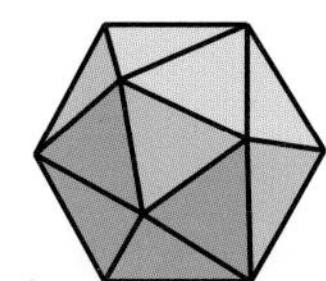

Icosahedron (20 equilateral triangles)

relation symbol A symbol used to express a relationship between two quantities.

Relation	Meaning
$=$	is equal to
$\neq$	is not equal to
$<$	is less than
$>$	is greater than
$\leq$	is less than or equal to
$\geq$	is greater than or equal to
$\approx$	is approximately equal to

rhombus A *parallelogram* with all *sides* the same length. All rhombuses are parallelograms. Every *square* is a rhombus, but not all rhombuses are squares. Also called a diamond. Plural is rhombuses or rhombi.

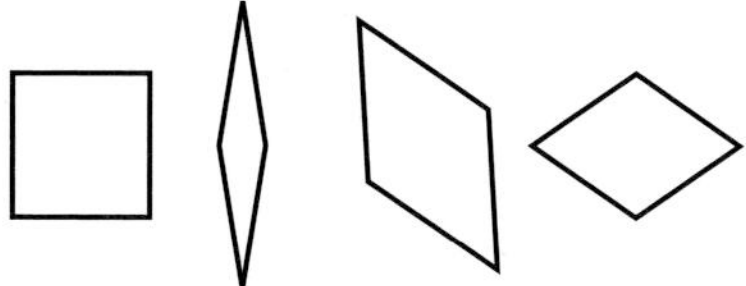

Rhombuses

rote counting Reciting a string of number words by rote, without understanding their significance. See *skip counting*.

round (1) To approximate a number to make it easier to work with, or to make it better reflect the precision of the *data.* "Rounding up" means to approximate larger than the actual value. "Rounding down" means to approximate smaller than the actual value. (2) Circular in shape.

row (1) A horizontal arrangement of objects or numbers in an array or table.

second (s) (1) A *unit* of time defined as $\frac{1}{31{,}556{,}925.9747}$ of the tropical year at midnight Eastern Time on New Year's Day, 1900. There are 60 seconds in a minute. (2) An *ordinal number* in the sequence *first, second, third, ...*

set A collection or group of objects, numbers, or other items.

side (1) One of the *line segments* that make up a *polygon.* (2) One of the rays or segments that form an angle. (3) One of the *faces* of a *polyhedron.*

situation diagram A diagram used to organize information in a problem situation in one of the addition/subtraction or multiplication/division use classes.

skip counting *Rote counting* by intervals, such as by twos, fives, or tens.

slate A lap-size (about 8-inch by 11-inch) chalkboard or whiteboard that children use in *Everyday Mathematics* for recording responses during group exercises and informal group assessments.

slide An informal name for a translation.

sphere The *set* of all *points* in space that are an equal distance from a fixed point called the center of the sphere. The distance from the center to the sphere is the radius of the sphere. The diameter of a sphere is twice its radius. Points inside a sphere are not part of the sphere.

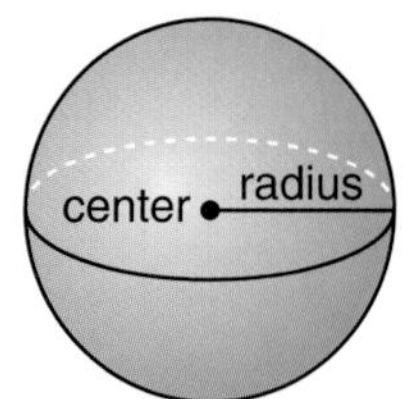

A sphere

square A *rectangle* with all sides of equal length. All angles in a square are *right angles.*

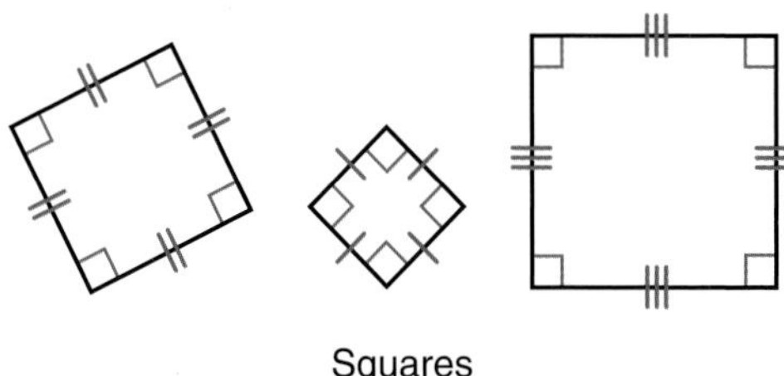

Squares

square corner A 90° angle.

standard unit A unit of measure that has been defined by a recognized authority, such as a government or a standards organization. For example, *inches, meters,* miles, *seconds, pounds,* grams, and acres are all standard units.

straightedge A tool used to draw *line segments.* Strictly speaking, a straightedge does not have a measuring scale on it, so ignore the marks if you use a ruler as a straightedge. Together, a compass and a straightedge are used to construct geometric figures.

sum The result of adding two or more numbers. For example, in 5 + 3 = 8, the sum is 8.

surface (1) The boundary of a *3-dimensional* object. The part of an object that is next to the air. Common surfaces include the top of a body of water, the outermost part of a ball, and the topmost layer of ground that covers Earth. (2) Any *2-dimensional* layer, such as a plane or a face of a *polyhedron.*

symmetry The balanced distribution of *points* over a line or around a point in a symmetric figure. See *line symmetry*.

A figure with line symmetry

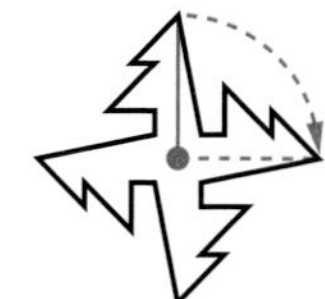

A figure with rotation symmetry

tally (1) To keep a record of a count, commonly by making a mark for each item as it is counted. (2) The mark used in a count. Also called "tally mark" and "tick mark."

tally chart A table to keep track of a *tally,* typically showing how many times each value appears in a *set* of *data.*

Number of Pull-Ups	Number of Children
0	卌 /
1	卌
2	////
3	//

A tally chart

temperature How hot or cold something is relative to another object or as measured on a standardized scale such as *degrees Celsius* or *degrees Fahrenheit.*

tessellation A pattern of shapes that covers a surface completely without overlaps or gaps. Same as a tiling.

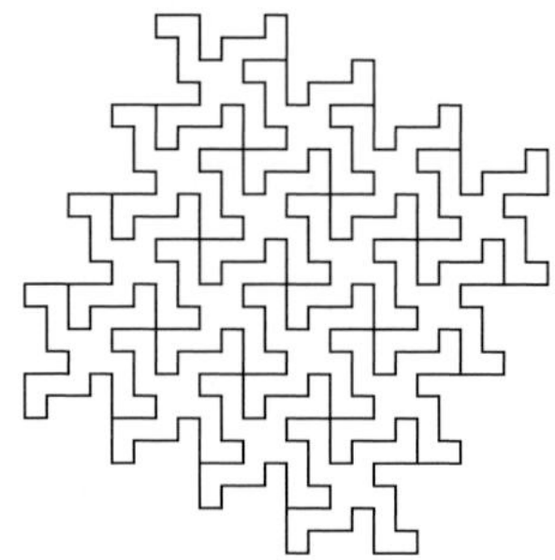

A tessellation

3-dimensional (3-D) figure A figure whose points are not all in a single plane. Examples include *prisms, pyramids,* and *spheres,* all of which have length, width, and height.

timeline A *number line* showing when events took place. In some timelines the origin is based on the context of the events being graphed, such as the birth date of the child's life graphed below. The origin can also come from another reference system, such as the year A.D. in which case the scale below might cover the years 2000 through 2005.

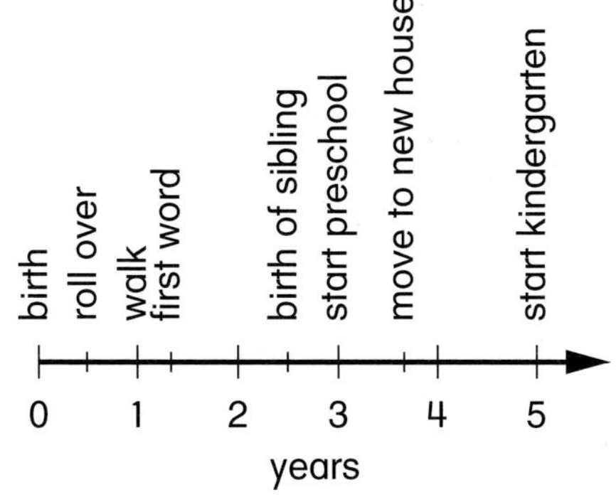

A timeline of a child's milestones

tool kit In *First* through *Third Grade Everyday Mathematics,* a bag or a box containing a calculator, measuring tools, and manipulatives often used by children in the program.

trapezoid A *quadrilateral* that has exactly one pair of parallel sides. In *Everyday Mathematics,* both pairs of sides cannot be parallel; that is, a *parallelogram* is not a trapezoid.

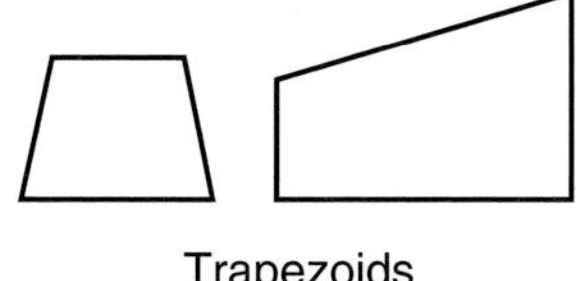

Trapezoids

triangle A 3-sided polygon.

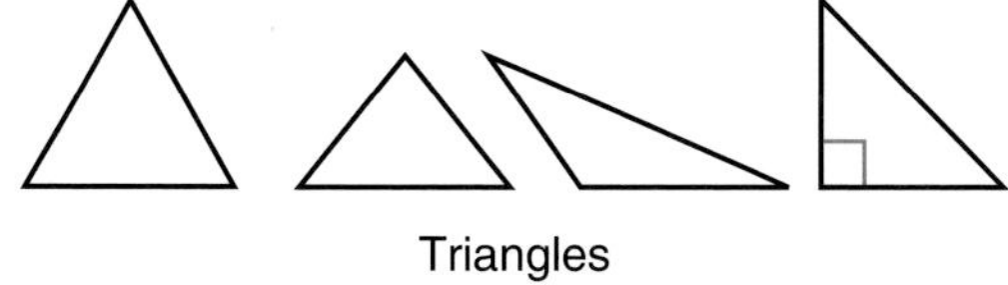

Triangles

triangular prism A *prism* whose bases are *triangles.*

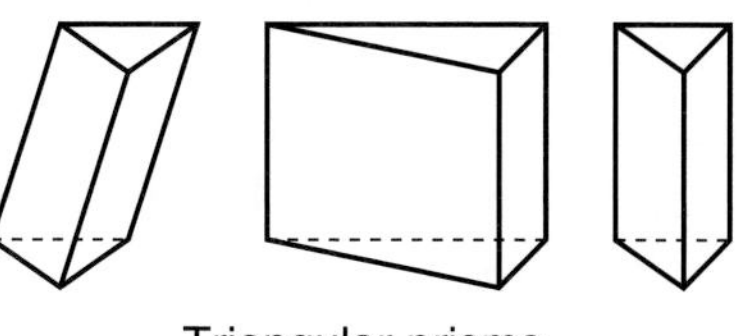

Triangular prisms

triangular pyramid A *pyramid* in which all *faces* are *triangles,* any one of which is the base. A regular tetrahedron has four equilateral *triangles,* four faces, and is one of the five regular *polyhedrons.*

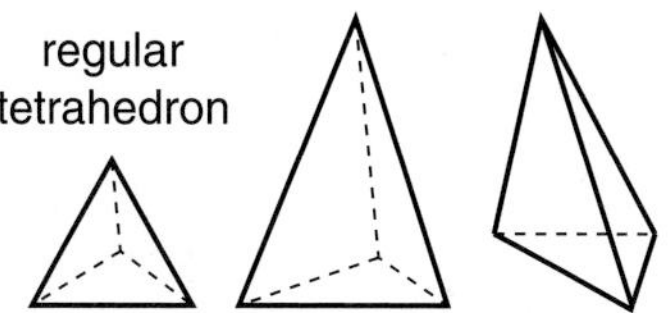

Triangular pyramids

turn An informal name for a rotation.

turn-around facts A pair of multiplication (or addition) facts in which the order of the factors (or addends) is reversed. For example, $3 \times 9 = 27$ and $9 \times 3 = 27$ are turn-around multiplication facts, and $4 + 5 = 9$ and $5 + 4 = 9$ are turn-around addition facts. There are no turn-around facts for subtraction or division. Turn-around facts are instances of the *Commutative Properties of Addition* and Multiplication.

2-dimensional (2-D) figure A figure whose points are all in one plane but not all on one *line.* Examples include *polygons* and *circles,* all of which have length and width but no height.

U

unit A label used to put a number in context. In measuring length, for example, *inches* and *centimeters* are units. In a problem about 5 apples, apple is the unit. In *Everyday Mathematics,* students keep track of units in *unit boxes.*

unit box In *Everyday Mathematics,* a box displaying the *unit* for the numbers in the problems at hand.

A unit box

unit fraction A *fraction* whose *numerator* is 1. For example, $\frac{1}{2}$, $\frac{1}{3}$, $\frac{1}{12}$, $\frac{1}{8}$, and $\frac{1}{20}$ are unit fractions. Unit fractions are especially useful in converting among units within measurement systems. For example, because 1 *foot* = 12 *inches* you can multiply a number of inches by $\frac{1}{12}$ to convert to feet.

U.S. customary system The measuring system used most often in the United States. *Units* for length include *inch, foot, yard,* and mile; units for *weight* include ounce and pound; units for volume or *capacity* include cup, pint, quart, gallon and cubic units; and the main unit for *temperature* change is *degrees Fahrenheit.*

V

Venn diagram A picture that uses *circles* or rings to show relationships between *sets.* In this diagram, 22 + 8 = 30 girls who are on the track team, and 8 girls are on both the track and the basketball teams.

Number of Girls on Sports Teams

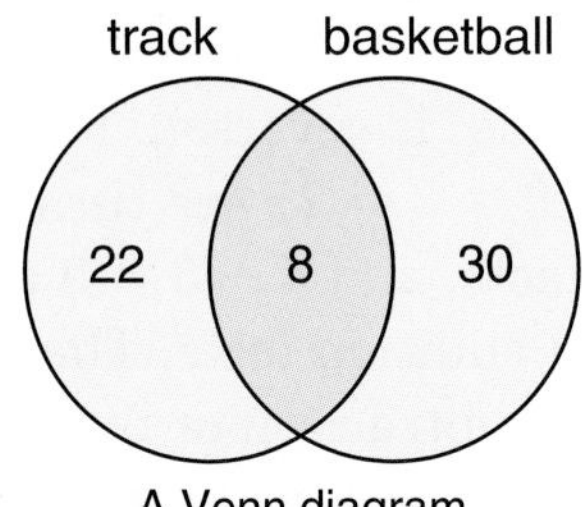

A Venn diagram

vertex The *point* at which the rays of an angle, the *sides* of a polygon, or the *edges* of a polyhedron meet. Plural is vertexes or vertices. In *Everyday Mathematics,* same as *corner.*

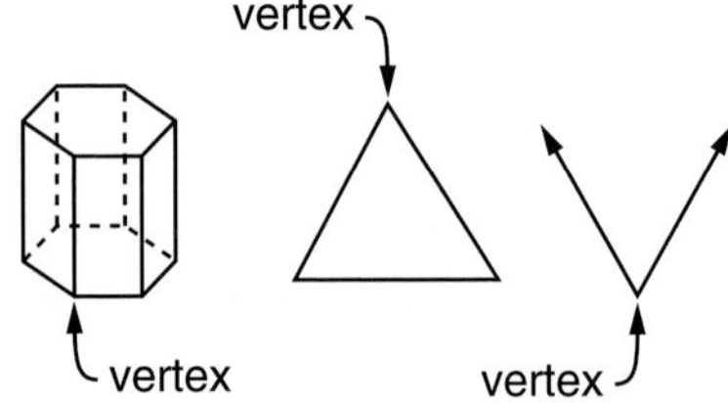

W

weight A measure of how heavy something is; the force of gravity on an object. An object's mass is constant, but it weighs less in weak gravity than in strong gravity. For example, a person who weighs 150 pounds in San Diego weighs about 23 pounds on the moon.

"What's My Rule?" problem In *Everyday Mathematics,* a problem in which two of the three parts of a *function* (*input, output,* and rule) are known, and the third is to be found out.

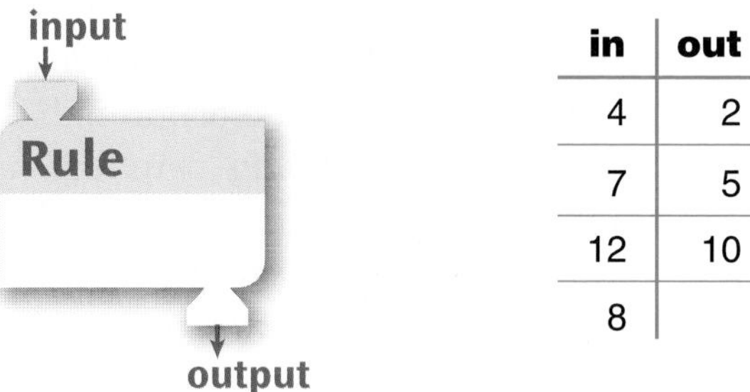

in	out
4	2
7	5
12	10
8	

A "What's My Rule?" problem

whole An entire object, collection of objects, or quantity being considered in a problem situation; 100%. Same as *ONE* and unit whole.

width of a rectangle The length of one side of a *rectangle* or rectangular object, typically the shorter side.

Y

yard (yd) A U.S. customary unit of length equal to 3 *feet,* or 36 *inches.* To Henry I of England, a yard was the distance from the tip of the nose to the tip of the middle finger. In *Everyday Mathematics,* it is the distance from the center of the chest to the tip of the middle finger.

Grade-Level Goals

Everyday Mathematics organizes content through Program Goals and Grade-Level Goals. The Grade-Level Goals Chart shows the units in which goal content is taught and then practiced and applied. For more information, see the *Assessment Handbook.*

The Grade-Level Goals are divided according to the content strands below.

Content Strands

How to Read the Grade-Level Goals Chart

Each section of the chart includes Grade-Level Goals organized by content strand. The three grade-level columns divided into units indicate in which units the goals are addressed.

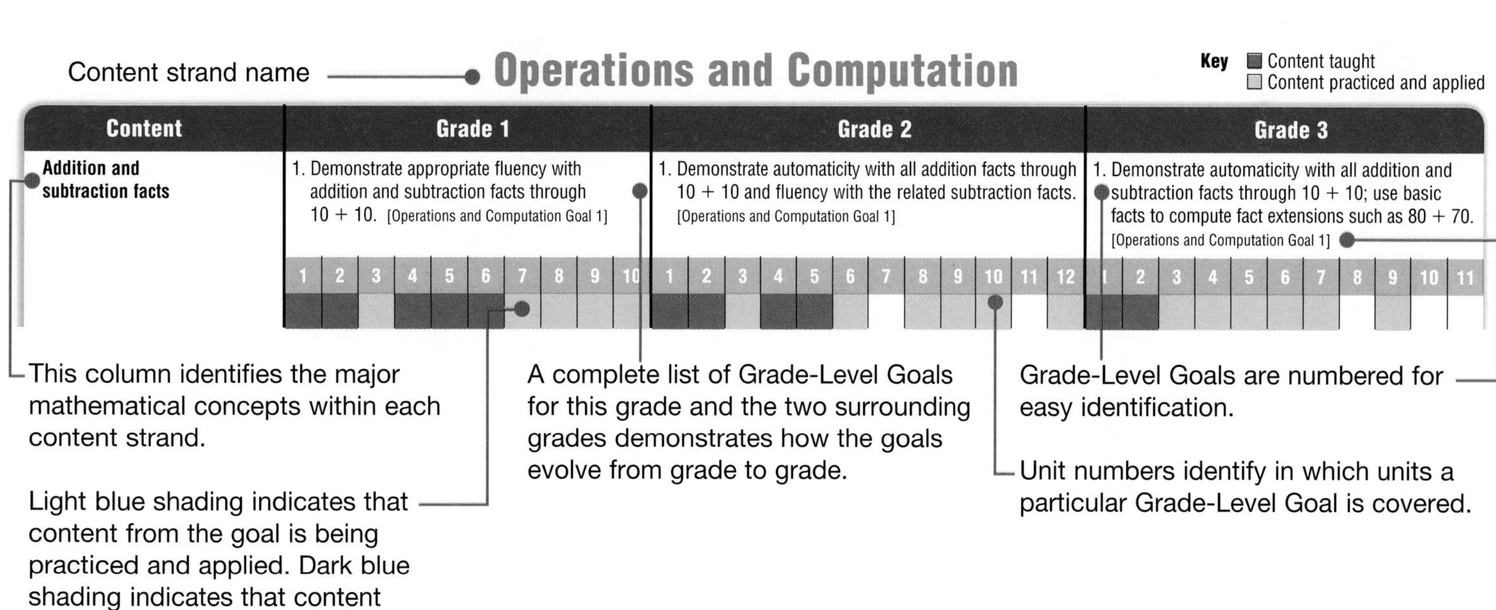

Number and Numeration

Key
- Content taught
- Content practiced and applied

Content	Grade 1	Grade 2	Grade 3
Rote counting	1. Count on by 1s, 2s, 5s, and 10s past 100 and back by 1s from any number less than 100 with and without number grids, number lines, and calculators. [Number and Numeration Goal 1] 1 2 3 4 5 6 7 8 9 10	1. Count on by 1s, 2s, 5s, 10s, 25s, and 100s past 1,000 and back by 1s, 10s, and 100s from any number less than 1,000 with and without number grids, number lines, and calculators. [Number and Numeration Goal 1] 1 2 3 4 5 6 7 8 9 10 11 12	1 2 3 4 5 6 7 8 9 10 11
Rational counting	2. Count collections of objects accurately and reliably; estimate the number of objects in a collection. [Number and Numeration Goal 2] 1 2 3 4 5 6 7 8 9 10	1 2 3 4 5 6 7 8 9 10 11 12	1 2 3 4 5 6 7 8 9 10 11
Place value and notation	3. Read, write, and model with manipulatives whole numbers up to 1,000; identify places in such numbers and the values of the digits in those places. [Number and Numeration Goal 3] 1 2 3 4 5 6 7 8 9 10	2. Read, write, and model with manipulatives whole numbers up to 10,000; identify places in such numbers and the values of the digits in those places; read and write money amounts in dollars-and-cents notation. [Number and Numeration Goal 2] 1 2 3 4 5 6 7 8 9 10 11 12	1. Read and write whole numbers up to 1,000,000; read, write, and model with manipulatives decimals through hundredths; identify places in such numbers and the values of the digits in those places; translate between whole numbers and decimals represented in words, in base-10 notation, and with manipulatives. [Number and Numeration Goal 1] 1 2 3 4 5 6 7 8 9 10 11
Meanings and uses of fractions	4. Use manipulatives and drawings to model halves, thirds, and fourths as equal parts of a region or a collection; describe the model. [Number and Numeration Goal 4] 1 2 3 4 5 6 7 8 9 10	3. Use manipulatives and drawings to model fractions as equal parts of a region or a collection; describe the models and name the fractions. [Number and Numeration Goal 3] 1 2 3 4 5 6 7 8 9 10 11 12	2. Read, write, and model fractions; solve problems involving fractional parts of a region or a collection; describe strategies used. [Number and Numeration Goal 2] 1 2 3 4 5 6 7 8 9 10 11

Key
- Content taught
- Content practiced and applied

Content	Grade 1	Grade 2	Grade 3
Number theory	5. Use manipulatives to identify and model odd and even numbers. [Number and Numeration Goal 5]	4. Recognize numbers as odd or even. [Number and Numeration Goal 4]	3. Find multiples of 2, 5, and 10. [Number and Numeration Goal 3]
	1 2 3 4 5 6 7 8 9 10	1 2 3 4 5 6 7 8 9 10 11 12	1 2 3 4 5 6 7 8 9 10 11
Equivalent names for whole numbers	6. Use manipulatives, drawings, tally marks, and numerical expressions involving addition and subtraction of 1- or 2-digit numbers to give equivalent names for whole numbers up to 100. [Number and Numeration Goal 6]	5. Use tally marks, arrays, and numerical expressions involving addition and subtraction to give equivalent names for whole numbers. [Number and Numeration Goal 5]	4. Use numerical expressions involving one or more of the basic four arithmetic operations to give equivalent names for whole numbers. [Number and Numeration Goal 4]
	1 2 3 4 5 6 7 8 9 10	1 2 3 4 5 6 7 8 9 10 11 12	1 2 3 4 5 6 7 8 9 10 11
Equivalent names for fractions, decimals, and percents		6. Use manipulatives and drawings to model equivalent names for $\frac{1}{2}$. [Number and Numeration Goal 6]	5. Use manipulatives and drawings to find and represent equivalent names for fractions; use manipulatives to generate equivalent fractions. [Number and Numeration Goal 5]
	1 2 3 4 5 6 7 8 9 10	1 2 3 4 5 6 7 8 9 10 11 12	1 2 3 4 5 6 7 8 9 10 11
Comparing and ordering numbers	7. Compare and order whole numbers up to 1,000. [Number and Numeration Goal 7]	7. Compare and order whole numbers up to 10,000; use area models to compare fractions. [Number and Numeration Goal 7]	6. Compare and order whole numbers up to 1,000,000; use manipulatives to order decimals through hundredths; use area models and benchmark fractions to compare and order fractions. [Number and Numeration Goal 6]
	1 2 3 4 5 6 7 8 9 10	1 2 3 4 5 6 7 8 9 10 11 12	1 2 3 4 5 6 7 8 9 10 11

Operations and Computation

Key
- Content taught
- Content practiced and applied

Content	Grade 1	Grade 2	Grade 3
Addition and subtraction facts	1. Demonstrate appropriate fluency with addition and subtraction facts through 10 + 10. [Operations and Computation Goal 1]	1. Demonstrate automaticity with all addition facts through 10 + 10 and fluency with the related subtraction facts. [Operations and Computation Goal 1]	1. Demonstrate automaticity with all addition and subtraction facts through 10 + 10; use basic facts to compute fact extensions such as 80 + 70. [Operations and Computation Goal 1]
	1 2 3 4 5 6 7 8 9 10	1 2 3 4 5 6 7 8 9 10 11 12	1 2 3 4 5 6 7 8 9 10 11
Addition and subtraction procedures	2. Use manipulatives, number grids, tally marks, mental arithmetic, and calculators to solve problems involving the addition and subtraction of 1-digit whole numbers with 2-digit whole numbers; calculate and compare the values of combinations of coins. [Operations and Computation Goal 2]	2. Use manipulatives, number grids, tally marks, mental arithmetic, paper & pencil, and calculators to solve problems involving the addition and subtraction of multidigit whole numbers; describe the strategies used; calculate and compare values of coin and bill combinations. [Operations and Computation Goal 2]	2. Use manipulatives, mental arithmetic, paper-and-pencil algorithms and models, and calculators to solve problems involving the addition and subtraction of whole numbers and decimals in a money context; describe the strategies used and explain how they work. [Operations and Computation Goal 2]
	1 2 3 4 5 6 7 8 9 10	1 2 3 4 5 6 7 8 9 10 11 12	1 2 3 4 5 6 7 8 9 10 11
Multiplication and division facts			3. Demonstrate automaticity with multiplication facts through 10 × 10. [Operations and Computation Goal 3]
	1 2 3 4 5 6 7 8 9 10	1 2 3 4 5 6 7 8 9 10 11 12	1 2 3 4 5 6 7 8 9 10 11
Multiplication and division procedures			4. Use arrays, mental arithmetic, paper-and-pencil algorithms and models, and calculators to solve problems involving the multiplication of 2- and 3-digit whole numbers by 1-digit whole numbers; describe the strategies used. [Operations and Computation Goal 4]
	1 2 3 4 5 6 7 8 9 10	1 2 3 4 5 6 7 8 9 10 11 12	1 2 3 4 5 6 7 8 9 10 11

* Children practice the basic facts using their Fact Triangles and record the ones they know at least once per unit.

Content	Grade 1	Grade 2	Grade 3
Computational estimation	3. Estimate reasonableness of answers to basic fact problems (e.g., Will 7 + 8 be more or less than 10?). [Operations and Computation Goal 3]	3. Make reasonable estimates for whole number addition and subtraction problems; explain how the estimates were obtained. [Operations and Computation Goal 3]	5. Make reasonable estimates for whole number addition, subtraction, multiplication, and division problems; explain how the estimates were obtained. [Operations and Computation Goal 5]
	Units 1 2 3 4 5 6 7 8 9 10	Units 1 2 3 4 5 6 7 8 9 10 11 12	Units 1 2 3 4 5 6 7 8 9 10 11
Models for the operations	4. Identify change-to-more, change-to-less, comparison, and parts-and-total situations. [Operations and Computation Goal 4]	4. Identify and describe change, comparison, and parts-and-total situations; use repeated addition, arrays, and skip counting to model multiplication; use equal sharing and equal grouping to model division. [Operations and Computation Goal 4]	6. Recognize and describe change, comparison, and parts-and-total situations; use repeated addition, arrays, and skip counting to model multiplication; use equal sharing and equal grouping to model division. [Operations and Computation Goal 6]
	Units 1 2 3 4 5 6 7 8 9 10	Units 1 2 3 4 5 6 7 8 9 10 11 12	Units 1 2 3 4 5 6 7 8 9 10 11

Data and Chance

Key
- Content taught
- Content practiced and applied

Content	Grade 1	Grade 2	Grade 3
Data collection and representation	1. Collect and organize data to create tally charts, tables, bar graphs, and line plots. [Data and Chance Goal 1]	1. Collect and organize data or use given data to create tally charts, tables, graphs, and line plots. [Data and Chance Goal 1]	1. Collect and organize data or use given data to create charts, tables, graphs, and line plots. [Data and Chance Goal 1]
	Units 1 2 3 4 5 6 7 8 9 10	Units 1 2 3 4 5 6 7 8 9 10 11 12	Units 1 2 3 4 5 6 7 8 9 10 11
Data analysis	2. Use graphs to answer simple questions and draw conclusions; find the maximum and minimum of a data set. [Data and Chance Goal 2]	2. Use graphs to ask and answer simple questions and draw conclusions; find the maximum, minimum, mode, and median of a data set. [Data and Chance Goal 2]	2. Use graphs to ask and answer simple questions and draw conclusions; find the maximum, minimum, range, mode, and median of a data set. [Data and Chance Goal 2]
	Units 1 2 3 4 5 6 7 8 9 10	Units 1 2 3 4 5 6 7 8 9 10 11 12	Units 1 2 3 4 5 6 7 8 9 10 11

Data and Chance (cont.)

Content	Grade 1	Grade 2	Grade 3
Qualitative probability	3. Describe events using *certain, likely, unlikely, impossible* and other basic probability terms. [Data and Chance Goal 3]	3. Describe events using *certain, likely, unlikely, impossible,* and other basic probability terms; explain the choice of language. [Data and Chance Goal 3]	3. Describe events using *certain, very likely, likely, unlikely, very unlikely, impossible,* and other basic probability terms; explain the choice of language. [Data and Chance Goal 3]
	1 2 3 4 5 6 7 8 9 10	1 2 3 4 5 6 7 8 9 10 11 12	1 2 3 4 5 6 7 8 9 10 11
Quantitative probability			4. Predict the outcomes of simple experiments and test the predictions using manipulatives; express the probability of an event by using "______ out of ______" language. [Data and Chance Goal 4]
	1 2 3 4 5 6 7 8 9 10	1 2 3 4 5 6 7 8 9 10 11 12	1 2 3 4 5 6 7 8 9 10 11

Measurement and Reference Frames

Key
- Content taught
- Content practiced and applied

Content	Grade 1	Grade 2	Grade 3
Length, weight, and angles	1. Use nonstandard tools and techniques to estimate and compare weight and length; measure length with standard measuring tools. [Measurement and Reference Frames Goal 1]	1. Estimate length with and without tools; measure length to the nearest inch and centimeter; use standard and nonstandard tools to measure and estimate weight. [Measurement and Reference Frames Goal 1]	1. Estimate length with and without tools; measure length to the nearest $\frac{1}{2}$ inch and $\frac{1}{2}$ centimeter; draw and describe angles as records of rotations. [Measurement and Reference Frames Goal 1]
	1 2 3 4 5 6 7 8 9 10	1 2 3 4 5 6 7 8 9 10 11 12	1 2 3 4 5 6 7 8 9 10 11
Area, perimeter, volume, and capacity		2. Partition rectangles into unit squares and count unit squares to find areas. [Measurement and Reference Frames Goal 2]	2. Describe and use strategies to measure the perimeter of polygons; find the areas of rectangles. [Measurement and Reference Frames Goal 2]
	1 2 3 4 5 6 7 8 9 10	1 2 3 4 5 6 7 8 9 10 11 12	1 2 3 4 5 6 7 8 9 10 11

Key
- Content taught
- Content practiced and applied

Content	Grade 1	Grade 2	Grade 3
Units and systems of measurement	Units: 1 2 3 4 5 6 7 8 9 10	3. Describe relationships between days in a week and hours in a day. [Measurement and Reference Frames Goal 3] Units: 1 2 3 4 5 6 7 8 9 10 11 12	3. Describe relationships among inches, feet, and yards; describe relationships between minutes in an hour, hours in a day, days in a week. [Measurement and Reference Frames Goal 3] Units: 1 2 3 4 5 6 7 8 9 10 11
Money	2. Know and compare the value of pennies, nickels, dimes, quarters, and dollar bills; make exchanges between coins. [Measurement and Reference Frames Goal 2] Units: 1 2 3 4 5 6 7 8 9 10	4. Make exchanges between coins and bills. [Measurement and Reference Frames Goal 4] Units: 1 2 3 4 5 6 7 8 9 10 11 12	Units: 1 2 3 4 5 6 7 8 9 10 11
Temperature	3. Identify a thermometer as a tool for measuring temperature; read temperatures on Fahrenheit and Celsius thermometers to the nearest 10°. [Measurement and Reference Frames Goal 3] Units: 1 2 3 4 5 6 7 8 9 10	5. Read temperature on both the Fahrenheit and Celsius scales. [Measurement and Reference Frames Goal 5] Units: 1 2 3 4 5 6 7 8 9 10 11 12	Units: 1 2 3 4 5 6 7 8 9 10 11
Time	4. Use a calendar to identify days, weeks, months, and dates; tell and show time to the nearest half and quarter hour on an analog clock. [Measurement and Reference Frames Goal 4] Units: 1 2 3 4 5 6 7 8 9 10	6. Tell and show time to the nearest five minutes on an analog clock; tell and write time in digital notation.* [Measurement and Reference Frames Goal 6] Units: 1 2 3 4 5 6 7 8 9 10 11 12	4. Tell and show time to the nearest minute on an analog clock; tell and write time in digital notation.* [Measurement and Reference Frames Goal 4] Units: 1 2 3 4 5 6 7 8 9 10 11

* Children record their start time at the top of journal pages on a daily basis.

Geometry

Content	Grade 1	Grade 2	Grade 3
Lines and angles		1. Draw line segments and identify parallel line segments. [Geometry Goal 1]	1. Identify and draw points, intersecting and parallel line segments and lines, rays, and right angles. [Geometry Goal 1]
Plane and solid figures	1. Identify and describe plane and solid figures including circles, triangles, squares, rectangles, spheres, cylinders, rectangular prisms, pyramids, cones, and cubes. [Geometry Goal 1]	2. Identify, describe, and model plane and solid figures including circles, triangles, squares, rectangles, hexagons, trapezoids, rhombuses, spheres, cylinders, rectangular prisms, pyramids, cones, and cubes. [Geometry Goal 2]	2. Identify, describe, model, and compare plane and solid figures including circles, polygons, spheres, cylinders, rectangular prisms, pyramids, cones, and cubes using appropriate geometric terms including the terms *face, edge, vertex,* and *base.* [Geometry Goal 2]
Transformations and symmetry	2. Identify shapes having line symmetry; complete line-symmetric shapes or designs. [Geometry Goal 2]	3. Create and complete two-dimensional symmetric shapes or designs. [Geometry Goal 3]	3. Create and complete two-dimensional symmetric shapes or designs; locate multiple lines of symmetry in a two-dimensional shape. [Geometry Goal 3]

Patterns, Functions, and Algebra

Key
- Content taught
- Content practiced and applied

Content	Grade 1	Grade 2	Grade 3
Patterns and functions	1. Extend, describe, and create numeric, visual, and concrete patterns; solve problems involving function machines, "What's My Rule?" tables, and Frames-and-Arrows diagrams. [Patterns, Functions, and Algebra Goal 1]	1. Extend, describe, and create numeric, visual, and concrete patterns; describe rules for patterns and use them to solve problems; use words and symbols to describe and write rules for functions involving addition and subtraction and use those rules to solve problems. [Patterns, Functions, and Algebra Goal 1]	1. Extend, describe, and create numeric patterns; describe rules for patterns and use them to solve problems; use words and symbols to describe and write rules for functions involving addition, subtraction, and multiplication and use those rules to solve problems. [Patterns, Functions, and Algebra Goal 1]

Key ■ Content taught ▒ Content practiced and applied

Content	Grade 1	Grade 2	Grade 3
Algebraic notation and solving number sentences	2. Read, write, and explain expressions and number sentences using the symbols +, −, and = and the symbols > and < with cues; solve equations involving addition and subtraction. [Patterns, Functions, and Algebra Goal 2]	2. Read, write, and explain expressions and number sentences using the symbols +, −, =, >, and <; solve number sentences involving addition and subtraction; write expressions and number sentences to model number stories. [Patterns, Functions, and Algebra Goal 2]	2. Read, write, and explain number sentences using the symbols +, −, ×, ÷, =, >, and <; solve number sentences; write expressions and number sentences to model number stories. [Patterns, Functions, and Algebra Goal 2]
Order of operations			3. Recognize that numeric expressions can have different values depending on the order in which operations are carried out; understand that grouping symbols can be used to affect the order in which operations are carried out. [Patterns, Functions, and Algebra Goal 3]
Properties of the arithmetic operations	3. Apply the Commutative and Associative Properties of Addition and the Additive Identity to basic addition fact problems. [Patterns, Functions, and Algebra Goal 3]	3. Describe the Commutative and Associative Properties of Addition and the Additive Identity and apply them to mental arithmetic problems. [Patterns, Functions, and Algebra Goal 3]	4. Describe and apply the Commutative and Associative Properties of Addition and Multiplication and the Multiplicative Identity; apply the Distributive Property of Multiplication over Addition. [Patterns, Functions, and Algebra Goal 4]

Grade 1 (Units)

Content	1	2	3	4	5	6	7	8	9	10
Algebraic notation and solving number sentences		■	■		■	■	■	▒	▒	▒
Order of operations										
Properties of the arithmetic operations				■	▒	■		▒	▒	

Grade 2 (Units)

Content	1	2	3	4	5	6	7	8	9	10	11	12
Algebraic notation and solving number sentences	■	■	▒	■	▒	■	▒	▒	▒	▒	■	▒
Order of operations												
Properties of the arithmetic operations		■		■	▒	▒	▒				▒	▒

Grade 3 (Units)

Content	1	2	3	4	5	6	7	8	9	10	11
Algebraic notation and solving number sentences	▒	■	▒	■	▒	▒	▒	▒	▒		
Order of operations							■	▒	■		
Properties of the arithmetic operations	▒	■		■	▒	▒	■		■		

Scope and Sequence Chart

Throughout *Everyday Mathematics*, children repeatedly encounter skills in each of the content strands. Each exposure builds on and extends children's understanding. They study important concepts over consecutive years through a variety of formats. The Scope and Sequence Chart shows the units in which these exposures occur. The symbol ● indicates that the skill is introduced or taught. The symbol ■ indicates that the skill is revisited, practiced, or extended. These levels refer to unit content within the *K–6 Everyday Mathematics* curriculum.

The skills are divided according to the content strands below.

Content Strands

Pages

How to Read the Scope and Sequence Chart

Each section of the chart includes a content strand title, three grade-level columns divided by units or sections, and a list of specific skills grouped by major concepts.

Routines

Projects

Number and Numeration — Content Strand

Key ● Content taught ■ Content practiced

	Kindergarten Sections										Grade 1 Units										Grade 2 Units											
Rote Counting	R	1	2	3	4	5	6	7	8	P	1	2	3	4	5	6	7	8	9	10	1	2	3	4	5	6	7	8	9	10	11	12
Perform rote counting	●	●	●	●	●	■	■	●	■	●	●	●	●	●	●	●	●	●	●	■	●	●	●	●			●			●	●	
Count by 2s, 5s, and 10s forward and backward (may include the use of concrete objects)	●			●	■	●	●	●	●	●	●	●	●	●	●	●	■	●	●	●	●	■	■	■	■	■	●	●		●	●	■
Count backward from 10 to 1		●		●	■	■	■	■	■																							
Count by numbers greater than 10																●			●	●	■	■	■		■					●		

This row identifies the major mathematical concepts within each content strand. A list of related skills appear below this head.

Find specific skills in this list and then follow across the row to find where they appear in Kindergarten or at each grade level.

The colored circle indicates where the skill is introduced or taught.

The colored square indicates where the skill is primarily revisited, practiced, or extended.

Number and Numeration

Key ● Content taught ■ Content practiced

	Kindergarten Sections										Grade 1 Units										Grade 2 Units											
Rote Counting	**R**	**1**	**2**	**3**	**4**	**5**	**6**	**7**	**8**	**P**	**1**	**2**	**3**	**4**	**5**	**6**	**7**	**8**	**9**	**10**	**1**	**2**	**3**	**4**	**5**	**6**	**7**	**8**	**9**	**10**	**11**	**12**
Perform rote counting	●	●	●	●	●	■	■	●	■	●	●	●	●	●	●	●	●	●	●	■	●	●	●	●			●			●	●	
Count by 2s, 5s, and 10s forward and backward (may include the use of concrete objects)	●			●	■	●	●	●	●	●	●	●	●	●	●	●	■	●	●	●	●	■	■	■	■	■	●	●		●	●	■
Count backward from 10 to 1		●		●	■	■	■	■	■																							
Count by numbers greater than 10																●			●	●	■	■	■		■					●		
Count by 25s																●			●	●			■									
Count by 100s																			●	●	●	■	■	■				●		●	●	■
Count up and back on a number grid						●	■	■				■	■	●	●		■	■	●		■	■				●	■	■	■	■		
Relate counting to addition and subtraction												●	●			●		■														
Locate numbers on a number line; count up and back on a number line; complete a number line	●			●	●		■	■			●	■	●	●					■		●	■		■		■						
Count using a calculator or calculator repeat key						●	●						●			●		●		■	●	■	■			■	●			●	■	■
Rational Counting	**R**	**1**	**2**	**3**	**4**	**5**	**6**	**7**	**8**	**P**	**1**	**2**	**3**	**4**	**5**	**6**	**7**	**8**	**9**	**10**	**1**	**2**	**3**	**4**	**5**	**6**	**7**	**8**	**9**	**10**	**11**	**12**
Perform rational counting	●	●	●	●	●	●	●	●	●	●	●	●	●	●	●	●	●	■	●	●	●	●	●	●	●	●	●	■	●	●	●	
Compare number of objects in sets of concrete objects	●	●	●	●	●	●	●	●	●																							
Estimate quantities of objects			●	■	■	■	■	■		●			■	■	●			●														
Place Value and Notation	**R**	**1**	**2**	**3**	**4**	**5**	**6**	**7**	**8**	**P**	**1**	**2**	**3**	**4**	**5**	**6**	**7**	**8**	**9**	**10**	**1**	**2**	**3**	**4**	**5**	**6**	**7**	**8**	**9**	**10**	**11**	**12**
Construct or use sets of objects to represent given quantities	●	●	●	●	●	●	●	●	●	●	●				●	■		●		■	●		●									
Read and write numbers to 20	●	●	●	●	●	●	●	●	●	●	●	●	●	●	●	●	●				●	●	■									
Read and write 2-digit numbers	●		●	●	●	■	■	■	■	●					●	■	●	●			●	●	●	●		●				●	●	
Read and write 3-digit numbers								●	●	●					●		●	●	■	●	●		●	■	■	■				●		
Read and write 4- and 5-digit numbers																				●	●		●	●						●	●	
Display and read numbers on a calculator					●	●	●		●			●	●		●	●		●		■	●	■	■			■				●		
Use multimedia and technology to explore number concepts					●	●	●		●																							
Read, write, or use ordinal numbers	●					●										●					■	■				■				●		

Key ● Content taught ■ Content practiced

Place Value and Notation (cont.)	R	1	2	3	4	5	6	7	8	P	1	2	3	4	5	6	7	8	9	10	1	2	3	4	5	6	7	8	9	10	11	12
Name the ordinal positions in a sequence and "next" and "last" positions	●																															
Identify the number that is one more or one less than a given number	●	●	■	■								■	■	■																		
Explore place value using a number grid						●		●	■	●			■		●				●											●		
Identify place value in 2-digit numbers	●							●	●				●		●	■		■	●	●	■		●	●		●				●	●	
Identify place value in 3-digit numbers																		●		●	●	■	●	●	■	■		■		●		■
Identify place value in 4-digit numbers																		●		●								■		●	■	■
Identify place value in larger numbers																							●					■	■	●		
Make exchanges among place values	●							●	●						●			●			●		●	●						●	●	
Make least and greatest numbers with randomly selected digits					●			●	■												■					■						
Write numbers in expanded notation																			■				■							●		
Use cents notation							●					●	●		■	■		■			●		●	■		●				●		
Use dollars-and-cents notation									●			●	●		■	■	●	●					●	●		●			■	●	●	
Use calculator to count/compute money amounts																		■				■								●		
Explore uses for decimals																		●												●		
Meanings and Uses of Fractions	**R**	**1**	**2**	**3**	**4**	**5**	**6**	**7**	**8**	**P**	**1**	**2**	**3**	**4**	**5**	**6**	**7**	**8**	**9**	**10**	**1**	**2**	**3**	**4**	**5**	**6**	**7**	**8**	**9**	**10**	**11**	**12**
Understand the meaning or uses of fractions							●	■	■								■	●	●	■								●	●	■	■	
Construct concrete models of fractions and equivalent fractions; identify fractions on a number line.																		●	●									●	■	■		
Identify pennies and dimes as fractional parts of a dollar																										●	■	●		●		■
Identify numerator and denominator																		●	●									●				
Shade and identify fractional parts of a region							●		■								■	●	●	■							■	●		■		
Shade and identify fractional parts of a set							●	■										●	■								■	●	●			■
Understand that the amount represented by a fraction depends on the size of the whole (ONE)																		■										●		●	■	
Use fractions in number stories																			■	■								●	■	■	■	

Number and Numeration (cont.)

Key ● Content taught ■ Content practiced

	Kindergarten Sections										Grade 1 Units										Grade 2 Units											
Number Theory	**R**	**1**	**2**	**3**	**4**	**5**	**6**	**7**	**8**	**P**	**1**	**2**	**3**	**4**	**5**	**6**	**7**	**8**	**9**	**10**	**1**	**2**	**3**	**4**	**5**	**6**	**7**	**8**	**9**	**10**	**11**	**12**
Explore or identify even and odd numbers		■					●	■					●	■	■	■	■		■		●	●	■	●	■		●		■			
Equivalent Names for Whole Numbers	**R**	**1**	**2**	**3**	**4**	**5**	**6**	**7**	**8**	**P**	**1**	**2**	**3**	**4**	**5**	**6**	**7**	**8**	**9**	**10**	**1**	**2**	**3**	**4**	**5**	**6**	**7**	**8**	**9**	**10**	**11**	**12**
Find equivalent names for numbers	●					●		●	●		●	●	■	■	●	●	■	■	■		●	●	●	●	■				●	●	●	■
Use Roman numerals																					■											
Equivalent Names for Fractions, Decimals, and Percents	**R**	**1**	**2**	**3**	**4**	**5**	**6**	**7**	**8**	**P**	**1**	**2**	**3**	**4**	**5**	**6**	**7**	**8**	**9**	**10**	**1**	**2**	**3**	**4**	**5**	**6**	**7**	**8**	**9**	**10**	**11**	**12**
Find equivalent fractions																			●								■	●	●	●		■
Comparing and Ordering Numbers	**R**	**1**	**2**	**3**	**4**	**5**	**6**	**7**	**8**	**P**	**1**	**2**	**3**	**4**	**5**	**6**	**7**	**8**	**9**	**10**	**1**	**2**	**3**	**4**	**5**	**6**	**7**	**8**	**9**	**10**	**11**	**12**
Compare and order numbers to 20	●		●	●	●	●	■	■		●	●	●	●	●	●	●				■	●		■		●		●		●			
Compare and order 2-digit numbers	●		●	●	●	●	■	●	■			●		●	●	●	■	■	■	●	●		■				●			●		●
Compare and order 3-digit numbers														●	●		■	■	■	●	●		●							●		
Compare and order 4- or 5-digit numbers												■									●									●		
Compare and order larger numbers																														●		●
Compare numbers using the symbols <, >, and =															●	■	■	■	●	■	●	■	●	■		■	■		■	■	■	■
Compare and order fractions; use manipulatives to identify/compare fractions																			●	■								●	●	●		
Compare fractions less than one																												●			■	■

Operations and Computation

	Kindergarten Sections										Grade 1 Units										Grade 2 Units											
Addition and Subtraction Facts	**R**	**1**	**2**	**3**	**4**	**5**	**6**	**7**	**8**	**P**	**1**	**2**	**3**	**4**	**5**	**6**	**7**	**8**	**9**	**10**	**1**	**2**	**3**	**4**	**5**	**6**	**7**	**8**	**9**	**10**	**11**	**12**
Find/use complements of 10		■	●	●		●	●	●	●	●		●	■	■	■	■					●				■		■	●	■			
Practice basic facts; know +/– fact families				●	●	●	■	●	●	●	●	●	■	●	●	●	●	■	■	■	●	●	■	■	■	●	■	■	■	●	■	●
Practice extensions of basic facts																			■					■								

Key ● Content taught ■ Content practiced

Addition and Subtraction Facts (cont.)	R	1	2	3	4	5	6	7	8	P	1	2	3	4	5	6	7	8	9	10	1	2	3	4	5	6	7	8	9	10	11	12
Make and solve number-grid puzzles														●					●	●	■	●										
Addition and Subtraction Procedures	**R**	**1**	**2**	**3**	**4**	**5**	**6**	**7**	**8**	**P**	**1**	**2**	**3**	**4**	**5**	**6**	**7**	**8**	**9**	**10**	**1**	**2**	**3**	**4**	**5**	**6**	**7**	**8**	**9**	**10**	**11**	**12**
Understand meaning of addition/subtraction; model addition/subtraction using concrete objects		■	●	●	●	■	■	●	●		●	●	●	●	●			■	●		●	■	●	●	●	●	●				●	
Investigate the inverse relationships between addition and subtraction			●	●	●	■	■	●	●			●		●	●	●		●		■	●	●		●							■	
Use mental arithmetic or fact strategies to add/subtract				●	●	●	■	●	●	●	●	●	●	●	●	●	●	●	■	■	●	●	■	●	■	●	■	■	■	■	■	■
Use addition to find the total number of objects in rectangular rays																								■	●	●		■			●	
Use addition/subtraction algorithms																										●	■	■	■	■	●	■
Explore calculator functions						●	●		■						●	●		■	■		●	■	■	■								
Make up and/or solve 1- or 2-step addition/subtraction number stories; determine operation needed to solve a problem	●		●	●	●	■	●	●	●		●	●	●	●	●	●	●	●	●	●	■	●	■	●	■	●	●		■	●	●	●
Use an Addition/Subtraction Facts Table															●	●						●										
Determine the value of the unknown number in an addition or subtraction problem													●	●	●	●						●	■	●	■	●				●		
Add/subtract using a number grid											●		■		●	■			●	■	●	■		■		●	●			■	■	
Add/subtract using a number line	●				●		■				●		●		■						●	●	■	●	●	●	●				■	●
Add/subtract using a calculator									●						●	●		■	■		●	●	■		■		●			■		
Add/subtract multiples of 10																			●	●	●	■		■		■				●		
Add 3 or more 1-digit numbers												●	●			●		●								●	■			■		●
Add/subtract 2-digit numbers															●	●		●	●	●	●			●	■	●	●	■	■	■	●	●
Add 3 or more 2-digit numbers																										●						●
Add/subtract 3- and 4-digit numbers																								●		●	■		●		●	●
Add/subtract money amounts/decimals; make change																●		●	●	●	●		●	●		●	●	■		●	●	■
Solve money number stories															●	●		●	●	●				■		■			■	●	●	■
Make change																		●	■	●		■		■	■				■	●	●	■

Operations and Computation (cont.)

Key ● Content taught ■ Content practiced

	Kindergarten Sections										Grade 1 Units										Grade 2 Units											
Multiplication and Division Facts	R	1	2	3	4	5	6	7	8	P	1	2	3	4	5	6	7	8	9	10	1	2	3	4	5	6	7	8	9	10	11	12
Practice multiplication/division facts																															■	●
Find complements for multiples of 10																											●					
Multiplication and Division Procedures	R	1	2	3	4	5	6	7	8	P	1	2	3	4	5	6	7	8	9	10	1	2	3	4	5	6	7	8	9	10	11	12
Use manipulatives, drawings/arrays, number sentences, repeated addition, or story problems to explain and demonstrate the meaning of multiplication/division							●							●				●							■	●	■	●		■	●	●
Understand meaning of multiplication/division and related vocabulary																									●	●	●				●	
Make up and/or solve multiplication/division number stories																										●	●				●	●
Investigate relationships between multiplication and division																										●					●	
Multiply/divide using a number line or number grid																										■					●	
Explore square numbers																															■	
Use a calculator to multiply or divide																															●	
Use a Multiplication/Division Facts Table																															●	
Use mental arithmetic to multiply/divide																															●	■
Identify factors of a number																															●	
Computational Estimation	R	1	2	3	4	5	6	7	8	P	1	2	3	4	5	6	7	8	9	10	1	2	3	4	5	6	7	8	9	10	11	12
Estimate reasonableness of answers to basic facts													●		■	■		■	●	■				■						■		
Use estimation strategies to add/subtract; make ballpark estimates													●							●				●		■	■			●	●	
Round whole numbers to the nearest ten															●		●	●	●											■		
Estimate costs																■		■						●						●	●	
Models for Operations	R	1	2	3	4	5	6	7	8	P	1	2	3	4	5	6	7	8	9	10	1	2	3	4	5	6	7	8	9	10	11	12
Solve change-to-more and change-to-less number stories/diagrams			●	●	●	■	■	●	●			●	●						●			●	●	●		●				■	●	
Solve parts-and-total number stories/diagrams			●	●	●	■	■	●	●				●	●	●	●		●					●	●		●		■	■	■		
Solve comparison number stories/diagrams							●											●		●		●			■	●				●	●	■
Solve equal-grouping and equal-sharing division problems							●																		■					■	■	

Data and Chance

Key ● Content taught ■ Content practiced

	Kindergarten Sections										Grade 1 Units										Grade 2 Units											
Data Collection and Representation	R	1	2	3	4	5	6	7	8	P	1	2	3	4	5	6	7	8	9	10	1	2	3	4	5	6	7	8	9	10	11	12
Collect data by counting	●			●		●	●	●	■	●	■							■		■			■			●	●					●
Collect data by interviewing	●						●													■						■						
Collect data by measuring														●						●							●		■	●	●	
Collect data from print sources and/or posters																										■			■	■		●
Collect data from a map																													●			
Use a weather map																				●												
Conduct a survey	●						●	■	■							■										●						
Make a tally chart or frequency table	●					●					●	●	●		●	●	■	■			■		●			●	●					■
Record data in a table/chart	●		■	●	●	■	●	●		●	●					●				●			●		■	●	●			■	■	●
Record days/events on a timeline	●					●								●											■							●
Create/interpret a bar graph, pictograph (picture graph), or Venn diagram	●	●	■	●		●	●		■					●	●	●	■	■	■	■			●		■	●	●					●
Create/interpret a line plot													●	●	■	■		■	■	●							●		■	●	●	●
Explore graphing software to make a bar graph or line plot													●	●		●				●						●						
Data Analysis	R	1	2	3	4	5	6	7	8	P	1	2	3	4	5	6	7	8	9	10	1	2	3	4	5	6	7	8	9	10	11	12
Read tables, graphs, and maps (including map scale, scale drawing)	●	●	■	●	●	●	●	●	■	●	●	●	●		●	●	■		■	●	●	●	●		■	●	●	■	●	■	■	●
Summarize and interpret data	●	●	■	●	●	●	●	●	■		●	●	●	●	●	●	■	●	●	●					■	●	●					●
Compare two sets of data; use calculator to compare data																				●			●			●	■				■	●
Make predictions about data	●	●	■	●	●	●	●	●	■		●	●				■							●			●						
Identify "more" or "less" from pictographs and bar graphs	●	●	■	●	●	●	●	●	■																							
Compare quantities from a bar graph	●	●	●	●	●	●	●	●	●				●		■	●						■	●					■				
Find the minimum/maximum of a data set																●		■	■	■		■					●			■	■	●
Find the range																●		■	■	■			●				●			■	■	●
Find the median														●				■	■	●		■	●			■	●		■	■	■	●

Data and Chance (cont.)

Key ● Content taught ■ Content practiced

	Kindergarten Sections										Grade 1 Units										Grade 2 Units											
Data Analysis (cont.)	R	1	2	3	4	5	6	7	8	P	1	2	3	4	5	6	7	8	9	10	1	2	3	4	5	6	7	8	9	10	11	12
Find the mode														●						●						■	■	■		■	■	●
Use data in problem solving	●											●	●	●		●						■				●	●			■	■	●
Qualitative and Quantitative Probability	R	1	2	3	4	5	6	7	8	P	1	2	3	4	5	6	7	8	9	10	1	2	3	4	5	6	7	8	9	10	11	12
Understand the language of probability to discuss likelihood of a given situation (using words such as certain, likely, unlikely, always, maybe, sometimes, never, possible, impossible)	●		●	●	■			■				■	■	■	●	■		■		■	■	■	■	■		■	■	■	■			
Explore equal-chance events					■										●	●		■														
Participate in games or activities based on chance			●	●	●	●	■	■	●	●																						
Predict outcomes; solve problems involving chance outcomes				●	●						●	●	■	■	■	■							●				■					
Conduct experiments; test predictions using concrete objects				●							●																■					
Find combinations (Cartesian products)	●		●	●	■			■										■									■	■				

Measurement and Reference Frames

Key ● Content taught ■ Content practiced

	Kindergarten Sections										Grade 1 Units										Grade 2 Units											
Length, Weight, and Angles	R	1	2	3	4	5	6	7	8	P	1	2	3	4	5	6	7	8	9	10	1	2	3	4	5	6	7	8	9	10	11	12
Name tools used to measure length						●	■		■			●		●										●			■		●			
Estimate, compare, and order lengths/heights of objects		●	■	●	■	●	■		■	●		●	■	●		●			●	●						■	●		●	■	■	
Compare lengths indirectly		●	●	●		●								●		●													■			
Measure lengths with nonstandard units				●	■	●	■		■	●				●										■					●			
Measure to the nearest foot						●								●															●			
Measure to the nearest inch														●	■				●					●			●	■	●			
Measure to the nearest $\frac{1}{2}$ inch														●															●			
Investigate the yard																													●			
Measure to the nearest yard																													●			
Measure to the nearest centimeter																●								●	■	■	●	■	●	■	■	
Measure to the nearest $\frac{1}{2}$ centimeter																													●			
Investigate the meter																●													●			
Measure to the nearest meter and/or decimeter																													●			
Solve length/height number stories																										●	●	■	■		■	
Investigate the mile and/or kilometer																													●		■	
Use words to describe distance										●																						
Estimate and compare distances																												■	●			
Solve distance number stories																													●		■	
Estimate, compare, and order weights				●					●										■			■		■			■	■	●			
Name tools used to measure weight				●					●	●																			●			
Order objects by weight																											■					
Use a pan balance				●		■			●						●	●					●	●										
Use a bath scale										●									■					■			●		●			
Use a spring scale																						●							●			
Choose the appropriate scale																													●			

Measurement and Reference Frames (cont.)

Key ● Content taught ■ Content practiced

	Kindergarten Sections										Grade 1 Units										Grade 2 Units											
Length, Weight, and Angles (cont.)	**R**	**1**	**2**	**3**	**4**	**5**	**6**	**7**	**8**	**P**	**1**	**2**	**3**	**4**	**5**	**6**	**7**	**8**	**9**	**10**	**1**	**2**	**3**	**4**	**5**	**6**	**7**	**8**	**9**	**10**	**11**	**12**
Solve weight number stories																								■			■		●			
Area, Perimeter, Volume, and Capacity	**R**	**1**	**2**	**3**	**4**	**5**	**6**	**7**	**8**	**P**	**1**	**2**	**3**	**4**	**5**	**6**	**7**	**8**	**9**	**10**	**1**	**2**	**3**	**4**	**5**	**6**	**7**	**8**	**9**	**10**	**11**	**12**
Investigate area															●	●								●					●			
Find the area of regular shapes concretely															●	●												■	●			■
Find the perimeter of regular shapes concretely, graphically, or with pictorial models																												■	●		■	■
Find the area of a rectangular region divided into square units																								■					●	●		
Partition rectangles into same-size squares; count to find the total																								■					●	●		
Find the area of irregular shapes concretely																												■	●	●		
Find the perimeter of irregular shapes concretely, graphically, or with pictorial models																												■	●		■	
Estimate area																													●			
Estimate perimeter																													■			
Compare perimeter and area																													●			
Name tools used to measure area																													●			
Estimate volume/capacity		●																	●									●				
Name tools used to measure volume and/or capacity										●																			●			
Find volume																												●				
Measure capacities of irregular containers																													■			
Compare and order the capacities of containers		●																	●										●			
Units and Systems of Measurement	**R**	**1**	**2**	**3**	**4**	**5**	**6**	**7**	**8**	**P**	**1**	**2**	**3**	**4**	**5**	**6**	**7**	**8**	**9**	**10**	**1**	**2**	**3**	**4**	**5**	**6**	**7**	**8**	**9**	**10**	**11**	**12**
Select and use appropriate nonstandard units to measure time							●					●																	■			
Estimate the duration of a minute									●			●																				
Investigate the duration of an hour									●			●																				
Investigate 1-minute intervals																															■	■
Identify equivalent customary units of length																													●			

Key ● Content taught ■ Content practiced

Units and Systems of Measurement (cont.)	R	1	2	3	4	5	6	7	8	P	1	2	3	4	5	6	7	8	9	10	1	2	3	4	5	6	7	8	9	10	11	12
Identify equivalent metric units of length																													●			
Identify customary and/or metric units of weight																													●			
Identify equivalent customary units of weight																													●			
Identify customary and/or metric units of capacity																			●										●			
Identify equivalent customary/metric units of capacity																													●			
Choose the appropriate unit of measure																													●			
Money	**R**	**1**	**2**	**3**	**4**	**5**	**6**	**7**	**8**	**P**	**1**	**2**	**3**	**4**	**5**	**6**	**7**	**8**	**9**	**10**	**1**	**2**	**3**	**4**	**5**	**6**	**7**	**8**	**9**	**10**	**11**	**12**
Recognize pennies and nickels		●	●	■		■	●	●	■			●	■		■			■			●	■	■	●	■	■	■	■	■	■	■	■
Recognize dimes		●	●	■		■	●	●	■				●	●			■	●	●		●	■	■	●	■	■	■	■	■	■	■	■
Recognize quarters		●		■		■		●	■							●	■	●			●	■	■	●					■	■		■
Recognize dollars									●									●			●	■		■				■	■	■		■
Calculate the value of coin combinations							●	●				●	●		■	●	●	●	■	●	●	■	●	●		■		■	■	●		
Calculate the value of bill combinations									●												●	■					■			●		
Calculate the value of coins/bills													●					●			●	■	●	●			●		■	●	■	■
Compare values of sets of coins or money amounts using <, >, and = symbols												■	■	■	●	■		■	■	■						■	■			●		
Identify equivalencies and make coin exchanges							●	■			●	●	●	■	●	●	■	●		■	■		●			●						
Identify equivalencies and make coin/bill exchanges									●									●	■	■			■			●	●		■	●		
Temperature	**R**	**1**	**2**	**3**	**4**	**5**	**6**	**7**	**8**	**P**	**1**	**2**	**3**	**4**	**5**	**6**	**7**	**8**	**9**	**10**	**1**	**2**	**3**	**4**	**5**	**6**	**7**	**8**	**9**	**10**	**11**	**12**
Compare situations or objects according to temperature	●								■																							
Use a thermometer	●								■		●		■	●	■				■	■	●	■	●	●		■						
Use the Fahrenheit temperature scale	●										●		■	●	■				■	●	●	■	●	●		■	■			■		
Use the Celsius temperature scale	●																			●			●	●						■		
Solve temperature number stories														●						●	●			●		■			■			
Time	**R**	**1**	**2**	**3**	**4**	**5**	**6**	**7**	**8**	**P**	**1**	**2**	**3**	**4**	**5**	**6**	**7**	**8**	**9**	**10**	**1**	**2**	**3**	**4**	**5**	**6**	**7**	**8**	**9**	**10**	**11**	**12**
Demonstrate an understanding of the concepts of time; estimates and measures the passage of time using words like *before, after, yesterday, today, tomorrow, morning, afternoon, hour, half-hour*	●					●	●		●		●	●		●							●			■								●

Measurement and Reference Frames (cont.)

Key ● Content taught ■ Content practiced

	Kindergarten Sections										Grade 1 Units										Grade 2 Units											
Time (cont.)	R	1	2	3	4	5	6	7	8	P	1	2	3	4	5	6	7	8	9	10	1	2	3	4	5	6	7	8	9	10	11	12
Order or compare events according to duration; calculate elapsed time	●					●	●					●		■						●	■		■				■	■				●
Name tools used to measure time	●					●	●		●												●		■									■
Relates past events to future events																●																
Investigate A.M. and P.M.	●											●									●	■	●	■	■	■	■	■	■	■	■	●
Name the seasons of the year										●																						
Use the calendar; identify today's date	●										●	■	■								●					■						●
Number and name the months in a year or days in the week	●										●	■	■	■						■	●					■		■		■		●
Investigate the second hand; compare the hour and minute hands									●			●	●								●		●									
Use an analog or digital clock to tell time on the hour	●								●			■	●	■		■		■		●	●	■	●	■	●	■	■			■		
Tell time on the half-hour													●	●	●	●	■	■		●	■	■	●	■	●					■		
Tell time on the quarter-hour														●	●	●	■	■		●		■	●	■			■			■		
Tell time to the nearest 5 minutes																●		■	●	●		■	●			■						●
Use digital notation*									●							●	■	■		●	■	■	●	■	●	■	■	■	■	■	■	■
Tell time to the nearest minute*																				●	■	■	●	■	■	■	■	■	■	■	■	■
Read time in different ways and/or identify time equivalencies									●							■												■				●
Solve time number stories																						■	●	■		■						
Coordinate Systems	R	1	2	3	4	5	6	7	8	P	1	2	3	4	5	6	7	8	9	10	1	2	3	4	5	6	7	8	9	10	11	12
Find and name locations with simple relationships on a coordinate system																			■													

*In Grade 2, children record the start time at the top of journal pages on a daily basis. In Grade 2, they use A.M. and P.M.

Geometry

Key ● Content taught ■ Content practiced

	Kindergarten Sections										Grade 1 Units										Grade 2 Units											
Lines and Angles	R	1	2	3	4	5	6	7	8	P	1	2	3	4	5	6	7	8	9	10	1	2	3	4	5	6	7	8	9	10	11	12
Identify and name line segments																									●						■	
Draw line segments with a straightedge																●									●		■	■				
Draw line segments to a specified length																■								■				■	■			
Draw designs with line segments																■																
Identify and name points																									●	■						
Model parallel lines on a geoboard																									●							
Draw parallel lines with a straightedge																									●							
Identify parallel, nonparallel, and intersecting line segments																									●							
Plane and Solid Figures	R	1	2	3	4	5	6	7	8	P	1	2	3	4	5	6	7	8	9	10	1	2	3	4	5	6	7	8	9	10	11	12
Explore shape relationships			●	■	●		●	■			●	■										■			●				●	■	■	■
Recognizes open and closed figures																	■				■	■		■								
Identify characteristics of 2-dimensional shapes; sort shapes by attributes		●	●	■	●	●	●	■			●					●	●	■	■	●	■	●		■	●							■
Distinguish between defining and non-defining attributes																■	●			●												
Explore 2-D shapes utilizing technology or multimedia resources							■										●															
Identify characteristics and use appropriate vocabulary to describe properties of 2-dimensional shapes			●	■	●	■	●	■	●		■	●			●	■	●			●					●							
Construct models of polygons using manipulatives such as straws or geoboards			●		●		●	●	●		■			●		●		●		●			●		●					●		
Match objects to outlines of shapes (on a Pattern-Block Template)		■			●					■																						
Draw 2-dimensional shapes (such as triangles and quadrilaterals); draw/describe objects in the environment that depict geometric figures		■	●		●		●	■			●	■				●	●		●	●		■		■	●			■	■	●	■	■
Create/extend designs with 2-dimensional shapes		●	●	■	■			●			■	■	●	■	■	■	●		■		●				●				■			■
Combine shapes and take them apart to form other shapes		●	●		●				●				●				●		■	●					●			●		●		
Record shapes or designs		■	●		●									●									●									
Identify and draw congruent or similar shapes																	●	■	■										■			

Geometry (cont.)

Key ● Content taught ■ Content practiced

	Kindergarten Sections										Grade 1 Units										Grade 2 Units											
Plane and Solid Figures (cont.)	R	1	2	3	4	5	6	7	8	P	1	2	3	4	5	6	7	8	9	10	1	2	3	4	5	6	7	8	9	10	11	12
Classify and name polygons											●		■	■		●									●							■
Compare 2-dimensional shapes			●	■	●	●					●	■					●	●							●							■
Compare polygons and non-polygons																	■								●							
Solve 2-dimensional shapes problems																						■		■	■							
Decompose shapes into shares																		●	●	■								●		■		
Identify/compare 3-dimensional shapes; sort shapes and/or describe attributes of each group						●	●	●	■		●					■	●	■	■	●				■	●		■			■	■	■
Construct 3-dimensional shapes								●	■											●					●				●			
Locate 2-D shapes on 3-D objects; compare 2- and 3-D shapes			●		●		●	●											■													
Explore 3-D shapes utilizing technology							■																									
Identify the number of faces, edges, vertices, and bases of prisms and pyramids																									●							
Identify the shapes of faces							●	■									■										■					
Explore slanted 3-dimensional shapes																											■					
Transformations and Symmetry	R	1	2	3	4	5	6	7	8	P	1	2	3	4	5	6	7	8	9	10	1	2	3	4	5	6	7	8	9	10	11	12
Identify symmetrical figures or symmetry in the environment			●		■		■			●							●	■	●					■	●							
Fold and cut symmetrical shapes			●		■		■			●							●	■							●							
Create/complete a symmetrical design/shape using concrete models, geoboard, and/or technology			●														●		●						●	■		■				
Identify lines of symmetry																	●		●						●	■	■		■	■		
Use objects to explore slides, flips, and turns; predict the results of changing a shape's position or orientation using slides, flips, and turns					●								●												■							
Spatial	R	1	2	3	4	5	6	7	8	P	1	2	3	4	5	6	7	8	9	10	1	2	3	4	5	6	7	8	9	10	11	12
Recognize that the quantity remains the same when the spatial arrangement changes		●		●								●																				
Arrange or describe objects by proximity, position, or direction using words such as *over, under, above, below, inside, outside, beside, in front of, behind*			●	■					■	●			●				●															

Key ● Content taught ■ Content practiced

Spatial (cont.)	R	1	2	3	4	5	6	7	8	P	1	2	3	4	5	6	7	8	9	10	1	2	3	4	5	6	7	8	9	10	11	12
Give or follow directions for finding a place or object			●							●							■		●											■		
Identify left hand and right hand			●							●																						
Identify structures from different views or match views of the same structures portrayed from different perspectives																●								■								
Use objects to explore slides, flips, and turns; predict the results of changing a shape's position or orientation using slides, flips, and turns					●																				■							

Patterns, Functions, and Algebra

	Kindergarten Sections										Grade 1 Units										Grade 2 Units											
Patterns and Functions	**R**	**1**	**2**	**3**	**4**	**5**	**6**	**7**	**8**	**P**	**1**	**2**	**3**	**4**	**5**	**6**	**7**	**8**	**9**	**10**	**1**	**2**	**3**	**4**	**5**	**6**	**7**	**8**	**9**	**10**	**11**	**12**
Identify, extend, and create patterns of sounds, physical movement, and concrete objects		●	●	●	●	●	●	●	■	●																						
Verbally describe changes in various contexts		●		■	●			●																								
Explore and extend visual patterns		●	●	●	●	●	●	●				■	●	■	■	●	●					■				■	●					
Find patterns and common attributes in objects/people in the real world	●	●	●	■	■	●	■	●	■			■		●	●	■						■		●	●	■						
Create and complete patterns with 2-dimensional shapes		●			●			●	■		■	■	●	■	■	■	■		■		■					■	●	●		●		
Identify and use patterns on a number grid			●			●	■	●					■	●	●				●	●	■	■		■	■		●			■		
Add and subtract using a number grid																			●		●	■			■					■	■	
Investigate even and odd number patterns; create, describe, extend simple number patterns/sequences			●			●	●	●	●				●	■							●	●	■									
Explore counting patterns using a calculator							●						●								●					■	●					
Solve "What's My Rule?" (e.g. function machine) problems					●			●	●						●	●		■	■	■		●	■	●			●			■	●	■
Solve Frames-and-Arrows problems with one or two rules													●	■	■	■			■	■	■	■	●	■		■		■	■	■	■	
Find patterns in addition and subtraction facts															●	●		●	■			●	■							■	■	
Explore patterns in doubling or halving numbers															●							●				■	●			■	■	
Find patterns in multiplication and division facts																											■				●	●

Patterns, Functions, and Algebra (cont.)

Key ● Content taught ■ Content practiced

	Kindergarten Sections										Grade 1 Units										Grade 2 Units											
Patterns and Functions (cont.)	R	1	2	3	4	5	6	7	8	P	1	2	3	4	5	6	7	8	9	10	1	2	3	4	5	6	7	8	9	10	11	12
Find patterns in multiples of 10, 100, and 1,000																							■							■	●	
Investigate square numbers																															■	
Algebraic Notation and Solving Number Sentences	R	1	2	3	4	5	6	7	8	P	1	2	3	4	5	6	7	8	9	10	1	2	3	4	5	6	7	8	9	10	11	12
Determine whether equations are true or false													●	■	●			■														
Use symbols ×, ÷, =																										●	●				●	●
Use symbols +, −, =; pictures; manipulatives; and models to organize, record, and communicate mathematical ideas					●	■	■	●	●			●	●	■	●	●	●	●	●	●	●	■	●	●	■	■	■		●	●	●	
Use a symbol or letter to represent the unknown number																								●		●						
Compare numbers using <, > symbols															●	■		■		■	●	■	●	■		■	■		■	■	■	■
Write/solve addition and subtraction number sentences					●	■	■	●	●			●					●	●	●	■	●	■	●	●	■	■	■		●	●	●	
Write/solve number sentences with missing addends									●						●							●				■	■		●	●	●	
Write and solve multiplication number sentences																										●	●				●	●
Write and solve division number sentences																															●	●
Write and solve number sentences with missing factors; know that symbols can be used to represent missing or unknown quantities									●															●		●					●	●
Order of Operations	R	1	2	3	4	5	6	7	8	P	1	2	3	4	5	6	7	8	9	10	1	2	3	4	5	6	7	8	9	10	11	12
Make up and/or solve number sentences involving parentheses																														●		
Properties of Arithmetic Operations	R	1	2	3	4	5	6	7	8	P	1	2	3	4	5	6	7	8	9	10	1	2	3	4	5	6	7	8	9	10	11	12
Investigate properties of addition/subtraction			●	●	●	■	■	●	●			●	●	●	●	●						●										
Investigate properties of multiplication/division																															●	●
Explore number properties (commutative, zero, and identity)		●													■							●										

Index

A

B

C

D

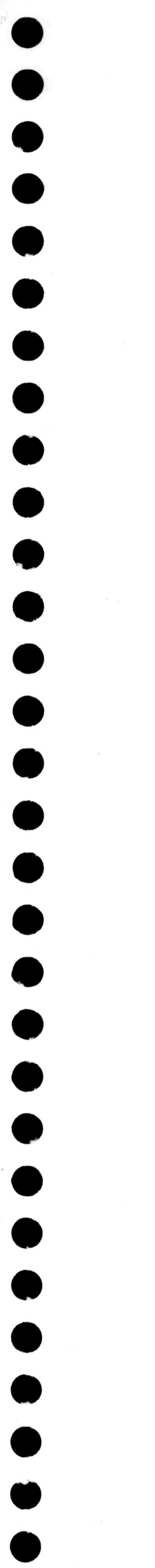